X-Rays
in Theory and Experiment

X-Rays
in Theory and Experiment

BY

ARTHUR H. COMPTON, Ph.D., Sc.D., LL.D.

NOBEL LAUREATE, 1927
Charles H. Swift Distinguished Service Professor of Physics
University of Chicago

and

SAMUEL K. ALLISON, Ph.D.

Associate Professor of Physics, University of Chicago

SECOND EDITION
of X-RAYS *and* ELECTRONS
By Arthur H. Compton

FOURTEENTH PRINTING

D. VAN NOSTRAND COMPANY, INC.
PRINCETON, NEW JERSEY

TORONTO

LONDON

NEW YORK

D. VAN NOSTRAND COMPANY, INC.
120 Alexander St., Princeton, New Jersey (*Principal office*)
24 West 40 Street, New York 18, New York

D. VAN NOSTRAND COMPANY, LTD.
358, Kensington High Street, London, W. 14, England

D. VAN NOSTRAND COMPANY (Canada), LTD.
25 Hollinger Road, Toronto 16, Canada

PREFACE

In 1926 I published a book on *X-rays and Electrons*, which gave an account of the physics of x-rays as known at that time. This volume was written just after experiments had shown the complete correspondence between x-rays and light in their major features of spectra, polarization and dispersion. Also the essentially quantum phenomena of the photo-electric effect and the change of wavelength of scattered x-rays had been studied enough to show that x-ray energy is transmitted in directed quanta. Attempts at correlation between these optical and corpuscular aspects of radiation were just beginning to meet with success.

Immediately after the publication of this book, the growth of quantum mechanics brought with it a rapid development of the theories underlying x-ray phenomena. Unique formulas were found for the intensity of scattered x-rays, which made possible application of the powerful methods of x-ray diffraction to the study of electron arrangement in atoms. The theory of dispersion was so developed as to give a connected account of x-ray refraction, reflection and absorption. Atomic theory was refined, and with the introduction of a vector atom with spinning electrons, x-ray spectra could be classified and interpreted with greatly improved clarity. These theoretical developments greatly stimulated also experimental studies, and with the continual advances in technique many of the lacunae in our knowledge of x-ray phenomena have been filled in, and a great mass of precise data, useful for testing the theoretical predictions, has accumulated.

With this widespread interest in the field of x-rays, the original printing and a revised second printing of *X-rays and Electrons* were soon sold out. Further printings were postponed with the hope of preparing a new edition. My attempts at revision could not, however, keep pace with the rapid growth of the subject. Professor Allison accordingly joined with me in the preparation of a more comprehensive discussion of x-rays than I could possibly have prepared by myself. Professor Allison has indeed taken the primary responsi-

v

bility for the greater part of the present volume, including the discussions of x-rays and crystals, dispersion and absorption, and x-ray spectra. It has been my privilege to prepare the introductory chapter and the discussion of the scattering of x-rays.

In the preface to *X-rays and Electrons* it was possible to write, "Perhaps no single field of investigation has contributed more to our knowledge of atomic structure than has the study of x-rays." The developments of the intervening years have emphasized this key position. We had then just shown with x-rays that radiation has the combined characteristics of waves and particles. It has since been found that electrons, protons and atoms likewise have these dual properties, thus forming the experimental basis of the principle of uncertainty, with all its fundamental implications. In the diffraction of x-rays we have found direct methods of observing the average positions and motions of electrons in atoms and of the thermal motions of atoms in crystals and molecules, establishing the correctness of the main predictions by the new quantum mechanics. The number of the electrons, their energy states, spin, magnetic moment, transition probabilities and other characteristics as revealed through studies of x-ray emission and absorption spectra, supply remarkably detailed tests of the predictions of theory. The intimate meeting of classical and quantum interpretations when dealing with x-ray phenomena makes this field one of unusual value in clarifying our ideas of the nature of atomic processes.

The admirable summary by F. Kirchner in his *Allgemeine Physik der Röntgenstrahlen*, as a part of the Wien-Harms *Handbuch der Experimental-physik*, gives as of 1930, a more detailed discussion of experimental technique than we have been able to include, as well as a good review of the results of the experiments. Likewise M. Siegbahn's "*Spektroskopie der Röntgenstrahlen,*" whose new edition (1931) appeared while this book was in preparation, has presented in excellent detail the experimental aspects of that subject. New treatments by W. L. Bragg, P. P. Ewald, R. W. G. Wyckoff and others have similarly appeared on the subject of crystal structure. The main objective of *X-rays in Theory and Experiment* is to present a comprehensive view of the whole field, to call attention to those aspects which seem of most fundamental physical significance, and especially to discuss the theory of the phenomena in sufficient detail that their meaning can be appreciated. Though we have made no attempt to supply an exhaustive bibliography, we have tried to give a fair impression of the present state of the subject, with references to all the more important contributions.

It is a pleasure to acknowledge the generous help of our colleagues Professor Carl Eckart, Professor W. H. Zachariasen, Dr. E. Dershem, Dr. E. O. Wollan and others, in preparing the manuscript; that of Dr. J. W. M. DuMond for supplying the photographs shown in Figs. III–49 and 50; Professor W. L. Bragg and The Macmillan Company for permission to reproduce Figs. VI–28 and VI–29; Professor S. J. M. Allen for supplying us with an advance copy of his x-ray absorption data, and many friends for placing at our disposal other information not available through the usual channels. We are also indebted to Ardis T. Monk for her assistance in reading proof and in preparing index material, and for her careful checking of many of the calculations.

CHICAGO   ARTHUR H. COMPTON.
July 26, 1934,

CONTENTS

CHAPTER I

The Discovery and Properties of X-rays

CHAPTER II

The Production of X-rays

CHAPTER III

The Scattering of X-rays

Part A.—Scattering by Independent Electrons

Part B.—Interference Phenomena with Scattered X-rays

Part C.—Corpuscular Aspects of Scattered X-rays

Part D.—Wave Mechanics Theory of X-ray Scattering

CHAPTER VII

PHENOMENA ASSOCIATED WITH THE EJECTION OF
PHOTO-ELECTRONS BY X-RAYS

CONTENTS

2. How X-rays are Produced

A typical arrangement of apparatus for producing x-rays is shown in Fig. I–1. The glass bulb X is evacuated to about 0.0005 mm of mercury pressure, and is excited by high potential current supplied by a step-up transformer T_1. For proper operation the current must pass through the tube only in one direction, which makes necessary a rectifying device of some kind if the high voltage is supplied by a transformer. In the figure this consists of a valve tube K, whose filament is heated by an auxiliary step-down transformer T_2 with a

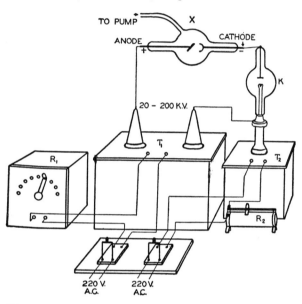

Fig. I–1.   X-ray Assemblage, with X-ray Tube X, High Voltage Transformer T_1, Rectifier K, and Electrical Controls.

secondary circuit highly insulated from the primary. The adjustable rheostats R_1 and R_2 control respectively the current through the primary of the main transformer, and hence through the x-ray tube, and the filament temperature. Some types of tubes are self rectifying. It is possible also to use other sources of high voltage, such as induction coils, static machines, or high voltage storage batteries, with which the rectifying devices are not essential.

If the current is allowed to flow through the x-ray tube while the exhaust is in progress, the appearance of the discharge changes as the

CHAPTER I

The Discovery and Properties of X-rays

1. *Roentgen's Early Experiments*

It was in the course of a systematic attempt to see if any radiation could be produced which would traverse matter opaque to ordinary light that Roentgen discovered the x-rays.[1] He was passing an electric discharge through a highly evacuated tube, and for the detection of any possible radiation had at hand a paper screen covered with crystals of platinum barium cyanide. With his discharge tube completely covered with opaque paper, he found that the screen fluoresced. From the fact that heavy objects placed between the tube and the crystal stopped the fluorescence, it was obvious that the effect was due to some type of radiation sent out by the discharge tube. This radiation was named by Roentgen "x-rays," indicating their unknown nature. The discovery of these rays attracted great interest, and experimenters the world over began to study their characteristics.

Besides producing fluorescence in certain salts, these rays were found to affect a photographic plate and to ionize gases, so that three methods, the visual, the photographic and the electrical, could be employed in their examination. It was shown that x-rays produce an effect, though a small one, directly upon the retina, giving rise to a faint illumination of the whole field of view. The rays were not subject to refraction nor reflection like ordinary light, nor were they bent by a magnetic field as were cathode rays. They were, however, diffusely scattered by all substances, and were partially absorbed by matter of all kinds. This absorption was much stronger by elements of high than by elements of low atomic weight.

[1] W. C. Roentgen, Sitzungsber. der Würzburger Physik-Medic. Gesellsch. Jahrg. 1895, reprinted in Ann. der Phys. **64**, 1 (1898). Translation by A. Stanton in Science, **3**, 227 and 726 (1896). For an excellent detailed account of Roentgen's discoveries, cf. Otto Glasser and Margret Boveri, "Wilhelm Conrad Röntgen, and the Early History of the Roentgen Rays." (1934). This includes translations of Roentgen's more important papers.

pressure falls. At pressures in the neighborhood of 1 mm of mercury the bulb is filled with an almost uniform pink glow. As the pressure is reduced still further, there appears a comparatively dark region surrounding the cathode, which is called *the cathode dark space*. At pressures between 0.1 and 0.001 mm, one observes a narrow bluish beam extending from the cathode toward the anode, or target. This is the beam of *cathode rays*. These rays can easily be deflected by bringing close to the bulb a permanent magnet, the direction of deflection indicating that they consist of a stream of negatively charged particles shot from the cathode. They are indeed *electrons*, whose paths are made visible by the excitation of the molecules of the rarefied air through which they pass. As the pressure falls below 0.001 mm the cathode rays fade from view, because their collisions with air molecules become infrequent. At the same time some of the cathode rays strike the glass wall of the bulb and make it glow with a green fluorescence. A fluoroscope now begins to reveal x-rays coming through the walls of the tube.

When the x-rays first appear they are very easily absorbed and are said to be *soft*. The flesh of the hand appears almost opaque when observed with a fluoroscope. As the pressure becomes lower, however, the voltage required to send a discharge through the tube increases, and the rays become more and more penetrating, until when the potential is over 100,000 volts even the bones in the hand cast only a faint shadow on the fluorescent screen. The rays are now described as *hard*. When the pressure has been reduced below about 0.0003 mm it is no longer possible with the voltages usually available to pass a discharge through the tube, and the x-rays cease.

The production of x-rays may be compared with the noise produced when a steel plate is bombarded by bullets from a rapid fire gun. The bullets correspond to the cathode rays, and the noise to the x-rays. The cathode rays are electrically charged, material particles, whereas the x-rays which they excite are electrically neutral rays, of the same nature as light.

The tube with which Roentgen made his original discovery was of the type shown in Fig. I–2. The tube was well evacuated with a mercury pump until a potential difference of about 40,000 volts was required to produce a discharge. The cathode rays, shot perpendicularly from the cathode's surface, then struck the broad end of the tube, producing a vivid fluorescence and at the same time giving rise to the x-rays. It was soon found that any substance struck by the cathode rays emitted x-rays, but that these rays were more intense from a target of high atomic weight. In order to obtain a point source of x-rays, the cathode was made concave, so that the cathode rays were focussed on a small spot at the target. This

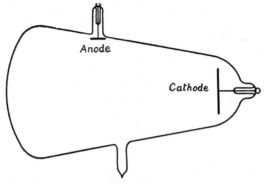

FIG. I–2. Roentgen's Original Form of X-ray Tube.

modification made necessary the use of a target of high melting point, in order to avoid damage due to the heat developed at the focus of the cathode rays. Thus the type of tube shown in Fig. I–3 was soon developed, which, with minor modifications, is still widely

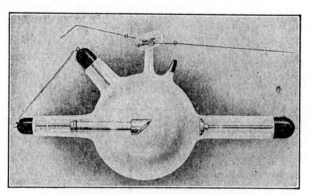

FIG. I–3. Low-pressure Gas-filled Tube.

used. It is a characteristic of the low pressure discharge tube that the potential difference between the anode and the cathode remains practically constant for large variations in the current through the tube. In order to change the voltage across the tube of this type, therefore, it is necessary to alter the pressure of the gas in the tube. In many of the tubes now in use, such changes can be effected by various ingenious devices. A tube which avoids this complication has been invented by Coolidge.[2] In this tube the cathode consists of a flat spiral of tungsten wire which is heated by an auxiliary current to such a temperature that it emits thermo-electrons. The tube is evacuated until there is no appreciable amount of gas remaining, so that all of the current through the tube is carried by the thermo-electrons. Thus the current through the tube is determined almost completely by the temperature of the filament, and the potential difference between the cathode and anode of the tube can be altered at will.

For the many uses that x-rays have found in science, technology

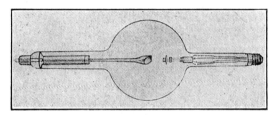

FIG. I–4. Coolidge Tube.

and medicine, a great many different forms of x-ray tubes have been built. In the laboratory it is usually found that the hot filament type is more easily subject to exact control.

3. *Measurement of X-rays*

The two most important distinguishing characteristics of a beam of x-rays are its intensity and its hardness or penetrating power. A rough estimate of the intensity of an x-ray beam may be made by observing *the brightness of the illumination produced on a fluorescent screen.* If a suitable standard of comparison is employed, this method may be used for approximate quantitative measurements, though it is subject to errors due to "fatigue" and deterioration of the fluorescent material, and can be used only for beams of relatively high intensity.

The photographic plate also affords convenient means of measuring

[2] W. D. Coolidge, Phys. Rev. **2**, 409 (1913). See also J. E. Lilienfeld and W. J. Rosenthal, Forts. auf d. Geb. d. Roentgenstrahlen, **18**, 256 (1912).

x-rays. It is capable of detecting very feeble rays if long exposures are made, and may be used over the complete range of x-ray wavelengths. Though it is usually employed to give only qualitative results, the photographic plate can also be adapted to precise quantitative comparisons of x-ray intensities. Let I_x and I_y be the intensities of two unknown beams x and y, the ratio of whose strengths is to be measured, and let y be the more intense. We may record beam y on the photographic plate by an exposure of say t seconds. A series of exposures of beam x may now be made on the same plate, of times t, $2t$, $3t$, and so on. When the plate is developed, the densities of the various images may be compared by means of a photometer. If the density of the image of y is the same as that of x exposed for a time nt, the beam y is n times as intense as x. It is obvious that interpolations may be made if the density of y lies between that of x for a time nt and for a time $(n + 1)t$.

In the case of light it is well known that the exposure cannot be expressed accurately by the product (intensity × time), that is, unit intensity of light exposed for 1/1000th second produces a greater photographic effect than 1/1000th unit intensity exposed for 1 second. For x-rays, however, tests have indicated that at least over a wide range of intensities the product It is a reliable measure of the exposure.

Figure I-5 shows an example of photographic intensity measure-

FILTERED

1 2 3 4 5 6 7 8 9 10 11

UNFILTERED

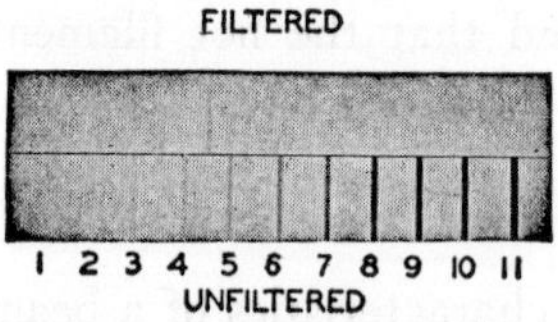

FIG. I-5. Comparison of Unknown Beam (above) with Differing Exposures of Standard Beam (below.)

ment. Above is the image produced by a certain beam of x-rays, filtered through 1 mm of aluminium, and exposed for 10 seconds. Below it are images made by the same x-ray beam, unfiltered, and exposed successively for 0.2, 0.4, 0.8, 1.2, 1.8, etc., seconds. A graph of the photometer readings for these images is shown in Fig. I-6. When a smooth curve is drawn through the density values for the unfiltered exposure, it is found that the density due to the filtered ray is equivalent to a 1.55 second exposure with the unfiltered beam. The ratio of the two intensities is thus 10/1.55 = 6.5.

The usual method of measuring x-ray intensities is however by means of *the ionization chamber*. We have noted that gases exposed to x-rays become conductors of electricity. This is due to the fact that the x-rays break up the gas molecules into electrically charged ions. A typical ionization chamber arranged to measure x-rays is

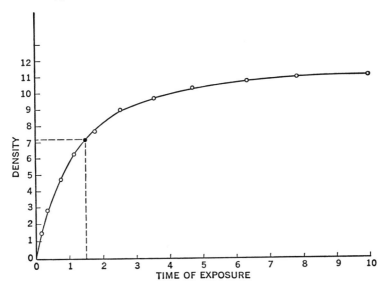

Fig. I-6. Typical Density vs. Exposure Curve.

shown diagrammatically in Fig. I-7. The chamber *I* may consist of a brass box, closed at one end with a window of thin celluloid or aluminium which will transmit the x-rays. Inside the chamber is an electrode insulated from the chamber, but connected to an electrometer or electroscope. The box may be raised to a potential of the order of a hundred volts by means of a battery.

When x-rays are admitted into the ionization chamber the ions of one sign which the x-rays produce are collected on the electrode, while those of the other sign migrate to the walls of the chamber.

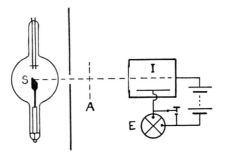

Fig. I-7. Ionization Chamber and Electrometer for Measuring X-ray Intensities.

The resulting ionization current is measured by the rate of charging of the electrometer. Figure I-8 is a typical graph of the variation of ionization current with the potential applied to the chamber. It will be seen that for the chamber employed and for potentials over 15 volts there is almost no change of current with potential. This means that all the ions produced are collected on the electrodes before they have time to recombine with each other to form neutral molecules. Under these conditions the ionization current is an accurate measure of the number of ions per second produced by the x-rays, which is in turn proportional to the intensity of the x-ray beam. The ratio of the intensities of two beams of the same wave-length can thus be found by merely determining the ratio of the ionization currents produced by the two beams.

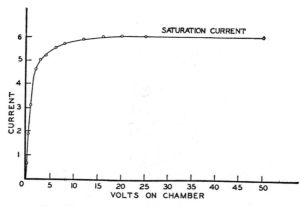

Fig. I–8.   Typical Ionization Saturation Curve.

If it is desired to compare the intensities of beams of different wave-lengths, it is necessary to take into account the different fractions of the two beams which are absorbed by the air in the chamber, and several other factors. A detailed discussion of this problem is given in Sec. 3, Chap. VII.

Absolute intensity determinations are perhaps most easily made by measuring the heat produced when the x-rays are absorbed. This may be done for example by allowing the x-rays to be absorbed by strips of sheet lead, well heat insulated, which form a bolometer. In this way one determines the ergs per cm² per second in the x-ray beam. Because of the small amount of energy in a beam of x-rays, such measurements can, however, be made only with x-rays of high intensity.

A practical unit of x-ray quantity which has been adopted internationally by radiologists[3] is the " Roentgen," r. This is that amount of x-rays which, when the secondary electrons are fully utilized and the wall effect of the chamber is avoided, will produce in one cubic centimeter of standard air one electrostatic unit of ions. The corresponding unit of intensity would be an x-ray beam of 1 roentgen per second. A Coolidge x-ray tube, operating at a constant potential of 100 kilovolts and 10 milliamperes gives a beam at one meter from the target whose intensity is about 0.34 r per second. This corresponds to about 390 ergs per cm^2 per second.[4] The ratio of r units to absolute units is, however, not the same for different wave-lengths, because of the correspondingly different absorption in air.

4. *Absorption of X-rays*

We have noticed that x-rays are much more strongly absorbed by some substances than by others. The reduction in intensity of x-rays as they traverse matter can be studied by the use of such apparatus as that shown in Fig. I–7. The ratio of the ionization current with an absorbing screen at A to the current without it, measures the relative intensity of the x-ray beam in the two cases.

In order to speak of the absorption quantitatively, it is convenient to define what is known as the *"absorption coefficient."* Let us suppose that the fraction dI/I of the intensity I of a beam of x-rays absorbed as they pass through a thin layer of matter is proportional to the thickness dx of this layer. Then

$$\frac{dI}{I} = -\mu dx,$$

where μ is the factor of proportionality, and the negative sign indicades a *decrease* in intensity. If the factor μ is constant, *i.e.*, independent of x, this equation gives on integration,

$$\log I = -\mu x + \log I_0,$$

taking $\log I_0$ as the constant of integration. This may be written,

$$\log \left(\frac{I}{I_0} \right) = -\mu x,$$

or

$$I = I_0 e^{-\mu x}. \tag{1.01}$$

[3] Third International Congress of Radiology, Paris, 1931.
[4] Cf. e.g., W. Rump, Zs. f. Phys. **43**, 274; and **44**, 396 (1927).

It is clear from the latter expression that I_0 represents the intensity of the rays when x is zero, whereas I is the intensity after traversing a layer of matter of thickness x. The quantity μ is the *absorption coefficient*, or *linear* absorption coefficient, and to differentiate it from other absorption coefficients will be represented by μ_l, where

$$\mu_l \equiv - dI/Idx,$$

that is, it is the fractional decrease in intensity per unit path through the absorbing medium.

If we consider a beam of x-rays 1 cm² in cross section, an equivalent definition of the linear absorption coefficient is the fraction of the energy of this beam which is absorbed per cm³ of the matter traversed. For many purposes, instead of the absorption per unit volume, we desire to know the fraction of the energy absorbed when a beam of unit cross section traverses unit mass of the material. This fraction is $\mu_m = \mu/\rho$, where ρ is the density of the material, and is called *the mass absorption coefficient*. The reason for the importance of this quantity is that it is characteristic of the absorbing substance, whereas the absorption per unit volume μ_l is not. Thus the linear absorption coefficient of a given beam of x-rays is much greater in water than in steam, whereas the mass absorption coefficient is the same in both. For in the latter case the amount of matter, 1 gram, traversed by an x-ray beam of unit cross section is independent of the density.

For purposes of calculation, we often wish to compare the amount of energy absorbed by an atom of each of several different elements. Since μ_l is the fraction of a beam of x-rays of unit cross section which is absorbed by unit volume of matter, the fraction of this beam absorbed by an individual atom is $\mu_a = \mu_l/n$, where n is the number of atoms per cm.³ This quantity is called the "*atomic absorption coefficient.*"

The remark has just been made that the mass absorption coefficient of water is the same whether in the form of liquid or of gas. This is an example of the experimental fact that the mass absorption coefficient of a substance for x-rays is independent of its physical state. It is also found that the fraction of the energy absorbed per atom or per unit mass of an element is independent of its state of chemical combinations.[5]

---

[5] Theoretically there should be very slight changes in μ_a with change of physical and chemical state, due to changes in the x-rays lost by scattering, and due to slight

This independence of the mass and atomic absorption coefficients from the physical and chemical state of an element sharply distinguishes x-rays from ordinary light. Thus, while liquid or solid mercury is opaque to light, its vapor is almost perfectly transparent. Carbon in the form of diamond is highly transparent, while in the form of graphite it absorbs light very strongly; but the mass absorption of both forms for x-rays is the same.

The absorption coefficient of the total radiation from an x-ray tube is found to depend chiefly upon two factors, the potential applied to the x-ray tube, and the atomic number of the absorbing screen. The penetration or "hardness" of the x-rays increases very rapidly as the voltage rises, the absorption coefficient in most substances varying inversely as the potential raised to some power between 2 and 3. Using the same beam of x-rays, the penetration decreases rapidly as the atomic weight, or more exactly the atomic number, of the absorbing material increases. There are, however, certain irregularities in the curve relating the atomic number and the absorption coefficients, which later will be considered in detail.

In deriving our expression 1.01 for the intensity of the x-ray beam after it has traversed a layer of matter, we assumed that the quantity μ was a constant for all values of x. Experiment shows that this assumption is valid only under very special conditions. When the direct radiation from an x-ray tube is studied, the first layers of the absorption screen remove a large fraction of the less penetrating, or "soft" radiations, so that only the more penetrating, or "hard" portions reach the final layers. The effective value of μ is accordingly greater for the rays which enter an absorbing screen than for those that leave. When, however, a ray is used which is all of the same wave-length, its absorption coefficient remains unchanged as it traverses matter. Such a ray is said to be *homogeneous*.

5. Secondary Radiations Produced by X-rays

When x-rays traverse matter, the matter becomes a source of secondary x-rays,[6] and of secondary high speed electrons[7] or β-rays.

changes of the energy levels of the valence electrons. These changes are however always so small that they can be detected only with great difficulty, if at all, by absorption measurements.

[6] Cf. M. I. Pupin, Science, 3, 538 (1896).

[7] Cf. Dorn, Lorentz Jubilee Volume, p. 595 (1900). The existence of secondary rays, whose nature was however unknown, was also recognized by Roentgen in 1896.

The intensity of the secondary rays is usually very small compared with the intensity of the primary radiation falling on the matter. This is necessarily the case. For in the first place, only a part of the energy of the primary beam which is dissipated in the secondary radiator reappears as x-rays or β-rays, and in the second place the reradiated rays spread in all directions, so that their intensity in any one direction is small.

The usual method of investigating secondary x-rays may be explained by reference to Fig. I–9. Radiation from the target S of

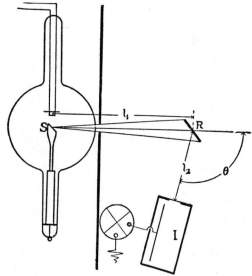

Fig. I–9. A Part of the X-rays Scattered in All Directions by Radiator R Enters the Ionization Chamber I.

an x-ray tube, or from some other source of x-rays, is allowed to traverse a radiator R. This radiator is then found to emit radiation in all directions. These rays may be investigated by means of an ionization chamber I which is carefully screened from the primary beam.

Scattered and Fluorescence X-rays.—It is found that many materials when used as radiators give rise to two distinct types of secondary x-radiations. One of these, known as " scattered " rays, is very nearly identical in absorption coefficient or wave-length with the primary beam. The other type, known as the " fluorescence " rays, is distinctly less penetrating, or of greater wave-length, than the primary x-rays. Scattered rays seem to be primary rays which have merely had their direction altered by the matter through which they pass. The fluorescence rays, on the other hand, are characteristic of the radiator, and do not change in character with change in wave-length of the primary beam as long as this beam is of sufficiently short wave-length to excite the fluorescence. Refined experiments show that the scattered rays are also somewhat less penetrating than the primary rays which produce them, though this change in hardness or wave-length is usually small compared with the change which occurs when fluorescence radiation is excited. The two types of radiation can however be distinguished by the fact that, whereas the wave-length of the fluorescence rays is characteristic of the radiator and independent of the wave-length of the primary rays, the wave-length of the scattered rays depends upon that of the primary beam and is nearly independent of the radiator.

The origin of the scattered ray becomes at once apparent if we think of the primary x-ray as an electromagnetic wave. When such a wave strikes an electron, the electron is accelerated by the electric field of the wave. But, according to electrodynamics, an accelerated electric charge must radiate. Consequently the electron radiates energy due to its forced oscillations under the action of the primary beam. Since these forced oscillations are of the same frequency as the incident wave, the rays produced by the oscillations must also be of the same frequency.

An alternative picture of the scattering process is presented if we think of the x-rays as corpuscular in nature. On this view an x-ray is scattered when one of the corpuscles, or *photons*, is deflected on passing close to an electron. If, as the quantum theory indicates, the mass of the photon is comparable with that of the electron, the electron will recoil from the impact, and will thus receive a part of the photon's energy. The deflected photon will thus have less energy after the collision than before, which corresponds on quantum principles to a reduced frequency. In this way it is possible to account for the slight change in wave-length that accompanies the scattering process.

When we wish to calculate the intensity of the scattered x-rays we thus turn to the wave theory; for the calculation of the wave-length we use the corpuscular theory. A wide variety of different experiments forces us to recognize these two apparently opposed aspects of radiation, as will become more and more evident as we try to interpret the properties of x-rays. As we shall see, however, at the close of this chapter, it is possible to formulate a unified theory of radiation which includes both its undulatory and its corpuscular aspects.

The fluorescence ray originates in the ionization and subsequent recombination of the atoms of the radiator. When the x-rays traverse matter, a part of their energy is spent in ejecting β-rays, or electrons, from some of the atoms. The remainder of the atom is in an ionized condition, and as it regains its normal state, energy is liberated which reappears as the fluorescence x-rays. We now have evidence that the ionized atom usually returns to its normal condition through a series of steps, and that at each step radiation is emitted whose frequency is proportional to the energy radiated.

If an electron is ejected from the innermost portion of the atom, where the energy is a minimum and the greatest amount of energy is therefore required to liberate the electron, a large amount of energy will correspondingly be liberated when an electron returns to the vacated position. The frequency of the fluorescence radiation emitted, being proportional to the energy radiated, will accordingly have the highest value possible for this atom.

There are two prominent types of fluorescence x-rays which may be excited in most of the elements, known as the K and the L characteristic radiations.[8] The former is apparently the most penetrating type of fluorescence radiation which the element is capable of radiating, and is thus presumably excited when an electron is ejected from the most stable position in the atom. The L radiation is much less penetrating, and occurs when electrons are ejected from the next most stable position. It is a remarkable fact that similar characteristic fluorescence radiations are emitted from all the elements, which differ by regular gradations in penetrating power or wavelength as one goes from one element to another.

Spectra of these characteristic radiations, taken however directly from the target of the x-ray tube instead of from fluorescing matter, are shown below (Figs. I–27 and I–28) for several elements.

Secondary Electrons Ejected by X-rays

The fact that x-rays ionize gases suggests that they eject electrons from the molecules of the gas. The most informative method of

---

[8] C. G. Barkla and C. A. Sadler, Phil. Mag. **16**, 550 (1908).

studying this phenomenon is that introduced by C. T. R. Wilson.[9]
He observed that a droplet of moisture will condense more readily
upon a charged ion than upon a neutral molecule, and has thus made
the ions visible by condensing water droplets upon them. The
principle on which his apparatus works is evident from Fig. I–10.
The chamber C has glass sides and top and is closed at the bottom
with a piston. In the chamber are air and some water. The piston
remains in position A until the air is saturated with moisture. Then
the piston is suddenly moved to B, producing an adiabatic expansion
and thus cooling the air until it is strongly supersaturated with
moisture. For a brief instant the shutter admits x-rays to the
chamber. If the air is free from dust, and there is just the right

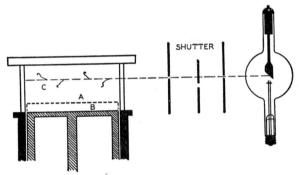

FIG. I–10.   Cloud Track Method of Making Visible Paths of High-speed Electrons.

degree of supersaturation, droplets of moisture will now form only
on the ions produced by the x-rays, which can be seen or photographed
with bright illumination.

A typical photograph thus obtained is shown in Fig. I–11. The
white lines here shown consist of rows of droplets, some of which
are separately visible, each formed upon an ion as a nucleus.
The part of the air exposed to the x-rays differs from the rest of
the air only in the fact that it is this region in which the curved lines
originate. In other words, the action of the x-rays is to eject from
the air high speed particles (β-rays) which break into ions the molecules through which they pass. Thus the process of ionization is to
a large extent an indirect one. Whereas in Fig. I–11 the x-rays
have ejected about 20 β-rays, these particles, while tearing their way

[9] C. T. R. Wilson, Proc. Roy. Soc. A 87, 277 (1912).

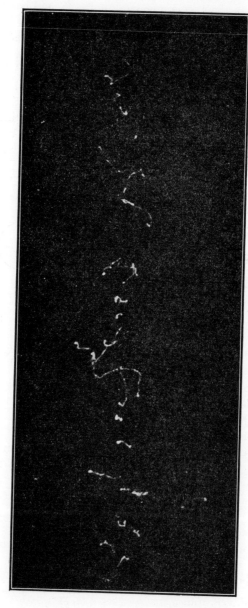

Fig. I-11.   Beta Rays Ejected by a Narrow Beam of X-rays.   (Wilson.)

through the air, have produced thousands of ions. It is the ions thus formed which give to air and other gases their electrical conductivity when exposed to x-rays.

In Fig. I–12 are shown two different types of β-rays, both ejected by the same x-ray beam. At the top and bottom of the figure are seen long trails of two high-speed electrons. Between them appear several short tracks due to electrons with much less energy. These two types of β-rays, which are easily distinguishable because of the difference in speed, are known respectively as *photo-electrons* and *recoil electrons*.

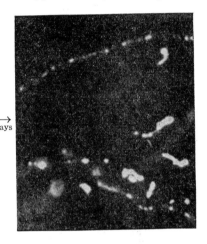

X-rays →

A study of the speed of these *recoil electrons* shows that they have the energy which should be given by the impact of a photon, according to the cor-

Fig. I–12.

puscular theory of x-ray scattering. The fact that these short tracks always point away from the x-ray tube supports this interpretation.

It seems that the *photo-electrons* are excited by the same process as that which occurs in the photo-electric effect with light. When light falls upon the alkali metals it has been found that electrons are ejected with a kinetic energy whose maximum value is given by Einstein's photo-electric equation as

$$\tfrac{1}{2}mv^2 = h\nu - w, \tag{1.02}$$

where w is the work done in pulling the electron out of the metal, ν is the frequency of the light, and h is a constant of proportionality known as "Planck's constant." When x-rays instead of light are employed, the photo-electrons are found to be ejected with different groups of velocities, but the energy of the fastest electrons in each group is again given by equation (1.02). The constant h keeps the same value, 6.56×10^{-27} erg seconds; but w, the work done in removing the electron from the atom, has a different value for the different groups of photo-electrons.

Relation between Photo-electrons and Fluorescence X-rays.—If it requires an amount of energy w_k to remove an electron from the lowest or K energy level, it is clear from equation (1.02) that such an electron cannot be ejected if $h\nu < w_k$, i.e., if the frequency of the incident x-rays is less than $\nu = w_k/h = \nu_k$.   But if the electrons are not removed from the K level, it is impossible for any K fluorescence radiation to be emitted.   This result has been fully verified by experiment, which shows that fluorescence radiation of the K or L type is not emitted by an element unless it is traversed by radiation whose frequency is greater than the critical value w_k/h or w_l/h required to eject photo-electrons from the corresponding energy levels.

It has been noted above that after ionization has occurred an atom usually returns to its normal condition through a series of steps.   One of these steps may be the transition of an electron from an L to a K energy level, in which case the amount of energy liberated is $w_l - w_k$, which can be determined by measuring the difference in energy of the photo-electrons ejected from these two levels.   It is interesting to note that the most prominent line in the spectrum of the fluorescence K radiation has the frequency $\nu = (w_l - w_k)/h$, where h is again Planck's constant.   It is thus natural to suppose that if the energy liberated during any change of the electron's position in the atom is w, the frequency of the radiation emitted during the process is w/h.   This statement is indeed a fundamental postulate of Bohr's theory of spectra, and as a part of that theory has received very strong support.

It is a consequence of this postulate that the highest frequency fluorescence ray that can be excited is no greater than the frequency of the primary ray.   For the greatest amount of energy which the primary ray can impart to an atom in ejecting an electron is $h\nu$, and this is therefore also the greatest amount of energy that can be liberated as a fluorescence ray when the atom returns to its normal condition.   It will of course usually happen that the frequency of the fluorescence ray is considerably lower than that of the primary ray.   This corresponds to Stokes' law in optics.   Though the law is by no means always valid in the visible region, in the region of x-rays it is doubtful whether any exceptions occur.

6. *Polarization of X-rays*

According to the electromagnetic wave theory of the scattering of x-rays given above, we should expect the rays scattered at an angle of 90° with the primary beam to be polarized.   For the electric vector of the primary wave is perpendicular to the direction of propagation, and the accelerations of the scattering electrons must therefore be perpendicular to this plane. If we were to look at these scattering electrons in a direction at right angles with the primary beam, their motions would all be in a plane which we should be seeing edge-on. Imagine, as in Fig. I–13, that the primary beam is propagated horizontally toward the north when it passes over the electron at e. The acceleration of this electron will then be in a vertical, east-west, plane. The electric vector of the wave which it emits toward the east must also lie in this plane, since there is no component of the acceleration of the scattering electron in any other direction.

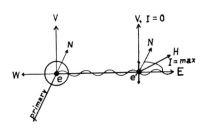

FIG. I–13. Polarization of X-rays by Scattering.

Consequently, the scattered ray reaching an electron at e', having its electric vector in a vertical plane, is completely plane polarized.

This polarization may be detected by examining the rays scattered by the electron e'. This electron is accelerated in a vertical direction. The amplitude of the electric vector of the wave emitted is, according to the usual electrodynamics, proportional to the sine of the angle between the acceleration and the direction of propagation. Thus the maximum intensity of the beam scattered by electron e' is in the horizontal plane, while in the vertical direction the intensity is zero. The polarization of the beam scattered by electron e is thus detected by comparing the intensity of the scattered rays from electron e' in the horizontal and vertical directions.

A test of this character was first made by C. G. Barkla[10] in 1906. In place of the electrons e and e', he used blocks of carbon to produce the scattering, and he compared the ionization produced in two chambers placed at H and V respectively. He found the ionization in the chamber H much more intense than in chamber V, thus proving that the rays scattered by the first radiator were strongly polarized. The fact that the scattered rays are thus polarized in the predicted manner gives strong evidence that the x-rays consist of electromagnetic waves or pulses.

[10] C. G. Barkla, Proc. Roy. Soc. A 77, 247 (1906).

7. Diffraction and Interference of X-rays

It was recognized early in their study that most of the properties of x-rays might be explained if they consisted of electromagnetic waves of wave-length much less than that of light.[11]   Many attempts were therefore made to secure diffraction of x-rays by passing them through a narrow slit.   Haga and Wind performed a careful series of experiments[12] to detect any possible diffraction through a wedge-shaped slit a few thousandths of a millimeter broad at its widest part. Photographs were obtained which showed a broadening where the rays passed through the narrow part.   The magnitude of the broadening was about that which would result[13] from rays of wave-length 1.3×10^{-8} cm.   Walter and Pohl repeated the experiments by yet more refined methods,[14] and came to the conclusion that if any diffraction effects were present, they were considerably smaller than Haga and Wind had estimated.   Later, A. Sommerfeld[15] recalculated the wave-lengths from Walter and Pohl's plates on the basis of photometric measurements performed by Koch.[16]   He thus found from their photographs that the effective wave-length of hard x-rays is about 4×10^{-9} cm., and that the wave-length of soft x-rays is measurably greater.   Though because of the experimental difficulties these results were not as convincing as their accuracy warranted, they are of historical significance because they inspired von Laue to carry out his epoch-making experiments on crystal diffraction, which are described below.

More recently experiments on the diffraction of x-rays have been performed with as perfect results as those obtained with light. Walter[17] and Rabinov[18] have published photographs showing definite diffraction effects using slits after essentially the same procedure as the earlier investigators, but with homogeneous x-rays of known wave-length (λ 1.54 and λ 0.71 A respectively).   Larsson[19] and Kellström,[20] using soft x-rays in a vacuum, have obtained remark-

[11] E. Wiechert, Sitzungsber. d. Phys-Okon. Ges. zu Königsberg, (1894).
[12] Haga and Wind, Wied. Ann. 68, 884 (1899).
[13] A. Sommerfeld, Phys. Zeits. 2, 59 (1900).
[14] Walter and Pohl, Ann. d. Phys. 29, 331 (1909).
[15] A. Sommerfeld, Ann. d. Phys. 38, 473 (1912).
[16] P. P. Koch, Ann. d. Phys. 38, 507 (1912).
[17] B. Walter, Ann. d. Phys. 74, 661 (1924); 75, 189 (1924).
[18] I. I. Rabinov, Proc. Nat. Acad. Sci., 11, 222 (1925).
[19] A. Larsson, Uppsala Univ. Årsskrift, No. 1, p. 97 (1929).
[20] G. Kellström, Nov. Act. Reg. Soc. Sci. Uppsaliensis 8, No. 5, (1932).

able results. Figure I–14 reproduces a diffraction pattern obtained by Larsson using x-rays of 8.3 A wave-length (Al $K\alpha$ line) and a slit of 0.0055 mm width.

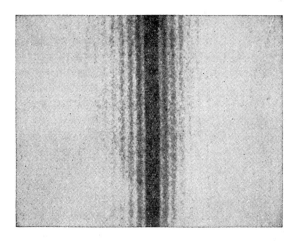

FIG. I–14. Enlargement of Diffraction Pattern of 8.3 A. X-rays Traversing 0.0055 mm Slit. (Larsson.)

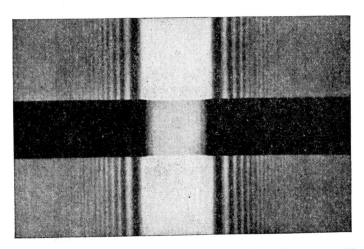

FIG. I–15. Diffraction of 8.3 A. X-rays by 0.038 mm Wire, Enlarged 73 Times. Middle portion printed darker. (Kellström.)

Figure I–15 shows a diffraction pattern obtained by Kellström using x-rays of the same wave-length, but with a tungsten wire of

0.038 mm diameter instead of a slit.   These diffraction patterns are found to agree accurately with the usual theory of the phenomena given in texts on physical optics.

8. *Diffraction by Ruled Gratings*

Though these photographs show definite diffraction effects, they have not enabled us to make any precise determination of the x-ray wave-lengths.   Absolute wave-lengths of x-rays have, however, been measured by means of ruled reflection gratings, similar to those used for visible light.   In the early experiments it was found impossible to reflect x-rays from a polished surface, but later work (described in Sec. 15) showed that such specular reflection does occur when the x-rays graze the surface at a sufficiently sharp angle.   Within this angle, of less than half a degree for ordinary x-rays, it is thus possible to use a reflection grating.

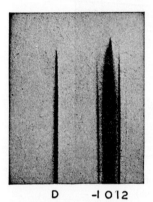

D   -1 0 1 2

Fig. I–16. Ruled Grating Spectrum of Mo $K\alpha_1$ Line, $\lambda = 0.71$ A. (Compton-Doan, 1925.)

One of the first spectra thus obtained[21] is reproduced in Fig. I–16. This shows the diffraction by a grating ruled on speculum metal of the $K\alpha_1$ line of molybdenum, $\lambda = 0.71$ A.   Figure I–17 shows the spectrum of the copper K lines (1.5 A) diffracted from a grating ruled on glass.[22] Figure I–18 is a spectrum of the carbon Kα line, $\lambda = 45$ A, obtained with a similar glass grating.[23]   In each case, D represents the direct beam (with the grating removed), O the specularly reflected beam (zero order), and the numbers refer to the order of the diffracted image.

These examples show how the method is applicable from x-rays of ordinary hardness, far into the region of soft x-rays.   Especially noteworthy are the pioneer studies of soft x-rays using ruled gratings in a vacuum made by Thibaud,[24] and Osgood,[25] culminating in

[21] A. H. Compton and R. L. Doan, Proc. Nat. Acad. Sci. **11**, 598 (1925).

[22] J. A. Bearden, Proc. Nat. Acad. Sci. **15**, 528 (1929).

[23] C. E. Howe, Rev. Sci. Inst. **1**, 749 (1930).

[24] J. Thibaud, J. de Phys. et le Radium, **8**, 447 (1927).

[25] T. H. Osgood, Phys. Rev. **30**, 567 (1927).

Osgood's extension of the spectrum into the region of the extreme ultraviolet. There is thus no longer any dividing line between optical and x-ray spectra, since the same spectroscopic technique can be used throughout the entire range of wave-lengths. On the other hand, Wadlund,[26] Bäcklin,[27] Bearden,[28] and others

FIG. I–17. Grating Spectrum of Copper K Lines, 1.5 A. (Bearden, 1929.)

have developed the technique of precision wave-length measurement with the ruled grating, until such determinations now probably give our most reliable wave-lengths for x-rays. The usual grating formula is used,

$$n\lambda = d(\sin i + \sin r).$$

For Fig. I–18, as an example, $d = 1/600$ mm, and λ for the Cu $K\alpha$ line was calculated to be $1.5422 \pm .0002$ A.

FIG. I–18. Grating Spectrum of Carbon K Line, 45 A. (Howe, 1930.)

9. Interference Phenomena

Of all optical phenomena, that which is usually considered to give the most conclusive evidence for the wave character of light is interference. Of course interference is an essential part of the action of a ruled grating—the region between the spectrum lines is dark because of the interference between the rays from the different lines in the grating. It is of interest however to note, as a series of beau-

[26] A. P. R. Wadlund, Phys. Rev. **32**, 841 (1928).
[27] E. Bäcklin, Thesis, Uppsala (1928).
[28] J. A. Bearden, Proc. Nat. Acad. Sci. **15**, 528 (1929).

tiful experiments by Kellström has shown,[29] that x-ray interference can be obtained also with the familiar Fresnel double-mirror and other similar methods.   Figure I–19 shows one of Kellström's photographs of the Fresnel interference fringes, using the aluminium $K\alpha$ line ($\lambda = 8.3$ A) and an angle between the two mirrors of 19.6 seconds of arc.

10. Diffraction of X-rays by Crystals

While these direct methods of measuring x-ray wave-lengths were being developed, and long before they were brought to a successful

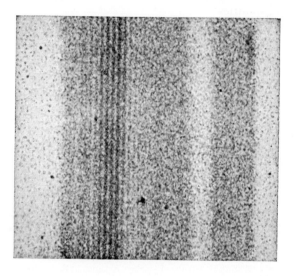

Fig. I–19.   Fresnel Interference Fringes with Al $K\alpha$ Line, 8.3 A.   Magnified 73 times.
(Kellström.)

conclusion, von Laue and his collaborators discovered the remarkable fact that crystals act as suitable gratings for diffracting x-rays.[30] From this discovery has grown on the one hand a surprisingly exact knowledge of the structure of many crystals, and on the other hand a means of studying x-ray spectra which is comparable in precision with our methods of studying optical spectra.

Sommerfeld had calculated from Walter and Pohl's diffraction

---

[29] G. Kellström, Nov. Act. Reg. Soc. Sci. Uppsaliensis 8, No. 5 (1932).
[30] W. Friedrich, P. Knipping and M. Laue, Ber. bayer. Akad. Wiss., 303 (1912).

experiments that the wave-length of ordinary x-rays must lie between 10^{-8} and 10^{-9} cm.   Von Laue calculated from the known number of molecules per unit volume that the average distance between the atoms in solids was between 10^{-7} and 10^{-8} cm.   Now in a crystal, in order to get the symmetry which is observed, we must suppose that there is a unit, presumably of atomic or molecular size, which arranges itself in a regular repeating order.   It is therefore natural to suppose that in a crystal there are layers of molecular units which are arranged successively at uniform distances not much greater than the wave-length of x-rays.   But these conditions are very similar to those which occur when light traverses an optical grating—regularly spaced discontinuities separated by distances several times the wave-

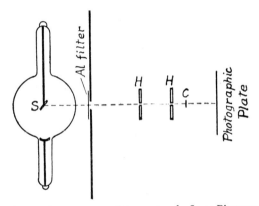

Fig. I-20.   Arrangement of Apparatus for Laue Photographs.

length of the light.   It therefore occurred to von Laue that a crystal might act toward x-rays in much the same manner as a grating acts toward light.   He accordingly asked Friedrich and Knipping to try the experiment of passing a narrow beam of x-rays through a crystal of zinc blende.

The apparatus which was used in the original experiments is shown diagrammatically in Fig. I-20.   X-rays from the target S, after being collimated by two circular holes HH, passed through the zinc blende crystal C onto the photographic plate.   In Fig. I-21 are shown three photographs of the type thus obtained.   Around the central spot, produced by the direct beam passing through the crystal, appears a group of symmetrically arranged spots.   The positions of these spots changed when the orientation of the crystals was altered,

A. X-rays perpendicular to cube face (100 plane).

B. X-rays perpendicular to cube edge (110 plane).

C. X-rays along cube diagonal (111 plane).

Fig. I–21. Laue Diffraction Patterns with Rock-salt.

and were different for different crystals. They formed exactly the type of pattern which might have been expected from a three dimensional grating.

A simple interpretation of these photographs was offered by W. L. Bragg.[31] He pointed out that each of the images surrounding the central spot could be interpreted as the reflection of the incident x-ray beam from some plane within the crystal which was especially rich in atoms. Consider a two-dimensional pattern of points as shown in Fig. I–22. It will be seen that the lines (corresponding to the planes in the three dimensional crystal) which have many points

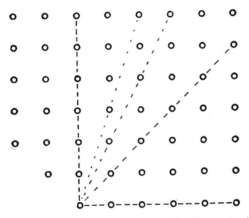

FIG. I–22.   A Two-dimensional Point Array.   The linear density of points is especially large along the dotted lines.

per unit length are those drawn at " simple " angles. Similarly the position of the spots to be expected in a Laue photograph with a cubic crystal can be calculated on Bragg's assumption merely from the crystal symmetry, the more intense spots being reflected from planes drawn at simple angles with the cubic axes. A comparison of the positions of the spots thus calculated with the positions of the spots in Friedrich and Knipping's photographs showed that the idea was sound.

The cleavage face of a crystal should be parallel to these " simple " planes which are rich in atoms. W. H. Bragg therefore tried the experiment of reflecting a beam of x-rays from the cleavage surface of a crystal, and found on the photographic plate a spot at the angle

[31] W. L. Bragg, Proc. Camb. Phil. Soc. 17, 43 (1912).

of reflection.[32]   He then replaced the photographic plate with an ionization chamber, mounted upon the arm of a spectrometer, and placed the crystal upon the prism table, so that both could be conveniently oriented at any desired angle with the primary beam.   A

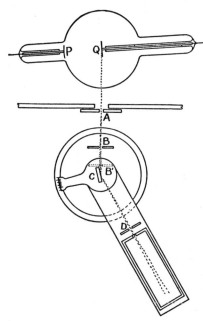

diagrammatic plan of the apparatus as thus employed is shown in Fig. I–23.   *A* and *B* are slits which collimate the primary x-ray beam, *C* is the crystal, *D* is a slit which defines the beam entering the ionization chamber *I*.   As the glancing angle θ at which the x-rays struck the crystal was varied, the angle between the ionization chamber and the primary beam was kept equal to 2θ, in order to receive the secondary beam reflected from the crystal.

A record of the intensity of ionization as the angle θ was varied is shown in Fig. I–24.   In this experiment x-rays from a tube containing a platinum target

FIG. I–23.   A Bragg X-ray Spectrometer.   were reflected by a crystal of rock-salt.   It will be seen that instead of varying uniformly with the angle, the ionization rises to large values at certain sharply defined angles.

An interpretation of this curve may be obtained if we examine further the manner in which x-rays are diffracted by a crystal.   Suppose that a wave comes from a source *S* and strikes a crystal, as in Fig. I–25.   A fraction of the wave is reflected by the first layer of atoms at an angle θ, equal to the incident glancing angle, and another fraction is reflected from the second layer.   It is clear from the construction of the figure that the difference in the length of the paths followed by these two rays is *ABC*.   But $AB = BC = OB \sin \theta$, so that the difference in path is $2OB \sin \theta$.   In order to secure coöperation between these beams, the difference between their paths

[32] It is interesting to note that Roentgen tried a rather similar experiment in 1895 using a crystal of calcite, but with negative results, due doubtless to underexposure.

must be an integral number of wave-lengths.   It follows, writing $OB = d$, that

$$n\lambda = 2d \sin \theta, \qquad (1.03)$$

where n is an integer, and represents the order of the diffraction. This relation is known as *Bragg's law*.

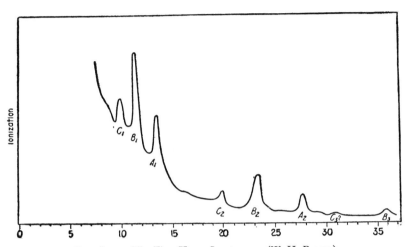

FIG. I-24.   The First X-ray Spectrum.   (W. H. Bragg.)

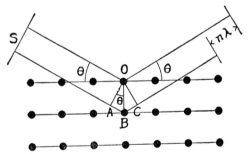

FIG. I-25.   Illustrating the Elementary Derivation of the Bragg Law.

According to this equation, a change of the angle θ should alter the wave-length of the rays reflected from the crystal.   It is therefore natural to suppose that the three peaks, A_1, B_1 and C_1 represent x-ray spectrum lines.   If this is the case, second orders of these lines should appear at angles whose sines are twice those of lines A_1, B_1 and C_1.   Such lines actually do appear at A_2, B_2 and C_2, and not only are their angles just what they should be according to eq. (1.03), but their relative intensities also are in the same ratio as those of the corresponding lines in the first order.

The fact that these lines are characteristic of the target from which the x-rays are emitted is shown by the fact that if an x-ray tube with a nickel target is substituted for the one with the platinum target, an entirely different type of spectrum is observed, two lines instead of three appearing, and at different angles.   If, on the other hand, the crystal is changed, the same lines appear with about the same relative intensity, but the angles at which they appear is changed, indicating, according to eq. (1.03), that the grating space between the layers of atoms is different for different crystals.   It is therefore clear that we are dealing here with true spectra of x-rays characteristic of the target, diffracted by a crystal grating.

11. *Wave-lengths of X-rays by Crystal Diffraction*

Measurements with the ruled gratings tell us the wave-length λ of the x-ray spectrum lines.   Thus it is possible from eq. (1.03) to calculate the distance between the layers of atoms from measurements of the angle θ at which a given x-ray line is diffracted.   For example, the first order of the $K\alpha$ line of copper is observed to be reflected from a cleavage face of rock salt at a glancing angle of 15° 50'. Bearden's measurement with a ruled grating shows that the wave-length of this line is 1.542 A, where 1 Angstrom = 10^{-8} cm.   By eq. (1.03) the distance between the atomic layers parallel to the cleavage face is

$$d = 1.542/[2 \sin (15° 50')]$$
$$= 2.826 \text{ A.}$$

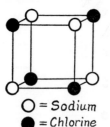

○ = Sodium
● = Chlorine

Fig. I–26.   Arrangement of Atoms in Rock-salt.   (Bragg.)

If we assume a definite arrangement of the atoms in a crystal, it is, however, possible to calculate the distance between the successive layers in terms of the number of molecules per gram molecule.   Thus if the atoms of sodium and chlorine are arranged alternately at the corners of a cubic array, as in Fig. I–26, the distance between adjacent atomic layers is $d = (1/n)^{1/3}$, where n is the number of atoms per cm.[3]   But the number of molecules per gram molecule is $N = 6.06 \times 10^{23}$, as Millikan finds from his oil drop measurements, the molecular weight of sodium chloride is $W = 58.45$, and its density ρ = 2.163. Thus $n = 2N\rho/W = 4.49 \times 10^{22}$ atoms per cm.^{3} The distance between the atomic layers should thus be

$$d(\text{calculated}) = (1/n)^{1/3} = 2.814 \text{ A},$$

which differs from the observed value by less than $\frac{1}{2}$ per cent.[33] It can be shown that there is no other arrangement of sodium and chlorine atoms on a cubic lattice which will give the relative intensities observed in different orders and from various crystal planes. This is discussed in Chap. V. It follows that the arrangement of the atoms shown in Fig. I–26 is the only one possible.

From a study of the crystal spectra themselves it was possible to select this arrangment of the atoms in rock salt with a high degree of probability years before it was possible to get a precise independent measurement of x-ray wave-lengths. This made it possible to assign absolute wave-lengths to the various x-ray spectrum lines. It would appear from recent measurements with ruled gratings that the wave-lengths thus assigned are in error by a small fraction of a per cent, but for most purposes this difference is negligible.

12. X-ray Spectra

A systematic study of the x-ray spectra of the different elements was first made by Moseley[34] in 1913–14. His experiments covered a range of from 0.4 to 8 A., using 38 different elements as targets of his x-ray tube. He found that the spectrum lines emitted by these elements belonged to two distinct series, which were identified with the K and L types of characteristic fluorescent radiation which had previously been observed by Barkla and Sadler. Moseley's photographs of the x-ray spectra of the K or shortest wave-length series lines from the elements of atomic weight between 40 and 65 are shown in Fig. I–27. Since in these spectra the wave-lengths are nearly proportional to the angles, the wave-lengths can be taken as nearly proportional to the distances of the lines from the left-hand side of the figure.

The most striking thing in this figure is the great regularity of the spectra. Each element exhibits a spectrum identical with that of the other elements except that the scale of wave-lengths is changed.

---

[33] A part of this difference is due to our neglect of the refraction of the x-rays in the crystal (cf. Chap. IX).

[34] H. G. J. Moseley, Phil. Mag. **26**, 1024 (1913); **27**, 703 (1914).

It will be noticed also that as one goes from the lighter to the heavier elements, the wave-length of the corresponding lines decreases in a regular manner.   Thus even if we did not know that there is an element scandium between the elements calcium and titanium, the large gap between the spectra of these two elements would have suggested strongly that such an element should exist.   An examination of these spectra revealed the fact that the square root of the frequency of either

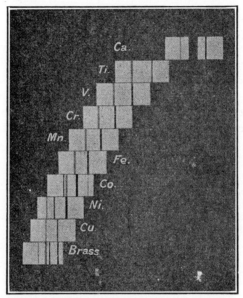

FIG. I–27.   Typical K series Spectra.   (Moseley.)

of the two lines in this spectrum is nearly proportional to the atomic number of the radiator, or more exactly, that the frequency is given by

$$\nu^{\frac{1}{2}} = K(Z - \sigma) \qquad (1.04)$$

Here K is a universal constant for all elements, Z is the number, and σ is another universal constant.   This is usually spoken of as Moseley's law.   It applies not only to the K series lines as shown in Fig. I–27, but also, with appropriate changes in the values of the constants K and σ, to the lines of the L series.   While precise experiments have shown that this law is not exact, it is nevertheless sufficiently accurate for many purposes, and affords, as we shall see, an important clue to the origin of these spectrum lines.

The appearance of the L series lines is beautifully shown by Siegbahn's photographs in Fig. I–28. The spectra of these elements also exhibit the same regular changes that are found in the spectra of the K series, but the spectrum has a considerably greater number of lines. Two series of still greater wave-length are known, an M series and an N series. These radiations are however so soft that they can be studied only with a vacuum spectrograph. Tables of

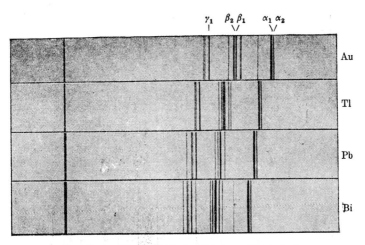

FIG. I–28.   Typical L Series Spectra.   (Siegbahn.)

the wave-lengths of the different x-ray spectrum lines are given in Appendix V.

13. X-ray Spectra According to Bohr's Theory

In order to understand the significance of the remarkable regularities observed in the x-ray spectra, we may profitably consider at this point Bohr's theory[35] of the origin of spectral lines. This theory is so well known that we need only recall its broad outlines. Its essential feature is the assumption that the atom may exist in any one of a series of discrete states, and that while in such a state no radiation is emitted. When however the atom changes from one state to another of less energy, the energy lost is radiated in a single unit, or *quantum*. If W_i is the energy of the atom in the initial

[35] N. Bohr, Phil. Mag. 6, 1, 476 and 857 (1913).

state and W_f that in its final state, Bohr assumes that the frequency of the emitted radiation is given by the relation,

$$h\nu = W_i - W_f. \qquad (1.05)$$

The similarity between this expression and Einstein's photo-electric equation (1.02) is at once evident. The normal state of the atom

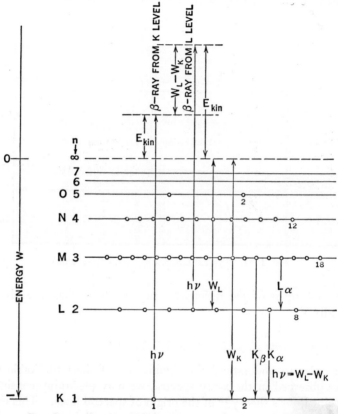

Fig. I–29. Energies of Electrons in the Molybdenum Atom.

is the state of the least possible energy. In this condition the atom cannot radiate, but may absorb radiation with a resulting change to an *excited* state of higher energy.

In our discussion of the origin of fluorescent x-rays and photo-electrons we have found evidence that the electrons occur at different energy levels within the atom. Let us represent by Fig. I–29 the energies of the various electrons in an atom of molybdenum. We suppose that since molybdenum is the 42nd element in the order of atomic weights (i.e., atomic number 42), it will have 42 electrons distributed around its nucleus. These are believed to be arranged in groups having different energies: 2 in the most stable or K group, 8 in the next group, and so on. At the outer part of the normal atom are the valence electrons, which are responsible for the chemical and optical properties of the atom. It is however the inner electrons which give rise to the x-ray spectra. It will be clear from this diagram that by measuring the energy E_{kin} of a photo-electron ejected from the K group by radiation whose frequency ν is known, we can determine the energy (of negative sign) of an electron in the K group, and similarly for any other group.

According to Bohr's theory, if an electron has been removed from the K group, the other electrons remaining in their normal positions, the atom is in an excited state. It may change to a state of lower energy if an electron falls from the L group into the vacant position in the K energy level. The energy difference between the two states is $W_L - W_K$, whence according to eq. (1.05) the frequency of radiation emitted should be:

$$\nu_{K\alpha} = \frac{1}{h}\,(W_L - W_K).$$

Measurements of the energies of photo-electrons enable us to evaluate the right-hand side of this equation, with results which completely confirm Bohr's frequency formula.

X-ray spectrum lines thus result from transfers of electrons between inner levels which are occupied in the normal atom. Optical spectra, on the other hand, are produced by electrons falling from possible outer levels that are normally unoccupied to other levels which may or may not be normally occupied. Thus optical spectra change their characteristics from element to element because of the marked changes in the energies of the outer electron groups. The inner electron groups are however similarly arranged for all except the very light elements, and the only spectral differences to be expected are those resulting from the different stability of these inner groups of electrons for different values of the nuclear charge.

Bohr has suggested a method of calculating the energy of the electron groups, which has been adapted by Moseley to the calculation of x-ray frequencies with remarkable results. He assumes that each electron revolves in a circular orbit, its centrifugal force being balanced by the electrostatic attraction of the nucleus, modified by the forces due to the other electrons in the atom. Of the infinite variety of orbits which are thus possible, only those are supposed to be stable for which the angular momentum is an integral multiple of $h/2\pi$, where h is again Planck's constant. These two assumptions are sufficient to specify the radius and the energy of the electron in its orbit. The radius is found to be

$$a = \frac{n^2 h^2}{4\pi^2 F e^2 m},\qquad(1.06)$$

and the energy of the electron in its orbit is

$$W = -\frac{2\pi^2 e^4 F^2 m}{n^2 h^2}.\qquad(1.07)$$

Here e and m are the charge and mass of the electron, n is an integer known as the quantum number, and F is the effective number of electronic units of charge on the nucleus. We may write, following Moseley,

$$F = Z - \sigma,\qquad(1.08)$$

where Z is the atomic number and σ, known as the *screening constant*, is the correction due to the repulsion by the other electrons in the atom. If an electron falls from an orbit of quantum number n_i to one of quantum number n_f, by combining eqs. (1.05) and (1.07) we find for the frequency of the emitted radiation,

$$\nu = RcF^2\left\{\frac{1}{n^2_f} - \frac{1}{n^2_i}\right\},\qquad(1.09)$$

where R is known as the Rydberg constant, defined by

$$R \equiv \frac{2\pi^2 e^4 m}{ch^3},\qquad(1.10)$$

and c is the speed of light.

Other methods of calculating these energies and frequencies have been proposed by Sommerfeld, Heisenberg, Schrödinger and others. From the standpoint of the nature of the assumptions involved these more recent theories are preferable; but the calculations are more complex and the results are very nearly the same as those reached by Bohr. It is probably safe to say that the Bohr theory offers as satisfactory a *picture* of what happens in the atom when radiation is emitted as can at present be supplied.

In the case of hydrogen, $F = Z = 1$ exactly, and substituting the values of e, m and h the frequencies of the various spectrum lines can be calculated. For $n_f = 2$ and $n_i = 3, 4, 5$, etc., this formula gives the frequencies of the visible hydrogen lines and those in the ultraviolet which compose what is known as the Balmer series. Within experimental error the agreement is exact. Thus for example, if $n_f = 2$ and $n_i = 3$, the calculated wave-length is $\lambda = c/v = 6.561 \times 10^{-5}$ cm, while the observed wave-length is 6.563×10^{-5} cm. For $n_f = 1$, the frequencies are much greater, and correspond exactly with those of the Lyman series of hydrogen. Similarly, for $n_f = 3, 4$ and 5, the various values of n_i give frequencies which agree with those of known lines in the infra red spectrum of hydrogen. Thus eq. (1.09) predicts accurately the position of all the known lines of atomic hydrogen, and does not predict any lines which do not occur under suitable conditions.

When we apply this formula to the case of x-ray spectra, for the $K\alpha$ line of molybdenum we have $Z = 42$, and supposing that the K series is emitted by electrons in the innermost energy level we may take $\sigma = 0.5$, as representing the repulsion of the other electron in the K energy level. Thus $F = 41.5$. Since the $K\alpha$ line is the longest of this series, we may take $n_f = 1$ and $n_i = 2$. Substituting these quantities in eq. (1.09) we find $\lambda = c/v = 0.70 \times 10^{-8}$ cm., which agrees very satisfactorily with the value 0.71×10^{-8} cm, determined experimentally. Similarly for the $L\alpha$ line of tungsten, we have $Z = 74$, σ may be taken as 5.5,[36] giving $F = 68.5$, $n_f = 2$, and $n_i = 3$. Thus $\lambda = 1.40 \times 10^{-8}$ cm, which again agrees acceptably with the experimental value 1.47×10^{-8} cm.

If we write

$$K^2 = R c \left(\frac{1}{n_f^2} - \frac{1}{n_i^2} \right)$$

and

$$F = Z - \sigma,$$

eq. (1.09) becomes

$$v^{\frac{1}{2}} = K (Z - \sigma),$$

[36] The value of σ may be written approximately as $\sigma = p + \frac{1}{2}(q - 1)$, where q is the number of electrons in the final energy level of the radiating electron, and p is the number of electrons in levels closer to the nucleus. Cf. X-rays and Electrons, p. 30.

which is identical with Moseley's experimental law (1.04). Moseley's law thus indicates that Z, the charge on the nucleus of the atom, increases by 1 electronic unit as we pass from one element to the element next higher in atomic weight. Moreover, since σ remains constant, the number of electrons in the inner shells must remain constant for the elements for which Moseley's law holds. These x-ray spectra, with the help of Bohr's theory, therefore supply very valuable evidence concerning the inner structure of the atom.

14. The Continuous X-ray Spectrum

The continuous portion of the x-ray spectrum also has some very

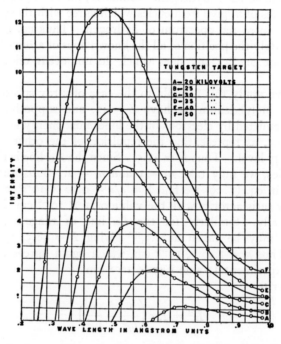

Fig. I-30.   Continuous X-ray Spectra at Different Constant Potentials. (Ulrey.)

interesting features. In Fig. I-30 is shown a series of spectra obtained by Ulrey from a tungsten target, taken with different potential differences across the x-ray tube. It will be seen that for a definite potential, no radiation occurs of wave-length less than a certain critical value. Having passed this wave-length, the intensity rises sharply to a maximum, and then gradually falls to a relatively low value.

Duane and Hunt have shown that the short wave-length limit of the spectrum is inversely proportional to the potential applied to the tube, or that the frequency of this limiting radiation is proportional to the potential. It is customary to state this fact thus:

$$Ve = h\nu_{max.} = hc/\lambda_{min.} \qquad (1.11)$$

In this expression, V represents the potential across the tube and e the charge on the electron, so that Ve is the energy with which the cathode ray strikes the target; c is the velocity of light, and h, the constant of proportionality, is the same as Planck's constant which we used in discussing the photo-electric effect. From careful determinations of the minimum wave-length $\lambda_{min.}$ corresponding to definite potentials V, Duane and his collaborators have found[37]

$$h = Ve\lambda_{min.}/c,$$

$$= 6.556 \times 10^{-27} \text{ erg sec.}$$

This is one of the most reliable direct determinations of Planck's constant.

Equation (1.11) is closely related to Einstein's photo-electric equation (1.02). Einstein's equation says that when a photo-electron is produced, all of the energy of the incident photon is spent in removing the electron from its parent atom and in giving it kinetic energy. Duane and Hunt's equation says that the maximum energy which a photon can receive is equal to the kinetic energy of the cathode electron which strikes the target. Thus Duane and Hunt's law is frequently referred to as the inverse photo-electric equation.

On the other hand this law may be considered as a special case of Bohr's frequency condition, eq. (1.05). We may consider the initial state to be a neutral atom plus a free electron with kinetic energy Ve. If the atom is to remain neutral after the impact of the cathode electron, the final state is a neutral atom plus a free electron with kinetic energy $V'e$, where V' is less than V. Thus any frequency of radiation may be emitted for which

$$h\nu = e(V - V'). \qquad (1.12)$$

[37] Duane and Hunt, Phys. Rev. 6, 166 (1915). Blake and Duane, Phys. Rev. 10, 624 (1917). Duane, Palmer and Chi-Sun-Yeh, J. Opt. Soc. Am., 5, 376 (1921).

The maximum frequency will occur when the final kinetic energy of the free electron is zero, i.e.,

$$h\nu_{max} = Ve,$$

which is Duane's and Hunt's law. Equation (1.12) thus predicts a continuous spectrum extending from $\nu = 0$ to $\nu = Ve/h$, in complete accord with the experiments.

15. *The Refraction of X-rays*

In his original examination of the properties of x-rays, Roentgen tried unsuccessfully to obtain refraction by means of prisms of a variety of materials such as ebonite, aluminium and water. Although these and other early direct tests for the refraction of x-rays were unsuccessful, Stenström found [38] that for x-rays whose wave-lengths are greater than about 3 A, reflected from crystals of sugar and gypsum, Bragg's law, $n\lambda = 2d \sin \theta$, does not give accurately the angles of reflection. He interpreted the difference as due to an appreciable refraction of the x-rays as they enter the crystal. Precise measurements by Duane[39] and Siegbahn[40] have shown that the same type of discrepancies occur, though they are very small indeed, when ordinary x-rays are reflected from calcite.

The direction of the deviations in Stenström's experiments indicated that the index of refraction of the crystals employed was less than 1. If this is the case also for other substances, total reflection should occur when x-rays in air strike a plane surface at a sufficiently sharp glancing angle, just as light in a glass prism is totally reflected from a surface separating the glass from the air if the light strikes the surface at a sufficiently sharp angle. The condition for total reflection is that $\sin r = (1/n) \sin i > 1$, where i is the angle of incidence, r is the angle of refraction, and $n = \sin i/\sin r$ is the index of refraction. For in this case the angle of refraction is imaginary, and all of the energy must be either reflected or absorbed. In terms of the glancing angle θ, which is the complement of the angle of incidence i, this may be written, $(1/n) \cos \theta > 1$, i.e., $\cos \theta > n$, or approximately,

$$\theta = \sin \theta < \sqrt{2}\sqrt{1 - n}. \qquad (1.13)$$

[38] W. Stenström, Dissertation, Lund (1919).
[39] Duane and Patterson, Phys. Rev. 16, p. 526 (1920).
[40] M. Siegbahn, Comptes Rendus, 173, p. 1350 (1921); 174, 745 (1922).

By measuring this critical angle for total reflection, we can thus measure the index of refraction of the x-rays.

The experiment was originally carried out by Compton[41] using the apparatus shown in Fig. I–31. A very narrow sheet of x-rays fell upon the mirror M, and was reflected onto the crystal of a Bragg spectrometer. It was found that the beam could be reflected from surfaces of polished glass and silver through angles of several minutes of arc. By investigating the spectrum of the reflected beam, it was possible to show that the critical glancing angle is approximately proportional to the wave-length, which means, according to eq. (1.13), that the index of refraction differs from unity by an amount pro-

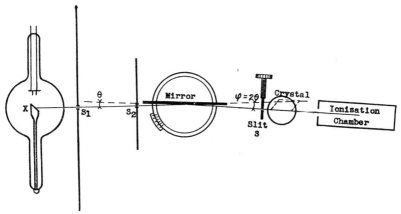

FIG. I–31. Apparatus for Studying Total Reflection of X-rays.

portional to the square of the wave-length. For glass and silver, also, the quantity $1 - n$ for a given wave-length is approximately proportional to the density. For the wave-length 1.279 A, crown glass of density 2.52 was found to have a critical angle of $\theta = 11'$, corresponding to an index of refraction $n = 1 - 5 \times 10^{-6}$. We shall see later (Chap. IV) that these total reflection experiments are in good accord with the usual electron theory of dispersion.

In 1924 Larsson, Siegbahn and Waller[42] finally succeeded in deviating an x-ray beam by means of a prism and in obtaining its dispersion spectrum. The principle of their arrangement is shown in

[41] A. H. Compton, Phil. Mag. 45, 1121 (1923).

[42] A. Larsson, M. Siegbahn and I. Waller, Naturwiss. 12, 1212 (1924); Phys. Rev. 25, 235 (1925).

Fig. I–32, and a photograph by Larsson using this method is shown in Fig. I–33. Their success was due to the fact that their x-rays

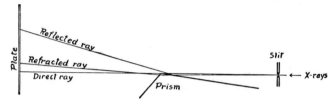

FIG. I–32.   Arrangement for Refracting X-rays with a Prism.

struck the face of the prism at a fine glancing angle, just greater than the critical angle for the refracted rays; whereas most of the earlier attempts had been made with the crystal set for minimum deviation. Experiments by Prins[43] and by Dershem[44] have carried the study of reflection and refraction of very soft x-rays up to wavelengths of 45 A, where it becomes evident that reflection is the same complex function of refractive index and absorption that is valid in the optical region. In fact it may now be truly said that the study of x-rays has become a branch of optics.

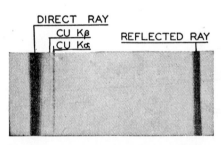

FIG. I–33.   Prism Spectrum of the K Lines of Copper ($\lambda = 1.5$ A), Using Arrangement of Fig. I–32. (Larsson.)

16. X-rays as Waves and as Particles

If x-rays are indeed of the same fundamental character as light, their apparently dual nature as waves and as particles becomes of vital significance. For if x-rays have this dual character, so then must light and heat rays, and electric waves. To every student of physics the phenomena of refraction and specular reflection suggest wave propagation. Diffraction and interference form crucial evidence for the existence of waves. If in addition polarization is observed, their transverse character is established. All of these phenomena have been observed for every one of the various types of

[43] J. A. Prins, Zeit. f. Phys. **47**, 479 (1928).
[44] E. Dershem, Phys. Rev. **33**, 659 and **34**, 1015 (1929).

electromagnetic radiation, including x-rays.   We accordingly cannot avoid the conclusion that light and x-rays have the characteristics of waves.

The Corpuscular Character of Light

The evidence that light consists of particles is no less convincing, though it is less familiar since it is more recent.   It may accordingly be worth while to review this evidence in some detail, though in doing so we must anticipate some of the work described in the later chapters.

The development of the modern conception of light quanta, or photons, began with Planck's ideas concerning heat radiation. Newton indeed had defended the hypothesis of light corpuscles; but the facts which he cited to support this view were later reconciled by Fresnel with the wave theory of light.   It was not until new problems were studied, such as the intensity of heat radiation and the electrical effects of light, that any real need arose for corpuscles as alternative or supplementary to the wave theory of light.

17. Planck's Theory of Heat Radiation

Planck was confronted[45] with the fact that the only theory of emission of radiation from hot bodies to which the classical mechanics and electrodynamics would lead, predicted rays much more intense than are actually observed, and of the wrong color.   It is a matter of common experience that as a body gradually becomes hotter it first glows a dull red, then orange, and bright gold and finally white. According to the formula developed from the classical kinetic theory, however, the light emitted should always be of the same blue color, differing only in intensity as the temperature changes.   Such a conclusion followed necessarily from the fact that all oscillators in thermal equilibrium with each other should have on the average the same kinetic energy, whatever their natural frequency of oscillation.   But the oscillators of higher frequency will be subject to greater acceleration if their kinetic energy is the same, and hence, according to electrodynamical principles, should radiate more energy than those of lower frequency.   Thus at all temperatures the theory predicted that the high frequency radiation should be more intense than the low frequency radiation.

[45] Planck, Verh. d. Deut. Phys. Ges. 2, 237 (1900). A complete account of Planck's studies of this problem is given in his "Wärmestrahlung" (1915), published by Blackiston in English translation by Masius.

Planck saw a possible way of escape from this difficulty if he were to suppose that at low temperatures only the oscillators of low frequencies could emit radiation, whereas at high temperatures those of higher frequencies could also radiate.   To accomplish this result he introduced the assumption that the oscillators in the hot body can emit radiation only in units, or quanta, whose energy is proportional to the frequency of the radiation, i.e.,

$$E = h\nu, \qquad\qquad (1.14)$$

where h is the constant of proportionality between the frequency and the energy E of the unit.   With this limitation it is possible for only those oscillators which have energy greater than $h\nu$ to emit a unit of radiation.   Thus at low temperatures, where the average energy of the oscillators is low, only low frequency rays can be emitted.   At higher temperatures the higher frequency oscillators will have enough energy to emit their larger units of radiant energy, and so as the temperature rises the center of gravity of the radiation will shift to higher and higher frequencies.   Thus with one bold assumption regarding the unitary nature of the emitted light, Planck was able to arrive at a reasonable explanation of the hitherto insoluble problem of the color of the light emitted by hot bodies.

It would take us too far afield to describe how Planck developed this idea of energy quanta to account quantitatively for the intensity as well as the spectral energy distribution of heat rays.   In his hands and those of others the theory has assumed a variety of forms, but it has always retained the essential feature that the rays from the hot body must be emitted in units whose energy is proportional to the frequency.

18. *The Photo-electric Effect*

The units of radiant energy introduced by Planck were not corpuscular.   He supposed that the radiation from an oscillator, though having a definite amount of energy, would spread itself through all space after the manner of a spherical electromagnetic wave.   It remained for Einstein[46] to bring back the conception of a corpuscular unit of radiation, or photon, as it is now called, in his effort to account for the photo-electric effect.

When Einstein approached this problem it was recognized that the speed with which photo-electrons are ejected from a surface

---

[46] A. Einstein, Ann. d. Physik **17**, 145 (1905).

increase with increasing frequency of the light, and it was generally supposed that the number of photo-electrons emitted was proportional to the intensity of the light striking the photo-electric surface. He saw that this proportionality would follow from the assumption that the light which excited the photo-electrons occurs as a stream of particles, each of which would spend its energy in ejecting an electron from an atom of the photo-electric material. If each of these particles had energy $h\nu$, as might be inferred from Planck's theory of heat radiation, this picture of the process would account also for the increase of speed with higher frequencies. If a certain amount of work w_0 is required to remove the electron from the atom, Einstein supposed that all the rest of the photon's energy is spent in giving kinetic energy to the electron, thus deriving his famous photo-electric equation,

$$E_{\text{kin}} = h\nu - w_0, \qquad (1.15)$$

which we have already had occasion to use eq. (1.02).

It was years before this theory received an adequate test. Experiments by Ladenburg[47] favored the view that the velocity rather than the kinetic energy was proportional to the frequency of the incident light, and different results were obtained with different metals. Richardson and Compton[48] and independently Hughes[49] showed that the differences found for different metals were due to the fact that the value of w_0 is different from metal to metal. They were indeed able to show that Einstein's equation was of the right form, and that the constant of proportionality h is approximately the same as Planck's constant. A few years later Millikan,[50] using greater care in securing strictly monochromatic light, was able by means of Einstein's equation to secure from photo-electric measurements one of the best experimental determinations that we have of Planck's constant.

The photo-electric effect is especially prominent with x-rays, for, as we have seen, these rays eject photo-electrons from all kinds of substances. It was M. de Broglie,[51] using his magnetic spectrograph, who showed that even for these very high frequencies Einstein's equation holds, if by w_0 we now mean the work required to

[47] E. Ladenburg, Phys. Zeits. 8, 590 (1907).
[48] O. W. Richardson and K. T. Compton, Phil. Mag. 24, 575 (1912).
[49] A. L. Hughes, Phil. Trans. Roy. Soc. A212, 205 (1912).
[50] R. A. Millikan, Phys. Rev. 7, 18 and 355 (1916).
[51] M. de Broglie, J. de Phys. et Radium, 2, 265 (1921).

remove the electron from the o level of the atom. Ellis, Meitner, Thibaud and others[52] have used eq. (1.15) as a means of determining γ-ray frequencies from the speed of the secondary β-rays. Recent measurements of these frequencies by crystal methods[53] have verified their results, thus showing that even for these exceedingly great energies Einstein's law holds. Over a range of kinetic energies corresponding to a drop through potential differences from two volts to a million volts Einstein's photo-electric equation has thus been verified to within an experimental error of about 1 per cent. It is thus one of the most thoroughly tested laws in the realm of physics.

It was while these photo-electric experiments were in progress that Duane and Hunt discovered what we have called the inverse photo-electric effect, which says that the highest frequency emitted by an x-ray tube is given by

$$h\nu_{max} = E_{kin},$$

where E_{kin} is the kinetic energy of the cathode electron as it strikes the target (cf. eq. (1.11)).

The significance of these phenomena will perhaps be more obvious if we imagine the following experiment: Let two x-ray tubes, A and B, be placed side by side. Tube A is operated at a constant potential of say 100,000 volts. A cathode electron with a kinetic energy E strikes the target of tube A and gives rise to an x-ray of frequency $\nu = E/h$. This ray strikes the target of tube B and ejects a photo-electron whose kinetic energy according to eq. (1.15) is $E - w_o$. This means that all of the energy of the cathode electron in tube A, except for w_o, which may be negligibly small, has been transmitted to the photo-electron ejected from the target of tube B. How is it possible for such a complete transfer of energy to be effected?

A precisely similar difficulty arises in connection with Bohr's picture of radiation and absorption by atoms, which was developed while these studies of the photo-electric effect were going on. According to this picture, if one atom radiates an amount of energy E, another similar atom, which may be as far away as the earth is from a distant star, may suddenly have its energy increased by the amount E when the radiation reaches it.

The impossibility that an electromagnetic wave whose energy spreads in all directions should effect such a sudden and complete

---

[52] Cf. Chap. VII.
[53] E.g., Frilley, Thesis, Paris (1928).

transfer of energy is obvious. It is equally clear that Einstein's photon conception affords a simple and adequate method of making the transfer. There have not been lacking, however, attempts to explain these phenomena without resorting to assumptions departing so completely from the electromagnetic waves of Maxwell.

One such attempt is the accumulation hypothesis, according to which the light energy is gradually accumulated by the atom, and the photo-electron is finally ejected when the accumulated energy exceeds a certain critical value. This process requires the existence of stored energy of all possible amounts within the atom, since the kinetic energy of the ejected photo-electron may have any value, depending upon the frequency of the radiation which traverses its parent atom. Furthermore this energy must remain stored for indefinitely long periods of time, for otherwise emission of photo-electrons would not occur at once upon exposure to the light—time would be required for the atom to accumulate sufficient energy. We are thus led to imagine an atom which may possess any energy whatever, and whose energy may gradually increase as radiation is absorbed. Such a picture is wholly inconsistent with Bohr's idea of an atom with definite energy states and which changes only suddenly from one such state to another. It is true that recent developments in quantum mechanics have led us to revise considerably Bohr's conception of electron orbits; but this hypothesis of definite energy states seems more firmly established than ever, and continues to be the fundamental principle of spectral analysis. We thus find it difficult to consider seriously an accumulation hypothesis which would mean atoms having all possible amounts of energy.

If the atom cannot gradually accumulate energy, since a spherical electromagnetic wave cannot give up its whole energy to a single atom, the occurrence of photo-electrons with the energy $h\nu$ means that we must either give up our old view that light comes in spherical waves or abandon the doctrine of the conservation of energy. Bohr, Kramers and Slater [54] at one time preferred to assume that energy is not conserved when an individual photo-electron is produced. They supposed that on the average the energy appearing in the photo-electrons is equal to that absorbed from the radiation, but under the stimulus of the incident waves any particular electron might suddenly escape at high speed without any corresponding loss in energy by the remainder of the system. That is, the conservation

[54] N. Bohr, H. A. Kramers and J. C. Slater, Phil. Mag. 47, 785 (1924).

of energy, and similarly the conservation of momentum, would become statistical laws. The authors of this theory assumed that, though the rays are propagated as spherical waves the motion of the photo-electrons would be the same as if they were ejected by photons. It has been difficult to devise a photo-electric experiment which would distinguish between this " virtual radiation " hypothesis and that of photons.

19. The Scattering of X-rays

We have seen that Einstein's hypothesis of corpuscular units of radiant energy gives a satisfactory account of the photo-electric effect. As Jeans significantly remarked, however, Einstein invented the photon hypothesis just to account for this one effect, and it was not surprising that it should account for it well. In order to carry any great weight the hypothesis should also be found applicable to phenomena of widely different character. The change in wavelength of the scattered rays, and the recoil electrons associated with them, which have been described above, are just such phenomena.

If we suppose that each x-ray photon is deflected by a single electron the electron will recoil from the impact. That is, part of the photon's energy is spent in setting the electron in motion, so the photon has less energy after deflection than before. The problem is very similar to that of the elastic collision of a light ball with a heavy one. If we assume that the energy and momentum are conserved in the process, we can calculate the loss in energy and hence by eq. (1.14) the increase in wave-length of a photon which is scattered at an angle ϕ with the primary ray. We thus find[55] for the increase in wave-length,

$$\delta\lambda = \frac{h}{mc} (1 - \cos \phi), \tag{1.16}$$

$$= 0.024 (1 - \cos \phi) \text{ Angstroms,}$$

where h is again Planck's constant, m is the mass of the electron and c is the velocity of light. The electron at the same time recoils from the photon at an angle θ given by

$$\cot \theta = - (1 + \alpha) \tan \tfrac{1}{2}\phi, \tag{1.17}$$

[55] Cf. Chap. III, Sec. 13.

where $\alpha = h/mc\lambda$, and the kinetic energy of the recoiling electron is

$$E_{\text{kin}} = \frac{h\nu 2\alpha \cos^2 \theta}{(1 + \alpha)^2 - \alpha^2 \cos^2 \theta}. \tag{1.18}$$

The agreement between eq. (1.16) and the observed change in wave-length, when light elements are used for which the electrons are effectively free, is found to be exact to within a small fraction of a per cent. From the close agreement between the theoretical and the observed wave-lengths of the scattered rays, the recoil electrons predicted by the photon theory of scattering were looked for with some confidence. Within a few months of their prediction, C. T. R. Wilson and W. Bothe independently announced their discovery. Figure I–12 shows one of Wilson's photographs.

Perhaps the most convincing reason for associating the short tracks found in such pictures with the scattered x-rays comes from a study of their number. Each photo-electron in a cloud photograph represents a quantum of truly absorbed x-ray energy. If the short tracks are due to recoil electrons, each one should represent the scattering of a photon. Thus the ratio of the number of short tracks to the number of long tracks should be the same as the ratio σ/τ of the scattered to the truly absorbed energy when the x-rays pass through air. The latter ratio is known from absorption measurements, and the former ratio can be determined by counting the tracks on the photographs. The satisfactory agreement between the two ratios for x-rays of different wave-lengths means that on the average there is about one quantum of energy scattered for each short track that is produced. The ranges of the tracks which start in different directions have also been studied,[56] using primary x-rays of different wave-lengths, with the result that eq. (1.18) has been satisfactorily verified.

In view of the fact that electrons of the recoil type were unknown when the photon theory of scattering was presented, their existence, and the close agreement with the predictions as to their number, direction and velocity, supply strong evidence in favor of the photon hypothesis.

It seems impossible to account for scattered rays of altered frequency, and for the existence of the recoil electrons, if we assume that x-rays consist of electromagnetic waves in the ordinary sense.

[56] Cf. Chap. III, Sec. 14.

There is nothing in these experiments, however, which is inconsistent with the idea of virtual oscillators continually scattering virtual radiation.   In order to account for the change of wave-length on this view, Bohr, Kramers and Slater assumed that the virtual oscillators scatter as if moving in the direction of the primary beam, accounting for the change in wave-length as a Doppler effect.   They then suppose that occasionally an electron, excited by the primary virtual rays, might suddenly move forward as if it had received the momentum of a photon.   Thus by treating the conservation of energy and momentum as statistical principles, they were able to make their theory include the type of motion that is actually observed.   It is difficult, however, to see how such a theory could by itself predict the change in wave-length and the motion of the recoil electrons.

The photon theory thus predicts quantitatively and in detail the change of wave-length of the scattered x-rays and the characteristics of the recoil electrons.   The virtual radiation theory is probably not inconsistent with these experiments, but is incapable of predicting the results.   The classical wave theory is altogether helpless to deal with these phenomena.

Directional Emission of Scattered X-rays.

A crucial test for corpuscular rays would be to follow a single corpuscle, or photon, from one encounter with an electron to the next.   According to the photon theory, we have a definite relation (eq. (1.17)) between the angle at which the photon is scattered and the angle at which the recoil electron is ejected.   But according to any form of spreading wave theory, including that of Bohr, Kramers and Slater, the scattered rays may produce effects in any direction whatever, and there should be no correlation between the direction in which a recoil electron proceeds and the direction in which the the scattered x-ray produces an effect.   A test to see whether such a relation exists has been made,[57] using a cloud expansion apparatus, in the manner shown diagrammatically in Fig. I–34.   Each recoil electron produces a visible track, and occasionally a secondary track is produced by the scattered x-ray before it escapes from the chamber. When but one recoil electron appears on the same plate with the track due to the scattered rays, it is possible to tell at once whether the angles satisfy eq. (1.17).   The experiments, which are described

[57] Cf. Chap. III, Sec. 15.

in detail on page 225, show that the angle ϕ at which the second electron appears is related to the angle θ according to eq. (1.17).

This result means that associated with each recoil electron there is scattered x-ray energy sufficient to produce a β-ray, and proceeding in a direction determined at the moment of ejection of the recoil electron. In other words, the scattered x-rays proceed in directed units of radiant energy. Other experiments with single photons of

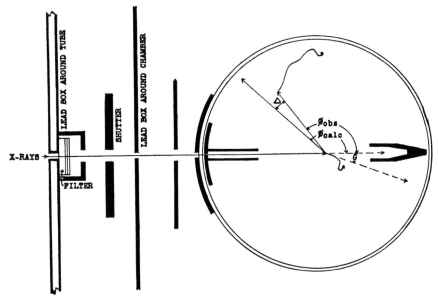

FIG. I–34. The scattered x-ray associated with an electron recoiling at angle θ produces effects only in direction ϕ determined by the laws of elastic collision, not in random directions as required by wave theory.

x-rays, which point in the same direction, are described below (p. 223).

Experiments on the photo-electric effect and on scattered x-rays, taken together with these experiments on the individual interactions of radiation and electrons, show therefore that radiation is emitted in units, is propagated in definite directions, and is absorbed again in units of undiminished energy. X-rays, and hence also light, thus have all the essential characteristics of particles. We have seen, however, that they have the characteristics of waves. How can these two apparently conflicting conceptions be reconciled?

20. *Electron Waves*

Before attempting to answer this question, let us notice that this dilemma applies not only to radiation, but also to other fundamental fields of physics.   When the evidence was growing strong that radiation, which we had always thought of as waves, had the properties of particles, L. de Broglie asked, may it not then be possible that electrons, which we have known as particles, may have the properties of waves?   He was able to show[58] that the dynamics of any particle may be expressed in terms of the propagation of a group of waves. That is, the particle may be replaced by a train of waves—the two, so far as their motion is concerned, may be made mathematically equivalent.   The motion of a particle in a straight line is represented by a plane wave.   The wave-length is determined by the momentum of the particle.   Thus just as the momentum of a photon is $h\nu/c = h/\lambda$ so the wave-length of a moving electron is given by $mv = h/\lambda$, or

$$\lambda = h/mv. \qquad (1.20)$$

In cloud expansion photographs such as Figs. I-10 and I-11, we have ocular evidence that electrons are very real particles indeed.   Nevertheless de Broglie's suggestion that they should act as waves was subjected to experimental test by Davisson and Germer[59] and later by G. P. Thomson, Rupp, Kikuchi and others.[60]

For our present purpose we may describe Thomson's experiment, which is typical of them all.   His experiment is analogous to those in which Debye and Scherrer and Hull[61] have secured diffraction patterns of x-rays by passing them through powdered crystals placed some distance in front of a photographic plate.   Thomson replaced the x-ray beam with a stream of cathode rays (falling through about 30,000 volts potential difference), and the mass of powdered crystals with a sheet of gold leaf.   In Fig. I-35 are shown (*a*) the diffraction pattern of an x-ray beam passing through a sheet of aluminium, as obtained by Hull, and (*b*) the diffraction pattern of an electron beam passing through gold leaf, as photographed by Thomson.   From the size of the electron diffraction rings the wave-length of the cathode rays can be calculated, and are found to be just that predicted by

[58] L. de Broglie, Phil. Mag. **47**, 446 (1924); Thesis, Paris (1924).

[59] C. J. Davisson and L. H. Germer, Phys. Rev. **30**, 705 (1927).

[60] For an excellent summary, cf. G. P. Thomson, "Wave Mechanics of Free Electrons," McGraw-Hill (1930).

[61] Cf. Chap. V.

de Broglie's formula (1.20). If the diffraction of x-rays by crystals proves that they are waves, this diffraction of cathode rays establishes equally the wave character of electrons.

We are thus faced with the fact that the fundamental things in nature, matter and radiation, present to us a dual aspect. In certain ways they act like particles, in others like waves. The experiments tell us that we must seize both horns of the dilemma.

A Suggested Solution.—During the last few years there has gradually developed a solution of this puzzle, which though at first rather

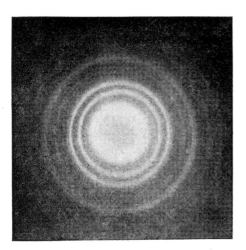

FIG. I–35. *a.* Diffraction of X-rays by Aluminium Foil. (Hull.)

b. Diffraction of Electrons by Gold Leaf. (Thomson.)

difficult to grasp seems to be free from logical contradictions and essentially capable of describing the phenomena which our experiments reveal. L. de Broglie, Duane, Slater, Schrödinger, Heisenberg, Bohr and Dirac, among others, have contributed to the growth of this explanation.[62] The point of departure of this theory is de Broglie's proof, mentioned above, that the motion of a particle may be expressed in terms of the propagation of a group of waves.

[62] A review of the development of this theory is given in the report of the fifth Solvay Congress, "Electrons et Photons," Brussels, 1928, written chiefly by W. L. Bragg, A. H. Compton, L. de Broglie, E. Schrödinger, W. Heisenberg and N. Bohr. Cf. also, W. Heisenberg, "The Physical Principles of the Quantum Theory," Univ. of Chicago Press, 1930.

In the case of the photon, this wave may be taken as the ordinary electromagnetic wave. The wave corresponding to the moving electron is generally called by the name of its inventor, a *de Broglie wave*.

Consider, for example, the deflection of a photon by an electron on this basis, that is, the scattering of an x-ray.[63] The incident photon is represented by a train of plane electromagnetic waves. The recoiling electron is likewise represented by a train of plane de Broglie waves propagated in the direction of recoil. These electron waves form a kind of grating by which the incident electromagnetic waves are diffracted. The diffracted waves represent in turn the deflected photon. They are increased in wave-length by the diffraction because the grating is receding, resulting in a Doppler effect.

In this solution of the problem we note that before we could determine the direction in which the x-ray was to be deflected, it was necessary to know the direction of recoil of the electron. In this respect the solution is indeterminate; but its indeterminateness corresponds to an indeterminateness in the experiment itself. There is no way of performing the experiment so as to make the electron recoil in a definite direction as a result of an encounter; the experiment itself is determinate only after the encounter is complete, and the observed direction of recoil supplies those parameters which the theory is incapable of defining.

It is not usually possible to describe the motion of either a beam of light or a beam of electrons completely without introducing both the concepts of particles and waves. There are certain localized regions in which at a certain moment energy exists, and this may be taken as a definition of what we mean by a particle. But in predicting where these localized positions are to be at a later instant, a consideration of the propagation of the corresponding waves is usually our most satisfactory mode of attack.

Attention should be called to the fact that the electromagnetic waves and the de Broglie waves are according to this theory waves of probability. Consider as an example the diffraction pattern of a beam of light or of electrons, reflected from a ruled grating, and falling on a photographic plate. In the intense portion of the diffraction pattern there is a high probability that a grain of the photographic plate will be affected. In corpuscular language, there is a high probability that a photon or electron, as the case may be, will strike this

[63] E. Schrödinger, Ann. d. Physik **82**, 257 (1927).

portion of the plate. Where the diffraction pattern is of zero intensity, the probability of a particle striking is zero, and the plate is unaffected. Thus there is high probability that a photon will be present where the " intensity " of an electromagnetic wave is great, and a lesser probability where this " intensity " is smaller.

It is a corollary that the energy of the radiation lies in the photons, and not in the waves. For we mean by energy the ability to do work, and we find that when radiation does anything it acts as particles.

In this connection it may be noted that this wave-mechanics theory does not enable us to locate a photon or an electron definitely except at the instant at which it interacts with another particle. When it activates a grain on a photographic plate, or ionizes an atom which may be observed in a cloud expansion chamber, we can say that the particle was at that point at the instant of the event. But in between such events the particle can not be definitely located. Some positions are more probable than others, in proportion as the corresponding wave is more intense in these positions. But there is no definite position that can be assigned to the particle in between its actions on other particles. Thus it becomes meaningless to attempt to assign any definite path to a particle. It is like assigning a definite path to a ray of light: the more sharply we try to define it by narrow slits the more widely the ray is spread by diffraction.

Perhaps enough has been said to show that by grasping both horns we have found it possible to overcome the dilemma. Though no simple picture has been invented affording a mechanical model of a light ray, by combining the notions of waves and particles a logically consistent theory has been devised which seems essentially capable of describing the properties of light as we know them. We continue to think of light as propagated as electromagnetic waves; yet the energy of the light is concentrated in particles associated with the waves, and whenever the light does something it does it as particles.

CHAPTER II

The Production of X-rays

1. Electromagnetic Radiation

According to the classical electron theory as developed by J. J. Thomson and by Lorentz on the basis of Maxwell's electrodynamics, an electron in accelerated motion should radiate energy in the form of a transverse electromagnetic wave. If, as in Fig. II–1, an electron

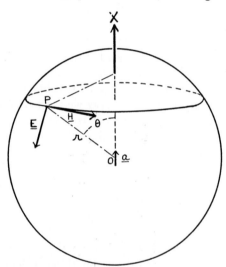

Fig. II–1. Showing the directions of *E* and *H* at a point *P* due to the acceleration of a positive charge at *O* in the direction of *a*.

of charge *e* is accelerated along the *X* axis with acceleration *a*, a wave consisting of an electric and a magnetic field is propagated in all directions with the velocity *c*, where *c* is the ratio of the electromagnetic to the electrostatic unit of charge.

The field due to the acceleration *a* will thus reach a point $P(r, \theta)$, after an interval of r/c. The directions of the electric and magnetic

56

fields are as shown in the figure, E lying in the plane POX and H being perpendicular to this plane. The magnitude of the electric and magnetic vectors is (cf. Appendix II)

$$E = H = \frac{ae}{rc^2} \sin \theta, \tag{2.01}$$

if the velocity with which the electron is moving is small compared with c. In this equation E is expressed in electrostatic units and H in electromagnetic units. In order to preserve the symmetry of our expressions, we shall always use electrostatic units to describe electrical quantities and electromagnetic units for magnetic quantities.

If the electron at the instant of its acceleration a is moving along the X axis with a velocity $v = \beta c$, the fields after a time r/c are given by (cf. Appendix I, eq. 33),

$$E = H = \frac{ae}{rc^2} \frac{\sin \theta}{(1 - \beta \cos \theta)^3}. \tag{2.02}$$

This is identical with eq. (2.01) when $\beta = 0$.

The rate at which energy flows past the point P may be calculated if we remember that the energy per unit volume in ergs per cm^3 of the electromagnetic field is given by the expression

$$\frac{E^2}{8\pi} + \frac{H^2}{8\pi}.$$

Since E is numerically equal to H this may be written as

$$\frac{E^2}{4\pi}.$$

The field is however propagated with a velocity c, so that the flow of energy per second across unit area taken perpendicular to the direction of propagation is

$$I = c\frac{E^2}{4\pi}, \tag{2.03}$$

where E is given by eq. (2.01) or (2.02). The quantity I is known as the *intensity* of the radiation at the instant under consideration, and is expressed in ergs per cm^2 per second.

The rate at which an electron loses energy by radiation may be calculated by integrating this energy flow over a spherical surface surrounding the electron. This is the *power*, or energy per unit time. From Fig. II–2 it is evident that

$$P = \int_0^\pi I \cdot 2\pi r \sin \theta \cdot r \, d\theta.$$

Substituting the value of I from eqs. (2.03) and (2.01), and integrating, we obtain

$$P = \frac{2e^2 a^2}{3c^3}. \tag{2.04}$$

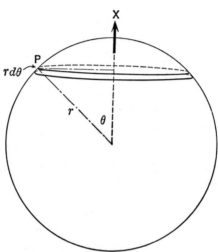

FIG. II–2. Showing the integration necessary to compute the total energy radiated per second by an electron.

It is frequently convenient to express these results in terms of the electric moment instead of the electric charge of an electron. If an atom is electrically neutral when the accelerated electron is at $x = 0$, when the electron moves to x an electric moment equivalent to that of a doublet of moment $M = ex$ is created. If then $a = d^2x/dt^2$, we may write

$$ae = d^2M/dt^2 = \ddot{M}.$$

Thus eqs. (2.01) and (2.04) may be written respectively

$$E = H = \frac{\ddot{M} \sin \theta}{rc^2} \tag{2.01'}$$

and

$$P = \frac{2\ddot{M}^2}{3c^3}.$$ (2.04′)

2. Energy and Intensity of Long Wave Trains

Let us then imagine that an electron in the target of the x-ray tube is executing simple harmonic motion in such a manner that its displacement in some direction is $z = A \cos(\omega t' + \delta)$, where A is the amplitude of the oscillation, and $\omega = 2\pi\nu$, ν being the frequency and δ the phase of the motion when $t' = 0$. The electron's acceleration will then be

$$a = \frac{d^2z}{dt^2} = -A\omega^2 \cos(\omega t' + \delta).$$

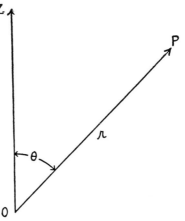

This motion will produce an electromagnetic disturbance which will arrive at the point $P(r, \theta)$, Fig. II–3, after a time r/c. The phase of the wave at this point at a time t is accordingly that of the wave which left the electron at the instant $t' = t - r/c$. But the acceleration of the electron at that instant was

$$a = -A\omega^2 \cos\left\{\omega(t - r/c) + \delta\right\}.$$

Fig. II–3.

By eq. (2.01), the electric intensity of the wave at the time t is therefore

$$E = -\frac{e \sin\theta}{rc^2} A\omega^2 \cos\left\{\omega(t - r/c) + \delta\right\}.$$ (2.05)

At a distance $r = ct$ the phase of the disturbance expressed by eq. (2.05) would remain constant. This means that the equation represents a wave propagated from the electron with the velocity c.

The rate at which energy is radiated by the oscillating electron from eq. (2.04) is

$$\frac{dW}{dt} = \frac{2e^2}{3c^3} A^2\omega^4 \cos^2\left\{\omega(t - r/c) + \delta\right\}.$$

To obtain the average rate of energy emission, we may integrate this expression over a complete oscillation, thus:

$$\overline{\frac{dW}{dt}} = \frac{\int_{t=0}^{t=2\pi/\omega} dW}{2\pi/\omega} = \frac{\omega}{2\pi} \int_0^{\frac{2\pi}{\omega}} \frac{2}{3} \frac{e^2 A^2 \omega^4}{c^3} \cos^2\{\omega(t - r/c) + \delta\} dt$$

$$= \frac{\omega}{2\pi} \cdot \frac{2\pi}{3} \frac{e^2 A^2 \omega^3}{c^3} = \frac{1}{3} \frac{e^2}{c^3} A^2 \omega^4. \qquad (2.06)$$

The energy per unit volume of the wave is as before $E^2/4\pi$. When this is averaged over a complete cycle, since the average value of $\cos^2 x$ is $\frac{1}{2}$, we obtain from eq. (2.05) the average energy per unit volume of the wave as

$$\frac{e^2 \sin^2 \theta}{8\pi r^2 c^4} A^2 \omega^4.$$

The energy passing unit area per second is c times this quantity, being thus

$$I = \frac{e^2 A^2 \omega^4}{8\pi r^2 c^3} \sin^2 \theta. \qquad (2.07)$$

I is called the intensity of the wave train.

3. *The Wave Mechanics Theory of Electromagnetic Radiation*

In the introductory chapter attention was called to various ways in which the classical electrodynamics fails to give an adequate account of the radiation process. On the other hand, in Sec. 13, Chap. I, we saw how Bohr, by introducing the concept of discrete or "quantized" energy states in which the angular momentum is an integral multiple of $h/2\pi$, and the postulate that the emitted frequency is given by

$$h\nu = W_i - W_f,$$

was able to account for many characteristics of optical and x-ray spectra. This theory of Bohr's does not enable us however to calculate the intensity of the radiation, which as we have seen in the last two sections the classical theory predicts in detail. A new form of quantum mechanics has recently been developed, largely by the efforts of L. de Broglie, Heisenberg, Dirac, and Schrödinger. This new mechanics appears to supply the kind of information offered by both the classical and the Bohr theories, enabling us to calculate both the wave-length and the intensity of radiation.

According to classical theory we assume that a homogeneous ray is emitted by a simple harmonic electronic oscillator. Bohr's theory, on the other hand, says that the ray is emitted when the atom changes from one stationary state to another, but does not describe the mechanism of emission. The new quantum mechanics ascribes the source of the radiation to " beats " between the electrical distributions of the initial and final states, which are very like the harmonic oscillator which the classical theory uses. Thus for many purposes the results of the classical theory may be counted upon to give reliable results.

Because its mathematical reasoning is more nearly similar to that used in other parts of this book, the wave-mechanics form of quantum dynamics as developed by de Broglie and Schrödinger will be discussed here rather than the Heisenberg or Dirac forms of the theory. There is little difference between the significance of the various forms of quantum mechanics, though the wave-mechanics form seems not to lend itself to relativistic treatment.

4. *L. de Broglie's Theory of the Equivalence of Particles and Wave-Groups*

Many years ago Hamilton called attention to the fact that a light ray will follow a path identical with that traversed by a particle moving in a field of force if the refractive index of the medium varies from point to point in a suitable manner. The necessary relation between the refractive index and the field potential may be found by comparing Fermat's principle of optics with Maupertuis' principle of mechanics.

Fermat showed that a light wave goes from one place A to another B in the shortest (or in rare cases the longest) possible time.[1] Thus for such a wave,

$$\delta \int_A^B \frac{ds}{u} = 0, \qquad (2.08)$$

where u is the phase velocity of the wave, i.e., the velocity with which an individual wave is propagated.

Maupertuis, and later more satisfactorily Hamilton, showed that in a conservative field of force a particle moving from A to B

[1] Cf., e.g. T. Preston, "The Theory of Light" (Macmillan, 1928, p. 102).

goes in such a manner that the line integral of the momentum over the path is a minimum (or rarely a maximum), i.e.,

$$\delta \int_A^B mv \, ds = 0, \qquad (2.09)$$

where v is the speed of the particle. This is the well-known Principle of Least Action.[2]

The two paths from A to B will become identical if v is proportional to $1/u$, i.e., if

$$u = C/mv, \qquad (2.10)$$

where C must be independent of s, and hence in general independent of the coordinates.

If the moving particle is to be equivalent to a wave group, it is necessary that the two shall not only traverse the same path, but that they shall traverse it at the same speed. We see from eq. (2.10) that the speed v of the particle is inversely proportional to the phase velocity u of the wave. If a particle is to correspond to a group of waves, however, it is not the velocity of propagation of the individual wave, but that of the boundaries of the wave group which should be equal to the velocity of the particle. Treatises on wave motion show[3] that the group velocity w is expressed by the equation

$$\frac{1}{w} = \frac{d}{d\nu}\left(\frac{\nu}{u}\right), \qquad (2.11)$$

where ν is the frequency of the wave.

To perform this differentiation we must express u as a function of ν. De Broglie has done this by taking the arbitrary constant C of eq. (2.10) equal to the total energy (kinetic and potential) W of the moving particle, and assuming that

$$C = W = h\nu \qquad (2.12)$$

in accord with usual quantum theory.[4] Remembering, however, that, if V is the potential energy, the kinetic energy is

$$\tfrac{1}{2}mv^2 = W - V,$$

---

[2] Cf., e.g. L. Page, "Introduction to Theoretical Physics," Van Nostrand, 1926, p. 166.
[3] Cf. Appendix III.
[4] What it is that oscillates with a frequency ν is not stated in de Broglie's theory. It is however suggested in Schrödinger's extension of the theory, as described below.

we have

$$v = \frac{1}{m} \sqrt{2m(W - V)}. \qquad (2.13)$$

Thus by eq. (2.10)

$$u = \frac{W}{\sqrt{2m(W - V)}}. \qquad (2.14)$$

From eqs. (2.11) and (2.12) therefore,

$$\frac{1}{w} = \frac{d}{dW}\left(\frac{W}{u}\right) = \frac{d}{dW}\sqrt{2m(W - V)}$$

$$= m/\sqrt{2m(W - V)}. \qquad (2.15)$$

Comparing this with (2.13) we see that

$$w = v, \qquad (2.16)$$

that is, the speed of the wave group is identical with the speed of the corresponding particle.

If then the refractive index is so adjusted that the phase velocity of the wave is inversely proportional to the momentum of the particle, and if the frequency of the wave is proportional to the total energy of the particle, *the particle and the wave group will traverse the same path at the same speed.* They are in fact dynamically indistinguishable.

The *wave-length* of the wave associated with the moving particle is $\lambda = u/v$, and since by (2.10) and (2.12) $u = hv/mv$, we have

$$\lambda = h/mv. \qquad (2.17)$$

The wave-train corresponding to a moving particle thus has a wave-length inversely proportional to the momentum of the particle. Equation (2.17) describes what is called a " de Broglie wave."[5]

The phase velocity of the waves is not definitely given by the theory as we have outlined it. We have, however, from eqs. (2.10) and (2.12),

$$uv = W/m = \text{constant}.$$

If we make use of the relativity result that the total energy of a particle is $W = mc^2$ (eq. (23), Appendix I), this becomes

$$uv = mc^2/m = c^2$$

[5] L. de Broglie, Comptes Rendus, **177**, pp. 507 and 548 (1923); **179**, 39 (1924); Phil. Mag. **47**, 446 (1924).

or

$$u = \frac{1}{\beta} c, \qquad (2.18)$$

where $\beta = v/c$. Thus the phase velocity is always greater than the speed of light.

We have already seen[6] how experiments by Davisson and Germer and others with cathode rays and by Dempster with positive rays have shown the wave characteristics of electrons and protons, whose properties as particles are well known. Conversely we have seen how light rays, with whose wave properties we have long been familiar, have the characteristics also of particles. In every case the relation between the length of the wave and the momentum of the associated particle is found to be that expressed by de Broglie's eq. (2.17). We may accordingly consider it established that the large scale dynamics of the fundamental elements, protons, electrons, and photons, may be expressed in terms either of waves or of particles.

5. Schrödinger's Theory of the Mechanics of Radiation

In the study of optics it is found that Fermat's principle holds strictly only when the wave-length of the light is small compared with the width of the beam of light. Refraction by a prism or lens can be accurately calculated on this basis, but there is no relation between Fermat's principle and the diffraction pattern due to a slit. It is to this difference that we refer when we distinguish between geometrical optics (where Fermat's principle holds) and physical optics (where Fermat's principle is not valid).

Similarly in our study of the dynamics of material particles we may expect Maupertuis' principle to hold (as it does) when the dimensions with which we are concerned are all large compared with the wave-length of the de Broglie waves associated with the particles. This is the case of ordinary dynamics. When, however, we deal with electronic orbits of the dimensions of a few wave-lengths, we may expect departures from the classical dynamics of particles such as should correspond to the diffraction of waves. The wave mechanics of de Broglie showed that large scale mechanics might be considered either as the motion of particles or the propagation of wave groups. Schrödinger has extended the wave-mechanics to cover

[6] Cf. Sec. 20, Chap. I.

problems without restriction as to the dimensions. His mechanics thus bears the same relation to Newtonian mechanics that physical optics bears to geometrical optics.

The Differential Equation of Wave Mechanics

We wish first to write down a differential equation which can be used to represent the wave corresponding to the motion of a particle in a field of force. Let us start with the differential equation for a three-dimensional wave,

$$\frac{\partial^2 \psi}{\partial x^2} + \frac{\partial^2 \psi}{\partial y^2} + \frac{\partial^2 \psi}{\partial z^2} - \frac{1}{u^2} \frac{\partial^2 \psi}{\partial t^2} = 0 \qquad (2.19)$$

or more briefly

$$\nabla^2 \psi - \frac{1}{u^2} \frac{\partial^2 \psi}{\partial t^2} = 0.$$

Here ψ is any quantity, a wave of which is being propagated with a velocity u. We shall consider the wave to be that associated with a particle having a velocity v. The wave-length is accordingly eq. (2.17),

$$\lambda = h/mv,$$

and the frequency

$$\nu = \frac{u}{\lambda} = \frac{mvu}{h}.$$

If ψ is a wave of frequency ν, i.e., $\psi = A \sin (2\pi\nu t + \delta)$,

$$\frac{\partial^2 \psi}{\partial t^2} = -4\pi^2 \nu^2 \psi,$$

whence

$$\frac{1}{u^2} \frac{\partial^2 \psi}{\partial t^2} = -4\pi^2 \frac{m^2 v^2}{h^2} \psi.$$

But by (2.13)

$$v^2 = \frac{2}{m} (W - V),$$

where W is the total energy of the particle and V its potential energy at any point. Thus

$$\frac{1}{u^2} \frac{\partial^2 \psi}{\partial t^2} = -\frac{8\pi^2 m}{h^2} (W - V)\psi.$$

Equation (2.19) then becomes

$$\nabla^2\psi + \frac{8\pi^2 m}{h^2}(W - V)\psi = 0. \tag{2.20}$$

This equation is the foundation of Schrödinger's wave mechanics.

Stationary States of a Simple Atom. The significance of this form of mechanics can best be made clear by applying it to a definite problem. Let us consider an atom consisting of a massive positive nucleus of charge $+Ze$ about which moves an electron of charge $-e$. The potential energy of the electron is then $-Ze^2/r$. Inserting this value for V in eq. (2.20), we have

$$\nabla^2\psi + \frac{8\pi^2 m}{h^2}\left(W + \frac{Ze^2}{r}\right)\psi = 0. \tag{2.21}$$

Schrödinger has shown[7] that solutions exist for this differential equation only if

$$W_n = \text{Const.} - \frac{2\pi^2 Z^2 m e^4}{h^2 n^2}\ [n = 1, 2, 3, \ldots\ldots], \tag{2.22}$$

or

$$W > \text{Const.} \tag{2.23}$$

If we consider the energy of the electron at rest at infinity to be zero, then

$$\text{Const.} = 0.$$

Equation (2.22) then represents the energy of the various Bohr orbits, just as in eq. (1.06). Equation (2.23), on the other hand, represents an electron which has enough kinetic energy to carry it away from the field of the nucleus.

The quantized states of the atom thus seem to be necessary consequences of the assumption, made in eq. (2.12), that there is a frequency associated with a particle of energy W such that $W = h\nu$.

Origin and Frequency of Radiation from an Excited Atom. Corresponding to any particular value W_k of W_n the solution of eq. (2.21) takes the form

$$\psi_1 = c_k\psi_k e^{2\pi i\ (\nu_k t\ +\ \theta_k)}, \tag{2.24}$$

where c_k and θ_k are arbitrary constants, ν_k is defined by the relation $h\nu_k = W_k$, where W_k is given by eq. (2.22), and ψ_k is an exponential

[7] E. Schrödinger, Ann. der Phys. **79**, 361 (1926).

function of the coordinates which rapidly approaches zero beyond the range of the Bohr orbits of quantum number k. The quantity ψ_1 thus oscillates with a frequency ν_k, which is identical with the characteristic frequency of the kth Bohr orbit.

The most general solution of eq. (2.21) for an unionized atom ($W < 0$) is the sum of all solutions of the type (2.24):[8]

$$\psi = \sum_{k=1}^{k=\infty} c_k \psi_k e^{2\pi i(\nu_k t + \theta_k)}. \tag{2.25}$$

We shall now assume that *the density of the electric charge at any point*[9] *is proportional to the value at the point of* $\psi\psi^*$ where ψ^* is the conjugate complex of ψ; i.e., we assume

$$\rho = -e\psi\psi^*$$
$$= -e\sum_k\sum_{k'} c_k c_{k'}{}^* \psi_k \psi_{k'}{}^* e^{2\pi i[(v_k - v_{k'})t + \theta_k - \theta_{k'}]}. \tag{2.26}$$

where e is the electronic unit charge. It will be seen that ρ depends upon the time only through the exponential factor of which the real part is $\cos 2\pi [(\nu_k - \nu_{k'})t + \theta_k - \theta_{k'}]$. Thus eq. (2.26) represents a fluctuation of the charge density at any point with frequencies

$$\nu_{kk'} = \nu_k - \nu_{k'} = \frac{1}{h}(W_k - W_{k'}). \tag{2.27}$$

This is precisely Bohr's frequency rule.

According to eq. (2.26) there is an actual vibration of electricity of the same frequency ($\nu_k - \nu_{k'}$) as the observed spectral line. This is an important advance over Bohr's theory, according to which nothing in the atom appeared to have the vibration period of the radiation. The amplitude of this electrical vibration at any point within the atom is determined by the coefficients c_k and $c_{k'}$, which depend upon the state of excitation of the atom. The functions ψ_k (known as "proper functions") describe the manner in which the

[8] Because of the spherical symmetry of the potential energy function $V = Ze^2/r$, there exist k^2 independent solutions, having identical values of ν, for $n = k$. When V is slightly unsymmetrical, due e.g. to applied electric or magnetic fields, these k^2 solutions give slightly different values of ν corresponding to the Stark and Zeeman effects. These interesting details need not, however, concern us here.

[9] It would appear that ρ should not be interpreted strictly as the volume density of a continuous electric charge, but rather as the probability that the electron will be at the point at any instant.

electric density varies from place to place within the atom. It can be shown[10] that the x component of the electric moment of the atom may be expressed by the equation,

$$M_x = - \sum c_k^2 a_{kk} - 2 \sum \sum c_k c_{k'}{}^* a_{kk'} \cos [2\pi(\nu_k - \nu_{k'})t + \theta_k - \theta_{k'}], \quad (2.28)$$

where

$$a_{kk'} = e \int \int \int x \psi_k \psi_{k'}{}^* dx dy dz.$$

This value of M_x is equivalent to ex, where x is the effective value of the displacement of the electron. The intensity of the radiation can now be calculated according to the usual principles of electrodynamics. Thus corresponding to our eq. (2.01) we have for the electric vector of the emitted radiation, due to the x component of the atom's electric moment,

$$E_{M_x} = \frac{\sin \theta}{rc^2} \frac{d^2 M_x}{dt^2}, \quad (2.29)$$

and similarly for the other components of M.

The adequacy of this theory of radiation has been tested by calculation of the relative intensities of spectrum lines, including the intensities and states of polarization of the various components of the Zeeman and Stark effects. The agreement with experiment has been found to be very satisfactory.

6. *Bohr's Correspondence Principle*

Before the introduction of the new quantum mechanics, Bohr had developed a qualitative interpretation of the relative intensities of different spectral lines on the basis of what he called the " correspondence principle." According to this principle the radiation should be an average between that calculated on classical theory for the initial and the final states. We may consider eq. (2.28) as stating explicitly how this average between the two states k and k' is to be taken. The results of the wave-mechanics are thus in complete agreement with the predictions of the correspondence principle, but the wave mechanics is expressed in a quantitative form.

There remain, however, many cases in which the correspondence principle offers a simpler mode of attack than does the wave-mechanics. From what has been said it appears that we may safely

---

[10] E. Schrödinger, loc. cit., or "Four Lectures on Wave Mechanics," (1928), p. 19.

use the Bohr atom and the correspondence principle as guides, though we may not be able by their help to secure a quantitative solution of some of our problems.

7. *Characteristics of Spectral Lines*

We have already noted that experiments which measure the energy required to remove electrons from inner energy levels of the atom support Bohr's postulate that the frequency of a spectrum line is given by

$$h\nu = W_i - W_f.$$

This relation has been obtained also from Schrödinger's wave-mechanics, eq. (2.27), describing the frequency of the electrical oscillations within an atom which may exist in both states i and f. We have calculated the intensity of the radiation emitted by an oscillating electron, and the formulas there developed should be immediately applicable to the radiation from the Schrödinger electrical oscillations within the atom. Thus in Sec. 10 of Chap. VIII, in treating the relative intensities of x-ray lines, we shall see that eq. (2.06) serves as a background for our calculations.

In Sec. 3 of Chap. IV we shall calculate the shape of the wave-train emitted by a classical electronic simple harmonic oscillator damped by its own radiation. Such a wave-train of varying amplitude appears as a frequency band in a spectroscopic instrument of sufficient resolving power, and we shall calculate the width of this band at half maximum intensity. The correspondence principle gives us confidence that by this procedure we will obtain a quantity which will be of the right order of magnitude for the width of spectrum lines, and we shall find our expectations fulfilled for x-ray lines, the width of $MoK\alpha_1$ being about 2.5 times the calculated value. The actual wave-mechanical computation of line widths is a problem of great complexity.

8. *Theoretical Treatments of the Probability of Ionization by Electron Impact*

The essential condition for the production of a line in the characteristic x-ray spectrum is that an electron be removed from an inner shell of some of the atoms in the radiator. In the target of an x-ray tube, this may be accomplished by the impact of a cathode ray with an atom, or by photo-electric absorption of general radiation produced in the target by another type of electron impact. There are of course tertiary processes which produce ionized atoms, but these will be disregarded, ionization by internal absorption of the characteristic radiation in the parent atom being included in the previously mentioned processes. We may thus distinguish between truly primary characteristic x-rays, coming from atoms ionized directly from cathode ray impact, and characteristic x-rays coming from atoms in the target ionized by secondary processes. We will first study the production of these primary characteristic x-rays.

We shall consider the power in these characteristic x-rays as a function of the voltage on the tube. Fundamental to these considerations is the study of the number of electrons ejected per unit length of path by a β-ray of uniform speed moving through the target material. This number will be a function of the energy of the β-ray, the density of the material it traverses, and the energy required to eject an electron. We shall call this function the "ionization function," $\Phi(E, E_q, n_q)$, defined by

$$di/dx = \Phi(E, E_q\, n_q), \qquad (2.30)$$

in which di/dx is the number of ionizations per unit path length, E is the energy of the impacting β-ray, E_q the energy required to remove an electron, and n_q the number of electrons per unit volume having the binding energy E_q.

We shall find that at present no experimentally satisfactory ionization function has been rigorously developed from a theoretical standpoint, neither on the basis of classical nor of wave-mechanics. In spite of this we shall reproduce the classical approach to the problem, because it illustrates many of the concepts upon which an adequate theory must be based.

In the development of the ionization function, we have to consider the transfer of energy from the incident β-ray to an electron in an atom. Mathematically, the problem is similar to the calculation of the energy transferred in molecular impacts in the kinetic theory of gases. This calculation was first carried out by Maxwell.[11] We shall take the result in a greatly simplified form. Maxwell's treatment was for any law of force between the impacting bodies; we shall only consider the case of the inverse square. For the case of two electrons, the two masses are the same, and we shall further assume

[11] J. C. Maxwell. The Scientific Papers of James Clerk Maxwell, edited by W. D. Niven. Librarie Scientifique J. Hermann, Paris (1927), Vol. II, pages 26 et seq.

that the electrons in the material may be considered at rest compared with the speed of the ionizing β-ray. This last assumption is most stringent, and we shall see later that it has been modified. The treatment given here neglects relativity effects. From Maxwell's work we obtain the result,

$$W = \frac{2e^4}{mS^2} \frac{1}{r^2 + \frac{4e^4}{m^2S^4}},$$

where W is the energy transferred in the impact, e the electronic charge, m the mass of the electron, S the speed of the cathode ray, and r is the impact parameter. More specifically, r is the perpendicular distance from the extended direction of the original velocity of the impacting electron to the position of the electron in the material of the target. If we solve the preceding expression for r, we obtain

$$r^2 = \frac{2e^4}{mS^2}\left(\frac{1}{W} - \frac{2}{mS^2}\right).$$

We will now introduce E as the energy of the β-ray, or $E = \frac{1}{2}mS^2$. Suppose that we are considering the ejection of an electron of the type q, whose binding energy is E_q. Then this consideration will impose an upper limit upon r, above which the energy transferred will be too small to achieve ejection from the atom. If this upper limit is r_q, we have

$$r_q^2 = e^4 E^{-1}(E_q^{-1} - E^{-1}).$$

This upper limit of the impact parameter will define an effective cross-section of the electron for ionization from the q-shell; the effective area will be πr_q^2. If the number of q-electrons per cubic centimeter is n_q, the number ejected from a thickness dx will be

$$di = \frac{\pi n_q e^4}{E}\left(\frac{1}{E_q} - \frac{1}{E}\right)dx,$$

or

$$\Phi_R(E, E_q, n_q) = \frac{\pi n_q e^4}{E}\left(\frac{1}{E_q} - \frac{1}{E}\right), \qquad (2.31)$$

which defines what we shall refer to as Rosseland's ionization function.[12]

---

[12] S. Rosseland, Phil. Mag. **45**, 65 (1923). J. J. Thomson, Phil. Mag. **23**, 449 (1912).

The problem has been reconsidered by Thomas,[13] from the viewpoint of the classical quantum theory, in which the electrons in the atom have orbital kinetic energy. Thus the assumption in Rosseland's treatment that the electrons in the atom may be considered at rest is not maintained. Furthermore the impinging electron will gain energy in the attractive field of the atom, and this appears in Thomas' treatment. The ionization function obtained by him is

$$\Phi_T(E, E_q, n_q) = \frac{\pi n_q e^4}{(E + E_q + k_q)} \left\{ \frac{1}{E_q} - \frac{1}{E} + \frac{2k_q}{3E_q^2} \left(1 - \frac{E_q^2}{E^2} \right) \right\}, \quad (2.32)$$

where k_q is the orbital kinetic energy of the q-electrons.

A further refinement of the classical quantum theory treatment has been introduced by Webster, Hansen, and Duveneck.[14] This is the consideration of the deflection of a β-ray by nuclear attraction within an atom, before it reaches the electron it is to eject. Especially in the case of the K electrons, which is the one considered by these authors, the effect of the nuclear attraction in deviating the β-particles toward the center of the atom and thus increasing the ionization probability, should be noticeable. In his discussion of the problem, Thomas showed that for a cathode ray to transfer classically to a K electron sufficient energy for ionization, it must approach the K electron to a distance so small compared with that of either electron from the nucleus that their relative motion is practically like that of two free electrons. Thus a spherical shell around the nucleus is defined whose thickness is only of the order $1/Z$ of the radius of the K orbit, and within this shell the ionizing impacts must take place. The problem then is to calculate the increased concentration of impinging electrons within this spherical shell due to nuclear attraction. Webster, Hansen, and Duveneck found that when this effect was considered, the ionization function of Thomas must be multiplied by a factor $(E + E_q + k_q)/E$, which gives

$$\Phi_W(E, E_q, n_q) = \frac{\pi n_q e^4}{E} \left\{ \frac{1}{E_q} - \frac{1}{E} + \frac{2k_q}{3E_q^2} \left(1 - \frac{E_q^2}{E^2} \right) \right\} \quad (2.33)$$

which we may call Webster's ionization function.

Wave-mechanical treatments of the problem have been published, but only in the cases where the velocity of the impinging electrons

[13] L. H. Thomas, Proc. Camb. Phil. Soc. **23**, 829 (1927).
[14] Webster, Hansen, and Duveneck, Phys. Rev. **43**, 839 (1933).

is very much greater than any orbital velocities has any definite result been attained. This restriction invalidates the application of the result to x-ray experimental problems to a large extent. Recently wave-mechanical calculations by Massey and Mohr, by Ochiai and by Møller have appeared.[15] In the work of Møller, relativity corrections are introduced. We shall quote an ionization function obtained non-relativistically by Bethe.[16] This is

$$\Phi_B(E, E_q, n_q) = \frac{n_q \pi e^4}{E_q} \, b_q \frac{1}{E} \, ln \frac{4E}{B_q}. \tag{2.34}$$

The value of b_q depends on the n, l value of the ejected electron. For the K-series of the heavier elements it is about 0.3. A definite value of B_q is not given, except that it is an energy of the order of E_q. Thus the wave-mechanical results, even in the high-velocity limiting case, do not lend themselves to precise evaluation.

9. *Experimental Tests of the Ionization Functions*

The best experimental method of treating these ionization functions in the x-ray region is to measure the intensity of an x-ray line as a function of voltage, using as a target a very thin foil. Such a foil must be used in order that the electron shall not lose an appreciable fraction of its energy in traversing the target. If a thick target is used, as in ordinary x-ray tubes, the line intensity which is measured is the result of ionizing impacts of the cathode rays during the process of being slowed down from their initial velocity to the minimum velocity for the ejection of a bound electron. This corresponds to integrating the ionization function over the possible range of velocities, and in the process many of the details of the function are smoothed over or disappear.

In eq. (8.46) of Chap. VIII, we have written an expression for the intensity of a spectrum line which is

$$I \sim \tilde{\nu}^4(i,f) \, F_i g_i P^2 \, (i,f), \tag{2.35}$$

where the symbols i, f refer to the initial and final states concerned in the production of the line, $\tilde{\nu}(i,f)$ is the frequency of the line, g_i the statistical weight of the initial state, and $P(i,f)$ is the amplitude of

[15] Massey, Proc. Roy. Soc. Lond. A **129**, 616 (1930). Massey and Mohr, ibid. **135**, 258; **136**, 289 (1932); **139**, 187 (1933). Ochiai, Proc. Phys. Math. Soc. Japan **11**, 43 (1929). Møller, Zeitschr. f. Physik **70**, 786 (1931); Annalen der Physik **14**, 531 (1932).
[16] Bethe, Annalen der Physik **5**, 325 (1930).

a virtual harmonic oscillator associated with the atom having a frequency $\tilde{\nu}(i,f)$. In the present treatment we are concerned with the relative intensity of the same x-ray line from a given thin target at various energies E of the impinging cathode rays. Thus we may disregard all the quantities in the above expression except F_i, and write

$$I \sim F_i.$$

F_i in eq. (2.35) is the ionization function for effectively one electron per cubic centimeter, or in other words, the probability that the impinging electron will lose an amount of energy greater than E_q in traversing a layer of material having effectively one electron per cubic centimeter. The word " effective " as used here is not necessary to interpret the classical ionization functions, but in Bethe's function, eq. (2.34), we find n_q multiplied by a factor b_q, and we would here speak of $n_q b_q$ as the " effective " number of q-electrons per cubic centimeter. The method of treatment adopted here is, when making the transition to the view-point exemplified by eq. (2.35), to consider those factors which contribute to the effective number of electrons as present in the g_i's. If all the corrections (discussed below) are properly made, so that the corrected I values correspond to ionizations made in a foil of effective thickness X by electrons of uniform kinetic energy E, we will have

$$F_i = [X\Phi(E, E_q, n_q)]/[n_q]_{\text{eff}},$$

where $\Phi(E, E_q, n_q)$ is the ionization function, as discussed in the preceding section. Thus we see that after correction, the relative values of I should give relative values of the ionization function.

The study of the excitation of characteristic radiation in thin foils has been undertaken largely by D. L. Webster and his associates.[17] The experimental difficulties are considerable, largely because of the thinness of the films. The silver films in the most recent paper varied from 1.70 to 17.00 $\times$ 10^{-6} cm thick. The thinner films of this group were formed by rapid vaporization of metallic silver onto a beryllium target, and were used with this backing in the x-ray tube. Because of the very low atomic number and low density of beryllium, the continuous radiation excited in it by electrons which penetrate the silver film is relatively weak, and no large correction

[17] Webster, Clark, and Hansen, Phys. Rev. 37, 115 (1931). Webster, Hansen, and Duveneck, Phys. Rev. 43, 839 (1933).

need be made for the K ionization of the silver due to absorption of general radiation from the backing material. It is important that the experiments so far performed only give the relative values of the ionization function at different values of the incident energy. The theoretical ionization functions give an absolute value for the number of electrons ejected so that experimental results must be compared with theory by fitting the two at a point, by means of an adjustable constant in the experimental curve. In the work of Webster, Hansen, and Duveneck some of the experimental and theoretical curves have been caused to coincide at a point $E = 2E_q$. It is easily seen by differentiation of the ionization function derived from classical theory that it has a maximum at this value.

The direct experimental results of line intensities from the foils must be corrected for minor effects. One of these is the retardation within the film, which means that in spite of the thinness, all the ionizing impacts are not made at the same speed. This correction will clearly depend on the initial speed, since any film which is not a monatomic layer will become effectively a thick film if the initial velocity is sufficiently small. If X is the effective thickness of the film, E the initial energy, and E_x the energy after traversing the film, we may write approximately,

$$E_x = E + X dE/dx,$$

in which of course dE/dx is intrinsically negative. We may then define an average value of E, $\bar{E}$, for traversing the film, which will be

$$\bar{E} = E + \tfrac{1}{2} X dE/dx.$$

The observed intensity from the film, which is proportional to the number of ionizing impacts in it, will be proportional to $X\overline{\Phi(E)}$, where $\overline{\Phi(E)}$ is an average value of the ionization function for the range of velocities in traversing the film. If we identify in our approximate calculation $\overline{\Phi(E)}$ and $\Phi(\bar{E})$ we obtain

$$X\overline{\Phi(E)} = X\Phi(E + \tfrac{1}{2} X dE/dx) = X\Phi(E) + \tfrac{1}{2}X^2 \frac{dE}{dx} \frac{d\Phi(E)}{dE},$$

where $X\overline{\Phi(E)}$ is proportional to the intensity observed, and $X\Phi(E)$ is proportional to the corrected intensity, considering the effect of retardation alone. The value of $d\Phi(E)/dE$ may be obtained by plotting the uncorrected results. dE/dx must be obtained from experiments on the retardation of cathode rays in passing through matter. It may be well to point out here that the major effect in this retarding is interaction with loosely bound outer electrons of the substance; a large loss of energy, such as the ejection of a K electron, is a relatively rare event. The Thomson–Whiddington[18] law,

$$\frac{dE}{dx} = -\frac{\text{const.}}{E}, \tag{2.36}$$

with values of the constant from measurements of Terrill,[19] might have been used, but recent work by E. J. Williams[20] has given a more reliable expression, which is

$$dV/dx = 1.06\rho\beta^{-1.4}.$$

In this expression, dV/dx is the energy lost per centimeter of path expressed in electron-kilovolts, ρ is the density, and β the ratio of the velocity of the impinging electrons to the velocity of light. If the loss of energy is expressed in ergs per centimeter, we obtain

$$dE/dx = 1.69 \times 10^{-9}\rho\beta^{-1.4}. \tag{2.37}$$

The experiments of Williams which gave rise to the above expressions were performed on mica, which contains only light atoms; for heavy atoms, Webster recommends multiplication of the above expression by a factor $2Z/A$, where Z is the atomic number and A the atomic weight. This takes account of the fact that the number of extra-nuclear electrons per unit of atomic weight is smaller for heavy than for light elements. From these considerations a correction factor for retardation may be calculated.

A further correction must be applied due to the effect of diffusion in the film. The electron tracks are not straight lines, but curves, and this has the effect of increasing the effective path length, so that X is greater than X_0, the actual foil thickness. A knowledge of the most probable angular deviation λ in radians produced in a thickness x cm of foil is needed. A formula, " for practical use " has been developed by Bothe,[21] which reads,

$$\lambda = \frac{800}{V} \frac{V+511}{V+1022} Z\sqrt{\frac{\rho x}{A}},$$

[18] R. Whiddington, Proc. Roy. Soc. Lond. A 86, 360 (1912).
[19] H. M. Terrill, Phys. Rev. 21, 476; 22, 107 (1923).
[20] E. J. Williams, Proc. Roy. Soc. Lond. A 130, 310 (1932).
[21] W. Bothe, Handbuch der Physik, Vol. 24, p. 18 (1927).

where V is the energy of the β-ray in kilovolt-electrons, Z the atomic number, ρ the density and A the atomic weight of the film material. From the consideration that the deviation in traversing a thickness of the material is independent in direction and magnitude of the deviation in the preceding thickness, an effective foil thickness X can be computed.

In the case of the films on beryllium backing, some of the electrons which pass through the film are deviated through 180° by the beryllium and strike the silver film twice, thus increasing the intensity observed. To correct for this effect a knowledge of the intensity versus angle distribution of β-rays scattered backward from a surface is required. It is important here to differentiate between rediffused primary electrons and secondary electrons, the latter having energies too low to produce characteristic x-rays in the film. From data presented in the results of Schonland,[22] and of Stehberger,[23] Webster estimates that the fraction of the incident β-rays scattered backward in beryllium is 0.04. From further information on their energy and angle distribution,[24] a correction for this effect can be computed.

Again, in the case of films mounted on a backing of beryllium, the general radiation produced in the beryllium by electrons which have passed through the film will to some extent be absorbed in the film and produce fluorescence K radiation in it. For the estimation of this correction, a knowledge of the distribution of energy in the general radiation from a light element such as beryllium and of the intensity at various angles from the cathode ray beam is needed. These factors are discussed in a later section of this chapter. The correction becomes relatively large at high incident energies, requiring multiplication of the observed intensity by a factor of 0.90 in the case of a 1400 angstrom silver film on beryllium when the incident voltage is 178 kv., corresponding to $E/E_K = 7$. For this reason, unsupported films were used at the higher voltages.

After a careful study of these corrections, Webster, Hansen, and Duveneck obtained the relative values of the ionization function listed in Table II–1.

Lorenz[25] has obtained data on the intensity of characteristic

[22] Schonland, Proc. Roy. Soc. Lond. A 108, 187 (1925).

[23] Stehberger, Ann. der Physik 56, 825 (1928).

[24] Wagner, Phys. Rev. 35, 98 (1930). Kovarik and McKeehan, Phys. Rev. 6, 426 (1915). Chylinski, Phys. Rev. 42, 393 (1932).

[25] E. Lorenz, Zeitschr. f. Physik 51, 71 (1928).

TABLE II-1

EXPERIMENTAL RELATIVE VALUES OF THE IONIZATION FUNCTION FOR K IONIZING
IMPACTS IN SILVER, ACCORDING TO WEBSTER, HANSEN, AND DUVENECK

E/E_K	$\Phi(E, E_K, n_q)$	E/E_K	$\Phi(E, E_K, n_q)$
1.2	0.404	3.5	1.153
1.5	0.733	4	1.145
2.0	(1.000)	5	1.123
2.5	1.103	6	1.099
3.0	1.138	7	1.072

radiation produced in an aluminium foil 8×10^{-5} cm thick by
incident cathode rays with velocities equivalent to energies up to
50,500 volts, or $E/E_K = 33$. Lorenz estimated that above 15 kilovolts, this aluminium sheet could be considered as an ideally thin
foil, but Webster, Hansen, and Duveneck have indicated that due
to diffusion in the foil the results of Lorenz can only be satisfactorily
interpreted between 25 and 30 kv. up to his higher limit.

It is doubtful whether the data of Webster and his associates
extend to values of E/E_K sufficiently large so that the approximation
on which Bethe's wave-mechanical ionization function, eq. (2.34), is
based, is valid. The best method of testing this equation is from
experiments on the passage of β-rays through gases.[26] The data
obtained by Lorenz at high values of E/E_K for aluminium presumably can be compared with Bethe's results, but it must be
remembered that only relative experimental values of the function
are known, and over the range specified Lorenz's results give a monotonically decreasing function without details. In the paper of
Webster and his associates, it is shown that if $b_q = 1$, the best values
of B_q to fit the trend of the curve are given by $B_q/E_q \sim 0$. The
test of the wave-mechanical function from an x-ray standpoint cannot therefore be said to be in a satisfactory state.

A comparison of the classical quantum theory ionization function

---

[26] For instance, the experiments of Hughes and Klein, Phys. Rev. **23**, 450 (1924);
K. T. Compton and C. C. van Voorhis, Phys. Rev. **26**, 436 (1925); **27**, 724 (1926); P. T.
Smith, Phys. Rev. **36**, 1293 (1930). These experiments were performed on helium. In
the paper of Webster, Hansen, and Duveneck these results are discussed, and it is
shown that in the range of E/E_q from 10 to 180, the best values of b_q and B_q in Bethe's
equation are 1.75 and $3E_q$ respectively.

eq. (2.33), with the experimental results of Table II–1, is shown in Fig. II–4. It is convenient to introduce the variables

$$U = E/E_q, \quad V = E/e \quad \text{and} \quad T = k_q/E_q.$$

Then eq. (2.33) can be written,

$$\Phi_C(U) = \frac{n_K \pi e^2}{V_K^2} \frac{1 - U^{-1} + \frac{2T}{3}(1 - U^{-2})}{U}. \qquad (2.38)$$

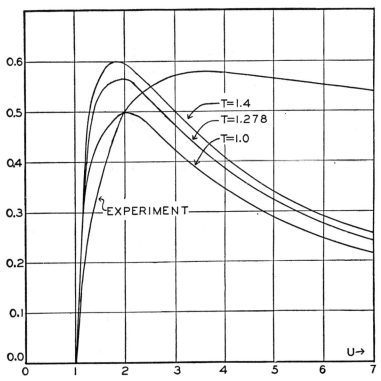

FIG. II–4. Comparison of the experimental and classical quantum theoretical ionization functions according to Webster, Hansen, and Duveneck. The scale of ordinates is arbitrary, since no absolute value is given by experiment.

where we are specifically considering ionization of the K shell, so that $q = K$. It is in this form that the classical quantum theory is tested in Fig. II–4. Curves are drawn for various values of T, the one indicated by the simple orbit theory being $T = 1.278$.

It is seen that the form of the classical quantum theory function is quite irreconcilable with experiment. All the theories of single ionizing impacts predict, and experiment shows, that the ionization function has a finite derivative at $E = E_q$.

As an empirical function fitting the experimental points, Webster, Hansen, and Duveneck give

$$I(U) = \left(\frac{2}{U}\right)^{0.783} \frac{\log U}{\log 2}. \qquad (2.39)$$

This function gives the arbitrary value unity at $U = 2$, and follows the experimental points closely.[27]

10. *The Intensity of Characteristic Radiation from a Thick Target*

In a thick target, as ordinarily used in x-ray tubes, the impinging cathode rays are slowed down to a very small residual speed by numerous impacts with atoms, and in the x-ray case we can consider that the entire original kinetic energy disappears. By far the largest part of the kinetic energy goes into the production of heat (see the treatment in a later section in this chapter); in some cases energy is lost in the production of general radiation, and occasionally an atom in the target is ionized in an inner shell. We are discussing here the intensity of the characteristic radiation resulting from such inner ionizations.

The present problem concerns the relative intensities of the same x-ray line at various voltages on the x-ray tube. Thus, as in the first paragraphs of the preceding section, we may consider the corrected intensity proportional to F_i, but at present we have

$$I \sim F_i = \left[\int_0^{x_q} \Phi\left(E', E_q, n_q\right) dx \right] \Big/ \left[n_q \right]_{\text{eff.}} \qquad (2.40)$$

Here the function Φ is the ionization function at the energy E', which is the energy possessed by the electrons after traversing a

---

[27] By a calculation similar to that leading to eq. (2.31), except that the inverse cube power of the distance is used as an expression for the variation of the repulsive force, instead of the ordinary inverse square, Webster, Hansen, and Duveneck derive the formula,

$$I_3\left(U\right) = \frac{6}{U\{(\frac{\pi}{2}\cos^{-1}U^{-\frac{1}{2}})^2 - 1\}},$$

which fits the experimental curve very well. The significance of this agreement is at present unknown.

certain thickness of target material. x_q is the length of path in the target material at which the incident cathode ray energy E has been reduced to E_q.

Before much attention had been paid to the rôle of the ionization function in this problem, x-ray spectroscopists had observed the increase in intensity of x-ray lines at voltages above the critical voltages, and obtained empirical formulae to fit the observations. The earliest of these was obtained by Webster and Clark[28] in 1917, and was of the form

$$I \sim (E - E_q)^n,$$

or in terms of the variable $U = EE_q^{-1}$,

$$I \sim (U - 1)^n. \tag{2.41}$$

Various values of n have been reported,[29] probably the most reliable being $n = 1.65$, which holds fairly well up to $U = 4$. The measurements of Stumpen, of Wooten, and of Nasledow and Scharawsky were carried out with unrectified, alternating potential, and it is doubtful if quantitative results can be deduced from them. Kettmann used an electrostatic induction machine as a source of high voltage, and extended his results to values of U as high as 7. In the work of Unnewehr the K radiation of targets of Cr, Cu, Rh, and Ag was studied up to 45 kv. In general it may be said that all experimenters found that the line intensity begins at zero at the excitation voltage, and increases according to the above-mentioned equation until approximately $U = 4$, then falls away from this rate of increase, presumably due to absorption in the target.

Stumpen found that the curves obtained for L group lines rose more rapidly with voltage after the K excitation voltage had been reached, as if the K radiation process increased the number of atoms in the target with vacancies in the L shell. Although such an effect was predicted by Smekal,[30] Kettmann failed to find positive evidence for it, and experimentally its existence does not seem to be satisfactorily demonstrated.

The expression of eq. (2.40) can be integrated if the functional

[28] D. L. Webster and H. Clark, Proc. Nat. Acad. Sci. USA 3, 181 (1917).

[29] B. A. Wooten, Phys. Rev. 13, 71 (1919). G. Kettmann, Zeitschr. f. Physik 18, 359 (1923). E. C. Unnewehr, Phys. Rev. 22, 529 (1923). H. Stumpen, Zeitschr. f. Physik 36, 1 (1926). D. Nasledow and P. Scharawsky, Zeitschr. f. Physik 43, 431 (1927). A. Jönsson, Zeitschr. f. Physik 36, 426 (1926). S. K. Allison, Phys. Rev. 32, 1 (1928).

[30] A. Smekal, Verh. d. D. Phys. Ges. 21, 149 (1919).

relationship between E' and x is known. If we assume that the Thomson-Whiddington law, eq. (2.36), is valid, using Rosseland's ionization function, eq. (2.31), we have

$$F_i = - C \int_E^{E_q} \frac{1}{E'} \left(\frac{1}{E_q} - \frac{1}{E'} \right) E' dE' = C \left(\frac{E - E_q}{E_q} - ln \frac{E}{E_q} \right). \quad (2.42)$$

Under similar conditions the integral of the ionization function of Thomas, eq. (2.32), is

$$F_i = C \left[(E - E_q) \left(\frac{2k_q}{E_q{}^2} + \frac{3}{E_q} \right) - \frac{2k_q}{(k_q + E_q)} \, ln \left\{ \frac{E(2E_q + k_q)}{E_q(E + E_q + k_q)} \right\} \right.$$

$$\left. - \left\{ 3 + (k_q + E_q) \left(\frac{2k_q}{E_q{}^2} + \frac{3}{E_q} \right) \right\} \, ln \left\{ \frac{E + E_q + k_q}{2E_q + k_q} \right\} \right]. \quad (2.43)$$

More accurate predictions probably could be based on the retardation function of eq. (2.37), found experimentally by E. J. Williams, and replacing the Thomson-Whiddington law.

Upon closer consideration, it appears that the emission from a thick target is complicated by various secondary effects. One of these is the production of ionized atoms in the target by photo-electric absorption of the general radiation, or the production of " indirect " characteristic x-rays. Another is due to the fact that the characteristic radiation is produced at depths within the target which vary with the initial velocity of the cathode rays, and hence is absorbed on its way out of the target through an effective thickness of material depending on the voltage. Also part of the cathode rays are rediffused, or reflected back from the target face, and do not enter it.

The first effect mentioned, namely the production of " indirect " line radiation by the photo-electric absorption of general radiation, has been investigated for the $K\alpha$ lines by Webster,[31] and by Webster and Stoddard.[32] An x-ray tube was used which had a target composed of a solid block of silver, over which a foil of palladium was placed. The thickness of the palladium foil was 0.010 cm for voltages up to 100 kv. At higher voltages, thicker foil was used, backed by aluminium. The criterion of foil thickness was that no primary electrons could penetrate the foil and excite radiation by electron impact in the silver underneath. Thus the silver radiation coming from such a composite target is all indirectly produced. The method

[31] D. L. Webster, Proc. Nat. Acad. Sci. **14**, 339 (1928).
[32] D. L. Webster and K. B. Stoddard, Phys. Rev. **43**, 701 (1933).

centers about the fact that 46Pd and 47Ag are so near together in atomic number that it is relatively easy to calculate from the observations what would be the state of affairs if the entire target were of palladium, and at the same time the spectrometer easily separates the silver K from the palladium K radiation. Confining our considerations to x-rays emerging normally from the target surface, let

$$P = \frac{\text{power in the direct } K\alpha \text{ radiation from a thick palladium target}}{\text{power in the indirect } K\alpha \text{ radiation from a thick palladium target}}.$$

Then the ratio $P/(P + 1)$ is the fraction of the normally emergent $K\alpha$ line radiation produced directly by electron impact. Values of P and $P/(P + 1)$ found by Webster and Stoddard are given in Table II–2. It is seen that the ratios are apparently independent of voltage.

TABLE II–2

P = Ratio of Direct to Indirect Pd$K\alpha$ Rays
$P/(P + 1)$ = Fraction of Normally Emergent Pd$K\alpha$ Rays Directly Produced

Kilovolts........	40	60	80	100	120	140	160	180
P..............	1.95	1.98	2.05	2.03	2.12	2.09	2.06	2.13
$P/(P + 1)$......	0.66	0.66	0.67	0.67	0.68	0.68	0.67	0.68

Wisshak[33] has attempted a calculation of the fractional amount of the observed characteristic radiation which is indirectly produced in the target. He assumes that the thickness of the target in which the continuous radiation is produced is very small compared to the thickness in which it is photo-electrically absorbed. Thus regions of the target contributing equally to the emergent indirect radiation lie in hemispherical shells, the centers of the spheres lying at the center of the focal spot. An analogous integration was carried out by Webster and Stoddard, but only for the purpose of estimating corrections to their observations. Wisshak, who computes the entire effect, arrives at $P/(P + 1)$ values which vary with voltage, in contrast to the results of Table II–2. The reason for this lack of agreement is not clear.

An experimental method for the estimation of the absorption in the target has been described by Kulenkampff,[34] and used by him

[33] K. Wisshak, Annalen der Physik 5, 507 (1930).
[34] H. Kulenkampff, Ann. der Physik 69, 548 (1922).

and by other investigators.   This is based on a comparison of the intensity of the characteristic radiation at various angles with the target face.   If it were true that all the characteristic radiation is produced in a thin layer at uniform depth X below the surface of the target, and that the target face is perfectly plane, then the rays emitted at a glancing angle β with the target face would have their intensity diminished by a factor

$$e^{-\mu X \cosec \beta},$$

where μ is the linear absorption coefficient.   A graph of the logarithm of the intensity against $\cosec \beta$ would in such a case be linear, and if it were extrapolated to $\cosec \beta = 0$, the extrapolated value would be free from absorption.

Andrew[35] has mentioned the doubtful point in this method, namely that the depth X is not a constant; characteristic radiations being produced at all depths up to the limiting one by primary processes, and indirect rays have on the average a still greater effective depth.   As a consequence of this, the above-mentioned graphs cannot be strictly linear, and accurate extrapolation is difficult.   The absorption correction obtained in this way is thus approximate. The lack of linearity will be more pronounced at higher voltages; thus the deviations from linearity observed by Wisshak in targets of 24Cr, 29Cu, 42Mo and 47Ag up to 32 kilovolts are within experimental error, but larger deviations appear in the work of Webster, Hansen, and Duveneck at 180 kilovolts with a silver target.

The correction for incident electrons re-diffused and thus leaving the target must be considered.   If the object of the experiments is merely to obtain the relative intensities of a given characteristic line at various voltages, a knowledge of the variation of the fraction of the incident electrons reflected with voltage is all that is required. Wisshak attempted to measure this by comparing the readings of a current measuring instrument in the tube circuit with the current calculated from the voltage on the tube and the measured rate of production of heat in the anode.   This method should give the total current actually reaching the target, and this may be less than indicated with a measuring instrument in the external circuit.   Wisshak found no change in the ratio of the calorimetrically measured current to the total current throughout a range of from 3 to 30 kv. in targets

[35] V. J. Andrew, Phys. Rev. **42**, 591 (1932).

of copper and silver. In the gas-filled tube used by him the ratio was 0.8 in Mo and Cu, and 0.6 in Ag. Webster, Hansen, and Duveneck calculated a correction for this effect, using the same sources of information mentioned previously in the correction of the observed intensities in backed foils for re-diffusion from the backing material. Their calculated corrections vary with voltage; if the factor for a silver target at $U = 1$ (25 kv.) is 1.00, the factor at $U = 7$ (180 kv.) is 1.31. This result differs from that of Wisshak, which however may itself be in error because it does not distinguish between cathode rays which strike and are absorbed in the focal spot, and rays which are reflected from the spot but return and strike the anode at some other point.

If the above-mentioned corrections have achieved their purpose, the corrected values of the observed intensities of the line at various voltages can be compared with the integrated ionization functions, for instance, eqs. (2.42) and (2.43). Such a comparison has been carried out by Wisshak, using the function of Rosseland, eq. (2.42), and a function obtained by integration of an empirical equation closely representing the thin target results of Webster and his associates.[36] Wisshak found that neither of these functions corresponded to his experimental results; the theoretical thick target curves rising more rapidly than the experiment indicates. Webster, Hansen, and Duveneck[37] have examined their corrected thick target results on the relative intensities of $AgK\alpha$ at various voltages for evidence as to the cathode ray retardation function.

Let $\Phi(E, E_q, n_q)$ be the ionization function, and $I(E)$ the corrected intensity from a thick target. Then the contribution to $I(E)$ from a layer of thickness dx at a depth x in the target is

$$dI(E) = k \, \Phi(E', E_q, n_q)dx$$

where k is independent of E, and E' is the value of E for the electrons incident on layer dx which have traversed target thickness x. From the above expression we may obtain, after dropping the prime,

$$\frac{dE}{dx} = k \frac{\Phi(E)}{dI(E)/dE}.$$

---

[36] This was not the function of eq. (2.39), but was $(1 - U^{-1})/(3+U)$ obtained in an earlier paper of Webster, Yeatman, Clark, and Hansen, Proc. Nat. Acad. Sci. USA **14**, 679 (1928).

[37] Webster, Hansen, and Duveneck, Phys. Rev. **44**, 258 (1933).

If the ionization function is considered as known, from the results of thin target measurements, and values of $dI(E)/dE$ are obtained from the experimental thick target curve, a set of values proportional to dE/dx for various values of E can be calculated. Absolute values of dE/dx depend on k, and Webster and his associates have not made this determination. If an equation like that of E. J. Williams for dE/dx (eq. (2.37)) is valid, a plot of log (dE/dx) against the logarithm of the cathode ray speed should be linear, with a slope of -1.4. Webster, Hansen, and Duveneck find that their data agree well with this exponent, giving independent evidence of the law of cathode ray retardation in traversing matter.

11. *Applications to the Problem of the Experimental Measurement of the Relative Intensities of X-ray Spectrum Lines*

The objective in the measurement of the relative intensities of two different lines is usually to obtain the ratio of the quantities $g_i P^2(i,f)$ which appear in eq. (2.35). Let I' represent the intensity of a line measured at the target surface, and let us distinguish between two lines by the subscripts 1 and 2. We may then write

$$\frac{[g_i P^2(i,f)]_1}{[g_i P^2(i,f)]_2} = \frac{I'_1 [\tilde{\nu}^4(i,f)]_2 [F_i]_2 a_2}{I'_2 [\tilde{\nu}^4(i,f)]_1 [F_i]_1 a_1}. \qquad (2.44)$$

The factors a_2 and a_1 are added to represent the necessary correction for the absorption in the target itself. This correction is very difficult to make, and it is probable that in none of the reported experiments on the relative intensities of x-ray lines has it been made in a thoroughly satisfactory manner. The experimental method of Kulenkampff described in the last section has not been used. The usual procedure has been either to neglect the correction entirely, or to attempt to calculate it by making simplifying assumptions. The effect of the diffusion of the cathode rays in the target material has been neglected, that is, it has been assumed that the path in the target is a straight line continuation of the incident path. Such an assumption will over-estimate the depth at which characteristic rays are produced. Also the indirect production of characteristic rays has been neglected. If the lines whose intensities are being compared have the same initial state, the effect of indirect production can only be to increase the effective depth of production. Thus at least it can be said that the two neglected factors will produce corrections in opposite directions in measurements on the lines of the K series, for instance.

Keeping in mind the above simplifying assumptions, we may write for classical ionization functions, where $n_q = [n_q]_{\text{eff.}}$

and

$$d(aF_i) = n_q^{-1}\Phi(E', E_q, n_q)\, e^{-\mu x\, \text{cosec}\, \beta}\, dx\, \text{cosec}\, \alpha$$

$$aF_i = n_q^{-1} \int_0^{x_q} \Phi(E', E_q, n_q) e^{-\mu x\, \text{cosec}\, \beta}\, dx\, \text{cosec}\, \alpha$$

In the above expression E' is the energy of the cathode rays incident upon the layer of thickness dx in the target (Fig. II–5), that is, the energy of the cathode rays after having traversed a distance x cosec α in the target material.

In order to complete the integration indicated above, the law of

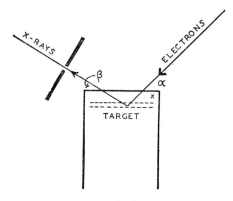

FIG. II–5.   Illustrating the notation used in the treatment of absorption in the target.

electron retardation must be known. Assuming the Thomson-Whiddington law, eq. (2.36), A. Jönsson[38] computed the above integral using Rosseland's ionization function, eq. (2.31). If we write eq. (2.36) in the form

$$dE'/ds = -\, b/2E'$$

where now s is used for the length of material traversed, we obtain by integration

$$E'^2 - E^2 = -\, bs \qquad\qquad (2.45)$$

[38] A. Jönsson, Zeitschr. f. Physik 43, 845 (1927).

since when $s = 0$, $E' = E$. In our present case, $s = x \operatorname{cosec} \alpha$, so

$$dx = - (2E'dE')/b \operatorname{cosec} \alpha.$$

If we now change the variable of integration from x to E' by means of the preceding relation, we obtain

$$aF_i = - \frac{2}{bn_q} \int_E^{E_q} \Phi(E', E_q, n_q) e^{-\kappa^2 \mu (E^2 - E'^2)} E' dE'$$

in which

$$\kappa^2 = \operatorname{cosec} \beta / b \operatorname{cosec} \alpha.$$

Using the ionization function of eq. (2.31), we may now write

$$aF_i = Ce^{-\kappa^2 \mu E^2} \left[E_q^{-1} \int_{E_q}^E e^{\kappa^2 \mu E'^2} dE' - \int_{E_q}^E E'^{-1} e^{\kappa^2 \mu E'^2} dE' \right]$$

This expression is not integrable, but Jönsson has given a series expansion which is recommended for small values of κ^2 and not too large values of E. This is

$$aF_i = Ce^{-\kappa^2 \mu E^2} \left[\frac{E - E_q}{E_q} - \log \frac{E}{E_q} + \frac{\kappa^2}{6E_q} (2E^3 - 3E^2E_q + E_q^3) \right.$$

$$\left. + \frac{\kappa^4}{40E_q} (4E^5 - 5E^4E_q + E_q^5) + \frac{\kappa^6}{252E_q} (6E^7 - 7E^6E_q + E_q^7) \ldots \right]$$

The value of b in eq. (2.45) is only roughly known; if E is measured in ergs and ρ is the density of the material,

$$b = 1.02 \times 10^{-12} \rho.$$

When the lines whose relative intensities are being measured belong to the same initial state, as in the K group, the ratio $[F_i]_2 a_2/[F_i]_1 a_1$ of eq. (2.44) differs from unity only because of absorption in the target, the two F_i factors being identical. Williams[39] has calculated the relative values of the a's for the $K\alpha_1$ and $K\beta_1$ lines of $_{24}$Cr at 31.8 kv., and finds

$$a_\alpha/a_\beta = 0.97$$

This result was obtained using the empirical ionization function of Webster, eq. (2.39), in the previous integration, rather than Rosseland's function, but retaining the use of the now somewhat out-

[39] J. H. Williams, Phys. Rev. **44**, 146 (1933).

moded Thomson-Whiddington law. In a series of experiments on the intensities of the K series lines the above represented the largest target correction in elements from 24Cr to 52Te at voltages ranging upward from roughly 30 kv. at 24Cr to 45 kv. at 52Te.

In cases where the relative intensity of two lines of different initial states is being measured, the factor $[F_i]_2 a_2/[F_i]_1 a_1$ may be large, because at a given incident energy E the two F_i's are different. The present considerations apply to the interesting problem of the relative intensities of the $L\beta_1$ ($L_{II} - M_{IV}$) and $L\alpha_1$ ($L_{III} - M_V$) lines of a given element. In order to treat this problem in a satisfactory manner, we need more information than experiments on the ionization function have so far given us. We need to know how $\Phi(E, E_q, n_q)$ varies with E_q, but the experiments only give Φ as a function of E with E_q constant. The theoretical classical ionization function, eq. (2.31) predicts that at values of E much greater than E_q for either line, the relative values of Φ will be

$$\left[\frac{\Phi_1}{\Phi_2}\right]_{E \gg E_q} = \frac{[E_q]_2}{[E_q]_1} \tag{2.46}$$

considering two functions having the same value of n_q, and this has been used as a guide in supplementing experimental data. To state the matter in another way, the empirical ionization functions such as eq. (2.39), involve an unknown multiplication factor; eq. (2.39) having been devised, for instance, to give the purely arbitrary value of unity at $U = 2$. The present question turns on the point as to whether this experimentally unknown factor contains E_q. The application to experimental results on the relative intensities of lines in the L group is discussed in the chapter on the interpretation of x-ray spectra.

12. *The Efficiency of X-ray Production*

Early experiments by Röntgen[40] showed that the amount of x-rays produced by a given beam of cathode rays increases with the atomic weight of the target and with the voltage applied to the x-ray tube. It was shown by Beatty[41] that the relation could be expressed to a close approximation by the simple formula

$$\frac{\text{x-ray energy}}{\text{cathode ray energy}} = kZV, \tag{2.47}$$

[40] W. C. Röntgen, Cf. Science, 3, 726 (1896).
[41] R. T. Beatty, Proc. Roy. Soc. 89, 314 (1913).

where Z is the atomic number, V is the potential applied to the tube, and k is a constant of proportionality. The following table shows various values of k which have recently been recorded:

TABLE II-3

Efficiency of X-ray Production

Observer	Excitation	Measurement	Date	k (per Volt)
Beatty......	Homogeneous cathode rays	Ionization	1913	20×10^{-10}
Bouwers......	Transformer	Bolometer	1924	5.6
Auren........	Continuous D.C.	Thermopile	1925	7.2
Rump........	Continuous D.C.	Calorimeter	1927	15.0

References:
  R. T. Beatty, Proc. Roy. Soc. Lond. A **89**, 314 (1913).
  A. Bouwers, Thesis, Utrecht, 1924.
  T. E. Auren, Medd. Nobelinst. v. 6 (1925).
  W. Rump, Zs. f. Physik **43**, 254 (1927).

Kulenkampff[42] estimates Bouwers' value as about 40 per cent low because alternating instead of continuous voltage was used, and Auren's value as about 20 per cent low, chiefly because of failure to correct for the electrons reflected from the surface of the target. Nicholas,[43] on the other hand, considers Rump's value to be some 30 per cent high due to the neglect of certain corrections. It would seem reasonable to take the value

$$\epsilon = 1.1 \times 10^{-9} \, ZV \qquad (2.48)$$

as probably correct within about 20 per cent. This would mean for a tungsten target tube ($Z = 74$) operated at 100,000 volts, an efficiency of x-ray production of about 0.8 per cent, or for a carbon target tube ($Z = 6$), operated at 10,000 volts, an efficiency of about 0.007 per cent.

13. *Energy Distribution of the Continuous Spectrum*

We have shown in Fig. I-30 typical spectral ionization curves obtained at different potentials from a massive target of tungsten. In order to interpret curves of this kind in terms of spectral energy

[42] H. Kulenkampff, Handbuch der Phys. (Geiger und Scheel) v. **23**, p. 445 (1926).
[43] W. W. Nicholas, Phys. Rev. **35**, 128 (1930).

distribution, it is necessary to assign different weights to different portions of the curve. Thus one takes into account the variation of the reflecting power of the crystal grating for different wave-lengths, the absorption of the x-rays in the x-ray bulb, the air and the window

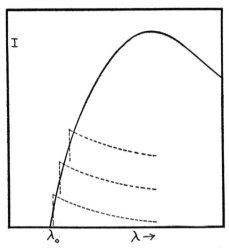

Fig. II–6. Analysis of a thick target spectrum into a series of thin target spectra. (Webster.)

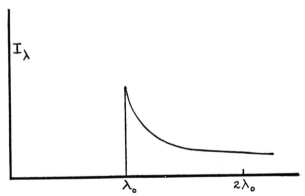

Fig. II–7. Energy distribution from a thin target, as calculated from the spectrum of a thick target. (Webster.)

of the ionization chamber, and the different ionization per unit energy produced by beams of different wave-length.

Webster has pointed out[44] that since the cathode rays quickly

[44] D. L. Webster, Phys. Rev. **9,** 220 (1917).

lose speed as they enter the target, the rays of maximum frequency can be emitted only from the surface of a thick target. A spectrum from such a target can indeed be analyzed into a series of thin target spectra, as suggested in Fig. II–6 in which, according to Webster, the distribution of energy from each thin layer should be that shown in Fig. II–7. The striking feature of this thin target spectrum is the sharp discontinuity at the spectral limit.

Recently Nicholas[45] has obtained spectra from targets consisting of thin gold and aluminium leaf, which show this same sharp break. Nicholas plots his results against the frequency, as shown in Fig. II–8. When plotted against the wave-length, as in Fig. II–9, we see

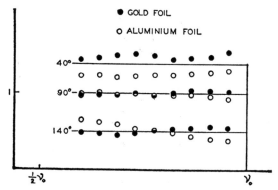

FIG. II–8. Experimental results on the energy distribution on a frequency scale in the continuous spectra from foils of gold and aluminium, observed at various angles from the cathode ray beam, according to Nicholas.

how closely his experiments confirm Webster's analysis of the thick target spectrum as shown in Fig. II–7. The transfer from an I versus ν curve to an I versus λ curve is based on the convention that $I_\lambda d\lambda = I_\nu d\nu$, which is necessary if the area under both curves is to be proportional to the energy in the spectrum. Thus $I_\lambda/I_\nu = -d\nu/d\lambda = \nu^2/c$, since $c/\nu = \lambda$. That is, $I_\lambda = (\nu^2/c)I_\nu$; and similarly, $I_\nu = (c/\nu^2)I_\lambda$.

Studies of the absorption of the rays emitted by thin targets, made by Kulenkampff[46] and by Duane,[47] have confirmed the distribution shown in Fig. II–8. Thus within experimental error we may express

[45] W. W. Nicholas, Bur. Stand. Jr. of Res. 2, 837 (1929).
[46] H. Kulenkampff, Ann. der Phys. 87, 579 (1928).
[47] W. Duane, Proc. Nat. Acad. Sci. USA 15, 805 (1929).

the spectral energy distribution of the x-rays produced in a very thin target by the equation

$$I_\nu d\nu = \text{const. } [\nu < \nu_0] \qquad (2.49)$$

This expression was first proposed by Kramers from theoretical considerations.

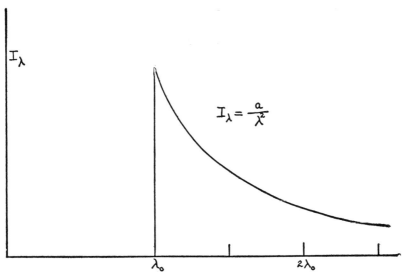

$$I_\lambda = \frac{a}{\lambda^2}$$

FIG. II-9.   The distribution $I(\nu) = $ const. plotted on a wave-length scale.

14. *Polarization of Primary X-rays*

Polarization of primary x-rays was first definitely established by Barkla,[48] using the apparatus shown diagrammatically in Fig. II-10.   The method consisted in using a scattering block R for the analyzer, in the manner described in Chap. I, Sec. 6.   The tube was placed alternately in positions A and B, and the ionization in chambers C and D compared.   The ionization chamber w which received the scattered ray proceeding at right angles to the cathode rays registered the greater current by 10 or 20 per cent.   These results have been extended by Haga,[49] Herweg,[50] Bassler,[51] and Vegard.[52]

[48] C. G. Barkla, Phil. Trans. Roy. Soc. 204, 467 (1905).
[49] H. Haga, Annalen der Physik 24, 439 (1907).
[50] J. Herweg, Annalen der Physik 24, 398 (1909).
[51] E. Bassler, Annalen der Physik 28, 808 (1909).
[52] L. Vegard, Proc. Roy. Soc. 83, 397 (1910).

These observers, especially Bassler, find that by filtering out the softer components of the primary beam the polarization can be increased, though increasing the speed of the cathode rays seems to diminish the polarization of the unfiltered rays. Experiments by Ross,[53] using a differential filter method, indicate that the portion of the primary x-rays which is at the high frequency limit of the spectrum is completely polarized. Wagner and Ott,[54] however, who separate the radiation near the spectral limit by reflection from a rock-salt crystal, find that the maximum polarization is 47 per cent. Here we define the magnitude of the polarization as

$$P = \frac{I_\perp - I_{||}}{I_\perp + I_{||}} \qquad (2.50)$$

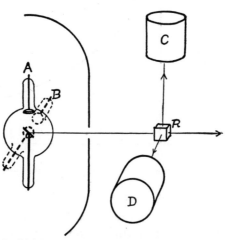

FIG. II-10.   Barkla's method for detecting polarization of primary x-rays.

where $I_\perp$ is the ionization in chamber D and $I_{||}$ that in chamber C of Fig. II-10, when the x-ray tube is in position A. The complete polarization found by Ross does not seem to be confirmed by other measurements using filter methods, such as those of Kirkpatrick,[55] who estimates the maximum polarization at the short wave-length limit for 58 kilovolts as about 10 per cent. It is possible that there may be some unsuspected error in Ross' differential filter method.

[53] P. A. Ross, Jour. Opt. Soc. Am. **16**, 375 (1928).
[54] E. Wagner and T. Ott, Ann d. Phys. **85**, 425 (1928).
[55] P. Kirkpatrick, Phys. Rev. **22**, 37; 226 (1923).

There can, however, be no doubt but that these limiting rays are strongly polarized.

This strong polarization of the rays of highest frequency, which are emitted only from the surface of a thick target, may imply that the smaller polarization of the total primary radiation is due to the deflection of the cathode electrons as they traverse the material of the target. If this is the case, the polarization of the total x-rays from very thin targets should likewise be strong. This is indeed the case. Thus Kulenkampff,[56] using a target of aluminium leaf and cathode rays of 38 kilovolts, finds 45 per cent polarization of the entire radiation and shows that under the conditions of his experiment the main stream of cathode rays has been only slightly diffused by passing through the target.

Dasannacharya[57] has extended this work by using a wide range of thicknesses of aluminium and several different voltages. Even for sheets as thin as 6×10^{-5} cm he finds the polarization increasing as the target is made thinner. Duane,[58] however, using as a target a jet of mercury vapor, finds no measurable difference in the polarization for jets of different densities. With cathode rays at 12.5 kilovolts he observes 50 per cent polarization. Dasannacharya notes that with these thin targets, just as with the thick ones, the polarization is smaller for cathode electrons of higher speed. For his thinnest aluminium leaf targets he finds at 27 kilovolts 47 per cent polarization, and at 56 kilovolts 38 per cent polarization. The deflection of the cathode electrons by the target is undoubtedly, however, greater at the lower than at the higher voltage, so that the lack of complete polarization in his experiments cannot be ascribed to this deflection. For targets of infinitesimal thickness, therefore, it seems that the polarization of the total is of the order of 50 per cent, that it is approximately independent of the atomic number of the atoms in the target (comparison of aluminium leaf and mercury vapor), and that it is somewhat less complete when excited by electrons of higher speed.

15. Spatial Distribution of X-rays Emitted from Thin Targets

A thorough study of the spatial distribution of the x-rays emitted from targets of thin aluminium leaf has been made by Kulenkampff.[56]

[56] H. Kulenkampff, Ann. d. Phys. 87, 597 (1928); Phys. Zeit. 30, 513 (1929).
[57] B. Dasannacharya, Phys. Rev. 35, 129 (1930).
[58] Wm. Duane, Proc. Nat. Acad. 15, 805 (1929).

In Fig. II–11 is reproduced a group of three curves showing the distribution for different portions of the spectrum excited by cathode rays of 31 kilovolts. It will be seen that the intensity has its maximum value at about 60 degrees, and that it approaches a minimum for 20 and 180 degrees. Duane[59] has measured the radiation from a target consisting of a jet of mercury vapor, at 0 and 90 degrees respectively with the cathode ray stream, and finds the intensity in the first case to be about 15 per cent of that in the second. This indicates that the minimum at $\theta = 0$ does not fall to zero intensity.

Measurements of the spectral distributions of the x-rays emitted

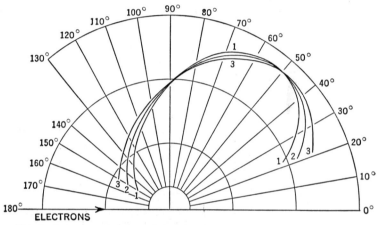

FIG. II–11.   Intensity of emission of various wave-lengths in the continuous radiation emitted from an aluminium foil as a function of angle from the cathode ray beam. Curve 1, radiation of about 0.43 A; 2, 0.53 A; 3, 0.73 A.   The incident cathode rays were accelerated by 31 kv.

in different directions from thin targets show only slight variations. The spectra obtained by Nicholas (Fig. II–8) from gold leaf have the same form at all three angles. Those from aluminium, however, show some predominance of the higher frequencies at the larger angles, though Nicholas doubts whether the effect is greater than the experimental error. Absorption measurements by Kulenkampff and by Duane, on the other hand, show that the rays emitted near the direction of maximum intensity are somewhat more penetrating than those at very small or at very large angles. These experiments are less subject to experimental errors than are the spectra obtained by

[59] W. Duane, Proc. Nat. Acad. 13, 662 (1927); 14, 450 (1928).

Nicholas. There is thus no decisive experimental evidence for a Doppler effect in connection with the frequency of primary x-rays.

This conclusion is contrary to that which was drawn in 1926 by one of the authors of this book.[60] Thus electrons at the surface of the target emit more strongly in the forward direction, whereas those which have traversed enough matter to move in approximately random directions, and which will emit softer radiation because of their speed, will radiate approximately equally in all directions. This results in a relatively greater intensity of the longer wave-lengths at the larger angles.

THEORIES OF THE CONTINUOUS SPECTRUM

16. *Stokes-Thomson Pulse Theory of X-rays*

The first hypothesis regarding the nature of x-rays which led to important results was that put forward by Stokes.[61] He supposed that x-rays consist of irregular electromagnetic pulses due to the irregular accelerations of the cathode particles as they are stopped by the atoms of the target. Thomson[62] simplified this hypothesis for purposes of calculation by assuming that the cathode electron is brought to rest by a uniform acceleration opposite to the direction of motion.

One immediate consequence of this hypothesis is that the x-rays should be polarized. For according to Fig. II–1 the electric vector is in the same plane as the acceleration, and hence on Thomson's theory in the plane of the cathode ray stream. In fact for a thin target in which the cathode electrons do not have their direction of motion altered before they suffer a collision resulting in radiation, this theory would require complete polarization. As we have seen in Sec. 15, strong polarization of x-rays from a thin target is observed in the predicted plane, though it is not found to be complete. This partial polarization, however, confirms Thomson's assumption that

[60] A. H. Compton, X-rays and Electrons, Van Nostrand (1926), p. 46. Experiments by Stark (Physikal. Zeitschr. 10, 902 (1909)) and Wagner (Jahrb. d. Rad. u. Elektron. 16, 212 (1919); Physikal. Zeitschr. 21, 623 (1920)) were quoted, which showed that the x-rays from thick targets are more penetrating in the forward than in the backward direction. It would now seem that this effect is due to the diffusion of the electrons in the anti-cathode, combined with the fact that the radiation emitted forward is more intense than in the reverse direction.

[61] G. Stokes, Proc. Manchester Lit. and Phil. Soc. (1898).

[62] J. J. Thomson, Phil. Mag. 45, 172 (1898); "Conduction of Electricity through Gases" (Cambridge Univ. Press), 2nd Ed., 658 et seq.

the accelerations to which the cathode electrons are subject are pre-
dominantly parallel to the cathode ray stream.

17. *Sommerfeld's Extension of the Pulse Theory*

Sommerfeld has used Stokes' pulse hypothesis as a basis for calculating the spatial intensity distribution of the primary x-rays.[63]
Let us assume that an electron, when it strikes the target, is subjected
to a constant negative acceleration in the direction of motion, which
continues until the electron has been brought to rest. Since the
cathode ray moves with a speed comparable to that of light, we must
use eq. (2.02) to represent the strength of the electric field. According to eq. (2.03) the intensity of the radiation at $P(r, \theta)$ is then

$$I = \frac{a^2 e^2}{4\pi r^2 c^3} \frac{\sin^2 \theta}{(1 - \beta \cos \theta)^6}. \qquad (2.51)$$

The total radiated energy traversing unit area at P due to stopping the electron is

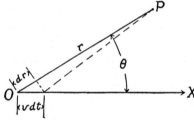

Fig. II–12.

$$S = \int I dt,$$

where the integral is taken over
the complete pulse. If t is the
time at which the radiation
reaches P which left the electron
at the instant t', then $t = t' + r/c$.
Thus $dt = dt' + dr/c$ where, as
a glance at Fig. II–12 will show, $dr = -vdt' \cos \theta = -\beta c \cos \theta \, dt'$,
and hence $dt = dt'(1 - \cos \theta)$. But $a = cd\beta/dt'$, whence $dt' = cd\beta/a$,
and

$$dt = \frac{c}{a} (1 - \beta \cos \theta) d\beta.$$

Thus

$$S = \int I dt = \int_{\beta}^{o} \frac{a^2 e^2}{4\pi r^2 c^3} \frac{\sin^2 \theta}{(1 - \beta \cos \theta)^6} \cdot \frac{c}{a} (1 - \beta \cos \theta) d\beta,$$

$$= \frac{ae^2}{4\pi r^2 c^2} \sin^2 \theta \int_{\beta}^{o} \frac{d\beta}{(1 - \beta \cos \theta)^5},$$

$$= \frac{|a|e^2}{16\pi r^2 c^2} \frac{\sin^2 \theta}{\cos \theta} \left[\frac{1}{(1 - \beta \cos \theta)^4} - 1 \right]; \qquad (2.52)$$

[63] A. Sommerfeld, Physikal. Zeitschr. **10**, 969 (1919); Atomic Structure and Spec-
tral Lines, English edition (Methuen), p. 33 (1923).

or for small values of β,

$$S_0 = \frac{|a|e^2\beta}{4\pi r^2 c^2} \sin^2 \theta. \qquad (2.53)$$

Spatial Intensity Distribution.—The energy as a function of the angle θ according to eq. (2.52) is plotted in Fig. II–13 for three values of β. There is a strong resemblance between these curves and those of Fig. II–11, taken from Kulenkampff's data. In particular the predominance of the forward over the backward radiation predicted by the theory is very similar to that which the experiments reveal.

There are two differences however between the theoretical and the experimental curves to which attention should be called. The first is the fact that the angle of maximum emission is smaller in the experiments than Sommerfeld's theory predicts. This difference may be explained by the fact that the thickness of the aluminium leaf used by Kulenkampff was so small that most of the cathode electrons were but slightly retarded on traversing it. Hence the effect of the forward motion on the intensity distribution should be characteristic of electrons moving with a speed almost equal to their initial velocity. Eq. (2.52), on the other hand, assumes that the cathode electron is brought to rest while it is radiating, so that the Doppler effect is that due to an average between the initial speed and zero. The difference between Figs. II–11 and II–13 is of just the order of magnitude to fit this explanation.

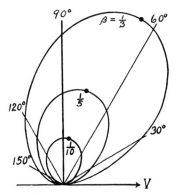

Fig. II–13. Movement of the direction of maximum emission toward the direction of the cathode ray beam at higher cathode ray energies, according to eq. (2.52).

The second difference, that the experimental intensity at $\theta = 0$ is not zero, is more fundamental. It must mean that there are accelerations of the cathode electrons perpendicular to the direction of motion, and hence that the Thomson-Sommerfeld assumption that only longitudinal accelerations occur is an unwarranted simplification. In fact, photographs obtained with the cloud expansion chamber show sharp curvatures in the paths of electrons traversing matter, which means strong transverse accelerations.

The Doppler Effect.—If, as in Fig. II–14 the electron moves from O to O' while the pulse is being radiated, the thickness of the pulse will be less at small angles θ than at large angles. In fact, the thickness

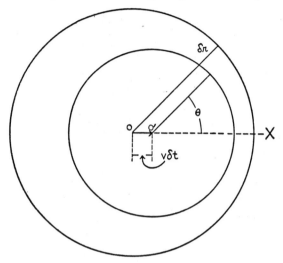

FIG. II–14. The Doppler effect in the emission from an accelerated electron.

of the pulse at a large distance r from the origin is given by the expression

$$\delta r = c\delta t - v\delta t \cos \theta = c\delta t(1 - \beta \cos \theta). \tag{2.54}$$

It can be shown[64] that a pulse of the form assumed in Sommer-

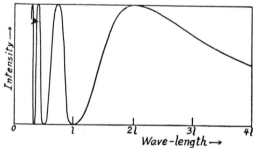

FIG. II–15. The Fourier analysis of a rectangular pulse.

feld's theory is equivalent to the spectral distribution represented by Fig. II–15. Here l, the thickness of the pulse, is the same as the

[64] A. H. Compton, X-rays and Electrons, van Nostrand (1926), p. 381.

δr of eq. (2.54). It will be seen from eq. (2.42) therefore that each peak of the original distribution curve of Fig. II–15 will occur at larger angles. This should result in a shorter effective wave-length for the total radiation, which is not in agreement with the experiments of Kulenkampff and Duane, quoted in Sec. 15.

If the spectral distribution is a continuous one, as indicated in Fig. II–8, the Doppler effect will result in a shift of the radiation which for $\theta = \pi/2$ lies between ν and $\nu + d\nu$ to the portion of the spectrum between ν' and $\nu' + d\nu$, where

$$\nu' = \nu/(1 - \beta \cos \theta) \qquad (2.55)$$

and

$$d\nu' = d\nu/(1 - \beta \cos \theta).$$

The result will be a continuous spectrum, expanded however along the frequency axis by the factor $1/(1 - \beta \cos \theta)$. Since, according to the quantum theory, the spectrum ceases abruptly at $\nu_{max} = Ve/h$, this need not in general result in any change in the average frequency of the radiation, for at small angles the portion of the radiation which should be shifted beyond ν_{max} does not appear in the spectrum. Thus the existence of the high frequency limit makes it impossible for the Doppler effect to show itself in the effective frequency of the radiation. By combining quantum principles with Sommerfeld's classical theory we can thus predict results in qualitative accord with the experiments. As we have seen above, however, an effect of the forward motion of the cathode electrons does appear in the longitudinal asymmetry of intensity of the x-rays.

18. X-ray Pulses Due to Motion of Cathode Electrons Past Atomic Nuclei

When electrons traverse matter, they suffer deflections due to close approach to other electrons and to atomic nuclei. Collisions with positive nuclei should be the more effective in producing radiation. If we neglect the effect of radiation in damping the electron's motion, its orbit about a positively charged nucleus should be an hyperbola. The acceleration of the electron at each point of its orbit should be along the line joining the two particles, and of magnitude Ze^2/mr^2, where Ze is the charge of the nucleus and r the radius vector.

It can be shown that the accelerations to which electrons are subject on passing through a group of such attracting centers have on the average a larger component opposite to the direction of motion than in other directions, and hence that there should be partial polarization. This is in qualitative accord with the experiments of Duane and others, as quoted above. No quantitative comparison, however, appears to have been made between the prediction of polarization by this theory and the experimental data from thin targets.

The spectral distribution of the radiation emitted by cathode electrons traversing such hyperbolic orbits about atomic nuclei has been calculated approximately by Kramers. The curve of Fig. II–16 shows his result. This is to be compared with Nicholas' experimental data shown in Fig. II–8. The shapes of the two curves show little similarity.

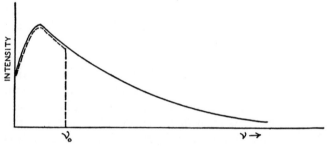

Fig. II–16. Spectral energy distribution of radiation due to electrons deflected by positive nuclei, calculated by classical electrodynamics (Kramers). The broken line represents his quantum theory.

19. *Necessary Failure of any Classical Theory of the Continuous X-ray Spectrum*

There is a serious difficulty in devising a theory on classical principles which will be consistent both with the fact that the x-ray spectrum has a sharp upper limit to its frequency and with the longitudinal asymmetry of the intensity described in Sec. 15. The latter phenomenon indicates that the source of radiation is moving forward at a speed approximately equal to that of the cathode electrons (Secs. 16 and 17), whereas the former fact makes necessary the assumption of an oscillator capable of emitting a long train of coherent waves. Such an oscillator, however, must be of atomic size, for so far as we know there is no mechanism which would enable a free electron to execute harmonic oscillations. Thus the sharp spectral limit seems to require atomic oscillators as the source of the continuous spectrum, whereas the Doppler intensity effect indicates that the source is a moving electron. The classical attempts to account for the continuous x-ray spectrum are accordingly blocked by an obstinate dilemma.

Several modes of escape from this difficulty have been proposed, but without satisfactory results. Thus Webster has suggested that the cathode electron may carry with itself a mechanism which is set into oscillation as it traverses matter.[65] Thus the cathode electrons would be moving radiators while they are passing among the atoms of the target. At one time there appeared to be several lines of confirmatory evidence[66] for the view that the electron might have a suitable structure for executing such oscillations. This auxiliary evidence has, however, almost completely fallen to the ground, and one hesitates to postulate such a complex structure for the electron for which no other use is found.

Several writers[67] have discussed the form of pulse necessary to give rise to the observed spectral distribution. For our present purpose the most interesting of these discussions is that of Nicholas,[68] who shows that the spectral energy distribution illustrated by the lines in Fig. II–8 is equivalent to an electromagnetic pulse whose electric vector is proportional to

$$\frac{\lambda_0}{2\pi ct} \sin \frac{2\pi ct}{\lambda_0},$$

where $\lambda_0 = h/mv_0$, v_0 being the initial speed of the cathode electron. This function is plotted in Fig. II–17. Such a pulse is in reality an infinite train of waves though the amplitude is very small except near the time interval λ_0/c.

Nicholas has attempted to account for the origin of such a pulse in a wave structure of the electron itself. He has to suppose however that the electric charge density of a uniform moving electron has a wave form similar to that of the electromagnetic pulse illustrated in Fig. II–17, whereas according to de Broglie's wave mechanics, if an electron moving at a definite speed is to be represented by

[65] D. L. Webster, Phys. Rev. 13, 303 (1919).

[66] D. L. Webster, Bull. Nat. Res. Council, 473 (1920); A. H. Compton, Phys. Rev. 14, 20 and 247 (1919); A. L. Parson, Smithsonian Misc. Coll. p. 65 (1915).

[67] A. Sommerfeld, Ann. d. Phys. 46, 721 (1915). E. H. Kennard, Phys. Zeits. 24, 372 (1923).

[68] W. W. Nicholas, Bur. Standards J. Research 2, 837 (1929).

a wave, the wave must be one whose amplitude diminishes only slowly on either side of the maximum. Difficulties arise in accounting on his theory for the incomplete polarization and for the Doppler effect on the wave-length and intensity; but this inconsistency with de Broglie's wave mechanics implies also an inconsistency with the experiments on electron diffraction, which seems to be fatal.

We are thus led to the conclusion that there seems no means, based on the usual electron theory and electrodynamics, of accounting

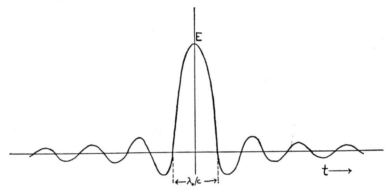

Fig. II–17. A pulse of this form would give the observed energy distribution of the continuous x-ray spectrum. (Nicholas.)

adequately for the characteristics of the continuous spectrum of x-rays.

20. *Quantum Theories of the Continuous Spectrum*

In some respects more success has attended the application of quantum principles to this problem, though as yet the solution is far from complete. Kramers[69] and Wentzel[70] have approached the question from the standpoint of the correspondence principle. If we consider the cathode electron in its initial state to have energy $W_i = \frac{1}{2}mv^2 = Ve$, and after the radiation collision to have energy $W_f = V'e$, the frequency of the radiation emitted, according to Bohr's frequency principle, should be

$$\nu = \frac{1}{h}(W_i - W_f) = (V - V')e/h \qquad (2.56)$$

[69] H. A. Kramers, Phil. Mag. **46**, 836 (1923).
[70] G. Wentzel, Zeits. f. Phys. **27**, 257 (1924).

Since the smallest possible value of V' is zero, there can be no radiation emitted of frequency higher than

$$\nu_{max} = Ve/h. \qquad (2.57)$$

This is in exact accord with Duane and Hunt's law of the high frequency limit of the x-ray spectrum.

Kramers has applied the correspondence principle to the radiation calculated classically for electrons moving past positive nuclei by simply neglecting the radiation which the classical theory predicts of frequency higher than ν_{max}, and assigning to radiation of lower frequency its full weight. This means, referring to Fig. II–16, that the spectral energy distribution for electrons traversing a thin target should be represented by the broken line. To a first approximation, Kramers calculates that the average energy emitted between frequencies ν and $\nu + d\nu$, due to a single electron with energy Ve traversing unit area which includes a small number A of atomic nuclei of atomic number Z, is

$$\left. \begin{array}{ll} i_\nu d\nu = \dfrac{16\pi^2 A}{3\sqrt{3}} \dfrac{Z^2 e^5}{mVc^3} d\nu & [\nu < \nu_0] \\[2mm] i_\nu d\nu = 0 & [\nu > \nu_0] \end{array} \right\}. \qquad (2.58)$$

For frequencies less than ν_0, this expression indicates an intensity independent of the frequency. This is not in strict agreement with the broken curve of Fig. II–16, and the difference shows the degree of approximation of the calculation. Equation (2.58) is however in good agreement with the thin target experiments. This is evident from Fig. II–8, in which the solid lines show the spectral distribution predicted by Kramer's theory.

In order to calculate the intensity of the radiation emitted from an x-ray tube with a solid target, Kramers takes into account the decrease in velocity of the electrons traversing the metal by applying the Thomson-Whiddington law, using Bohr's theoretical value of the constant. For the energy between frequencies ν and $\nu + d\nu$ radiated per electron impact he thus finds,

$$I_\nu d\nu = \dfrac{8\pi}{3\sqrt{3}l} \dfrac{e^2 h}{mc^3} Z(\nu_0 - \nu) d\nu, \qquad (2.59)$$

approximately, where l is a numerical factor of the order of magnitude of 6.   This result is in good accord with Kulenkampff's empirical formula[71]

$$I_\nu = CZ(\nu_0 - \nu) + BZ^2,\qquad (2.60)$$

in which the first term is ordinarily much more important than the second.

A quantitative test of the theory is afforded by the calculation of the efficiency of production of x-rays.   The formula obtained is,

$$\epsilon = \frac{4\pi}{3\sqrt{3}l}\frac{e^3}{mhc^3}ZV$$

$$= 9.2 \times 10^{-10}\,ZV,\qquad (2.61)$$

where the potential V is expressed in volts.   Not only does the efficiency as thus calculated vary with the potential and the atomic number in the way shown by experiment (cf. Sec. 12), but also the numerical coefficient is in good accord with the value 11×10^{-10} which represents an average of the experimental results.

Kramers does not attempt to make any estimate of the polarization of the x-rays.   To the degree of approximation with which eqs. (2.59–2.61) hold, however, he finds that the x-rays may be considered as being emitted by electrons traversing parabolic orbits. For such orbits most of the radiation is emitted when the acceleration is nearly opposite to the initial direction of the cathode rays, and there should thus be a strong polarization with the electric vector in the plane of the cathode rays.   There would seem to be no reason to expect any considerable differences in polarization for different parts of the spectrum, though the polarization should on this theory approach zero for rays emitted at 0 and 180 degrees with the cathode ray stream.   These qualitative results are in satisfactory accord with the rather uncertain data described in Sec. 14.

Wentzel has applied the correspondence principle in a different manner.[72]   Instead of arbitrarily cutting off the radiation at ν_0, he compares the radiation from an hyperbolic orbit with that from an elliptic orbit.   In the latter case the classical theory analyzes the radiation into a series of harmonics whose frequencies are integral multiples of the frequency of revolution in the elliptic orbit.   The amplitudes of the successive terms diminish, approaching zero as the

[71] H. Kulenkampff, Ann. d. Phys. 69, 548 (1922).
[72] G. Wentzel, Zeits. f. Phys. 27, 258 (1924).

term number increases indefinitely.   Bohr has shown that the line spectrum radiated by an electron which jumps from one elliptic orbit to another may be represented by a similar infinite series of terms which instead of approaching infinite frequency, approaches the limit $\nu_{max} = W_f/h$, where W_f is the final energy.   There is further-more a one to one correspondence between the amplitude of the nth term of the classical Fourier series and the nth term of Bohr's series. In fact Bohr was able in this manner to estimate the relative inten-sities of the different lines, and their state of polarization.   In Fig. II–18 is shown (*a*) a comparison of a classical line spectrum of har-

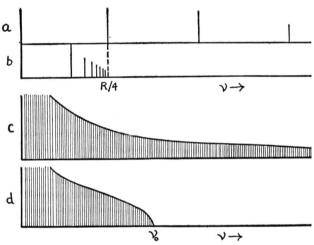

FIG. II–18. *a* and *b* compare the classical line spectrum of an harmonic oscillator, *a*, with an observed series spectrum, *b*. *c* and *d* compare the classical radiation from an hyperbolic orbit, *c*, with the observed continuous x-ray spectrum, *d*.

monic components with the corresponding Bohr spectrum (*b*) ap-proaching a limit at a finite frequency.

Wentzel applies a similar argument to the radiation from an electron traversing an hyperbolic orbit.   In this case there is no fundamental frequency, and the classical theory leads not to a Fourier series, but to a Fourier integral, in fact that corresponding to the intensity distribution shown in Kramers' classical curve of Fig. II–16.   Wentzel now supposes that this energy distribution, instead of continuing to indefinitely high frequencies, approaches instead ν_0 as a limit, as suggested in curves (*c*) and (*d*) of Fig. II–18. Unfortunately, as we have seen above, the correspondence principle does not state quantitatively how the transfer from one type of series to the other is to be made. Hence the exact shape of the spectral energy distribution curve cannot be definitely predicted. Wentzel uses a transformation formula which he has found applicable to line spectra, and thus obtains a spectral distribution curve of the form shown in Fig. II–19, which is not in satisfactory accord with the observed spectra from thin targets. It would however be possible,

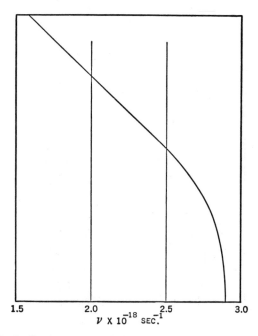

Fig. II–19. A distribution curve calculated by Wentzel for the continuous x-ray spectrum.

consistent with the fundamental basis of Wentzel's theory, to obtain a curve agreeing closely with the experiments.[73]

Wentzel's theory will necessarily lead to an expression for the efficiency of x-ray production which is of the same order of magnitude as that of Kramers, and hence in reasonably good agreement

[73] For though the "terms" of higher frequency become of lower and lower amplitude, they are in Bohr's series packed closer and closer together on a frequency scale. It accordingly becomes possible that the mean spectral energy density may not diminish as the frequency approaches ν_0.

with the experiments. The exact magnitude of the efficiency will however depend upon the way in which the transformation from the classical spectrum to the quantum spectrum is made.

According to classical theory the radiation of highest frequency emitted by a group of electrons of the same speed traversing a family of orbits about a nucleus is that due to the electron which approaches closest to the nucleus, and at that part of the orbit where it is closest, namely at perihelion. Such a close orbit is however nearly parabolic, and at perihelion the acceleration is opposite to the initial direction of motion of the electron. Thus the radiation of highest frequency should be strongly polarized, with the electric vector in the plane of the cathode ray stream. On Kramers' theory this radiation of highest frequency should not appear in the spectrum, since its frequency is greater than ν_0. According to Wentzel, however, such radiation should be strongly concentrated near the high frequency limit. Thus for radiation from a thin target, Wentzel's theory would predict a stronger polarization near ν_0 than for lower frequencies, whereas Kramers' theory would predict little if any difference. The experiments of Ross, described in Sec. 14 of this chapter, would favor the former prediction.

Though these theories of Kramers and Wentzel seem inherently adequate to account for the major features of the continuous x-ray spectrum, they were based on the correspondence principle, and therefore suffer from the lack of precision of that principle in its older form, the nature of the average between the amplitudes of the Fourier components of the classical motions in the initial and final states being left indefinite. The wave mechanics, however, leads to a definite prediction of spectrum line intensities, as we have seen in Sec. 5.

In a nucleus electron system, we may set the energy of the system equal to zero when the two are an infinite distance apart, and the electron is at rest. If we adopt this convention, the energies of states in which the electron is in a quantized configuration, corresponding to a stage in its capture by the nucleus, are negative. These are the quantized states of the ordinary optical term table. We may, however, have states of positive energy, the excess energy above zero representing the kinetic energy of the electron. When such positive energy states are examined by Schrödinger's equation, it is found that discrete energies are not predicted, as in the negative energy range, but that a continuous set of energies is permissible. If we

assume a certain positive energy, the corresponding proper or characteristic function can be computed, and the intensity of the radiation
emitted in a transition between two such states estimated from the
electric moment as given by eq. (2.28).

The actual calculations have been approached along two different
lines. One of these is typified by the work of Oppenheimer,[74] some
errors of which have been corrected by Gaunt,[75] and the work of
Sugiura.[76] In these calculations the analytical procedure according
to Schrödinger was followed, matrix elements being calculated from
characteristic functions corresponding to states of positive energy
before and after the interaction of the electron and the bare nucleus.

Sommerfeld,[77] on the other hand, introduced plane waves representing the oncoming and leaving electron beam as an explicit element
of the problem. The incident cathode ray beam is represented as
an electronic wave, present in entire space, both before and behind
the nucleus. It is necessary to take account of the fact that after
deflection the electron may leave the vicinity of the nucleus in any
direction. The problem was first studied by Sommerfeld assuming
that the electron leaving the nucleus could be represented as a plane
wave of the de Broglie type having the same direction as the wave
representing the incident electrons. This restriction was soon realized
to be too stringent, and the problem re-examined by summing over
all possible emergent orientations. This is analogous to the procedure used in calculating intensities of spectrum lines, in which one
has to sum over all the different orientations of the atom in a magnetic
field, giving them each unit weight.

Both the incident and the emergent de Broglie waves exist in
all space, before and behind the nucleus, and are diffracted by the
electric field of the nucleus. The abandonment of the "cause and
effect" models used in the classical explanations is obvious here.
From the overlapping of these waves, the effective values of the
electric moment to use in the classical expression for the radiation

[74] J. R. Oppenheimer, Zeitschr. f. Physik, 55, 725 (1929).

[75] J. A. Gaunt, Phil. Trans. Roy. Soc. 229, 163 (1930).

[76] Y. Sugiura, Sci. Pap. Inst. Phys. Chem. Res. Tokyo 11, 193 (1929); ibid. 11, 251
(1929); 13, 23 (1930); 15, 37 (1930); 17, 89 (1931). Of these papers the last one is
more nearly final, several errors in the preceding communications having been corrected.

[77] A. Sommerfeld, Proc. Nat. Acad. Sci. 15, 393 (1929). Annalen der Physik 11,
257 (1931). The problem has also been discussed by F. Sauter, Annalen der Physik 18,
486 (1933), and by Eckart, Phys. Rev. 34, 167 (1929).

from a dipole may be computed by a procedure analogous to that indicated in eq. (2.28), and hence the intensity of the radiation may be obtained.

If one sets the final velocity of the electron equal to zero, the short wave-length limit of the general radiation should be obtained. One of the most interesting results of the theoretical calculation of this region is that the polarization here is not necessarily complete, independent of the velocity of the impinging cathode rays, as might be expected on a simple deceleration model. In discussing the results of the calculations, Sommerfeld introduces the so-called "depolarization ratio," D, where

$$D = M_z^2/M_x^2.$$

This refers to a set of rectangular coordinates in which the nucleus lies at the origin, and the incident cathode ray approaches it along the x-axis, moving in the positive direction of x. The observer is supposed to be situated on the y-axis, and hence observing the radiation emitted in a direction perpendicular to the cathode ray beam. Then M_z is the effective electric moment along the z-axis, and M_x that along the x-axis. The early experiments on polarization of the continuous radiation from thick targets indicated that it is partially polarized in the sense that the electric vector is stronger in a direction parallel to the cathode ray beam than perpendicular to it, or in the present teminology, $M_x > M_z$. According to the definition of D, if $D = 0$, the radiation is 100 per cent polarized with its electric vector parallel to the cathode ray beam.

Sommerfeld finds that if the velocity of the impinging electrons corresponds to an accelerating voltage which is large compared to the K critical ionization voltage of the atoms of target, for radiation near the short wave-length limit $D = 0$, that is, we have 100 per cent polarization of the radiation emitted perpendicular to the cathode ray beam. This is confirmed by the results of Kulenkampff[78] who examined the radiation from an aluminium foil ($Z = 13$) when the incident electrons were accelerated by a voltage of about 30 kv. The theory predicts a depolarization ratio of 0.02 under these conditions and Kulenkampff's experiments indicated that the radiation near the short wave-length limit was completely polarized. The theoretical depolarization ratio increases rapidly as the voltage is lowered, and is in the neighborhood of 0.23 when the

---

[78] H. Kulenkampff, Physikal. Zeitschr. 30, 513 (1929).

electrons are accelerated by a voltage equal to the K ionization voltage of the atoms of the target. At the lower limit of velocity of the incident cathode rays the theoretical depolarization ratio approaches 0.25, which means that the polarization, defined as in eq. (2.50), approaches 80 per cent.

A further theoretical result concerning the short wave-length limit is that the intensity falls abruptly to zero from a finite value, in agreement with the curves of Fig. II–8.

If we now consider cases in which the velocity of the electron is not zero after the interaction with the nucleus, we can investigate the entire continuous spectrum and not confine ourselves to the region immediately adjacent to the short wave-length limit. Sommerfeld has computed the depolarization factor for four wave-lengths longer than the minimum wave-length. These are the wave-lengths corresponding to the frequencies

$$\tfrac{3}{4}\nu_{max.}, \quad \tfrac{1}{2}\nu_{max.}, \quad \tfrac{1}{4}\nu_{max.}, \quad 0.$$

The computed polarizations, P, where

$$P = \frac{1 - D}{1 + D},$$

are given in Table II–4.

TABLE II–4

THEORETICAL POLARIZATION OF THE CONTINUOUS RADIATION

Frequency	Per cent Polarization
$\nu = \nu_{max}$	100
$\nu = \tfrac{3}{4}\nu_{max}$	82
$\nu = \tfrac{1}{2}\nu_{max}$	57
$\nu = \tfrac{1}{4}\nu_{max}$	24
$\nu = 0$	−100

These computed values refer to an experimental case like that of Kulenkampff, where the initial electrons have an energy far above that of the K electrons of the atoms in the medium. The value −100 per cent for the polarization at the long wave-length end of the continuous spectrum means that the electric vector of the radiation emitted at right angles to the cathode ray stream is perpendicular to the cathode ray direction. The predicted points are compared with the observations of Kulenkampff on aluminium foil at 30 kv. in Fig. II–20.

As regards the intensity distribution in the continuous radiation, the theory gives, for observations at 90° to the cathode ray beam, a spectrum agreeing well with that experimentally observed, shown in Fig. II–8. When the dependence of the spectral energy distribution is examined as a function of the angle of observation, measured from the cathode ray beam, the theory agrees well with experiment. Perhaps the most interesting feature is the question of the intensity observed in the forward direction of the cathode rays. The theory

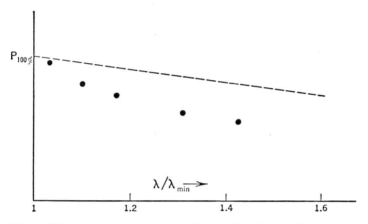

Fig. II–20. The dashed curve shows the theoretical prediction of the polarization of various wave-lengths in the continuous spectrum, if the energy of the incident electrons is high. Experimental points by Kulenkampff are indicated.

predicts that in this direction the intensity of radiation of frequency near the maximum frequency will be zero if the incident cathode rays have high energy compared to the K ionization energy of the atom. However, the intensities at longer wave-lengths in the spectrum will not approach zero here, so that a finite intensity should be observed, and this is confirmed by experiment. The older form of the theory in which the stopping of the electrons was assumed to take place along the direction of incidence only, predicted zero intensity at every wave-length in the forward direction.

The theoretical interpretation of the fact that the direction of maximum emission of the continuous x-rays is not in a plane normal to the direction of the cathode rays but is tilted forward of this plane, lies in the assumption that the electrons are emitting while in motion, as we have seen in Sec. 16. In calculating the intensity of spectrum lines by means of the matrix elements, one considers the radiation of a stationary dipole, but clearly a complete theory of the x-ray continuous radiation must take account of the motion of the source. At first Sommerfeld attempted this by a straightforward relativity transformation of the matrix elements, but in the present stage of the application of relativity theory to quantum mechanics this procedure cannot be completely justified. In his later calculations he proceeds by the method of retarded potentials in which the results previously obtained by relativity transformation methods appear automatically, although in a somewhat changed form.

For wave-lengths near the high frequency end of the spectrum, the theoretical result that the angle of maximum emission should satisfy the differential equation

$$\frac{d}{d\theta} \frac{\sin^2 \theta}{(1 - \beta \cos \theta)^4} = 0$$

is obtained. For small values of β, the value of θ is given by

$$\cos \theta \sim 2\beta.$$

The extent of the agreement with the experiments of Kulenkampff is shown in Table II–5. The experiments were performed using a narrow band of wave-lengths in the vicinity of the high frequency limit.

TABLE II–5

COMPARISON OF THEORETICAL AND OBSERVED DIRECTIONS OF MAXIMUM INTENSITY
OF EMISSION OF RADIATION NEAR THE SHORT WAVE-LENGTH LIMIT

Voltage (Kv.)	β	θ (Obs.)	Cos θ (Obs.)	Cos θ (Calc.)
16.4	0.248	63°	0.454	0.447
24.0	0.296	59°	0.515	0.514
31.0	0.333	55°	0.574	0.562
37.8	0.364	51°	0.629	0.598

Theoretical investigation of the effect of introducing retarded potentials on the longer wave-lengths in the continuous spectrum leads to the somewhat unexpected result that the angle of maximum emission for these wave-lengths is less than that for radiation near the high frequency limit. This, however, is found experimentally, as can be seen in Fig. II–11, in which curve 3, representing radiation of wave-length about 0.73 A has a maximum more in the forward direction than does curve 1, representing the distribution for wave-lengths near 0.43 A.

CHAPTER III

The Scattering of X-rays

1. *Wave and Corpuscular Aspects of Scattered X-rays*

Perhaps our most important source of information regarding the world around us is the light which is scattered into our eyes. By its aid we acquire precise and detailed information regarding the size, position and motion of the objects which scatter the light. In a similar way, scattered x-rays carry information regarding the molecules, atoms and electrons which scatter them. Because of their much shorter wave-length, the information thus obtainable from x-rays is in certain cases much more detailed than that given by scattered light. It was from the intensity of scattered x-rays that Barkla made the first accurate calculation of the number of electrons in an atom. Their diffraction by crystals (a special case of scattering) has made possible the precise study of the arrangement of atoms in solids. Similarly, investigations of the scattering of x-rays by liquids are now giving us new information about the arrangement of the atoms in liquid molecules, and from the scattering by gases we are learning the distribution of the electrons in the atoms themselves. We have in this phenomenon, therefore, an invaluable tool for investigating the more intimate aspects of matter.

As we have seen in our first chapter, not all the aspects of scattered x-rays can be described in terms of light waves. In certain respects they show the characteristic properties of discrete particles. It was in fact in connection with the scattering of x-rays that the dual wave and particle characteristics of nature were first made evident. It is desirable therefore to consider in some detail both the limiting cases of photons colliding with electrons and of the scattering of electromagnetic waves. We shall then notice how by the help of the wave mechanics it is possible to formulate a unified theory of the scattering process.

A. SCATTERING BY INDEPENDENT ELECTRONS

2. *Theory of J. J. Thomson*

We have already noticed that if x-rays are electromagnetic waves they should set into forced oscillation the electrons which they traverse, and these electrons in virtue of their accelerations should themselves radiate energy. If we suppose that the electrons in the scattering material are not subject to any appreciable forces of constraint, and if they are arranged in such a random manner that no definite phase relations exist between the rays scattered by the different electrons, J. J. Thomson has shown how to calculate very simply the intensity of the scattered beam.[1]

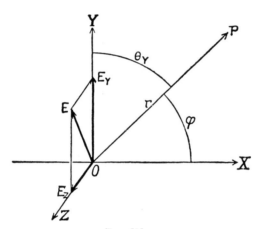

Fig. III-1.

If a wave whose electric intensity is E traverses an electron of charge e and mass m, the acceleration of the electron is Ee/m. According to eq. (2.01) this electron will radiate a wave whose electric intensity at a distance r is

$$E_\theta = \frac{e \sin \theta}{rc^2} \cdot \frac{Ee}{m} = \frac{Ee^2 \sin \theta}{rmc^2},$$

where θ is the angle between the electron's acceleration and the ray which we are considering. Since the intensities of both the primary

---

[1] This calculation follows in principle that performed by J. J. Thomson, "Conduction of Electricity through Gases," 2d Ed., p. 325.

and the secondary rays are proportional to the square of their electric vectors, the ratio of their intensities is

$$\frac{I_\theta}{I} = \frac{E_\theta{}^2}{E^2} = \frac{e^4 \sin^2 \theta}{r^2 m^2 c^4}. \tag{3.01}$$

If the primary ray is unpolarized, the acceleration of the scattering electron will be in a random direction in a plane perpendicular to the primary beam, OX, Fig. III–1. Let us take two rectangular axes in this plane, OY and OZ, such that one of them OY is in the plane POX in which lies the scattered ray which we are studying. The electric vector of the primary ray may be resolved into two components, E_y and E_z, such that $E_y{}^2 + E_z{}^2 = E^2$. Since the direction of E in the YOZ plane is random, E_y is on the average equal to E_z, whence on the average,

$$E_y{}^2 = E_z{}^2 = \tfrac{1}{2}E^2.$$

Thus

$$I_y = I_z = \tfrac{1}{2}I,$$

where I_y and I_z represent the intensities of the Y and Z components of the primary beam. The intensity of the scattered beam at P due to the Y component of the incident ray is, by eq. (3.01),

$$I_{\theta_y} = I_y \frac{e^4 \sin^2 \theta_y}{r^2 m^2 c^4},$$

or

$$I_{\phi_y} = \tfrac{1}{2}I \frac{e^4}{r^2 m^2 c^4} \cos^2 \phi, \tag{3.02}$$

where ϕ is the angle between the primary and the scattered rays. Similarly, that due to the Z component is

$$I_{\phi_z} = I_z \frac{e^4 \sin^2 \theta_z}{r^2 m^2 c^4}$$

$$= \tfrac{1}{2}I \frac{e^4}{r^2 m^2 c^4}, \tag{3.03}$$

since $\theta_z = \pi/2$. Thus if the primary beam is unpolarized, the intensity of the beam scattered by a single electron is

$$I_e = I_{\theta_y} + I_{\theta_z}$$

$$= I \frac{e^4}{2r^2 m^2 c^4} (1 + \cos^2 \phi). \tag{3.04}$$

If a number n of electrons are independently effective in scattering, the intensity of the scattered beam is then

$$I_s = \frac{Ine^4}{2r^2m^2c^4}(1 + \cos^2 \phi).\qquad(3.05)$$

The calculation of the total power in the scattered beam is effected most directly by integrating equation (3.05) over the surface of a sphere of radius r, thus:

$$P_s = \int_0^\pi I_s \cdot 2\pi r \sin \phi \cdot r d\phi$$

$$= \frac{\pi Ine^4}{m^2c^4} \int_0^\pi (1 + \cos^2 \phi) \sin \phi d\phi$$

$$= \frac{8\pi}{3} \frac{ne^4}{m^2c^4} I.$$

If n represents the number of electrons in a cubic centimeter, since I is the energy in the primary beam per square centimeter per second, the fraction of the primary energy which is scattered per cm of path is

$$\sigma = \frac{P_s}{I} = \frac{8\pi ne^4}{3m^2c^4}.\qquad(3.06)$$

This quantity σ is called the *scattering coefficient*, and should represent the fraction of the incident x-rays scattered per cm^3 of the irradiated material. The mass scattering coefficient, $\sigma_m = \sigma/\rho$, correspondingly represents the fraction scattered per gram of matter traversed by the x-rays. It is worth noting that these results have been obtained without assuming any particular form of electromagnetic pulse. They are thus independent of the wave-length and of the degree of homogeneity of the x-rays.

3. Experimental Tests of Thomson's Theory

a. The Polarization of Scattered X-rays

A significant confirmation of the principles underlying Thomson's theory of x-ray scattering comes from a study of the polarization of scattered x-rays. We notice that equation (3.02) represents the energy in the component of the scattered ray whose electric vector lies in the plane POX (Fig. III–1) including both the primary and the scattered ray. According to eq. (3.02), the intensity of this component is zero at right angles with the primary beam ($\phi = \pi/2$), whereas the oppositely polarized component, eq. (3.03), keeps its normal intensity. Thus in this direction the scattered beam should be completely plane polarized.

Such polarization can be detected by scattering again the polarized beam, and comparing the intensity of the scattered beam in two different directions, as already described on page 18. Barkla, in his classic measurement of the polarization of x-rays,[2] found that at 90 degrees the secondary rays from carbon were approximately 70 per cent polarized. This result has been confirmed by many experimenters.[3]

There are, however, two sources of error in these experiments

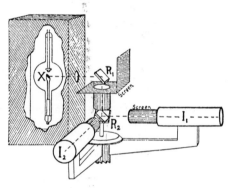

Fig. III–2.   Polarization of scattered x-rays, arrangement of Compton and Hagenow.

which have the effect of making the polarization appear incomplete. One of these, whose presence was recognized by Barkla, is the fact that in order to secure sufficient intensity in the beam after being twice scattered, the solid angle subtended by the scattering blocks at the source of x-rays must be very appreciable. The result is that most of the scattering does not occur at exactly 90 degrees, so that neither the polarization nor the analysis of the beam can be complete. The magnitude of this "geometrical error" as calculated in a typical case is of the order of 5 per cent. The second source of error is the multiple scattering at angles other than 90 degrees which occurs in both the polarizing and the analyzing radiators. Experiments by

[2] C. G. Barkla, Proc. Roy. Soc. **77**, 247 (1906).

[3] *E.g.*, Haga, Ann. d. Phys. **23**, 439 (1907).   E. Wagner, Sitz.-Ber. d. Würzburger phys.-med. Ges. **51**, No. 1 (1926). H. Mark and L. Szilard, Zs. f. Phys. **35**, 743 (1926).

Compton and Hagenow[4] have shown that when this multiple scattering is eliminated by using very thin radiators, and when the geometrical error is allowed for, the polarization of the scattered x-rays is complete within an experimental error of 1 or 2 per cent. The x-rays employed were the complete radiation from a tungsten tube excited at about 130,000 volts, and the test was made on scattering blocks of paper, carbon, aluminium and sulphur. These polarization experiments are therefore in complete accord with the electromagnetic theory of x-ray scattering.

b. *The Intensity of Scattered X-rays*

In Fig. III–3 are plotted the observed x-ray scattering coefficients of various different elements for a wide range of wave-lengths. The data have been collected by many different experimenters[5] using a wide variety of methods. The scattering coefficient is expressed in terms of σ_0, the value calculated from eq. (3.06), so that when $\sigma/\sigma_0 = 1$, the observed scattering is equal to that predicted by Thomson's theory. It will be seen that there is approximate agreement for light elements when the wave-length is between 0.1 and 1.0 A. That is, under these conditions the scattering coefficient is nearly independent of the wave-length and proportional to the atomic number.

For wave-lengths shorter than 0.1 A, the scattering coefficient for all elements rapidly becomes less than the theory predicts. This phenomenon is associated with the change in wave-length of the scattered rays, which also becomes prominent at these short wave-lengths. It is due to the recoil of the scattering electrons from the impact of the deflected photons, which for these wave-lengths have a mass comparable with that of the electron.

For the heavier elements the scattering coefficient is greater than Thomson's theory indicates, and increases rapidly with increasing

[4] A. H. Compton and C. F. Hagenow, J. O. S. A. and R. S. I., p. 487 (1924).

[5] The values of the scattering coefficients shown in Fig. III–3 are based chiefly on the data of E. O. Wollan, Phys. Rev. **37**, 862 (1931), E. N. Coade, Phys. Rev. **36**, 1101 (1930), G. Herzog, Helv. Phys. Acta, **6**, 508 (1933) and Owen, Fleming and Fage, Proc. Phys. Soc. **36**, 355 (1924). We wish especially to thank Dr. Wollan for supplying us with his heretofore unpublished data for σ for the gases here mentioned. Data from the following authors have also been useful: C. G. Barkla and J. G. Dunlop, Phil. Mag. **31**, 229 (1916). C. G. Barkla and R. Sale, Phil. Mag. **45**, 743 (1923). C. W. Hewlett, Phys. Rev. **20**, 688 (1922); **17**, 284 (1921). S. J. M. Allen, Phys. Rev. **24**, 1 (1924). N. Ahmad, Proc. Roy. Soc. **105**, 507 (1924); **109**, 206 (1925). C. S. Barrett, Phys. Rev. **28**, 891 (1926). P. Mertz, Phys. Rev. **36**, 1101 (1930).

wave-length. This effect occurs when the wave-length is great compared with the distances between the electrons in the atoms, so that the phases of the rays scattered from the different electrons are nearly the same, resulting in an increased total intensity. Indeed, if the distances between the electrons were negligible compared with the wave-length of the x-rays, all the electrons in the atom would act as

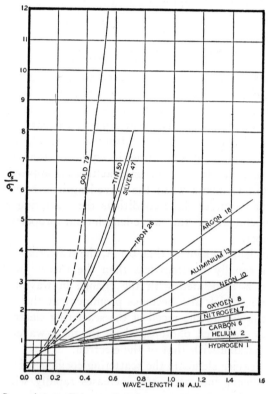

FIG. III–3. Scattering coefficients of various elements for different wave-lengths, relative to Thomson's calculated value, σ_0.

a unit. If Z is the number of electrons in the atom, the intensity of the ray scattered by a single atom would then be (eq. (3.04))

$$I'_a = I\frac{(Ze)^4}{2r^2(Zm)^2c^4}\,(1 + \cos^2\phi)$$

$$= \frac{IZ^2e^4}{2r^2m^2c^4}\,(1 + \cos^2\phi) = I_eZ^2. \qquad (3.07)$$

whereas if the electrons scatter independently the intensity should be (eq. (3.05))

$$I_a = \frac{IZe^4}{2r^2m^2c^4} (1 + \cos^2 \phi) = I_e Z.$$

According to the degree of concentration of the electrons near the center of the atom, the intensity of the scattered x-rays may thus vary by a factor of Z. The fact that for the light elements the scattering per atom is proportional to the first power of the atomic number, rather than to its square, thus indicates that in these atoms the electrons are spaced at distances which are considerable when measured in terms of x-ray wave-lengths. The fact that for the heavier elements the intensity of the scattering increases more rapidly than the atomic number indicates that in these atoms some of the electrons are close together when measured on this scale.

Determination of the Number of Electrons per Atom.—In the region of low atomic numbers and moderate wave-lengths we may thus apply Thomson's theory with some confidence. Now Hewlett[6] has measured the intensity of the x-rays of wave-length 0.71 A scattered from carbon over angles extending almost from $\phi = 0$ to $\phi = \pi$. He was thus able to perform experimentally the integration required to obtain σ, and finds for the mass scattering coefficient, $\sigma/\rho = 0.20$. According to eq. (3.06) the number of effective electrons per gram of carbon is

$$\frac{n}{\rho} = \frac{\sigma}{\rho} \cdot \frac{3m^2c^4}{8\pi e^4}.$$

Taking $\sigma/\rho = 0.20$, and using the usual values of e, m and c, this gives

$$\frac{n}{\rho} = 3.0 \times 10^{23} \text{ electrons per gram.}$$

But the number of carbon atoms per gram is

$$\frac{N}{M} = 6.06 \times \frac{10^{23}}{12} = 5.05 \times 10^{22} \text{ atoms per gram,}$$

where N is the number of molecules per gram molecule and M is the atomic weight of carbon. Thus the number of electrons per atom which scatter x-rays is $3.0 \times 10^{23}/5.05 \times 10^{22} = 6.0$, which is the atomic number of carbon.

[6] C. W. Hewlett, Phys. Rev. **19**, 266 (1922); **20**, 688 (1922).

It will be recalled that Rutherford[7] and Chadwick[8] have shown
by their experiments on the scattering of alpha particles that the
charge on the nucleus of the atom is equal to the atomic number.
A comparison of these two results means that all of the electrons exte-
rior to the atomic nucleus are effective in scattering x-rays. His-
torically, an x-ray scattering experiment of this type performed by
Barkla[9] afforded our first accurate estimate of the number of mobile
electrons in the atom.

As will be seen from Fig. III–3, if Barkla and Hewlett had performed their experiments under considerably different conditions of
wave-length and atomic number, their estimates of the number of
electrons would have been by no means so satisfactory. In eq.
(4.46) of Chap. IV, we have a method of estimating the number of
electrons per atom from the unit decrement of the index of refraction
for x-rays, and this method is more nearly independent of the wave-
length, and hence more reliable. The agreement between observed
and calculated values of this decrement shown in Table IV–2 may
at present be considered as a confirmation of the idea that the number of electrons per atom is equal to the atomic number, for without
this, the observed agreement would not have appeared. Thus refraction confirms the result of x-ray scattering studies in indicating a
number of mobile electrons equal to the atomic number.

c. *Variation of Intensity with Scattering Angle*

An experimental test of eq. (3.05), describing the relative intensity
at different angles, leads to equally interesting results. In Fig. III–4
are plotted the intensities of x-rays of two widely different wave-
lengths, scattered from substances of low atomic number. The
upper curve, representing Hewlett's data from liquid mesitylene
$[C_6H_3(CH_3)_3]$, shows that for moderate x-ray wave-lengths Thomson's $(1 + \cos^2 \phi)$ relation (eq. 3.05) is valid to a close approximation, except for small angles ϕ, where the phase differences between
the rays scattered from the different electrons in an atom are small.
At these small angles the cooperative interference between the rays
scattered by neighboring electrons and neighboring atoms leads to
an excess scattering.

The lower curve, showing Compton's data on the scattering of

[7] E. Rutherford, Phil. Mag. 21, 669 (1911).

[8] J. Chadwick, Phil. Mag. 40, 734 (1920).

[9] C. G. Barkla, Phil. Mag. 21, 648 (1911).

hard γ-rays by iron, reveals a much lower scattering coefficient at large angles than the theory predicts. This departure from the predictions of Thomson's theory, like the low value of the scattering coefficient observed for wave-lengths less than 0.1 A, is due to the effect of the recoil of the electrons which scatter the x-ray photons. The photons which are deflected through the greater angles make the

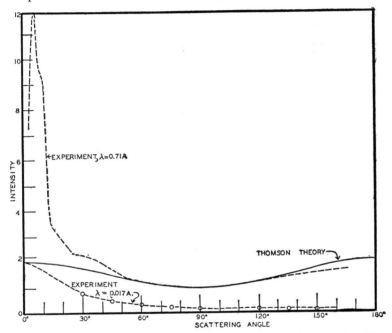

Fig. III-4. Scattered x-rays are more intense at small than at large angles. Upper curve, mesitylene (liquid), lower curve, iron.

scattering electrons recoil with greater speed, resulting in a larger reduction in intensity.

d. The Wave-length of Scattered X-rays

If the incident beam of x-rays consists of a train of waves of definite frequency, as for example an x-ray spectrum line, the electrons traversed will be set into forced oscillation with the same frequency. Thus, in the special case of a free electron traversed by a wave whose electric field at O is given by

$$E = E_0 \cos (pt + \delta),$$

the acceleration of the electron is

$$a = \frac{Ee}{m} = \frac{E_o e}{m} \cos (pt + \delta).$$

The ray scattered by this electron to a point $P(r, \theta)$ (Fig. III–1) will have an electric field given by the equation

$$E_\theta = \frac{e \sin \theta}{rc^2} \cdot \frac{E_o e}{m} \cos \left\{ p\left(t - \frac{r}{c}\right) + \delta \right\} \qquad (3.08)$$

$$= E_o' \cos (pt + \delta').$$

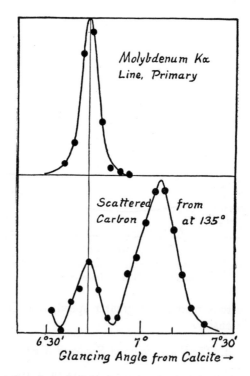

FIG. III–5. Spectrum of scattered x-rays, showing change of wave-length.

The frequency of this scattered ray is thus the same, $\nu = p/2\pi$, as that of the primary ray. It can be shown that the effect of constraints and damping on the motion of the scattering electron is to modify the amplitude and phase of the scattered ray, but not its frequency. The present theory accordingly demands that the two frequencies be identical.

The remark was made in the first chapter that refined measurements show that the wave-length of the scattered x-rays is not identical with that of the primary ray. The result of a typical experiment is shown [10] in Fig. III–5. The upper curve represents the spectrum of the $K\alpha$ line of molybdenum taken direct from the target. The lower curve represents, on a much larger scale, the spectrum of the same line after being scattered by graphite at $\phi = 135°$. A part of the scattered beam has the same wave-length as the primary, but the greater part is of a slightly greater wave-length.

The suggestion at first occurs that the " modified " ray represents a type of fluorescence radiation, and that only the " unmodified " ray is truly scattered. There are, however, strong arguments against this view. In the first place, the wave-length of the modified ray is determined by that of the primary ray and not by the nature of the radiator, contrary to the case of other fluorescence radiation. In the second place, we have seen that the secondary radiation at $90°$, which includes the modified ray, is completely polarized; but no form of fluorescence radiation has ever been shown to be polarized.[11] And finally, so large a part of the secondary energy is in the modified ray that if the intensity of the scattered beam is to be at all comparable in magnitude with that calculated from the electromagnetic theory the modified as well as the unmodified ray must be considered as scattered x-rays.

The magnitude of this change of wave-length is given within experimental error by the formula,

$$\delta\lambda = 0.0242(1 - \cos\phi), \qquad (3.09)$$

where $\delta\lambda$ is expressed in angstroms, and ϕ is the angle of scattering. As will be shown below (eq. (3.117)), this equation can be derived simply on the basis of the photon theory of x-rays. It will be noted that this change is independent of the wave-length. It is hence relatively less important, i.e., $\delta\lambda/\lambda$ is smaller, for wave-lengths large

[10] A. H. Compton, Phys. Rev. 22, 409 (1923).

[11] An apparent exception to this statement occurs in the experiments of Wood and Ellet (Phys. Rev. 24, 243, 1924) in which the resonance radiation excited in mercury vapor by polarized radiation from a mercury arc is found to be partially polarized. It is doubtful, however, whether such radiation can properly be classed as fluorescence, since both the primary and secondary rays are of the same wave-length.

compared with 0.0242 A.   This result is in accord with the experiments on the intensity of the scattered rays, in indicating that Thomson's theory is a valid approximation only for x-rays of the greater wave-lengths.

4. *Scattering by a Pair of Electrons*

From these comparisons between the experiments and the classical electron theory of scattering we see the importance of investigating

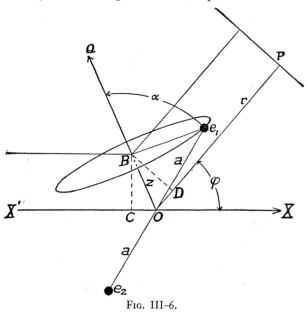

Fig. III–6.

the interference of the x-rays scattered by groups of electrons.   The suggestion that the electrons in an atom cooperate in their scattering seems to have been made first by Webster,[12] and was first stated in a satisfactory form by Darwin.[13]   The simplest problem of this type, which is also representative of the more general problem, is that of the scattering by two electrons at a distance s apart.

Imagine, as in Fig. III–6, that a beam of x-rays, of wave-length λ and frequency $\nu = p/2\pi$, is moving in the direction OX, and traverses

[12] D. L. Webster, Phil. Mag. **25**, 234 (1913).
[13] C. G. Darwin, Phil. Mag. **27**, 325 (1914).

two electrons e_1 and e_2 separated by a distance $s = 2a$. Take the point O, midway between these electrons, and let OP be the direction of the scattered beam which we are considering. The plane POX is in the plane of the paper, but in general the line e_1Oe_2 does not lie in this plane. Its position can be defined with sufficient precision by stating that it is at an angle α with the line OQ which bisects the angle $X'OP$.

Suppose the electric intensity at O of the component of the incident wave which lies in the plane XOP is

$$E_{11} = A \cos (pt + \delta).$$

If an electron were at O, its acceleration would be $E_{11}e/m$, and the electric intensity at P at the time t would be, by eq. (3.08),

$$E_{po} = \frac{e \cos \phi}{rc^2} \cdot \frac{Ae}{m} \cos \left\{ p\left(t - \frac{r}{c} \right) + \delta \right\}$$

where, as compared with eq. (3.08), $\phi = \dfrac{\pi}{2} - \theta$, and $Ae/m = Ap^2 =$ the maximum acceleration of the electron. Since pr/c is the constant phase difference between O and P, we may write $\delta - pr/c = \Delta$, and our expression becomes,

$$E_{po} = \frac{Ae^2 \cos \phi}{rmc^2} \cos (pt + \Delta). \qquad (3.10)$$

If a plane is described through e_1 perpendicular to OQ and intersecting this line at B, it will be seen from Huyghen's principle that wherever in this plane the electron lies, the phase of the wave scattered to the plane P will be the same. Thus the phase is the same as if the electron were at B. But from B the total length of the path of the ray reaching P is less than that from O by the distance COD. Since $\angle CBO = \angle OBD = \phi/2$, and writing $OB = z$, this difference in path is

$$COD = 2z \sin \frac{\phi}{2}.$$

The phase difference at P between rays scattered from these two points is therefore $\dfrac{2\pi}{\lambda} \cdot 2z \sin \dfrac{\phi}{2}$. The electric intensity at P due to the electron e, is accordingly

$$E_{p1} = A_\phi \cos \left(pt + \Delta + \frac{4\pi z}{\lambda} \sin \frac{\phi}{2} \right), \qquad (3.11)$$

where, as compared with eq. (3.10) we have written

$$A_\phi = \frac{Ae^2 \cos \phi}{rmc^2}.$$

But the path of the ray scattered from e_2 is obviously greater than that from O by the same amount that the path from O is greater than that from e_1. Thus the electric intensity at P due to the ray scattered from e_2 is

$$E_{p2} = A_\phi \cos \left(pt + \Delta - \frac{4\pi z}{\lambda} \sin \frac{\phi}{2} \right). \tag{3.12}$$

Putting $a = pt + \Delta$ and $b = \frac{4\pi z}{\lambda} \sin \frac{\phi}{2}$, since

$$\cos (a + b) + \cos (a - b) = 2 \cos a \cos b,$$

we have for the total electric intensity at P,

$$E_p = E_{p1} + E_{p2} = 2A_\phi \cos b \cos (pt + \Delta).$$

This is a harmonic function, whose maximum occurs when $\cos (pt + \Delta) = 1$, so that its amplitude is

$$A_p = 2A_\phi \cos b. \tag{3.13}$$

We may now write the general principle that the energy or intensity of a wave is proportional to the square of its amplitude in the form,[14]

$$I = \beta A^2.$$

The intensity of the beam scattered to P is thus

$$I_p = 4\beta A_\phi{}^2 \cos^2 b. \tag{3.14}$$

In order to obtain the average value of this intensity for all possible orientations of the line $e_1 O e_2$, let us express I_p as a function of α. Referring again to Fig. III–6, we notice that $z = a \cos \alpha$, where a is the distance Oe_1, whence

$$b = \frac{4\pi a}{\lambda} \sin \frac{\phi}{2} \cos \alpha,$$

---

[14] In the present case, where A is the amplitude of the electric vector and I is the energy in the wave per cm.² per second, $I = c\frac{A^2}{8\pi}$, whence $\beta = c/8\pi$, c being the velocity of light.

or writing

$$h = \frac{4\pi a}{\lambda} \sin \frac{\phi}{2},$$ (3.15)

$$b = h \cos \alpha.$$

Then

$$I_p = 4\beta A_\phi^2 \cos^2 (h \cos \alpha).$$

But the probability that α will lie between α and $\alpha + d\alpha$ is $2\pi \sin\alpha \, d\alpha/4\pi$, or $\frac{1}{2} \sin\alpha \, d\alpha$. The average value of I_p is thus

$$\bar{I}_p = \int_0^\pi 4\beta A_\phi^2 \cos^2 (h \cos \alpha) \cdot \tfrac{1}{2} \sin \alpha d\alpha$$

$$= 2\beta A_\phi^2 \left(1 + \frac{\sin 2h}{2h} \right),$$

or substituting the value of A_ϕ,

$$\bar{I}_p = \frac{2\beta A^2 e^4 \cos^2 \phi}{r^2 m^2 c^4} \left(1 + \frac{\sin 2h}{2h} \right)$$ (3.16)

Since A is the amplitude of the component of the electric vector of the primary beam lying in the plane XOP, it follows from our definition of β that the intensity of this component is $I_{||} = \beta A^2$, whence eq. (3.16) becomes

$$\bar{I}_p = 2 \frac{I_{||} e^4 \cos^2 \phi}{r^2 m^2 c^4} \left(1 + \frac{\sin 2h}{2h} \right).$$ (3.17)

If the component of the primary beam had been considered whose electric vector is perpendicular to the plane XOP, eq. (3.10) would have been modified only by the omission of the factor $\cos \phi$, since the scattered beam would always be at right angles with the electron's acceleration. The analysis for this component would have been otherwise the same, leading to an intensity of the scattered beam at P, corresponding to expression (3.17),

$$\bar{I}_p' = 2 \frac{I_\perp e^4}{r^2 m^2 c^4} \left(1 + \frac{\sin 2h}{2h} \right).$$

Thus the intensity at P due to an unpolarized primary ray is

$$I_\phi = \tfrac{1}{2}(\bar{I}_p + \bar{I}_p') = \frac{I e^4 (1 + \cos^2 \phi)}{r^2 m^2 c^4} \left(1 + \frac{\sin 2h}{2h} \right)$$ (3.18)

Since the intensity of the ray scattered by a single independent electron is (eq. (3.04)),

$$I_e = \frac{Ie^4(1 + \cos^2 \phi)}{2r^2m^2c^4},$$

this result may be written,

$$I_\phi = 2I_e\left(1 + \frac{\sin x}{x}\right), \qquad (3.19)$$

where

$$x = 2h = \frac{8\pi a}{\lambda}\sin\frac{\phi}{2} = \frac{4\pi s}{\lambda}\sin\frac{\phi}{2}, \qquad (3.20)$$

s being the distance between the two electrons.

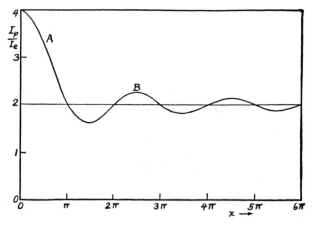

Fig. III–7.   X-ray scattering by pair of electrons, according to eq. (3.19).

According to this result, if x is small, that is, for great wavelengths, small distances between the electrons, or small angles of scattering, the intensity of the ray scattered by the electron pair approaches a value 4 times that for a single electron.   If, however, x is large, $\sin x/x$ becomes small, and the intensity approaches 2 times that due to a single electron—in other words, the electrons scatter independently of each other.   The manner in which I_ϕ/I_e varies with the value of x is shown in Fig. III–7.   It will be seen that the value of I_ϕ/I_e approaches its final value of 2 by a series of oscillations in intensity.

It is frequently convenient to use the quantity

$$S \equiv \frac{I}{ZI_e},\qquad(3.21)$$

where Z is the number of electrons per atom.   In the present case $Z = 2$, and

$$S = \left\{1 + \frac{\sin x}{x}\right\}.\qquad(3.22)$$

This quantity, which may be called the *scattering factor*, is the ratio of the actual scattering to that which would occur if each electron acted independently of the others.

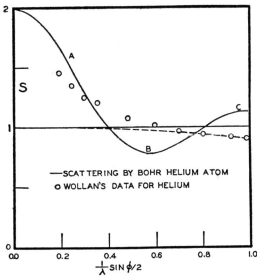

FIG. III–8.   X-ray scattering by Bohr helium atom, compared with experiments.

Test of Bohr Helium Atom

At one time Bohr proposed a theory of the helium atom[15] according to which the two electrons in helium revolve in the same orbit at opposite ends of a diameter.   According to his calculation this diameter is 0.63×10^{-8} cm.   Equations (3.19) and (3.22) should according to this theory apply exactly to the scattering by helium gas. In Fig. III–8 Wollan's experimental values of the scattering by

[15] N. Bohr, Phil. Mag. 26, 489 (1913).

helium[16] are compared with the scattering factor S calculated from eq. (3.22), using $s = 0.63 \times 10^{-8}$ cm. For comparison, the solid line at $S = 1$ represents the scattering by randomly arranged electrons on Thomson's theory, whereas the broken line takes into account the recoil of the electrons (cf. eq. (3.137) below).

According to the theory based on Bohr's atom, excess scattering should become prominent for about the angles (portion A of the curve) for which the experiments show a marked increase. This means that the size of the atom as calculated by Bohr is approximately correct. The data give no indication however of minima and maxima such as those predicted at B and C. Thus the details of Bohr's proposed structure do not agree with the scattering data. It seems that the absence of maxima and minima in the data here shown requires a kind of diffuseness in the atomic structure, such as a widely variable distance between the electrons in the helium atom.

5. *Investigation of Electron Distributions in Atoms with Scattered X-rays*

Many attempts have been made to find agreement between experimental scattering values and those calculated for the various types of atoms suggested by different theories.[17] Until the advent of the new quantum mechanics, which predicts atoms with a diffuse electron atmosphere, these attempts have been uniformly unsuccessful. However Debye[18] and Thomson[19] solved independently the important problem of the scattering of x-rays by atoms consisting of a group of electrons arranged at fixed distances from each other. Their result may be put in the form,

$$S = \frac{1}{Z} \sum_{m}^{Z} \sum_{n}^{Z} \frac{\sin x_{mn}}{x_{mn}}, \qquad (3.23)$$

where

$$x_{mn} = \frac{4\pi s_{mn}}{\lambda} \sin \frac{\phi}{2},$$

and s_{mm} is the distance from the mth to the nth electron. It will be

---

[16] E. O. Wollan, Phys. Rev. **37**, 862 (1931).

[17] *E.g.*, G. A. Schott, Proc. Roy. Soc. **96**, 695 (1920). A. H. Compton, Washington University Studies, 8, 98 (1921). R. Glocker, Zs. f. Phys. **5**, 54 (1921).

[18] P. Debye, Ann. der Phys. **46**, 809 (1915).

[19] J. J. Thomson, ms. read before the Royal Institution in 1916 and loaned to A. H. C.

noted that when $Z = 2$, this expression becomes identical with our eq. (3.22). It has not been found possible by the application of this formula to calculate accurately the scattering from any real atom, due presumably to the fact that the electrons do not remain at fixed distances from each other. The formula has nevertheless been found useful as a guide, and is directly applicable to certain problems of scattering by molecules (cf. Sec. 3 of this chapter).

When the change of wave-length due to scattering became known, about 1922, it became clear that the classical methods of applying electrodynamics to the scattering of x-rays were inadequate. Until a more reliable theoretical procedure could be developed, attempts to study the interference between the rays scattered by electrons in the same atom were held in abeyance. In 1927 Wentzel showed[20] on the basis of quantum mechanics (cf. Sec. 19, below) that the x-rays scattered by an atom should consist of two distinct components. For one component the rays from the different electrons were coherent (in definite phase relation to each other), while for the other component the rays were incoherent. The coherent portion, according to this theory, should be scattered in precisely the manner predicted by the classical electrodynamics. The incoherent part should be subject to the effect of electron recoil, and corresponds to the line of increased wave-length in the spectrum of the scattered x-rays. The following year, Raman[21] showed also from purely classical considerations that two such distinct components should exist. His classical calculation has been developed by Woo[22] to give a coherent ray identical with that from Wentzel's quantum theory, and an incoherent ray which differs from Wentzel's only due to the effect of the recoil of the scattering electrons. It has thus become clear how the results of the classical calculations are to be interpreted. The results of diffraction studies of atoms can accordingly now be interpreted with the same confidence as diffraction studies of crystals.

Scattering by an Electron Cloud

Let us first calculate the intensity of the x-rays scattered by a group of electrons moving independently of each other about an

[20] G. Wentzel, Z. P. **43**, 1 and 779 (1927). This result has been confirmed and extended by I. Waller, Z. P. **51**, 213 (1928); I. Waller and D. R. Hartree, Proc. Roy. Soc. A124, 119 (1929). Wentzel's work was an elaboration of that of O. Klein, Z. P. **41**, 407 (1927).

[21] C. V. Raman, Indian J. of Physics, **3**, 357 (1928). Classical incoherent scattering was noted but not developed by A. H. Compton, X-rays and Electrons, p. 171 (1926).

[22] Y. H. Woo, Phys. Rev. **41**, 21 (1932).

atomic nucleus.[23]   Let δ_1, δ_2 ... δ_Z be the phases of the waves scattered by the Z electrons to the distant point $P(r, \phi)$ (Fig. III–9). If A_e is the amplitude of the wave at P due to 1 electron, the sum of the vibrations from the Z electrons is

$$E = A_e[\cos(pt + \delta_1) + \cos(pt + \delta_2) + \ldots + \cos(pt + \delta_Z)],$$

$$= A_e\sqrt{(\cos \delta_1 + \ldots + \cos \delta_Z)^2 + (\sin \delta_1 + \ldots + \sin \delta_Z)^2}\ \cos(pt + \delta),$$

where δ is the phase of the resultant vibration. The intensity is accordingly,

$$I = \frac{cA^2}{8\pi} = \frac{c}{8\pi} A_e^2\,[(\cos \delta_1 + \ldots + \cos \delta_Z)^2 + (\sin \delta_1 + \ldots + \sin \delta_Z)^2]$$

$$= I_e\,[Z + \sum_1^Z \sum_1^Z {}_{(m \neq n)} \cos(\delta_m - \delta_n)], \qquad (3.24)$$

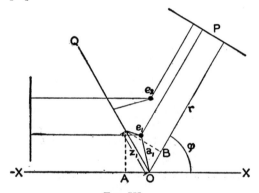

FIG. III–9.

where as before,

$$I_e = \frac{c}{8\pi} A_e^2$$

is the intensity due to one electron.

Referring to Fig. III–9, and eq. (3.11) it will be seen that

$$\delta_m = \frac{4\pi z_m}{\lambda} \sin \frac{\phi}{2}$$

$$= k\mu_m a_m$$

[23] This problem has been solved independently by C. V. Raman, Ind. J. of Phys. **3**, 357 (1928) and by A. H. Compton, Phys. Rev. **35**, 925 (1930).   The derivation here given follows closely that of Raman.

where

$$k = \frac{4\pi}{\lambda} \sin \frac{\phi}{2} \qquad (3.25)$$

and $\mu_m \equiv z_m/a_m$ is the direction cosine of a_m with respect to the line OQ which bisects the angle XOP. If $u(a)da$ is the probability that any particular electron will lie between a and $a + da$, the chance that the phase of the mth electron will lie within the range $d\delta_m$ is

$$dP_m = u(a_m)da_m d\mu_m.$$

The statistical average of $\cos(\delta_m - \delta_n)$ is accordingly,

$$\int_0^\infty \int_0^\infty \int_{-1}^1 \int_{-1}^1 \cos k(\mu_m a_m - \mu_n a_n) u(a_m)da_m d\mu_m u(a_n)da_n d\mu_n.$$

Since the variables are all independent, this can be integrated with respect to μ_m and μ_n, giving

$$\left[\int_0^\infty u(a) \frac{\sin ka}{ka} da \right]^2 = f^2 \qquad (3.26)$$

The quantity f is called the *electronic structure factor*.[24]

The double summation of eq. (3.24) contains $Z^2 - Z$ terms, each of which taken as a statistical average is the same and equal to f^2. Thus eq. (3.24) becomes

$$I = I_e[Z + (Z^2 - Z)f^2]. \qquad (3.27)$$

It is clear that eq. (3.27) represents an average intensity, which is continually fluctuating due to the changing phases of the rays

[24] Unfortunately the notation in this book concerning the various form factors is not uniform. This reflects, however, the lack of a consistent notation in the articles published on the subject. Throughout Chap. III, f is used to represent the electronic structure factor. In the remainder of the book, this concept does not appear, and f there denotes the atomic structure factor, which in Chap. III is denoted by F. The relations are given in the following table.

NOTATION USED FOR FORM FACTORS

Factor	Chap. III	Other Chapters
Electronic structure factor...................	f, f_n, f_{kk}	does not appear
Atomic structure factor.....................	F	f
Crystal structure factor.....................	does not appear	F

from the electrons moving within the atom. In order to identify the part of this radiation which is to be considered as coherent, we may calculate the intensity scattered by an atom having a continuous distribution of electricity equal to the average distribution of the electrons in the atom just treated, and having the same value of e/m as the electron. The electric charge between radii a and $a + da$ will then be

$$Zeu(a)da.$$

The element of this lying between the direction cosines μ and $\mu + d\mu$ is

$$Zeu(a)dad\mu.$$

Noting that for this element the phase of the scattered ray is $\delta = k\mu a$, we get for the amplitude of the vibration from this continuous charge distribution,

$$A_c = \frac{A_e}{e} \int_0^\infty \int_{-1}^1 \cos (k\mu a) Zeu(a) dad\mu$$

$$= ZA_e \int_0^\infty u(a) \frac{\sin ka}{ka} da$$

$$= ZA_e f, \qquad\qquad (3.28)$$

where A_e is the amplitude due to one electron and f is defined by eq. (3.26). It follows that the intensity of the ray scattered by such an atom would be,

$$I_c = I_e Z^2 f^2. \qquad\qquad (3.29)$$

If this quantity I_c represents the continuous, coherent radiation due to the average atom, we may consider the remaining part of I of eq. (3.27) as the fluctuating, incoherent scattered rays. Their intensity is

$$I_i = I - I_c = I_e Z(1 - f^2). \qquad\qquad (3.30)$$

In order to distinguish more clearly between the physical signifi-cance of its terms, eq. (3.27) would thus better be written,

$$I = I_e[Z^2 f^2 + Z(1 - f^2)] \qquad\qquad (3.31)$$

or

$$S \equiv \frac{I}{ZI_e} = \underbrace{Zf^2}_{\text{coherent}} + \underbrace{(1 - f^2)}_{\text{incoherent}}. \qquad\qquad (3.32)$$

In further justification of this qualitative distinction between the two terms in this scattering formula, Raman calls attention to the fact that the second term of eq. (3.31) is proportional to Z instead of Z^2. Such a summation of intensities instead of amplitudes can represent the statistical average only when the effects considered are completely uncorrelated in phase. This corresponds exactly with Wentzel's conclusion (cf. eq. (3.174), below) that this term represents the modified scattered radiation, each photon of which must be scattered from a single electron.

We may note at once that the incoherent term of eqs. (3.31) and (3.32) is found by experiment to be less intense than here indicated. According to Wentzel's quantum theory, all of this incoherent radiation should appear in the modified line of the scattered x-ray spectrum. For x-rays scattered by free electrons, the modified rays are however reduced in intensity as compared with the classically calculated value by a factor R, where

$$R = 1 \Big/ \left(1 + \frac{h}{mc\lambda} \text{ vers } \phi\right)^3, \qquad (3.33)$$

according to Breit and Dirac (cf. eqs. (3.137) and (3.139) below). Assuming that the incoherent rays scattered by bound electrons are reduced by the same ratio, we should expect the observed scattering to be expressed by the formula,

$$S = Zf^2 + R(1 - f^2), \qquad (3.34)$$

where f is defined by eq. (3.26).

This analysis has been based upon the assumption that each electron in the atom has the same probability of occurring at a given position as every other electron. There would thus be no distinction between K, L, M, etc., electrons. Such electron groups would be distinguished merely as regions of greater electron density. The further assumption is made that the electron distribution has spherical symmetry.

Woo[25] and Jauncey[26] have placed the calculation on a somewhat more general basis by considering each electron in the atom to have its own probability $u_n(a)da$ of lying between distances a and $a + da$ from the center of the atom. If these values of u_n are the same for all the electrons in the atom, this assumption becomes identical with

[25] Y. H. Woo, Phys. Rev. 41, 21 (1932).

[26] G. E. M. Jauncey, Phys. Rev. 37, 1193 (1931).

that used by Raman and Compton, leading to eqs. (3.32) and (3.34). If the values of u_n differ from each other, Woo finds instead of eq. (3.31),

$$I = I_e \left\{ \left(\sum_1^Z f_n \right)^2 + Z - \sum_1^Z f_n^2 \right\}, \qquad (3.35)$$

or

$$S = \frac{1}{Z} F^2 + 1 - \frac{1}{Z} \sum_1^Z f_n^2. \qquad (3.36)$$

Here

$$F \equiv \sum_1^Z f_n = \sum_1^Z \int_0^\infty u_n(a) \frac{\sin ka}{ka} \, da. \qquad (3.37)$$

It is known as the " atomic structure factor." Another expression for the same concept occurs in eq. (6.96), Chap. VI. The form in which the right-hand member of eq. (3.37) appears shows more clearly the steps which would be taken in the calculation of F from a wave-mechanical atom model, in which a probability density is assigned to each electron and then summed.

Equation (3.35) is exactly that derived by Wentzel (3.175) from quantum mechanical considerations. Before comparison with experiment, we must introduce again the recoil factor R (eq. (3.33)), giving instead of eq. (3.36),

$$S = F^2/Z + R(1 - \Sigma f_n^2/Z). \qquad (3.38)$$

It will be noted that this expression still lacks generality in that only electron distributions having spherical symmetry are considered.[27] According to current atomic theories, this should be true for the completed electron shells, but should not hold for the valence electrons at the surface of the atom. In the experimentally important case of the scattering by the noble gases, all the electron shells are complete. From our present quantum theories of the atom we should thus expect eq. (3.38) to be strictly valid.

6. *Experiments with Monatomic Gases*

The problem of measuring experimentally the scattering by gases of x-rays of a definite wave-length and at a definite angle is one which has made extreme demands upon x-ray technique. Its solution has been primarily a matter of getting sufficient intensity.

---

[27] Note however that if f is defined as in eq. (3.173), this limitation of spherical symmetry is removed.

Secondary x-rays from air were recognized by several of the early experimenters,[28, 29, 30] and Barkla,[31] Crowther,[32] and Herzog[33] made valuable quantitative measurements of the scattered and fluorescent x-rays from many gases. This work was done, however, using the total beam of x-rays traversing large volumes of gas, and scattering over a wide range of angles. For data which will be comparable with our theoretical calculations, we must know both the wave-length of the rays and the angle at which they are scattered. Experiments affording this information have recently been reported by Barrett,[34] and Wollan,[35] using ionization methods, and by

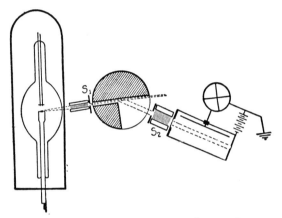

Fig. III-10. Apparatus for measuring scattering of x-rays by gases, as used by Wollan.

Scherrer and Staeger,[36] by Debye, Bewilogua and Ehrhardt[37] and by Herzog,[38] using photographic technique.

[28] M. I. Pupin, *Science* 3, 538 (1896).

[29] W. C. Roentgen, Ann. Phys. Chem. 44, 18 (1898).

[30] G. Sagnac, Comptes Rendus 126, 521 (1898).

[31] C. G. Barkla, Phil. Mag. 5, 685 (1903); 7, 543 (1904).

[32] J. A. Crowther, Phil. Mag. 14, 653 (1907).

[33] G. Herzog, Helv. Phys. Acta 2, 217 (1929).

[34] C. S. Barrett, Proc. Nat. Acad. 14, 20 (1928); Phys. Rev. 32, 22 (1928).

[35] E. O. Wollan, Proc. Nat. Acad. 17, 475 (1931); Phys. Rev. 37, 862 and 38, 15 (1931).

[36] P. Scherrer and A. Staeger, Helv. Phys. Acta 1, 518 (1928).

[37] P. Debye, L. Bewilogua and F. Ehrhardt, Phys. Zeits. 30, 84 (1929); Sächs. Akad. Ber. 81, 29 (1929).

[38] G. Herzog, Helv. Phys. Acta 2, 169 (1929); Zeits. f. Phys. 69, 207 (1931); 70, 583 and 590 (1931).

The measurements made by Wollan seem to have yielded the best quantitative results. Figure III–10 shows the arrangement of his apparatus. The x-ray source is an oil-immersed, water-cooled tube with a molybdenum target. The rays pass through a filter F, are collimated by a pile of parallel slits S_1, and traverse the gas contained within the airtight chamber G. Rays scattered by this gas at an angle ϕ pass through the parallel slits S_2 into an ionization chamber filled with methyl bromide vapor. Under these conditions the

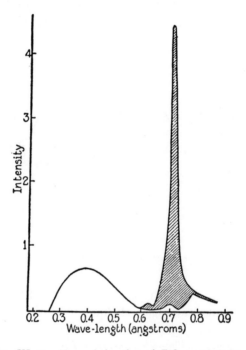

FIG. III–11. Transmission through ZrO_2 and SrO filters.

ionization current is between 10^{-15} and 10^{-14} amperes, and the individual measurements are reproducible to within about 5 per cent.

It will be clear from the figure that the angle of scattering can be sharply defined by the collimating slits, except at small angles ϕ, where the height as well as the width of the slits must be considered.

It was the development by Ross[39] of the double filter F, for securing data as from a monochromatic x-ray beam, which finally made

[39] P. A. Ross, Phys. Rev. 28, 425 (1926). Cf. Chap. VII, Sec. 7.

possible securing the desired data.   The K absorption limit of
zirconium lies between the $K\alpha$ and $K\beta$ lines of molybdenum.   Strontium has its absorption limit at a wave-length slightly longer than
the molybdenum $K\alpha$ lines.   It is thus possible so to adjust filters of
ZrO_2 and SrO that except in the immediate neighborhood of the $K\alpha$
lines the absorption by the two filters will be very nearly the same.
The difference between the radiation transmitted by the two filters

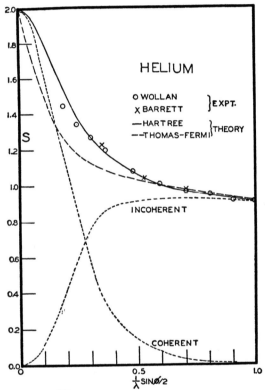

FIG. III-12.   Scattering of x-rays by helium.

is then due almost entirely to the $K\alpha$ line of molybdenum.   The
spectral energy distribution curve of Fig. III-11 shows the degree of
homogeneity of the rays used by Wollan.   The unshaded curve represents the radiation transmitted by the strontium filter, whereas the
total curve is that transmitted by the zirconium.   The difference is
thus represented by the shaded portion, which, as will be seen, represents a large fraction of the total radiation.

In order to obtain absolute values for the scattering factor S, Wollan compared all of his observed values with that for hydrogen at 90 degrees. According to all theoretical calculations, hydrogen should show no measurable coherent scattering at this angle, and we should have,

$$S_{H90} = R_{90} = 0.91. \qquad (3.39)$$

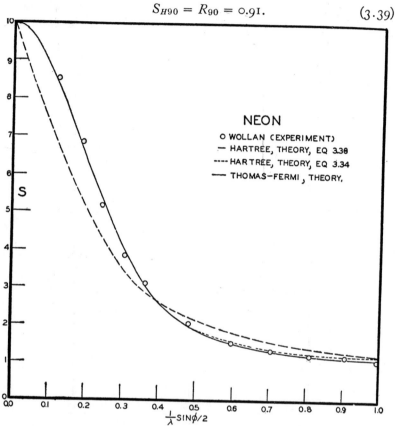

Fig. III–13.   Scattering of x-rays by neon.

In Figs. III–12, 13, 14 and 15 are shown scattering data for helium, neon, argon and mercury vapor. In the case of argon the results of Wollan, Barrett and Herzog are compared. Since the data of the latter two observers are relative rather than absolute, they have been made to fit Wollan's values at a definite value of $(\sin \phi/2)/\lambda$. The excellent agreement between the data of the different observers gives confidence in their reliability.

a. *Test of Various Atomic Theories*

We have already noted (p. 134) that the observed scattering by helium gas does not fit acceptably with the values calculated on the basis of Bohr's original theory of the helium atom. Can we get better agreement on the basis of modern atomic theories?

Except in the case of hydrogen-like atoms, the new quantum mechanics has not led to exact calculations of electron distributions.

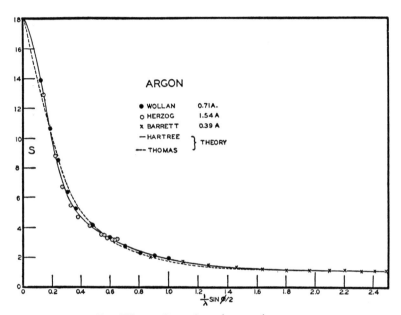

Fig. III–14. Scattering of x-rays by argon.

Of the several approximate methods that have been proposed, those of Thomas[40] and Fermi[41] and of Hartree[42] have been found the most useful.

The theory of Thomas and Fermi, though presumably not as exact a formulation of the quantum concepts, is much the simpler. They consider the electrons as a gas surrounding the nucleus, whose charge density is a function only of the distance from the center.

[40] L. H. Thomas, Proc. Camb. Phil. Soc. 23, 542 (1927).
[41] E. Fermi, Zeits. f. Phys. 48, 73 (1928); Leipsiger Vorträge, 1928.
[42] D. R. Hartree, Proc. Camb. Phil. Soc. 24, 89 and 111 (1928).

It is found that the following simple relation holds between the charge density ρ_e and the electric potential V at any point,

$$\rho_e = \frac{2^{9/2}\pi m^{3/2}e^{5/2}}{3h^3} \, V^{3/2}. \tag{3.40}$$

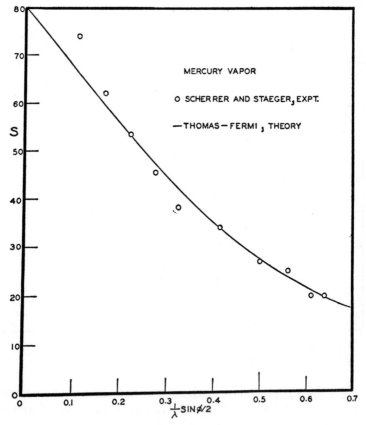

Fig. III–15. Scattering of x-rays by mercury vapor.

Taking into account the average shielding effect of the electrons on the electric potential, the probability that a particular electron will lie between a and $a + da$ from the center of an atom may be shown to be

$$u(a)da = 2.13Z^{1/3}\left(\frac{a}{\alpha}\right)^{1/2}\left[\phi\left(\frac{a}{\alpha}\right)\right]^{3/2}da \tag{3.41}$$

where Z is as usual the atomic number, α is a radius characteristic of atomic number Z defined by

$$\alpha = \left(\frac{3}{32\pi^2}\right)^{2/3} \frac{h^2}{2me^2} Z^{-1/3} = 0.47/Z^{1/3} \text{ angstroms,} \qquad (3.42)$$

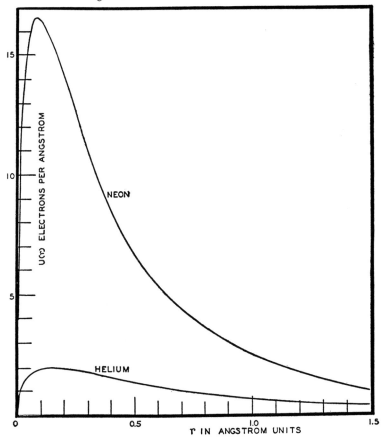

Fig. III–16.   Typical radial electron distributions by Thomas-Fermi theory.

and ϕ is a function of (a/α) whose numerical values have been tabulated by Fermi.   The function $u(a)$ is thus similar for all values of Z, being somewhat more concentrated at smaller radii for the larger atomic number.   In Fig. III–16 are plotted the values of the radial electron density,

$$U = \sum_{1}^{Z} u_n, \qquad (3.43)$$

for helium and neon as calculated from eq. (3.41). Since according to Fermi's theory all values of u_n are the same, eq. (3.43) becomes

$$U = Zu.$$ (3.44)

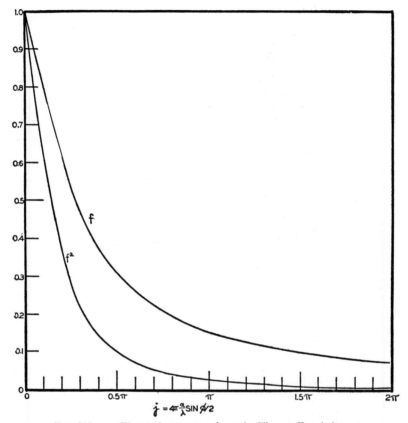

FIG. III–17. Electronic structure factor by Thomas-Fermi theory.

If the value of $u(a)$ given by eq. (3.41) is substituted in eq. (3.26), we obtain[43] for the electronic structure factor,

$$f = \int_{-\infty}^{\infty} \frac{1}{j} \frac{[\phi(x)]^{3/2}}{x^{1/2}} \sin (jx)dx$$ (3.45)

$$= f(j)$$

[43] This calculation has been published by W. L. Bragg and S. West, Zeits. f. Kristallog., **69**, 118 (1929); P. Debye, Phys. Zeits. **31**, 419 (1930); and Y. H. Woo, Sci. Reports Nat. Tsing Hua University **1**, 55 (1931).

where $j = k\alpha = 4\pi \dfrac{\alpha}{\lambda} \sin \dfrac{\phi}{2}$, and $x = a/\alpha$. This integral can be evaluated graphically, with the result plotted in Fig. III–17. The atomic structure factor as defined by eq. (3.37) for any atom should on this theory be $F = Zf$, and the corresponding scattering factor should be, by eq. (3.34),

$$S = Zf^2 + R(1 - f^2),$$

where the values of f for any value of $j(Z, \lambda, \phi)$ may be read directly from Fig. III–17. The values thus calculated for helium, neon, argon and mercury vapor are shown by the broken curves in Figs. III–12, 13, 14 and 15.

In the case of helium, it will be seen from Fig. III–12 that the scattering as thus calculated does not agree well with the experimental data. For progressively heavier atoms however the fit becomes better, until in the case of mercury vapor no systematic departure from the predictions of the theory is evident. Since the approximations made by Thomas and Fermi approach exactness to the quantum theory for very heavy atoms, the result of this comparison is very satisfactory.

The exact method of arriving at the value of $U(r)$, and hence of f, would be to solve Schrödinger's wave equation for ψ, and place

$$U(r) = 4\pi a^2 |\psi|^2. \tag{3.46}$$

Such an accurate solution for an atom with Z electrons would however involve an equation with $3Z$ variables, and becomes impractical. The most accurate approximate method that has been developed seems to be that of Hartree's " self-consistent fields." This method applies to completed electron groups, which are supposed to have spherical symmetry. The electrons within each electron group are assigned identical values of $u(a)$, but each group has its own characteristic value of $u(a)$. Thus for determining the atomic structure factor it is necessary to apply eq. (3.37) rather than the simpler eq. (3.26).

Values of $u(a)$ have been calculated by Hartree for a number of atoms and ions up to atomic number 37, and James and Brindley[44] have published values of f for the various electron groups in typical atoms, based on Hartree's values of $u(a)$. In Appendix IV are given

[44] R. W. James and G. W. Brindley, Phil. Mag. **12**, 81 (1931); Zeits. f. Kristallographie, **78**, 470 (1931).

the values of F_a which they have thus determined. In Figs. III–12, 13 and 14, are shown solid curves representing the values of the scattering as thus calculated from Hartree's electron distributions, using eq. (3.38). It will be seen that the agreement with the experimental data is in every case satisfactory. It is noteworthy that the electron distributions as thus calculated from the quantum mechanics theory of atomic structure are the only ones that have been found to fit with experimental scattering data. This must be taken as a very strong confirmation of the present theory of atomic structure.

b. *Direct Determination of Atomic Electron Distributions*

If we suppose that the atom has spherical symmetry, we can use eq. (3.34) to determine directly from measurements of x-ray scattering what the electron distribution is. The importance of such a calculation lies in the fact that it is probably the most direct method which physics now offers for learning how electrons are arranged in atoms.

The small errors introduced by using eq. (3.34) for this purpose instead of eq. (3.38), which is in some cases more exact, are not serious. In the case of helium atoms, since both electrons have the same radial distribution, eqs. (3.38) and (3.34) become identical. For a heavy atom like mercury, as we have seen, the results of Hartree's electron distribution become practically indistinguishable from that of Thomas-Fermi, to which eq. (3.34) strictly applies. Thus, as Wollan has pointed out, it is for intermediate atomic numbers such as neon, where the differences between the results of eq. (3.34) and eq. (3.38) should be greatest. In Fig. III–13 the broken line represents the same electron distribution as the solid line, but calculated from eq. (3.34) using for $u(a)$ the average electron distribution. In no range of the experiments does the difference between the two curves become great enough for the data to permit a decisive choice. We should thus anticipate only small errors resulting from the use of eq. (3.34) in place of the sometimes more exact eq. (3.38).

Solving eq. (3.34) for f we get,

$$f = \left\{ \frac{S - R}{Z - R} \right\}^{\frac{1}{2}}. \tag{3.47}$$

Since R and Z are known, this equation serves to give the experimental value of f in terms of the measured scattering factor S.

Equation (3.26) thus becomes an integral equation, which is to be solved[45] for $u(r)$ in terms of the experimentally determined f.

Let us initially assume that the spherically symmetrical atom has a finite radius b beyond which $u(a) = 0$. We may then express the probability function u as a Fourier series, thus:

$$u(a) = \sum_{1}^{\infty} A_n a \sin n\pi \frac{a}{b}. \qquad (3.48)$$

We do not include cosine terms in the series, since a finite cosine term would give a finite value of $u(0)$, which would mean an infinite density $\rho = u/4\pi a^2$ at the center of the atom. This consideration also eliminates the term $n = 0$. Substituting this value of $u(a)$ in eq. (3.26) we get,

$$f = \pm \sum_{1}^{\infty} \int_{0}^{b} \frac{A_n}{k} \sin (n\pi a/b) \sin (ka) da.$$

Integration shows that all terms are zero except that for which $n\pi/b = k$, whence

$$f_n = \pm \frac{A_n}{k} \int_{0}^{b} \sin^2 (n\pi a/b) da$$

$$= \pm A_n b/2k.$$

Thus

$$A_n = \pm \frac{2k}{b} f_n, \qquad (3.49)$$

where f_n is the experimental value of f determined by eq. (3.45) from the value of S for which $k = n\pi/b$. The coefficients of the terms of the Fourier series (3.48) are thus determinable in terms of the experimental values of f.

It is however more satisfactory to evaluate u in terms of a Fourier integral. In eq. (3.48) we write $n\pi/b = k$; $\delta k = (\pi/b)\delta n = \pi/b$; $A\delta k = A_n$, or $A = bA_n/\pi$.

Thus

$$u(a) = \sum_{1}^{\infty}{}_{n} A a \sin ka \delta k.$$

[45] A. H. Compton, Phys. Rev. **35**, 925 (1930).

If we pass toward the limit where b approaches ∞, and δn becomes dn, this sum approaches the value

$$u(a) = \int_0^\infty Aa \sin (ka)dk.$$

Writing for A its value $bA_n/\pi = \pm 2kf/\pi$, by eq. (3.49) this becomes

$$u(a) = \pm \frac{2a}{\pi} \int_0^\infty fk \sin (ak)dk. \qquad (3.50)$$

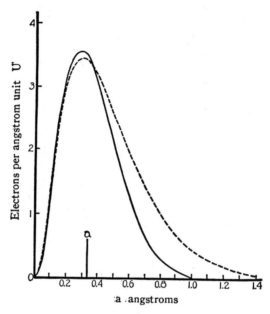

FIG. III–18. Radial electron distribution in helium. Solid line, experiment; broken line, Hartree theory. (Wollan.)

In order to obtain positive probabilities, it is necessary to choose the positive sign.

This equation can be evaluated graphically for any desired value of a, using the experimental values of f calculated according to formula (3.45). The values of $fk \sin (ak)$ are plotted against k and the curve is integrated with a planimeter.[46] Figure III–18 shows

[46] The technique of this integration has been discussed by A. H. Compton, *loc. cit.* and by E. O. Wollan, Rev. Mod. Physics **4**, 203 (1932).

the value of $U(a) = Zu(a)$ thus obtained by Wollan[47] for an atom of helium.

It will be noted that our formula (3.50) for obtaining the electron distribution in the atom from the experimental values of f is independent of any theory of atomic structure. Two assumptions are made (1) that the atoms possess spherical symmetry, and (2) that all electrons have the same value of f. We have noted that it makes little difference whether the latter assumption is correct. Trial shows also that a lack of spherical symmetry produces less effect on the intensity of scattering than does a slight change in the radial electron distribution. A curve such as that shown in Fig. III–18 thus represents an electron distribution calculated directly, though only approximately if these assumptions are wrong, from the experimental values of the scattering. In the case of helium, auxiliary information indicates that both assumptions are strictly correct. The experimental $U(a)$ curve[48] should accordingly be a good representation of the structure of the atom.

We see that the observed region of maximum electron density is close to the distance 0.33 A calculated by Pauling for the radius of the first Bohr orbit in helium. On Bohr's theory, there should occur no electrons except at this radius, i.e., $U(a)$ should be zero except at $a = 0.33$ A, where it should rise to a large value. The wide spread of the observed distribution along the a axis thus confirms the diffuseness of the atom as indicated by the wave theory, but shows also that Bohr's theory gives a good first approximation as to the size of the atom.

In Fig. III–19 is shown Wollan's analysis of the electron distribution in an atom of neon, obtained from his experimental data by a similar procedure. Here it is especially noteworthy that the K and L groups of electrons in the atom are resolved, and that they have about the predicted radii. A similar analysis of argon, as shown in Fig. III–20, fails to distinguish the K and L electron groups, but shows evidence of separation of the L and M electrons.

A comparison of the results for argon and neon shows some interesting limitations of this method of analysis. In the first place, the factor a in eq. (3.50) makes the absolute error in $u(a)$ increase rapidly with the radius. Thus for argon the results become unreli-

---

[47] E. O. Wollan, Phys. Rev. **38**, 15 (1931).

[48] Note that $U(a) = \sum_n u_n(a)$, and represents the number of electrons between a and $a + da$.

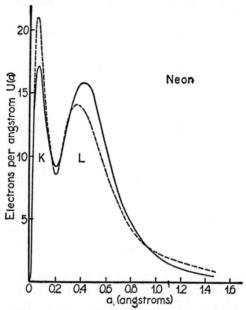

FIG. III-19. Radial electron distribution in neon. Solid line, experiment; broken line, Hartree theory. (Wollan.) Note resolution of *K* and *L* electron groups.

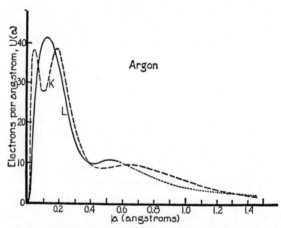

FIG. III-20. Radial electron distribution in argon. Solid line, experiment; broken line, Hartree theory. (Wollan.) Note failure to resolve *K* and *L* electron groups.

able for $a > 0.6$ A. For atoms as heavy as argon, therefore, we get by this method no information of value regarding the arrangement of the outer (valence) electrons. It is only for the light atoms that this is possible.

More significant is the failure to resolve the K and L groups of electrons in the case of argon. Let us assume that two electrons can be distinguished if the waves scattered by them traverse paths differing by more than half a wave-length. At the most favorable orientation of the two electrons, this will occur when

$$\frac{\lambda}{2} = 2\delta \sin (\phi/2),$$

or

$$\delta = \lambda/4 \sin (\phi/2), \qquad (3.51)$$

where δ is the minimum distinguishable distance. Equation (3.51) may be used to define the resolving power δ of the x-ray diffraction method. It applies equally in the case of scattering and crystal reflection of x-rays.

In Wollan's experiments on argon, $\lambda = 0.708$ A, and $(\phi)_{max} = 90°$. Thus $\delta = 0.25$ A. It will be seen that in the case of neon, where the distance between the electrons is greater than this distance, the K and L groups are distinctly resolved. In the case of argon, on the other hand, the failure to resolve the K and L groups is clearly due to the lack of resolving power. With shorter wave-lengths such resolution could presumably be accomplished.

c. The " X-ray Microscope "

It is of interest to present these experimental electron distributions as they would appear if the atoms could be viewed with an x-ray microscope. What would be seen would be the projection of the atom on a plane surface. Let us represent the atom in cylindrical coordinates, as in Fig. III–21, and let us project the electrons on the plane $h = 0$. The number of electrons projected on the element of area $rd\theta dr$ will then be

$$Prd\theta dr = 2 \int_0^\infty (\rho rd\theta dr)dh, \qquad (3.52)$$

where

$$\rho = U/4\pi a^2$$

is the volume density of distribution of the electrons. Writing $h = \sqrt{a^2 - r^2}$, eq. (3.52) becomes

$$P(r) = \frac{1}{2\pi}\int_r^\infty \frac{U(a)}{a\sqrt{a^2 - r^2}} da. \qquad (3.53)$$

From equations (3.44), (3.45) and (3.50), $U(a)$ may be written as

$$U(a) = \frac{2Za}{\pi}\int_0^\infty \left\{\frac{S - R}{Z - R}\right\}^{\frac{1}{2}} k \sin (ak) dk.$$

Thus eq. (3.53) becomes

$$P(r) = \frac{Z}{\pi^2}\int_r^\infty \int_0^\infty \left\{\frac{S - R}{Z - R}\right\}^{\frac{1}{2}} \frac{k \sin (ak)}{\sqrt{a^2 - r^2}} dk da. \quad (3.54)$$

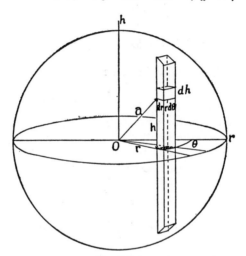

Fig. III–21.

Of the quantities on the right hand side of this equation, it will be noted that $S = I\phi/ZI_e$ is determined directly by the observed intensity of the scattered x-rays, Z is the atomic-number, and R is determined according to eq. (3.33) by the conditions of the experiment. $P(r)$ as thus defined is a purely experimental quantity, as independent of any theory of atomic structure as is a photograph taken with a lens.

We now plot P in polar coordinates, as in Fig. III–22, which represents the experimental value of P calculated for helium from Wollan's x-ray data according to eq. (3.53) or (3.54). If this shaded figure is rotated at uniform rate about the origin, and is uniformly illuminated, the light per unit area scattered by the portion of the figure at radius r will be proportional to $P/2\pi$, and hence to the projected density of the electron distribution P. Figure III–23 A, B, C, shows photographs[49] of the light reflected from rotating templates cut in this manner to represent the x-rays scattered respectively from helium, neon and argon, as measured by Wollan.

These photographs thus represent atoms as observed with x-rays of 0.71 angstrom, in which instead of using a lens, the image of the object has been formed from the observed scattered x-rays by mathematical and mechanical methods. The magnification is equal to the ratio of the unit on which r is plotted in Fig. III–22 to the unit in which the atom is measured, in the present instance a magnification

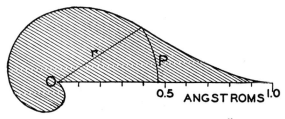

FIG. III–22.   Template which when rotated about O gives " appearance " of helium atom as observed with x-rays.

of about 2×10^8 times. The resolving power, determined jointly by the wave-length and the " aperture " of the spectrometer (maximum angle of x-ray scattering) is as noted above, about 0.25 A, which is sufficient to distinguish the detailed structure of neon, but is not high enough to show the finer details of the inner structure of argon.

Considered as analogous to a lens, the " image " produced by our mathematical-mechanical process is subject to two types of aberration. The photographs shown in Fig. III–23 represent the true electron distributions accurately if (1) the atoms are spherical, and (2) each electron has the same chance as any other of occurring at any place in the atom. If these assumptions are incorrect, the images are somewhat faulty. Auxiliary evidence indicates that assumption (1) is valid for all atoms of the noble gas group, and that (2) is exact for helium, very approximately valid for argon, and

[49] E. O. Wollan and A. H. Compton, Jour. Opt. Soc. Am. **24**, 229 (1934).

Fig. 23*A*   Fig. 23*B*

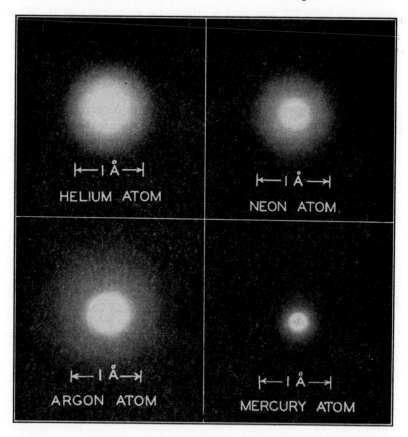

Fig. 23*C*   Fig. 24

Fig. III–23. Photographs showing "appearance" of atoms of *A*, helium; *B*, neon; and *C*, argon, as observed with x-rays of wave-length 0.71 A and a spectrometer working to an angle of 90°.

Fig. III–24. Photograph showing "appearance" of mercury 'atom, based on Thomas-Fermi electron distribution, as supported by x-ray scattering experiments (Fig. III–15). This picture represents closely, except for differences in scale, the appearance of any atom heavier than argon.

not seriously in error for neon. Thus the appearance of the helium, neon and argon atoms as shown in these photographs should correspond very closely to their true forms. In fact, the most serious error in the photographs is that introduced by the failure of the photographic emulsion accurately to reproduce differences in brightness.

The x-ray diffraction experiments under discussion accordingly supply us with just the same information that would be available if we could look at the atom with an x-ray microscope. The size of the atom is clearly observed, and diffuse groups of electrons show themselves within the atom. As interpreted on our classical theory of scattering, *we must assume the atom's atmosphere to consist of discrete electrons*—not of a continuous charge distribution. In order to arrive on this basis at a scattering formula corresponding to that derived from quantum mechanics, we must suppose also that *the individual electrons belong to specific electron groups.* We thus speak properly of K electrons, L electrons, and so on.

These studies of x-ray scattering by gases thus supply us with a more definite picture of the atom than has been secured in any other way. Of all the many theories of atomic structure that have been presented, the experiments pick out that supplied by the new quantum mechanics as the only one which is adequate to account for the observations. The theoretical electron distributions have in fact been checked at enough points to give confidence in their essential correctness. Our x-ray scattering experiments indicate further that for purposes of classical calculation we interpret the atom more correctly as composed of discrete electrons than as diffuse electricity.

7. Scattering by Polyatomic Gases

When x-rays are scattered by monatomic gases, we need to consider only the interference effects due to the electrons in the same atom.[50]   In the case of gases composed of polyatomic molecules, the interference between the rays from the component atoms of the molecule must likewise be considered. If F_m is the atomic structure factor for the mth atom (eq. (3.37)), a simple extension of Debye's formula (3.23) gives for the coherent scattering by the molecule,

$$I_c = I_e \sum_m^p \sum_n^p F_m F_n \frac{\sin x_{mn}}{x_{mn}}. \qquad (3.55)$$

[50] At very high pressures, however, the molecules approach each other so closely that their positions are no longer fortuitous. The effect of the resulting regularity has been considered theoretically by P. Debye, Phys. Zeits. 28, 135 (1927).

Here I_e is again the scattering per electron by eq. (3.04), p is the number of atoms in the molecule, and

$$x_{mn} = 4\pi \frac{s_{mn}}{\lambda} \sin \tfrac{1}{2}\phi,$$

where s_{mn} is now the distance from the mth to the nth atom in the molecule. There is also the incoherent scattering from the atoms, which plays no part in the interference phenomena. This, according to eqs. (3.32), (3.36) and (3.38) is

$$I_i = RI_e \sum_1^p (Z_m - \sum_1^{Z_m} f_i^2), \qquad (3.56)$$

where as before,

$$R = \left(1 + \frac{h}{mc\lambda} \text{vers } \phi\right)^{-3},$$

Z_m is the number of electrons in the mth atom, and f_j is the structure factor for the jth electron in the mth atom. The total scattering by the molecule is $I_M = I_c + I_i$, or [51]

$$I_M = I_e\left\{\sum_m \sum_n F_m F_n \frac{\sin x_{mn}}{x_{mn}} + R\sum_m(Z_m - \sum_j f_i^2)\right\}. \qquad (3.57)$$

An important simple case is that of diatomic molecules consisting of two similar atoms. Our formula then reduces to

$$I_2 = 2I_e\{F^2(1 + (\sin x)/x) + R(Z - \sum f^2)\}. \qquad (3.58)$$

In applying these formulas, it is usually assumed that the structure factors f and F are the same in the molecule as in the individual atom. It is evident however that the electron distributions will be somewhat distorted by the presence of neighboring atoms. The effect of such distortion should be a maximum for hydrogen, since the only electrons present are " valence " electrons. The theory of x-ray scattering by a hydrogen molecule has been examined more exactly by Massey,[52] using the ψ function for the molecule as devel-

[51] The coherent term of this expression has been given by P. Debye (Phys. Zeits. **31**, 419 (1930) and Proc. Phys .Soc. London **42**, 340 (1930)). The term for incoherent scattering was added independently by G. E. M. Jauncey, Phys. Rev. **38**, 194 (1931), Y. H. Woo, Proc. Nat. Acad. Sci. **17**, 467 (1931), and L. Bewilogua, Phys. Zeits. **32**, 740 (1931). This equation was first given in the equivalent of the form here used by Y. H. Woo, Phys. Rev. **41**, 21 (1932).

[52] H. S. W. Massey, Proc. Cambridge Phil. Soc. **27**, 77 (1930).

oped by Wang.[53]   For values of x greater than $3\pi/2$ he finds as a close approximation for the coherent scattering from the molecule,

$$I_{H_2} = 0.96 \times 2I_e F_H{}^2 \left(1 + (\sin x)/x\right), \quad [x > 3\pi/2] \qquad (3.59)$$

differing only by the factor 0.96 from eq. (3.58).   For smaller values of x, the more rigid calculation approaches even closer to eq. (3.58), becoming identical for $x = 0$.   It is thus doubtful whether in any case the error introduced by assuming an undistorted atom will be experimentally detectable.

a. *Comparison with Experiment*

Comparison of these results with experiment may be expected to give information both with regard to the distance between the atoms in the molecule (through the value of x) and with regard to the electron distributions (through the values of F).   Our studies of the scattering by monatomic gases has confirmed the structure factor calculations based on Hartree's approximation to the wave mechanics atomic structures.   We may accordingly use the factors as thus calculated for comparison with experiment.   In Appendix IV are tabulated the values of F as thus determined chiefly by James and Brindley[54] for a number of different atoms, and also the values of Σf^2 which are required for calculating the incoherent scattering.

Measurements of the scattering by the *diatomic molecules* H_2, N_2 and O_2 have been made by Barrett[55] and Wollan.[56]   Figure III–2; shows Wollan's values for oxygen and hydrogen compared with the values calculated by eq. (3.58).   The values of the structure factor used in the calculation are those given in Appendix IV, and s for oxygen is taken as 1.22 A, which gives the best fit with the data.   For hydrogen, s is taken as 1.1 A, in accord with Rasetti's determination[57] of the moment of inertia.   In the case of oxygen, the agreement is reasonably good except in the neighborhood of 0.4. For hydrogen, if there were no interatomic interference, the data should all lie close to the line $S = 1$.   The upward trend of the data at angles close to the predicted value of about 15 degrees shows the existence of such interference.   The differences between the theo-

[53] S. C. Wang, Phys. Rev. **31**, 579 (1928).
[54] R. W. James and G. W. Brindley, Phil. Mag. **12**, 104 (1931).
[55] C. S. Barrett, Phys. Rev. **32**, 22 (1928).
[56] E. O. Wollan, Phys. Rev. **35**, 1019 (1930); Proc. Nat. Acad. **17**, 475 (1931).
[57] F. Rasetti, Phys. Rev. **34**, 367 (1930).

retical curve and the experiments in this case are probably due to the non-homogeneity of the x-rays which Wollan found it necessary to use in order to get sufficient intensity of scattered x-rays from hydrogen. This source of error is absent in his experiments with oxygen and nitrogen.

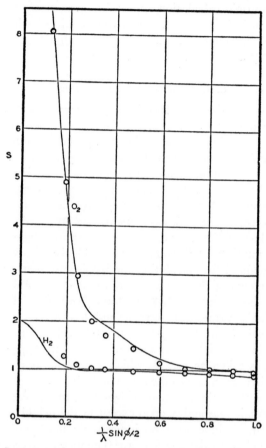

Fig. III-25. Scattering of x-rays by hydrogen and oxygen. Experimental points, Wollan. Curves, calculated from eq. (3.58).

A more interesting comparison is obtained by plotting the values of

$$X = [I_2/2I_e - R(Z - \Sigma f^2)]/F^2 \qquad (3.60)$$

as a function of $(\sin \frac{1}{2}\phi)/\lambda$. According to eq. (3.58) we should have

$$X = 1 + (\sin x)/x. \qquad (3.61)$$

The values of X from eq. (3.60), obtained using Wollan's experimental values of I_2/I_e and the values of Σf^2 and F^2 tabulated in Appendix IV, are shown in Figs. III–26 and III–27 for nitrogen and oxygen.

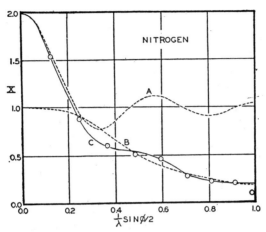

FIG. III–26. Scattering function X for nitrogen. Experiments, Wollan. Curve $A = 1 + (\sin x)/x$. B = correction curve for atomic structure factor. $C = A \times B$.

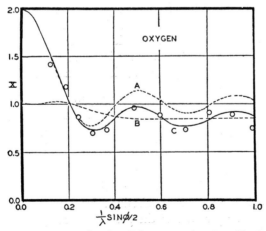

FIG. III–27. Scattering function X for oxygen, based on data by Wollan.

Two features of these curves are noteworthy. The humps corresponding to the maxima of $(\sin x)/x$ now become evident in the experimental data, making possible a precise determination of the distance between the atoms of the molecule. On the other hand, instead of oscillating about the value $X = 1$, the experimental values of X fall markedly below 1 for the larger values of $(\sin \frac{1}{2}\phi)/\lambda$. This can only mean that the values of F and of Σf^2 taken from our table are inaccurate. Nor is this surprising, since the approximations underlying Hartree's electron distributions assume nearly spherical atoms, which is not true for oxygen or nitrogen. Moreover, the values tabulated for nitrogen are obtained by an interpolation method, which introduces further uncertainties.

The broken line B in these figures is accordingly drawn in such a way that when multiplied by $(1 + (\sin x)/x)$ the best fit with the data will be secured. Its departures from unity indicate the inaccuracies of our assumed structure factors. Noting that the experimental error increases rapidly with $(\sin \frac{1}{2}\phi)/\lambda$, the best fit with the experimental data is secured if the first maximum ($x = 5\pi/2$) for oxygen occurs at $(\sin \frac{1}{2}\phi)/\lambda = 0.51$ and for nitrogen at 0.575. From the relation,

$$s = x/\{4\pi (\sin \tfrac{1}{2}\phi)/\lambda\}, \tag{3.62}$$

we thus find for the interatomic distances in oxygen and nitrogen, 1.22 A and 1.09 A respectively.

On the basis of Rasetti's measurements of the moments of inertia of the O_2 and N_2 molecules from his studies [58] of the Raman spectra, Woo calculates[59] these interatomic distances as 1.21 A and 1.10 A respectively. The agreement is within our experimental error, and affords a valuable confirmation of the less direct though more precise spectroscopic method of measuring these distances.

b. *Polyatomic Molecules*

An extensive series of measurements by Debye and his collaborators has resulted in detailed information regarding the structures of some of the more complicated molecules. Photographs of the diffraction pattern from carbon tetrachloride vapor were the first to show clearly interatomic interference. Figure III–28 is a photometer record of such a photograph obtained by Debye, Bewilogua and Ehrhardt.[60] The presence of the peaks at about $36°$ and $60°$ in the figure is evident.

[58] F. Rasetti, Phys. Rev. **34**, 367 (1930).
[59] Y. H. Woo, Proc. Nat. Acad. **17**, 470 (1931).
[60] P. Debye, L. Bewilogua and F. Ehrhardt, Phys. Zeits. **30**, 84 (1929); Ber. der Math.-Phys. Klasse der Sächs. Ak. Wiss. zu Leipsig, **81**, 29 (1929).

An approximate calculation of the expected scattering can be made from eq. (3.57) if the effect of the carbon atom is neglected, and the four chlorine atoms are assumed to lie at the corners of a tetrahedron. The term representing the interatomic interference is then proportional to

$$1 + 3 \frac{\sin x}{x},$$

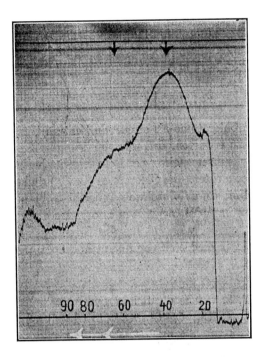

FIG. III–28.   Photometer record of diffraction of x-rays by carbon tetrachloride vapor. (Debye, Bewilogua, and Ehrhardt.)

and the peaks shown in the photometer curve correspond to $x = 2.5\pi$ and 4.5π respectively. In Figs. III–29 and 30 are shown comparisons by Bewilogua[61] of similar curves as calculated from eq. (3.57) and as measured from his diffraction photographs, for CCl_4 and CH_2Cl_2 respectively. In both cases the similarity between the two curves is close, though not exact. Precise measurements,[61] using three dif-

[61] L. Bewilogua. Phys. Zeits. **32**, 265 (1931).

ferent wave-lengths, give the following values for the distances between the Cl atoms:

TABLE III–1

INTERATOMIC DISTANCES BY X-RAY DIFFRACTION

Substance	s (Cl — Cl)			
	λ 1.539 A	λ 0.71 A	λ 1.94 A	Mean
CCl$_4$	2.99	2.98	3.00	2.99 A
CHCl$_3$	3.11	3.11	3.10	3.11 A
CH$_2$Cl$_2$	3.23	3.18	3.28	3.23 A

Similar measurements by other observers have given the following results:

TABLE III–2

INTERATOMIC DISTANCES BY X-RAY DIFFRACTION

Substance	Atoms	Spacing	Observer
H$_2$	H–H	1 A	1, 2
N$_2$	N–N	1.09	1, 2, 3, 6
O$_2$	O–O	1.22	1, 2, 3, 6
CCl$_4$	Cl–Cl	2.99	4, 5
CHCl$_3$	Cl–Cl	3.11	4, 5
CH$_2$Cl$_2$	Cl–Cl	3.28	4, 5
CH$_3$Cl	C–Cl	1.8	5
CS$_2$	S–S	3.0	6
CO$_2$	O–O	2.2	6
SiCl$_4$	Cl–Cl	3.35	7

1. Y. H. Woo, Proc. Nat. Acad. Sci. **17**, 467 and 470 (1931).
2. E. O. Wollan, Proc. Nat. Acad. Sci. **17**, 475 (1931).
3. Supra, p. 161.
4. P. Debye, L. Bewilogua, F. Ehrhardt, Sächs, Ak. **81**, 29 (1929).
5. L. Bewilogua, Phys. Zeits. **32**, 265 (1931).
6. H. Gajewski, Phys. Zeits. **33**, 122 (1932).
7. R. W. James, Phys. Zeits. **33**, 737 (1932).

c. *Effect of Temperature*

It will be seen in Figs. III–29 and 30 that the amplitude of the oscillations of the experimental intensity curves is not as great as that of the theoretical curves. James[7] has investigated the possibility that this may be due to an oscillation of the atoms about their mean positions, which would reduce the effect of the interatomic interference especially at the larger angles. He compares his theory with

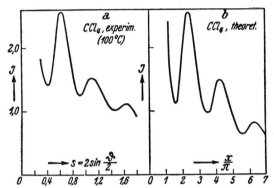

Fig. III–29. Experimental and theoretical scattering curves from carbon tetrachloride vapor. (Bewilogua.) Note that the calculated height of humps is greater than shown by experiment.

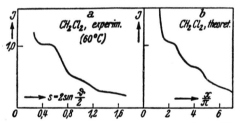

Fig. III–30. Observed and calculated scattering from CH_2Cl_2 vapor.

his own experiments on SiCl$_4$ at temperatures of 100° C. and 300° C. In accord with the predictions of the theory, such a temperature difference does not produce any detectable change in the x-ray diffraction. There is an appreciable effect due to the " zero point oscillations" of the atoms, though the predicted effect is not sufficient to bring the calculated amplitude of the interference maxima into complete agreement with experiment.[62]

[62] W. van der Grinten, Phys. Zeits. **34**, 609 (1933), has recently shown that most of this difference disappears if monochromatic x-rays are used.

The rather complex formula which James derives assumes the following relatively simple form for the case of a molecule composed of two similar atoms:

$$I = 2I_e\left\{F^2\left[1 + \frac{\sin x}{x}e^{-A} + \sqrt{2\pi A}\frac{J_{3/2}(x)}{x^{3/2}}\right] + R(Z - \Sigma f^2)\right\}. \quad (3.63)$$

Here

$$A = \frac{2h}{mv}\coth\frac{hv}{2kT}\left\{\frac{\sin\frac{1}{2}\phi}{\lambda}\right\}^2,$$

$J_{3/2}(x)$ is Bessel's J function of the 3/2 order, and the other quantities have the same significance as in eq. (3.58). The most significant effect of the oscillation is that introduced by the factor e^{-A}. For all practicable temperatures kT is so small compared with hv, where v is the natural frequency of the atom's oscillation, that $\coth(hv/2kT)$ is nearly unity. Thus we may take

$$A = \frac{2h}{mv}\left(\frac{\sin\frac{1}{2}\phi}{\lambda}\right)^2, \quad (3.63)$$

which corresponds to an oscillation with an energy of $hv/2$ (the zero state of a harmonic oscillator, according to quantum mechanics). No experiments with diatomic molecules have yet been performed of sufficient precision to give this equation an adequate test, though as noted above, comparison of the corresponding more complicated expressions with the tetrahedral molecules gives the calculation partial confirmation.

8. Scattering by Liquids

Since liquids have neither the calculable periodicity of crystals nor the completely random character of gases, the detailed study of their diffraction of x-rays presents formidable difficulties. Nevertheless the information gained from these studies has thrown important new light upon the structure of substances in the liquid state. It is found that the arrangement of the molecules in the liquid state is far from random. There appears rather an almost crystalline arrangement, which, however, is continually changing and retains a regular form for only a small number of molecular layers.

When in 1912 von Laue and his collaborators first observed diffraction of x-rays by crystals, liquids were also used to demonstrate the effect of amorphous materials.[63]   Though no diffraction spots were observed, the intensity of the scattered x-rays was not uniformly distributed at different angles.   Debye[64] and Ehrenfest,[65] several years later, called attention to the interference which must occur even in amorphous substances, due both to the fact that the molecules approach each other in a liquid to a rather definite distance, and also to the existence of interference within the individual molecules.   The latter type of interference is the same as that which we have considered under monatomic and polyatomic gases.   Interference of the former kind is closely analogous to that observed with powdered crystals.   It was, in fact, while testing the predictions of this theory

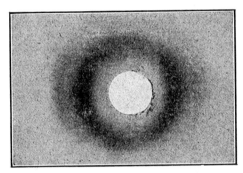

Fig. III-31.   Diffraction haloes from water.   (Keesom and de Smedt.)

that Debye and Scherrer first observed[66] the diffraction of x-rays by powders.

Figure III-31 shows a photograph obtained when the $K\alpha$ ray of copper is diffracted by water.[67]   It will be noticed that close to the primary beam, where the scattering angle ϕ is small, the intensity of the scattered ray is very low.   This is shown also in Fig. III-4 where liquid mesitylene is used, and in Fig. III-37 which represents diffraction by liquid mercury.   In the case of gases, on the other hand, as for example in Fig. III-13 the intensity approaches a maximum as

[63] W. Friedrich, P. Knipping and M. v. Laue, Sitzber. Bayr. Ak. 315 (1912) W. Friedrich, Phys. Zeits. 14, 397 (1913).

[64] P. Debye, Ann. d. Phys. 46, 809 (1915).

[65] P. Ehrenfest, Ak. Amsterdam Versl. 23, 1132 (1915).

[66] P. Debye and P. Scherrer, Nachr. d. Göttingen Ges. 1 and 16 (1916).

[67] W. H. Keesom and J. de Smedt, Ak. Amsterdam Versl. 31, 87 (1922); Jour. de Phys. 4, 144 (1923).

ϕ approaches zero. When this difference was noticed,[68] it was at once ascribed to destructive interference at small angles between the rays scattered from neighboring molecules in the liquid. This means that there is enough regularity in the arrangement of the liquid molecules to produce interference similar to that obtained with crystals at angles less than that given by $\lambda = 2d \sin \theta$.

Following a theoretical paper by Raman and Ramanathan,[69] a series of studies of the diffraction of x-rays by liquids at small angles was made by Sogani and others of the Calcutta school.[70] One of the chief objectives of this work was to test the theoretical predictions of the effect of fluctuations in density of the liquid due to thermal motions in accord with the theories of Smoluchowski and Einstein. These density fluctuations occur over distances varying from that between molecules up to that of the containing vessel. If the density were uniform, no scattering whatever should occur, for the interference would be complete. If we let a be the distance between parallel planes which would diffract x-rays at the angle given by $\lambda = 2a \sin \frac{1}{2}\phi$, the density fluctuations for such planes are calculable in terms of the density, compressibility and temperature. As long as a is large compared with d, the spacing between the molecules, i.e., at very small angles of scattering, this macroscopic thermal theory seems to give an adequate account of the phenomenon. For scattering angles such that a approaches d, however, Raman and his collaborators conclude that it is the shape of the molecule which determines the intensity of the scattered x-rays.

The almost crystalline regularity of the molecular arrangement in liquids, due both to molecular shapes and inter-molecular forces, has been emphasized especially by Stewart.[71] To this condition of the

---

[68] C. W. Hewlett, Phys. Rev. **19**, 266 (1922). A. H. Compton, Bull. Nat. Res. Council, No. 20, p. 14 (1922).

[69] C. V. Raman and K. B. Ramanathan, Proc. Indian Assn. Cultivation Sci. **8**, 127 (1923). C. V. Raman, Phil. Mag. **47**, 671 (1924).

[70] C. M. Sogani, Indian J. Phys. **1**, 357 (1927); **2**, 97 (1927); **2**, 377 (1928). P. Krishnamurti, Indian J. Phys. **2**, 355, 491, 501 (1928); **3**, 225, 303, 331 (1929); **4**, 449 (1930). S. S. Ramasubramaniam, Indian J. Phys. **3**, 371, 391 (1929). V. S. Vaidyanathan, Indian J. Phys. **3**, 371, 391 (1929). K. Banerjee, Indian J. Phys. **4**, 541 (1930). Cf. also E. H. Collins, Phys. Rev. **27**, 242 (1926).

[71] Cf. especially G. W. Stewart, Rev. Mod. Physics **2**, 116 (1930) and Faraday Society Discussion, 1933, p. 982, for summaries; also, G. W. Stewart and M. Morrow, Phys. Rev. **30**, 232 (1927); Stewart and E. W. Skinner, Phys. Rev. **31**, 1 (1928); G. W. Stewart, Phys. Rev. **32**, 153 (1928); **33**, 889 (1929); **35**, 291, 296, 726, 1426 (1930); **38**, 931 (1931).

molecules he assigns the name of *cybotactic state* (cybotaxis = space grouping).   As typical of the impressive evidence which he presents, we may quote that of the relative scattering by the normal alcohols, in which the shape of the molecule is a determining factor in the liquid structure;   the scattering by ether as it is carried through the critical point, where the molecular arrangement assumes a regularity

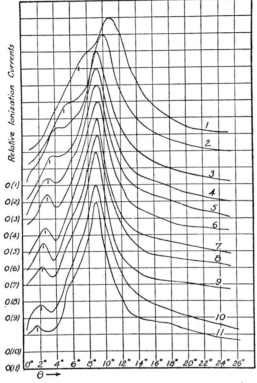

Fig. III–32.   Diffraction curves from normal alcohols containing from 1 to 11 carbon atoms.   (Stewart and Morrow.)

which depends more upon the volume occupied than upon the temperature;   and the interesting case of liquid crystals.   In the same direction points also the work of Bernal and Fowler[72] on the structure of water, and the experiments of Todd[73] on the effect of agitation on the scattering of x-rays by nitrobenzol.

[72] J. D. Bernal and R. H. Fowler, J. Chem. Phys. 1, 515 (1933).   Cf. also, W. H Good, Helvetica Physica Acta, 3, 205 (1930).

[73] F. C. Todd, Phys. Rev. 44, 787 (1933).

Scattering by normal alcohols. Figure III–32 shows Stewart's experimental curves for the diffraction of the filtered $K\alpha$ radiation from molybdenum by the primary normal alcohols, from CH_3OH to $CH_3(CH_2)_{10}OH$. The number of carbon atoms per molecule is indicated by the number of the curve. In order to avoid confusion each curve has a different zero. A major feature is the presence of two peaks for each of these curves, in the neighborhood of 3 degrees and 9 degrees respectively. This can be satisfactorily interpreted if we suppose that the molecules are elongated, and become arranged somewhat as cigars in a box. Then the main peak, at 9 or 10 degrees, is due to interference between molecules piled side by side, and measures the diameter of the carbon chain. The small peak near 3 degrees similarly represents interference between molecules piled end to end. The distances are approximately calculable[74] from Bragg's law. This interpretation accounts satisfactorily for the fact that as the number of carbon atoms in the molecule increases the angle at which

---

[74] Strictly speaking, Bragg's law is applicable only when interference occurs over a large number of regularly spaced layers. In the case of liquids the number of such layers that may be considered as regularly spaced is probably not large. In the extreme case of only two diffracting centers, we find from eqs. (3.19) and (3.20) that the diffraction maxima occur when the function $(\sin x)/x$ is a maximum, i.e. when $x = \dfrac{\pi}{2}(4n + 1)$ approximately, or when

$$(n + \tfrac{1}{4})\,\lambda = 2s \sin \tfrac{1}{2}\phi. \tag{3.65}$$

This differs from Bragg's law by only the factor $(n + \tfrac{1}{4})/n$, and indicates that the distances calculated from that law can never be greatly in error.

The fact that eq. (3.66) below is the sum of terms representing atoms taken in pairs has been used to justify the application to liquids of the theory for pairs of diffracting particles, i.e., the validity of eq. (3.65). If all possible interatomic distances were considered, the argument would be satisfactory. Usually, however, only the value of $n = 1$ in eq. (3.65) has been used, giving

$$\tfrac{5}{4}\,\lambda = 2s \sin \tfrac{1}{2}\phi. \tag{3.65a}$$

That this relation cannot be in general valid is evident from the case of a crystal with random orientation, to which also eq. (3.65) applies. Here the position of the first maximum is given by Bragg's law as

$$\lambda = 2s \sin \tfrac{1}{2}\phi. \tag{3.65b}$$

The difference arises from the neglect, when eq. (3.65a) is used, of diffraction by atoms at distances ns apart, which when n is large give maxima at positions approaching that given by eq. (3.65b). Thus for a real liquid the correct formula will be intermediate between (3.65a) and (3.65b), but can in no case differ greatly from Bragg's law.

the first peak occurs grows smaller, while that of the second peak approaches a constant value.

Experiments of this type indicate that for molecules containing many carbon atoms the chain diameters of the normal monobasic fatty acids and of the normal alcohols have the same value, 4.55 A, whereas the paraffin molecules have the slightly greater diameter, 4.64 A.[75] The additional length contributed by each carbon atom in the chain is 1.24 A. This is less than the effective diameter of the

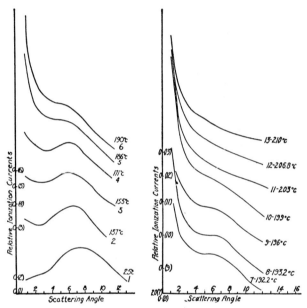

FIG. III–33.   Diffraction curves from ether under 43.5 kg./cm.² pressure, at different temperatures. (Noll.)

carbon atom, 1.5 A, as found from crystal measurements. The carbon atoms in a paraffin chain are thus apparently not arranged in a straight but in a zigzag line, somewhat similar to the lines that can be drawn connecting carbon atoms in diamond.

Scattering by ether near the critical point.—A comparison of the diffraction by ether at different temperatures near the critical value

---

[75] B. E. Warren, Phys. Rev. **44**, 969 (1933), using the more exact method of Zernicke and Prins (eq. (3.86)) for calculating the distances, finds from these data a diameter of 5.4 A.

is shown[76] in Fig. III–33. The pressure used, 43.5 kg/cm², is somewhat greater than the critical pressure, 36.7 kg/cm². It will be
noted that the distinct rise which appears in the diffraction curve for
liquid ether at about 7 degrees scattering angle, disappears soon after
the critical temperature (194.6°) is exceeded. Further experiments
by Spangler, as yet unpublished,[77] indicate that the volume occupied
by the ether is much more important than its temperature in determining whether this hump in the curve shall appear. Thus even at
a temperature well above the critical value, the hump is present if
the volume is less than the critical volume, but vanishes completely
if the volume is greater.

Clearly this peak in the diffraction curve is due to an ordered
arrangement of the ether molecules. It occurs normally in the
liquid phase but is present in the gaseous phase only when compressed
into so small a volume that regularity is demanded by the requirements of close packing.

Scattering by liquid crystals.—Liquid para-azoxyanisol occurs in a
milky, liquid-crystalline condition between 117.4° C. and 134° C.
Above this temperature the liquid is transparent and apparently
homogeneous. Experiments by Kast[78] and Stewart[79] show that
whereas in the solid and in the clear liquid condition a powerful
magnetic field has no effect on the diffraction of x-rays by this substance, in the liquid crystalline condition, it is strongly affected by a
magnetic field. Figure III–34 shows the nature of the effect when
the magnetic field is applied in the plane perpendicular to the spectrometer axis and perpendicular to the x-ray beam. It will be seen
that the main diffraction peak, due presumably to the regular periodicity transverse to the carbon chains, practically disappears. This
means that the molecules in the liquid crystals orient themselves in
the magnetic field like a pile of compass needles, so that no transverse
periodicity occurs in the direction necessary to give observable diffraction. Stewart shows that this phenomenon is subject to quantitative explanation if in the liquid crystal state groups of molecules
having a total magnetic moment of from 10^4 to 10^5 Bohr magnetons
are so regimented as to turn as a unit in the magnetic field. Both

[76] F. H. W. Noll, Phys. Rev. 42, 337 (1932).

[77] Cf. G. W. Stewart in Faraday Society Discussion, 1933, p. 982, for some of
Spangler's new data.

[78] W. Kast, Ann. d. Phys. 73, 145 (1924); 83, 418 (1927).

[79] G. W. Stewart, Phys. Rev. 38, 931 (1931).

this magnetic effect and the optical anistropy would thus seem to require a high degree of regularity in the molecular structure of such liquid crystals.

When, however, the temperature of the liquid is raised to 143° C., where the substance is optically homogeneous and no magnetic effect is observable, the x-ray diffraction experiments show a peak almost identical with that for the liquid crystal with no magnetic field (Fig. III–34). That is, there is sufficient regularity in the grouping of the molecules in the clear liquid to give diffraction effects practically

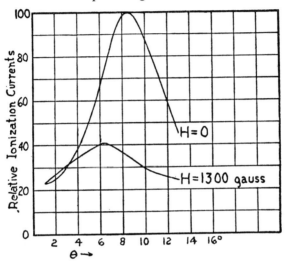

FIG. III–34. Scattering by para-azoxyanisol in the liquid-crystalline state, with and without a strong magnetic field applied perpendicular to the x-ray beam. (Stewart.)

identical with those in the liquid crystal state where regimentation is known to exist.

Scattering by water.—The liquids so far considered have large molecules, in which a regular grouping is required because of the molecular shapes. A notable example of a small molecule in which intermolecular forces play a determining part is that of water, whose structure has been analyzed by Bernal and Fowler.[72] Raman spectra and absorption spectra agree in showing that the molecule in liquid water is simply H_2O, and is identical in form with the molecule of gaseous water. The results of band spectra [80, 81] indicate that

[80] Mecke and Baumann, Phys. Zeits. 33, 833 (1932).
[81] R. S. Mulliken, Phys. Rev. 41, 756 (1932).

this molecule has very nearly the symmetry of a tetrahedron, at the center of which is the oxygen nucleus. Near two corners are the protons, giving positive polarity, and at the other two corners are concentrations of negative electricity. This obviously gives a strongly polar molecule. Its " radius," as calculated from the closest approach of water molecules in ice, is 1.38 A.

In Fig. III–35 are shown the experimental diffraction data for water at room temperature as compared with the calculated scatter-

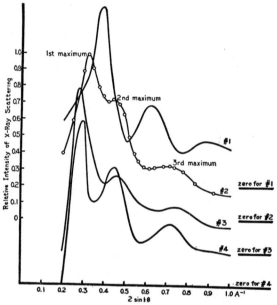

FIG. III–35. X-ray scattering curves for water. (Bernal and Fowler.) 1, irregular close-packing; 2, experiment; 3, quartz-like distribution; 4, ice-tridymite-like distribution of water molecules.

ing for three different types of crystal-like structure. Bernal and Fowler conclude that below 4 degrees centigrade the molecular grouping is like that of ice or tridymite. Between 4 degrees and 200 degrees, as suggested by Fig. III–35, the structure is quartz-like. From 200 degrees to the critical temperature it resembles more nearly a close-packed arrangement, similar to that found for liquid mercury and liquid ammonia. These various forms are not distinct, and pass continuously into each other. In addition to accounting quantitatively for the x-ray diffraction by such structures, they show also that many other properties, including the anomalous density changes of water, can thus be explained.

a. More Exact Determination of Intermolecular Distances in Liquids

In the case of liquids which consist of spherical molecules it is possible to calculate directly from measurements of the scattering of x-rays at different angles the average distances between the molecules, using a method developed by Zernicke and Prins.[82] Following a procedure identical with that used above for calculating the intensity due to an atom with many electrons (eq. (3.24)) it is found [83] that the instantaneous intensity of the coherent scattering due to a portion of the liquid containing N molecules is

$$I = I_m \sum_m^N \sum_n^N \cos \delta_{mn}, \qquad (3.66)$$

where I_m is the intensity of the coherent scattering due to a single molecule, and δ_{mn} is the phase difference between the rays scattered from the mth and nth molecules. I_m is given by eq. (3.55), or by $I_e F$, where I_e is the scattering per electron (eq. (3.04)), and F is the molecular structure factor (eq. (3.37)). Referring to Fig. III-9 and eq. (3.25), it will be seen that

$$\delta_{mn} = \frac{4\pi}{\lambda} \sin \frac{\phi}{2} \mu_{mn} a_{mn}, \qquad (3.67)$$

where a_{mn} is the distance between the two molecules, and μ_{mn} is the direction cosine of the line $\overline{mn}$ with respect to the line OQ.

We may write the probability that the molecule m has its midpoint in the volume element dv_m at the same time that n lies in the element dv_n as

$$P \frac{dv_m}{V} \frac{dv_n}{V},$$

where V is the whole volume of the scattering material. If all positions were equally probable, we should have everywhere $P = 1$. At large distances a_{mn} this will in fact be nearly correct, though for distances shorter than that of closest approach of two molecules it must have the value $P = 0$. In general, we may assume that for a liquid consisting of spherical molecules, the conditions will be isotropic, so

[82] F. Zernicke and J. A. Prins, Z. Phys. **41**, 184 (1927).

[83] This derivation follows closely that given by P. Debye and H. Menke, Forts. d Röntgenforschung **2**, 1 (1931).

that P will be a function of a only. The probable intensity of the rays scattered by the whole volume may then be written,

$$\bar{I} = I_m \sum_m \sum_n \int \int \cos \delta_{mn}\, P \frac{dv_m}{V} \frac{dv_n}{V}, \qquad (3.68)$$

where each integration is taken over the whole volume V.

In this double sum there are N terms for which $m = n$, and for which the double integral has the value 1. All of the remaining terms have the same value,

$$X = \int \int \cos \delta_{mn}\, P \frac{dv_m}{V} \frac{dv_n}{V}. \qquad (3.69)$$

Let us now write, $P = 1 - (1 - P)$, and separate X into two parts

$$X_1 = \int \int \cos \delta_{mn} \frac{dv_m}{V} \frac{dv_n}{V}, \qquad (3.70)$$

and

$$X_2 = \int \int \cos \delta_{mn}\, (1 - P) \frac{dv_m}{V} \frac{dv_n}{V}, \qquad (3.71)$$

so that

$$X = X_1 - X_2. \qquad (3.72)$$

Evaluation of X_1 and X_2 will then mean solution of eq. (3.68), i.e., the calculation of the intensity of the scattering in terms of a known molecular distribution within the liquid.

Integral (3.70) can be evaluated as to order of magnitude if we write

$$\int \cos \delta_{mn} \frac{dv_m}{V} = \frac{1}{V} \int_{-1}^{1} \int_{0}^{R} \cos (k\mu_{mn} a_{mn}) 2\pi a^2 da d\mu,$$

where R is the effective radius of the scattering material, and as before, $k = (4\pi/\lambda) \sin (\phi/2)$. If we write also $V = \frac{4}{3}\pi R^3$, we find on integration,

$$\int \cos \delta_{mn} \frac{dv_m}{V} = 3 \frac{\sin kR - kR \cos kR}{(kR)^3}. \qquad (3.73)$$

Carrying through the second integration with respect to dv_n introduces the same factor again, giving approximately[84]

$$X_1 = \left[3 \frac{\sin kR - kR \cos kR}{(kR)^3} \right]^2. \qquad (3.74)$$

[84] This value is only approximate, since the limit of integration R has no exact relation to the boundary of the scattering liquid.

The quantity $kR = (4\pi R/\lambda) \sin (\phi/2)$ is of the order of magnitude of R/λ, which is very large compared with 1. Hence we may neglect the term $\sin kR$, and find that X_1 is of the order of $1/(kR)^4$, i.e., of $(\lambda/R)^4$.

We have noted above that the double sum of eq. (3.68) has N terms equal to 1. There are $N(N-1)$, or approximately N^2 terms equal to X_1. Thus if the contribution by the individual molecules is proportional to N, that due to the X_1 terms is given by N^2X_1. We may now define a mean molecular distance d as

$$d^3 \equiv V/N, \qquad (3.75)$$

or $N = V/d^3$. Thus the ratio of the contribution of the X_1 terms to that due to the individual atoms is

$$\frac{N^2X_1}{N} = NX_1 \sim N\frac{\lambda^4}{R^4} = \frac{V}{d^3}\frac{\lambda^4}{R^4},$$

or writing $V = \frac{4}{3}\pi R^3$,

$$NX_1 \sim \frac{4}{3}\pi\frac{\lambda^3}{d^3}\frac{\lambda}{R}. \qquad (3.76)$$

Using x-rays, d is at least as large as λ, and R is very large compared with λ. Thus

$$NX_1 \ll 1,$$

and this term may be neglected.

The quantity X_2 can be readily evaluated if we assume that P depends only upon a, and that $1 - P$ vanishes at a distance from the origin that is small compared with the dimensions of the scattering material. Because of the latter fact, one of the two integrations of eq. (3.71) represents merely the evaluation of $\frac{1}{V}\int dv$ over the whole volume, giving 1. Thus we have,

$$X_2 = \int \cos \delta_{mn}(1 - P)\frac{dv_m}{V}$$

$$= \frac{1}{V}\int_{-1}^{1}\int_{0}^{\infty} (1 - P) \cos (k\mu a)2\pi a^2 da d\mu, \qquad (3.77)$$

where k, μ and a have the same significance as before. The limits 0 to ∞ are used for a because the quantity $(1 - P)$ vanishes within a few molecular distances from the origin of integration, so that the limit may be made indefinitely large without affecting the result. Since P is independent of μ, one integration may be effected directly. Writing also Nd^3 instead of V, we thus get,

$$X_2 = \frac{4\pi}{Nd^3} \int_0^\infty (1 - P) \frac{\sin ka}{ka} a^2 da. \tag{3.78}$$

Since there are $N(N - 1)$ or very nearly N^2 such terms in the double sum of eq. (3.68), we thus have,

$$N^2 X_2 = \frac{4\pi N}{d^3} \int_0^\infty (1 - P) \frac{\sin ka}{ka} a^2 da. \tag{3.79}$$

From eq. (3.68) we thus have, since $X = X_1 - X_2$,

$$\bar{I} = NI_m \left\{ 1 - \frac{4\pi}{d^3} \int_0^\infty (1 - P) \frac{\sin ka}{ka} a^2 da \right\}. \tag{3.80}$$

Using the dimensionless variable $u = a/\lambda$, and writing $s = 2\sin(\phi/2) = k\lambda/2\pi$, this becomes

$$\bar{I} = NI_m \left\{ 1 - \frac{\lambda^3}{d^3} \frac{2}{s} \int_0^\infty (1 - P) \sin(2\pi u s) u \, du \right\}. \tag{3.81}$$

This equation represents only the coherent part of the scattering. To get the total observed intensity, we should add the incoherent scattering, which may be written as NI_i, where I_i, the incoherent radiation from a molecule, is given by eq. (3.56). The total scattered intensity is thus

$$I = \bar{I} + NI_i$$

$$= N \left\{ I_i + I_m \left[1 - \frac{\lambda^3}{d^3} \frac{2}{s} \int_0^\infty (1 - P) \sin(2\pi u s) u \, du \right] \right\}. \tag{3.82}$$

If the spatial distribution of the molecules P were known, this expression would enable us to calculate the intensity of the scattered x-rays.

Let us now suppose the intensity curve has been observed, so that I is known as a function of s. We may then write

$$I = N[I_i + I_m E(s)], \tag{3.83}$$

or

$$E = \frac{I}{NI_m} - \frac{I_i}{I_m}, \tag{3.84}$$

where, since I is observed, and N, I_m and I_i are known, $E(s)$ is given by the experimental data.

Comparison of eq. (3.83) with eq. (3.82) gives

$$\frac{sd^3}{\lambda^3}(1 - E) = 2\int_0^\infty (1 - P)\sin(2\pi us)u\,du. \qquad (3.85)$$

Fourier's theorem may, however, be stated in the following form: if

$$f(w) = 2\int_0^\infty \phi(u)\sin(2\pi wu)du,$$

then [85]

$$\phi(u) = 2\int_0^\infty f(w)\sin(2\pi wu)dw. \qquad (3.86)$$

We may thus write at once,

$$u(1 - P) = 2\frac{d^3}{\lambda^3}\int_0^\infty s(1 - E)\sin(2\pi us)ds. \qquad (3.87)$$

This is Zernicke and Prins's formula, except that in their derivation the term representing the incoherent scattering was omitted from eq. (3.84).

Structure of liquid mercury.—A good example of the application of this method of analysis to the study of liquid structure is given by liquid mercury, which has been examined by Debye and Menke.[86] Their method consisted in observing the diffuse scattering when x-rays from a copper target fell upon the liquid surface of mercury. Figure III–36 shows a photometer curve of the measured scattering, and Fig. III–37 gives the value of E as a function of s as calculated from this curve. In calculating E from the observed intensity, according to eq. (3.84), the term I_i/I_m is of negligible importance in this case, because of the high atomic number of the mercury. With the help of a harmonic analyser and a planimeter the integration required by eq. (3.87) was performed for various values of x, giving the probability distribution of the molecules shown in Fig. III–38. Here are shown also the locations of the atoms in a close-packed array, indicated by the heavy vertical lines, and a curve (the broken one) showing how

[85] It will be seen that this is precisely equivalent to the transformation made above (eq. (3.50)) and below (eq. (6.96)).

[86] Debye and H. Menke, Phys. Zs. **31**, 797 (1930). Cf. also ref. 83.

these spacings might appear if the positions of the atoms are only approximately rather than exactly those of the close-packed array.

There is an obvious discrepancy between the two curves in the region $a < 2$ A, where for part of the range the atomic density is calculated as less than zero. This impossible result is due to the fact that the density in this region, as calculated from eq. (3.85), is determined chiefly by the values of $(1 - E)$ at relatively large values of s, where the quantity is small compared with E and is hence difficult to measure with precision. The negative probability accordingly has little physical significance. With this exception the agreement between the experimental full-lined curve and the broken curve is so good that we may fairly consider the close-packed arrangement of molecules as the predominant one in liquid mercury.

Equations (3.81) and (3.82) form the basis for most of the present study of liquid structure. Bernal and Fowler in their analysis of water used (3.81) for calculating the theoretical curves of Fig. III–35. Buchwald[87] has made similar computations on the diffraction by para-azoxyanisol, which,

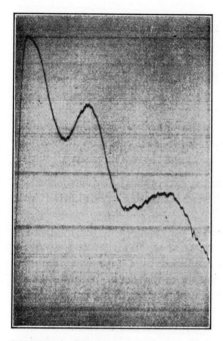

Fig. III–36. Photometer curve of the scattering by liquid mercury. (Debye and Menke.)

as we have seen above, occurs either as a clear liquid or as a liquid crystal. He finds agreement with experiment in the position of the main peak if the molecules are grouped with axes parallel, six surrounding one, and each 5.4 A from its neighbor. Likewise Warren[88] has found the same kind of arrangement for the molecules in liquid normal paraffins, the distance between neighboring molecular chains being 5.4 A.

[87] E. Buchwald, Ann. d. Phys. **10**, 558 (1931).
[88] B. E. Warren, Phys. Rev. **44**, 969 (1933).

Unless the data have been obtained with high precision over a large range of s values, it may be questioned whether we arrive at a more reliable value of the spacing by application of eq. (3.87) than by Bragg's law. In any case the values found by the two methods differ by only a few per cent. The chief value of the present method is rather that it makes possible a quantitative comparison of the

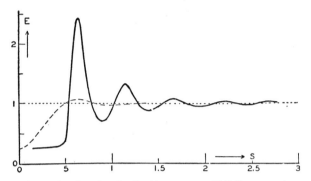

FIG. III-37. Scattering function for liquid mercury. Full line, experiment; broken line, theory based on random arrangement of atoms.

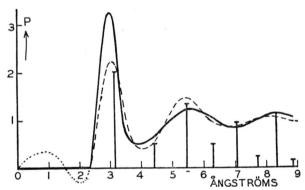

FIG. III-38. Radial probability distribution of mercury atoms. Full line, based on observed intensity of scattering; broken line, irregular close packing of spheres.

intensities of the observed peaks with those characteristic of various types of molecular arrangements.

Scattering by Liquids at Small Angles.—The equations we have developed enable us also to calculate the scattering at small angles. In expression (3.82), the incoherent scattering I_i approaches zero as s becomes small, as will become evident from eq. (3.56), in which f_i

approaches unity for small angle scattering. The term containing the integral may be written in the form

$$4\pi \frac{\lambda^3}{d^3} \int_0^\infty (1 - P) \frac{\sin 2\pi us}{2\pi us} u^2 du. \tag{3.88}$$

If s is small, the quantity $\sin (2\pi us)/2\pi us$ is nearly unity unless u is large. But we have supposed that at large values of u the quantity $(1 - P)u^2$ approaches zero (the condition for random position of the particles). Thus as s approaches zero, expression (3.88) approaches the value

$$4\pi \frac{\lambda^3}{d^3} \int_0^\infty (1 - P)u^2 du. \tag{3.89}$$

In the case of a gas we may assume as a close approximation that the distribution of the molecules is random, i.e., $P = 1$, at all points outside of a sphere of volume $\tau = \frac{4\pi}{3}\rho^3$, where τ is approximately related to Van der Waal's constant b by the relation $b = N_m\tau$, N_m being Avogadro's number. Within the volume τ, P will have the value 0. Thus expression (3.89) becomes, in view of eq. (3.75),

$$4\pi \frac{\lambda^3}{d^3} \int_0^{\rho/\lambda} u^2 du = \frac{4}{3}\pi \frac{\rho^3}{d^3} = \frac{N\tau}{V} = \frac{b}{V_m}. \tag{3.90}$$

Here b/V_m is the ratio of the volume of exclusion of all the molecules to the total volume occupied by the gas. For a gas at small values of s, eq. (3.82) thus approaches,

$$I_0 = NI_m(1 - b/V_m), \tag{3.91}$$

or by (3.84),

$$E_0 = 1 - b/V_m. \tag{3.92}$$

For close-packed spheres, $\frac{b}{V_m} = \frac{\pi}{6}\sqrt{2} = 0.74$. Though for molecules of other shapes the ratio might be somewhat larger, we may reasonably take $E_0 = 1/4$ as the approximate minimum value that should be approached for the scattering of molecules arranged at random.

Debye[89] has extended this discussion to include the scattering at larger angles, for a gas in which $P = 1$ beyond the sphere of action

[89] P. Debye, J. Math. and Phys. 4, 153 (1925); Phys. Zeits. 28, 135 (1927).

of the origin molecule. His result may be written in the form, comparable with eq. (3.82),

$$I = N\left\{I_i + I_m\left[1 - \frac{b}{V_m}\frac{3}{x^3}(\sin x - x\cos x)\right]\right\}, \qquad (3.93)$$

where $x = 2\pi us = 4\pi\dfrac{\rho}{\lambda}\sin\tfrac{1}{2}\phi$, having the same significance as in
eq. (3.90).

Some recent experiments by Harvey[90] on nitrogen at high pressure are in good qualitative accord with the results of eq. (3.93).
Because of the random positions of the gaseous molecules such agreement is to be expected. If on the other hand, this theory is applied
to liquid mercury, the result is unsatisfactory. The broken line of
Fig. III–37 is thus calculated, assuming $\lambda = 1.54$ A, and to get the
best agreement possible, $b/V_m = 0.75$ and $\rho = 2.2$ A. The difference
between this curve, which represents scattering from atoms with
random arrangement, and the experimental curve shows clearly the
effect of the pseudo-crystalline regularity of the arrangement of the
mercury atoms.

Similarly the experiments with ether, as shown in Fig. III–33
show that at room temperature the scattering at 1 degree is only
about 12 per cent as great as at 210° C., a difference much too great
to account for on the simple theory of a dense gas. The data taken
at small angles are thus sufficient to show a considerable degree of
regularity in the arrangement of liquid molecules.

*Sharpness of Diffraction Peaks and the Regularity of Molecular Arrange-
ment in Liquids*

A rough lower limit to the number of layers of molecules which is
effective in the interference phenomena with liquids is calculable from
the observed width of the main diffraction peak. It can be shown[91]
that if there are m regularly spaced layers of atoms at a distance d
apart, the intensity of the diffraction pattern may be expressed as

$$I = C\sin^2(m\omega)/\sin^2\omega, \qquad (3.94)$$

where C is a quantity which depends upon the structure factor, the

[90] G. G. Harvey, Phys. Rev. **45**, 848 (1934); **46**, 441 (1934).
[91] Cf. e.g., A. A. Michelson, "Studies in Optics," University of Chicago Press, 1927,
p. 65.

geometry, etc., but does not change rapidly with ω, and $\omega = \dfrac{2\pi d}{\lambda} \sin \frac{1}{2}\phi$. The maxima occur when $\omega = n\pi$, where the integer n represents the order of the diffracted line. If we confine our attention to the region near the first maximum, we may write $\omega = \pi + \epsilon$. After some reduction, eq. (3.94) then becomes,

$$I_\epsilon = C \frac{\sin^2 m\epsilon}{\sin^2 \epsilon}. \tag{3.95}$$

At the first maximum $\epsilon = 0$, and this has the value

$$I_1 = m^2 C.$$

Thus,

$$\delta I = I_1 - I_\epsilon = C\left(m^2 - \frac{\sin^2 m\epsilon}{\sin^2 \epsilon}\right),$$

which neglecting 4th and higher orders of small quantities is,

$$\delta I = \tfrac{1}{3}C\epsilon^2(m^4 - m^2).$$

Thus

$$\frac{\delta I}{I_1} = \frac{\epsilon^2}{3}(m^2 - 1). \tag{3.96}$$

This expression may be solved for the number of diffracting layers, giving

$$m^2 = 1 - \frac{3}{\epsilon^2}\frac{\delta I}{I_1}. \tag{3.97}$$

Since a range of $\epsilon = \pi$ corresponds to the angle θ_1 between one diffraction maximum and the next, for the small values of ϵ which are used, we may write,

$$\epsilon = \pi\delta\theta/\theta_1.$$

Thus

$$m^2 = 1 + \frac{3}{\pi^2}\left(\frac{\theta_1}{\delta\theta}\right)^2 \frac{\delta I}{I_1}. \tag{3.98}$$

This means that the width of the line is approximately inversely proportional to the number of atomic layers in the diffracting unit.

As typical examples we may use the diffraction by liquid mercury as shown in Fig. III–37, and that of lauryl alcohol, from Fig. III–32. In the former case, for $\delta\theta/\theta_1 = 0.08$, $\delta I/I_1 = 0.18$. According to eq. (3.98) we thus find $m = 3.0$. Similarly from curve 11 of Fig. III-32 we find that for $\delta\theta/\theta_1 = 0.05$, $\delta I/I_1 = 0.13$, whence $m = 4.1$ layers of atoms. These small numbers represent the effective number of atomic layers which are so uniformly spaced that the x-rays scattered from them may all be considered coherent. Since the diffraction peak may be broadened by other factors, the number of co-operating molecular layers as thus calculated is to be considered as a lower limit. Such a degree of uniformity over even so short a distance as several molecular diameters would seem, however, to require appreciable influence of the position or orientation of one molecule on another at considerably greater distances. In this way it is possible to account for the high dielectric constant of water as discussed by Bernal and Fowler, the effect of agitation on the scattering of x-rays by nitrobenzene, as found by Todd, the orientation of liquid crystals by a magnetic field, and similar phenomena.

The Structure of Liquids.—It thus becomes evident that the arrangement of molecules in liquids shows a considerable degree of order. As Stewart describes it, in a gas the molecules are lone soldiers; in a liquid, they are ordered into companies; in liquid crystals the companies form regiments; and in crystals the army moves as a unit.

One of the major results of the x-ray analysis of crystals was to show that in many solids no particular small group of atoms can be isolated as a distinct molecule.[92] Rather the whole crystal is a single molecule, in the sense that the forces holding the atoms together are of the same type throughout the volume of the crystal. This seems to be universally true for crystals which have ionic lattices; and even where individual molecules can be distinguished within the crystal, it has become evident that the forces holding neighboring molecules together are of essentially the same kind as the chemical binding force. The x-ray studies here considered indicate that the molecules in a liquid are held together with an arrangement which is a crude imitation of a crystal. The passage from the solid to the liquid state appears thus not to represent the separation into independent molecules, as in a gas, but rather the expansion of the lattice, under thermal agitation, to such an extent that the atomic groupings which in the solid are immutable become in the liquid readily interchangeable.

[92] Cf. e.g., A. H. Compton, J. Franklin Inst. **185**, 745 (1918).

9. Scattering by Solids

A typical curve showing the intensity of x-rays scattered at different angles by a solid is shown in Fig. III–39, which represents the scattering of λo.71 A by powdered graphite as observed by Hewlett.[93] The peaks and valleys in this curve are much more pronounced than those in the corresponding curves (e.g., Fig. III–4) for liquids. The maxima are in fact identical with the lines of the powdered crystal diffraction pattern, as discussed from a different viewpoint in Chap. V. It will be noted however that in between the lines the intensity does not fall to zero. There is rather a background of diffuse scattering on which the lines are superposed.

If the atoms in a crystal were all identical and arranged with perfect regularity, the rays at any angle other than near

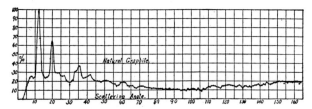

Fig. III–39.   Scattering of λo.71 A from graphite.   (Hewlett.)

$\sin^{-1}(n\lambda/2d)$ should be completely extinguished by interference. That diffuse scattering from a crystal should appear was, however, shown by Debye[94] to be a necessary consequence of the thermal agitation of the atoms in the crystal. Experiments by Jauncey[95] and his collaborators showed, however, that there occurs much stronger diffuse scattering than can thus be accounted for. Compton[96] called attention to the fact that incoherent scattering from the individual electrons within the atoms of the crystal must contribute to this diffuse scattering; and the more complete study of Woo,[97] Jauncey,[98] and Harvey[99] has shown that the two factors introduced

[93] C. W. Hewlett, Phys. Rev. **20**, 700 (1922).

[94] P. Debye, Ann. der Phys. **43**, 49 (1914).

[95] G. E. M. Jauncey, Phys. Rev. **20**, 421 (1922), and later papers.

[96] A. H. Compton, *X-rays and Electrons*, p. 171 (1926).

[97] Y. H. Woo, Proc. Nat. Acad. **17**, 467 (1931); Phys. Rev. **38**, 1 (1931); **41**, 21 (1932).

[98] G. E. M. Jauncey, Phys. Rev. **37**, 1193; **38**, 1 (1931).

[99] G. G. Harvey, **44**, 133 (1933).

by Debye and Compton are adequate to account completely for the phenomenon.

Average Scattering by Solids.—The early experiments of Barkla and others, which were used as the basis for determining the number of electrons in atoms, were mostly done by scattering from solids a beam of x-rays of a wide range of frequencies and receiving them into the ionization chamber over a wide range of angles. Under these conditions a wide range of the peaks and valleys of Fig. III–39 is averaged in each measurement. It can be shown that in this case the intensity scattered by n atoms is just n times that scattered by a single atom, which is the assumption used by Barkla and which we also made above in discussing the scattering by gases. The proof follows:

Let

$$E_n = A_n \cos pt$$

be the electric field of the ray scattered from a group of n atoms, and

$$E_1 = A_1 \cos (pt + \delta_1)$$

be the electric field of the ray from an additional atom. The total electric field is then

$$E_{n+1} = E_n + E_1 = A_n \cos pt + A_1 \cos (pt + \delta_1).$$

The instantaneous value of the intensity of the composite scattered ray being proportional to the square of the amplitude, may then be written as

$$I_{n+1} = \beta E_{n+1}{}^2$$

or

$$I_{n+1} = \beta A_n{}^2 \cos^2 pt + 2\beta A_1 A_n \cos pt \cos (pt + \delta_1)$$
$$+ \beta A_1{}^2 \cos^2 (pt + \delta_1)$$
$$I_{n+1} = \beta E_n{}^2 + \beta E_1{}^2 + 2\beta A_1 A_n \cos pt \cos (pt + \delta_1). \qquad (3.99)$$

If all values of δ_1 are equally probable, $\cos (pt + \delta_1)$ has equal chances of being positive and negative, and the average value of the last term in eq. (3.99) is zero. Thus the average over all values of δ_1 is

$$I_{n+1} = I_n + I_1, \qquad (3.100)$$

i.e., the average addition to the intensity due to adding the rays from one atom with random phase is equal to the intensity due to this atom alone.

This proposition was established many years ago by Lord Rayleigh in his study of the scattering of light by gases. Its importance here lies in the fact that it enables us to use the total scattering from matter in any physical state for determining the scattering per atom if we are careful to average the observations over a large enough range of angles or wave-lengths to ensure random phase relations.

Experiments by Coven[100] and by Jauncey and Pennell[101] have completely confirmed these calculations, showing that the total scattering per gram from a powdered crystal of KCl, for example, is nearly the same as that from argon gas. This is to be expected, since the average atomic number of potassium and chlorine is the same as that of argon. In order better to satisfy the conditions for

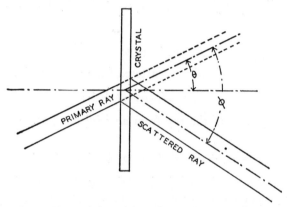

Fig. III–40.   Transmission method of scattering x-rays from a crystal.

averaging over a wide range of phases, Jauncey and Pennell used a continuous band of x-ray wave-lengths filtered through a suitable thickness of aluminium. The convenience of using solids for such experiments is evident, and it makes possible measurements at considerably larger values of $\sin(\phi/2)/\lambda$ than can conveniently be made with gases.[102]

Diffuse Scattering from Crystals.—Jauncey has introduced a method for measuring the diffuse scattering from single crystals,

[100] A. W. Coven, Phys. Rev. **41**, 422 (1932).

[101] G. E. M. Jauncey and Ford Pennell, Phys. Rev. **43**, 505; **44**, 138 (1933).

[102] Cf. *e.g.* A. W. Coven, Phys. Rev. **38**, 1424 (1931). Because of the change in wave-length of the scattered x-rays, earlier data obtained with short wave-lengths have been of little value in calculating structure factors. Coven and later workers have reduced their results with the help of the relations developed below (p. 192).

which consists in passing the primary beam through a thin slab of the crystal as indicated in Fig. III–40. As the crystal is turned, leaving ϕ constant, a Laue spot occurs at $\theta = \phi/2$. The diffuse scattering at $\phi/2$ is determined by interpolation between the intensities observed on either side of the spot, as will be seen in Fig. III–41. At this angle, $\theta = \phi/2$, the direct beam traverses the same thickness as the reflected beam, and the only correction necessary for absorption is that due to the change in wave-length. Fig. III–42 shows the S values for the diffuse scattering by NaCl as thus measured by Jauncey and Harvey.[103]

A theoretical expression for the intensity of the diffuse scattering

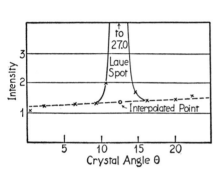

FIG. III–41. Jauncey method of determining diffuse scattering at $\theta = \phi/2$.

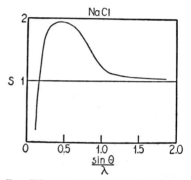

FIG. III–42. Diffuse scattering from rock salt. (Jauncey and Harvey.)

by a crystal has been developed independently by Jauncey and Harvey[103] and by Woo.[104] If the molecules are arranged at random, as in a gas, the coherent scattering per electron should be given, according to eq. (3.38), by

$$S_{coh} = F^2/Z, \qquad (3.101)$$

where F is the atomic structure factor. The mean intensity per electron in the lines reflected from a crystal is, however, in view of eq. (3.100),

$$S_R = F_T{}^2/Z, \qquad (3.102)$$

where F_T is the structure factor of the atom as calculated from its

[103] G. E. M. Jauncey and G. G. Harvey, Phys. Rev. **37**, 1203 (1931).
[104] Y. H. Woo, Phys. Rev. **38**, 1 (1931) and **41**, 21 (1932).
Our treatment follows more closely that of Woo.

mid-point in the crystal lattice. F_T differs from F due to the thermal oscillation of the atom. This effect is discussed in Sec. 17, Chap. VI. It is mentioned there that

$$F_T = Fe^{-M}. \tag{3.103}$$

Waller[105] has corrected the earlier result of Debye[106] for the value of M, so that we must use the result given in eq. (6.100), which shows M as a function of the temperature and the angle of scattering. Since the average coherent scattering by the crystal must, according to eq. (3.100) be the same as that for a gas (eq. (3.101)), there will be diffuse scattering of a coherent type given by

$$S_D = (F^2 - F_T^2)/Z. \tag{3.104}$$

This formula has been confirmed by a detailed calculation by Debye.[106]

The incoherent scattering due to the random motion of the electrons in the atoms is not affected by interference, and is hence independent of the crystalline grouping of the atoms. By eq. (3.38) its magnitude is

$$S_I = R(1 - \Sigma f_n^2/Z), \tag{3.105}$$

where as before R is the recoil factor, and f_n is the electronic structure factor for electrons of type n. Thus the total x-rays scattered diffusely by a crystal should be given by the expression,

$$S_c = (F^2 - F_T^2)/Z + R(1 - \Sigma f_n^2/Z). \tag{3.106}$$

Noting that the total scattering by a gas is the sum of expressions (3.101) and (3.105), we may also write,[107]

$$S_G = S_c + F_T^2/Z, \tag{3.107}$$

where S_G is the scattering per electron by the substance in the form of gas, S_c the diffuse scattering from the crystal, and F_T is the lattice structure factor obtained from measurements of the intensity of reflection of x-rays by crystals, as described in Chap. VI. From this relation it should be possible to obtain from measurements of the scattering and reflection of x-rays by crystals, all the information that is given by scattering data from gases.

Equation (3.107) is thoroughly confirmed by experiment, as will

[105] I. Waller, Uppsala Dissertation, 1925.
[106] P. Debye, Annalen der Physik 14, 65 (1914).
[107] G. E. M. Jauncey and G. G. Harvey, Phys. Rev. 38, 1071 (1931).

be evident from Fig. III-43, which combines the scattering data from KCl crystals and argon gas. As the temperature increases, F_T decreases, and the diffuse scattering from a crystal approaches the value to be expected from a gas of the same density. Figure III-44, due to Harvey,[108] shows this phenomenon clearly for sylvine (KCl) over a wide range of temperatures. For a temperature close to the melting point, for values of sin $(\phi/2)/\lambda$ greater than 0.5, the scattering is indistinguishable from that by a gas.

The curves shown in this figure were calculated by Harvey directly

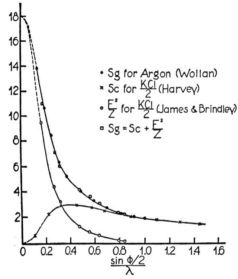

FIG. III-43. Comparison of scattering by gases and crystals. (Wollan.)

from eq. (3.106), using the values of the structure factors given in Appendix IV. To obtain F_T, the experimental values of e^{-M} as measured by James and Brindley were used rather than the Debye-Waller calculated exponent. At low temperatures the difference was unimportant; but at the highest temperature curve D results from the theoretical exponent, whereas E is based on the experimental value. The difference between the data and the theoretical curve D indicates

[108] G. G. Harvey, Phys. Rev. 44, 136 (1933). In order to facilitate calculation, the values of S_I used in this figure have been multiplied by $1/R$, thus giving the scattering per electron S_{class}, which should be present if there were no recoil of the scattering electrons.

that our knowledge of the thermal motion of atoms in crystals near the melting point is yet incomplete. However, the very satisfactory agreement of the scattering data with the other calculated curves gives additional assurance of the satisfactory state of our theory of x-ray scattering.

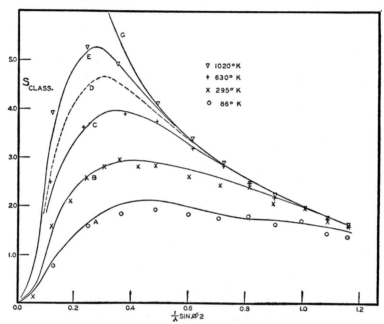

FIG. III–44.　Diffuse scattering by sylvine at different temperatures. (Harvey.)

10. *Scattering of Short Wave-lengths at Large Angles*

We have noticed in Figs. III–4, III–12, and elsewhere that for large values of sin $(\phi/2)/\lambda$ the scattering per electron becomes less than predicted by Thomson's theory. This fact has long been known for the scattering by gamma rays, whereas Fig. III–4 shows the intensity of the scattered rays is only a small fraction of the predicted value. For hard x-rays the effect is partially obscured by the change in wave-length, which makes the scattered rays more effective in ionizing the gas in the ionization chamber. Nevertheless the fact that for hard x-rays also the scattering is less than the simple theory would predict was observed and emphasized by Barkla and White[109] in 1917. They found that the total absorption of these

[109] C. G. Barkla and M. P. White, Phil. Mag. **34**, 275 (1917).

hard x-rays fell below the value which eq. (3.06) predicts for the absorption due to scattering alone.

Several attempts have been made on the basis of classical electrodynamics to account for this reduced scattering. It is evident from Fig. III–7 that though at certain angles the intensity of the rays scattered by a pair of electrons may be less than the sum of the rays scattered by two independent electrons, on the average the effect is to increase the intensity of the scattered rays. Moreover, the reduction in the strength of the scattered rays occurs for such large values of sin $(\phi/2)/\lambda$ that, as our study above has shown, no appreciable interference between neighboring electrons is to be anticipated. It is thus impossible to account for the small scattering of hard x-rays by interference between different electrons.

Constraining and Damping of Electrons' Motions.—A valiant attempt to reconcile the experiments with classical theory was made by Schott,[110] who investigated the effect of various types of constraining and damping forces. If one supposes that the constraining force is proportional to the displacement, and that the damping force is proportional to the velocity, the equation of motion of the forced oscillation of the electron due to the primary wave is:

$$m\frac{d^2x}{dt^2} + rm\frac{dx}{dt} + q^2mx = Ae\cos pt, \qquad (3.108)$$

where $A\cos pt \equiv E_x$ is the electric field due to the incident wave. The solution of this equation after the system has reached a steady state of oscillation, is

$$x = -A_1\cos(pt + \delta), \qquad (3.109)$$

where

$$A_1 = \frac{Ae}{mp^2}\Big/\left\{\left(1 - \frac{q^2}{p^2}\right)^2 + \frac{r^2}{p^2}\right\}^{1/2},$$

and

$$\delta = \tan^{-1}\left\{\frac{r}{p}\Big/\left(1 - \frac{q^2}{p^2}\right)\right\}.$$

The acceleration of the electron is thus

$$a = \frac{d^2x}{dt^2} = p^2A_1\cos(pt + \delta)$$

$$= \frac{Ae\cos(pt + \delta)}{m}\Big/\left\{\left(1 - \frac{q^2}{p^2}\right)^2 + \frac{r^2}{p^2}\right\}^{1/2}.$$

110 G. A. Schott, Proc. Roy. Soc. A 96, 395 (1920).

But if the electron were free its acceleration would have been

$$a_f = \frac{Ae}{m} \cos pt.$$

In view of the fact that the electric vector of the scattered wave is proportional to the acceleration of the scattering electron, and since the intensity of the ray is proportional to the square of the amplitude of the electric vector, we can say at once that the ratio of the intensity of the ray scattered by the electron under consideration to that scattered by a free electron is

$$\frac{I'_e}{I_e} = \frac{a_{max}^2}{a_{fmax}^2} = 1 \bigg/ \left\{ \left(1 - \frac{q^2}{p^2}\right)^2 + \frac{r^2}{p^2} \right\}. \qquad (3.110)$$

An examination of this equation shows that if the frequency of the x-ray is greater than the natural frequency of the electron ($p > q$) the intensity of the scattered ray will always be greater for a bound electron than for a free electron. The intensity of the scattered ray becomes smaller than that for a free electron only if $2p^2 < q^2$, that is for frequencies considerably smaller than the natural frequency of the electron. Thus the effect on the scattered x-rays of constraining forces on the scattering electrons should be greatest at comparatively low frequencies, and should become negligible at very high frequencies. Experiment, on the other hand, shows that at moderate frequencies the scattering by light elements is about that anticipated from free electrons, while the great departure is at the highest frequencies. Constraining forces on the electrons are thus inadequate to account for the reduced scattering at high frequencies.

An increase in the damping constant r would, as is evident from eq. (3.110), reduce the intensity of the scattered ray. But in order that this effect should not approach zero at high frequencies r must increase rapidly as p increases.

Let us suppose that this damping is due to the energy radiated by the scattering electron. We have noticed that the mean rate of energy loss from an oscillating electron due to its own radiation is (eq. (2.06))

$$\frac{\overline{dW}}{dt} = \frac{1}{3} \frac{e^2}{c^3} A_1^2 p^4,$$

where A_1 is the amplitude of the electron's displacement. But from eq. (3.108) the rate of energy loss at any instant due to damping is

$$\frac{dW_r}{dt} = rm \frac{dx}{dt} \frac{dx}{dt} = rm \left(\frac{dx}{dt}\right)^2,$$

which, according to (3.109) is

$$\frac{dW_r}{dt} = rm \cdot p^2 A_1^2 \sin^2 (pt + \delta).$$

When averaged over a complete cycle, this becomes

$$\overline{\frac{dW_r}{dt}} = \frac{1}{2} rmp^2 A_1^2. \tag{3.111}$$

If then we suppose that the damping is due to the radiation, we have at once that

$$\tfrac{1}{2} rmp^2 A_1^2 = \frac{1}{3} \frac{e^2}{c^3} A_1^2 p^4,$$

or

$$r = \frac{2}{3} \frac{e^2 p^2}{mc^3}. \ast \tag{3.112}$$

Thus

$$\frac{r^2}{p^2} = \frac{4}{9} \frac{e^4 p^2}{m^2 c^6}. \tag{3.113}$$

For the highest frequencies at which scattering experiments have been made, i.e., for γ-rays of wave-length 0.02 A, the value of this ratio is 0.000035. It follows from eq. (3.110) that the effect of this damping on the intensity of the scattered x-rays is wholly negligible.

We have seen that for hard x-rays traversing light elements the absorption coefficient falls below the value calculated from the classical theory for the absorption due to scattering alone. When we examine the absorption of x-rays on the classical theory we shall see that the absorption coefficient is proportional to the damping constant r, and thus the observation that the absorption coefficient is less than the theoretical scattering coefficient would mean that the damping constant must be even less than the value given by (3.112), so that the effect of the damping in eq. (3.110) will be wholly negligible. Thus we are forced to the conclusion at which Schott

---

* $\frac{1}{2}r$ as here defined is the same as the b of eq. (4.12), Chap. IV.

arrived, that neither by forces of constraint nor by damping forces can we account for the fact that at very high frequencies the scattering by an electron is less than that calculated for a free electron.

The Large Electron

It would seem that the only escape from our difficulty, consistent with classical electrodynamics, is to suppose either that the force on an electron at rest is for high frequencies less than the value Ee, as assigned by Lorentz's force equation, or that the electric field due to an accelerated electron is less than is calculated from the usual electron theory. The possibilities in this direction resulting from assuming a new force equation have been investigated by Maizlish.[111] At best, such an assumption can supply a solution of only half of our problem. We have seen that as the frequency of the x-rays increases, the rays scattered at large angles decrease in intensity more rapidly than those at small angles, with the result that an asymmetry appears, similar to that due to interference when soft x-rays are used. This asymmetry is shown clearly in Fig. III–4, which represents the scattering of hard γ-rays by iron. It is clear that a mere modification of the force equation will only modify the absolute intensity of the scattered beam, but can have no effect on its angular distribution.

A suggestion that at one time seemed to be very promising was that the electron, instead of being sensibly a point charge, has instead dimensions comparable with the wave-length of hard gamma rays.[112] The effect of this hypothesis is to make possible interference between the rays scattered from different parts of the electron. For wavelengths considerably greater than the diameter of the electron, this interference would be negligible, and the electrons would act as described by the usual electron theory. If the wave-length is shorter, since the phase differences from different parts of the electron are larger for rays scattered backward than for those scattered at small angles, the intensity in the reverse direction should fall off the more rapidly. Qualitatively, therefore, this hypothesis is adequate to account for both the reduced intensity and the asymmetry of the scattered x-rays of very short wave-length. The radius of the electron required to reduce the scattered x-rays by the observed amount as a result of such interference is of the order of $h/mc = 0.024$ A, a

[111] I. Maizlish, Jour. Franklin Inst. **197**, 667 (1924).

[112] A. H. Compton, Jour. Washington Acad. Sci., **8**, 1 (1918); Phys. Rev. **14**, 20 (1919).

unit of length which is of significance in the quantum theory of scattering (eq. (3.117)). The calculated intensity of the rays scattered at different angles from a spherical electron of such a radius is found to be in surprisingly good accord with the experimental values.

This theory fails, however, as any theory based upon the classical electrodynamics must fail, to account for the change in the wavelength of the scattered x-rays. In view of the fact that the quantum theory which leads to a correct expression for the change of wavelength suggests also an adequate explanation of the reduced intensity of scattered x-rays of very high frequency, such arbitrary assumptions regarding the nature of the electron are unnecessary.

11. Summary

The classical electromagnetic theory of scattering in its simplest form is quantitatively applicable to the scattering of comparatively soft x-rays by elements of low atomic weight. But when heavier elements are employed as radiators, the interference between the rays scattered by the different electrons becomes appreciable, giving rise to what is known as " excess scattering." We find that it is possible to choose electron distributions within the atom which will give closely the observed intensity of scattering of ordinary x-rays, thus affording a means of studying these electronic arrangements. For very short waves, however, we find that the intensity of the scattered x-rays is less than can be accounted for on the theory of electromagnetic waves, the difference being greater when the scattered ray makes a large angle with the primary ray. This fact, coupled with the observation that the wave-length of the scattered rays is always greater than that of the primary beam, indicates that the classical explanation of x-ray scattering is not wholly adequate.

C. CORPUSCULAR ASPECTS OF SCATTERED X-RAYS

12. Scattered X-rays as Directed Quanta

We have seen that many of the properties of scattered x-rays may be accounted for on the basis of the classical theory of electromagnetic waves, as developed by Thomson, Debye, and others. The accuracy of Barkla's determination of the number of electrons in an atom, and the success in extending the theory to cover the diffraction of x-rays by crystals, led physicists to class scattering with interference and refraction as being completely explicable according to our classical theories of electrons and electromagnetic waves. Then appeared a new set of scattering phenomena—the change of wave-length of scattered x-rays, recoil electrons associated with scattered rays, etc., which could be interpreted only on the assumption that x-rays are corpuscular in nature. It is only within the last few years that it has become possible to describe all the scattering phenomena in terms of a single theory.

The evidence leading to this dramatic development of our ideas regarding the dual nature of x-rays, and hence of all radiation, will now be presented. Later in this chapter we shall consider how a unified theory of radiation can be developed.

13. *The Change in Wave-length of Scattered X-rays.*

Early Experiments.—The earliest experiments on secondary x-rays and γ-rays showed a difference in the penetrating power of the primary and the secondary rays.[113] In the case of x-rays, Barkla and his collaborators showed that the secondary rays from the heavy elements consisted largely of fluorescent radiations characteristic of the radiating element, and that it was the presence of these softer rays which was chiefly responsible for the greater absorption of the secondary rays.[114] When later experiments showed a measurable difference in penetration even for light elements such as carbon, from which no fluorescent K or L radiation appears, it was only natural to ascribe this difference to a new type of fluorescent radiation, similar to the K and L types, but of shorter wave-length.[115] Careful absorption measurements failed however to reveal any critical absorption limit

[113] For γ-rays, see A. S. Eve, Phil. Mag. 8, 669 (1904); R. D. Kleeman, Phil. Mag. 15, 638 (1908); J. P. V. Madsen, Phil. Mag. 17, 423 (1909); D. C. H. Florance, Phil. Mag. 20, 921 (1910); J. A. Gray, Phil. Mag. 26, 611 (1913); D. C. H. Florance, Phil. Mag. 2, 225 (1914); K. W. F. Kohlrausch, Phys. Zeit. 21, 193 (1920); A. H. Compton, Phil. Mag. 41, 749 (1921); *et al.*

In the case of x-rays scattered by light elements, the early experiments of Barkla and his collaborators indicated a slight softening of the secondary rays (C. G. Barkla, Phil. Mag. 7, 550, 1904; R. T. Beatty, Phil. Mag. 14, 604, 1907), but the difference seems to have been considered within the experimental error. (Barkla and Miss Ayers, Phil. Mag. 21, 271, 1911.) Experiments showing the softening of secondary x-rays have been performed by C. A. Sadler and P. Mesham, Phil. Mag. 24, 138 (1912); J. Laub, Ann. der Phys. 46, 785 (1915); J. A. Gray, Franklin Inst. J. 190, 633 (1920); A. H. Compton, Phys. Rev. 18, 96 (1921); Nature 108, 366 (1921); J. A. Crowther, Phil. Mag. 42, 719 (1921).

[114] C. G. Barkla and C. A. Sadler, Phil. Mag. 16, 550 (1908).

[115] J. Laub, Ann. der Phys. 46, 785 (1915); J. A. Crowther, Phil. Mag. 42, 719 (1921).

for these assumed "J" radiations similar to those corresponding to the K and L radiations. Moreover, direct spectroscopic observations failed to reveal the existence of any spectrum lines under conditions for which the supposed J rays should appear.[116] It thus became evident that the softening of the secondary x-rays from the lighter elements was due to a different kind of process than the softening of the secondary rays from heavy elements where fluorescent x-rays are present. Some carefully designed absorption measurements by Gray[117] showed that this softening was indeed a direct result of the scattering process.

It was at this stage that the first spectroscopic investigations of the secondary x-rays from light elements were made.[118] According to the usual electron theory of scattering it is obvious that the scattered rays will be of the same frequency as the forced oscillations of the electrons which emit them, and hence will be identical in frequency with the primary waves which set the electrons in motion. Instead

[116] For discussion of J series radiation, *cf.* e.g. *X-rays and Electrons*, p. 188. *Barkla's J-transformation* is an interpretation of the softening of secondary x-rays which is essentially different from that of fluorescence. It is supposed rather that the rays are scattered without change of wave-length, but are in some way modified as they traverse matter after being scattered. Following are references to the more important papers in which this suggestion is developed: C. G. Barkla and R. Sale, Phil. Mag. 45, 748 (1923); R. T. Dunbar, Phil. Mag. 49, 210 (1925); C. G. Barkla and S. R. Khastgir, Phil. Mag. 49, 251; 50, 1115 (1925); 4, 735 (1927); C. G. Barkla, Nature 112, 723 (1923); Phil. Mag. 5, 1164 (1928); C. G. Barkla and G. I. Mackenzie, Phil. Mag. 1, 542 (1926); C. G. Barkla and W. H. Watson, Phil. Mag. 2, 1122 (1926); S. R. Khastgir, Phil. Mag. 14, 99 (1932); C. G. Barkla and J. S. Kay, Phil. Mag. 16, 457 (1933).

Among the critical discussions of the J-transformations have been the following: A. H. Compton, Nature 113, 160 (1924); R. T. Dunbar, Phil. Mag. 5, 962 (1928); B. L. Worsnop, Phys. Soc. Proc. 39, 305 (1927); O. Gaertner, Phys. Zeits. 28, 493 (1927); N. S. Alexander, Phys. Soc. Proc. 42, 82 (1930); I. Backhurst, Phil. Mag. 13, 28 (1932).

Even in the hands of Barkla and his collaborators the J-transformations appear erratic and are not reproducible. Outside of his laboratory the phenomena do not appear to have been observed. Thus Alexander (*loc. cit.*) concludes, "The results obtained in no case provide any evidence for this phenomenon, and, considered in conjunction with the work of Dunbar, Worsnop and Gaertner, the experimental results suggest that the J-phenomenon has no real existence as an x-ray absorption effect." Likewise Backhurst states, "There seems to be no reason why the existence of such phenomena should be postulated."

[117] J. A. Gray, Franklin Inst. Jour., Nov. 1920, p. 643.
[118] A. H. Compton, Bulletin Nat. Res. Council. No. 20, p. 16 (1922); Phys. Rev. 21, 715 and 22, 409 (1923).

of showing scattered rays of the same wave-length as the primary rays, however, these spectra revealed lines in the secondary rays corresponding to those in the primary beam but with each line displaced slightly toward the longer wave-lengths.

A diagram of the apparatus employed, such as Fig. III–45, may help in understanding the significance of the result. X-rays proceed from the molybdenum target T of the x-ray tube to the carbon radiator R, and are thence scattered at an angle ϕ with the primary beam through the slits 1 and 2 to the crystal of a Bragg spectrometer. Thus is measured the wave-length of the x-rays that have been scattered at an angle ϕ. This angle may be altered by shifting the

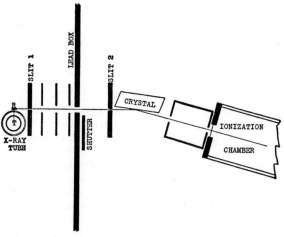

FIG. III–45. Compton's apparatus for studying the spectrum of x-rays scattered from a graphite block at R.

radiator and the x-ray tube, and the spectrum of the primary beam may be obtained by merely shifting the x-ray tube without altering the slits or the crystal.

Spectra of the molybdenum $K\alpha$ line after being scattered by carbon at different angles are shown in Fig. III–46. The upper curve is the spectrum of the primary ray, and the curves below are the spectra, using the same slits, of the rays scattered at 45 degrees, 90 degrees and 135 degrees respectively. It will be seen that though in each case there is one line of exactly the same wave-length as the primary, there also occurs a second line of greater wave-length. These spectra show not only that the wave-length of the secondary ray differs from that of the primary, but also the fact that the difference increases rapidly at large angles of scattering.

In Fig. III–48 is shown a similar spectrum of x-rays scattered at 120° by lithium, in which no appreciable line appears of the same wave-length as the primary beam.[119] We have seen (p. 121) that the energy of the whole secondary x-radiation from light elements is very nearly equal to that calculated from Thomson's classical theory for the scattered rays. If there is any scattering from lithium it must therefore be the radiation which appears in the spectrum as the shifted line M. Similarly we must ascribe both lines in the spectrum of the secondary rays from carbon to scattered x-rays.[120]

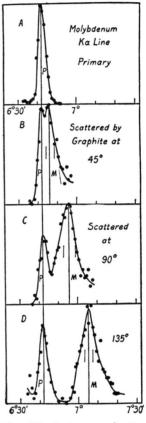

The fact that the scattered rays are of greater wave-length when scattered at large angles with the primary beam suggests at once a Doppler effect as from particles moving in the direction of the primary radiation. This would be similar to the change in wave-length of the Fraunhofer lines in the sunlight reflected to us by

[119] Y. H. Woo, Phys. Rev. 27, 119 (1926).

[120] It is now possible to identify this scattered radiation of changed wave-length with the incoherent radiation discussed above (p. 138). The views have at times been defended that the shifted or modified line is due to a form of fluorescence radiation (A. H. Compton, Phil. Mag. 41, 749 (1921); Phys. Rev. 18, 96 (1921) or tertiary x-radiation produced by the impact of photoelectrons (G. L. Clark and W. Duane, Proc. Nat. Acad. Sci. 9, 422 (1923) and later papers). These hypotheses suggest no reason why the energy in the modified rays from lithium should be that calculated on Thomson's theory of the scattered rays. They also fail to account for the fact that the secondary x-rays at 90° are completely polarized—a property characteristic of scattered rays.

Fig. III–46. Spectra of x-rays scattered by graphite at different angles, showing modified line wider than primary, and displaced to theoretical position M. (Compton.)

In applying the name "scattered rays" to those here studied, we mean the rays which correspond most closely to those described by Thomson's original theory of scattering.

Venus, because of the Doppler effect from the motion of the planet. According to the classical idea of the scattering process, however, every electron in the matter traversed by the primary x-rays is effective in scattering the rays. In order to account for such a Doppler effect on this view, therefore, all of the electrons in the radiating matter would have to be moving in the direction of the primary beam with a velocity comparable with that of light—an assumption obviously contrary to fact. It is clear that if any elec-

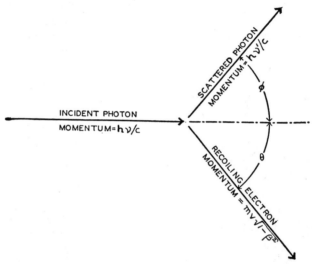

FIG. III–47. When an x-ray photon is scattered by an electron at an angle ϕ, the electron recoils at an angle θ, using some of the photon's energy and hence reducing its frequency.

trons move in this manner it can be only a very small fraction of the whole number in the scattering material, and that it must be this small fraction which is responsible for the scattering. The idea thus presents itself that an electron, if it scatters at all, scatters a complete quantum of the incident radiation; for thus the number of electrons which move forward would just be equal to the number of scattered quanta.

Theory of Photons Scattered by Free Electrons

This suggestion that each quantum of x-rays is scattered by a single electron supplies a simple means of accounting for the observed change of wave-length.[121] For if we consider the primary rays to proceed in quanta so definitely directed that they can be scattered by individual electrons, along with their energy $h\nu$ they will carry[122] momentum $h\nu/c$. Such a definitely directed quantum of radiant energy is called a *photon*. The scattered photon, proceeding in a different direction from the primary, carries with it a different mo-

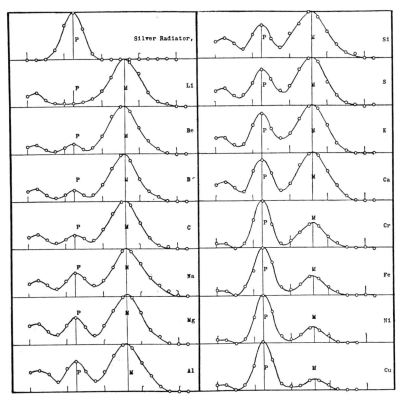

FIG. III-48. Spectra of silver $K\alpha$ line scattered by different elements, showing the increase in prominence of the unmodified line with increasing atomic number. (Woo.)

mentum. Thus by the principle of the conservation of momentum, the electron which scatters the ray must recoil with a momentum equal to the vector difference between that of the primary and that

[121] A. H. Compton, Bulletin Nat. Res. Council No. 20, p. 19 (1922); Phys. Rev. 21, 207 and 483 (1923). P. Debye, Phys. Zeits. 24, 161 (1923).
[122] Cf. equation 25 of Appendix I.

of the scattered photon (Fig. III–47). But the energy of this recoiling electron is taken from that of the primary photon, leaving a scattered photon which has less energy and hence a lower frequency than has the primary photon.

From the principle of the conservation of energy we have

$$hv = hv' + mc^2 \left(\frac{1}{\sqrt{1 - \beta^2}} - 1 \right), \qquad (3.114)$$

where v is the frequency of the incident ray, v' that of the ray scattered by the electron, and $mc^2 \left(\dfrac{1}{\sqrt{1 - \beta^2}} - 1 \right)$ is the kinetic energy of the recoiling electron.[123] The principle of conservation of momentum supplies the additional equations,

$$\text{(X-component)} \quad \frac{hv}{c} = \frac{hv'}{c} \cos \phi + \frac{m\beta c}{\sqrt{1 - \beta^2}} \cos \theta \qquad (3.115)$$

$$\text{(Y-component)} \quad 0 = \frac{hv'}{c} \sin \phi + \frac{m\beta c}{\sqrt{1 - \beta^2}} \sin \theta. \qquad (3.116)$$

For a definite angle of scattering ϕ there are in these equations three unknown quantities, v', β and θ, the angle of recoil of the electron. By a straightforward solution of the three equations we can calculate these quantities. It is more convenient, however, to express the result in terms of the scattered wave-length $\lambda' = c/v'$, and the kinetic energy of the recoiling electron. We obtain,[124]

$$\lambda' = \lambda + \frac{h}{mc} (1 - \cos \phi),$$

or

$$\left. \begin{array}{l} \delta\lambda = \lambda' - \lambda = \dfrac{h}{mc} (1 - \cos \phi) \\[2mm] = \gamma \text{ vers } \phi, \end{array} \right\} \qquad (3.117)$$

---

[123] Cf. equation 21 of Appendix I.
[124] For the detailed solution, cf. e.g., *X-rays and Electrons*, p. 393.

where $\gamma = h/mc = 0.0243$ A, and vers $\phi = 1 - \cos \phi$. Also

$$E_{kin} = h\nu \cdot \frac{\alpha \text{ vers } \phi}{1 + \alpha \text{ vers } \phi}$$

$$= h\nu \cdot \frac{2\alpha \cos^2 \theta}{(1 + \alpha)^2 - \alpha^2 \cos^2 \theta}, \qquad (3.118)$$

and

$$\cot \theta = - (1 + \alpha) \tan \tfrac{1}{2}\phi,$$

or

$$\cot \tfrac{1}{2}\phi = - (1 + \alpha) \tan \theta, \qquad (3.119)$$

where

$$\alpha \equiv h\nu/mc^2 = \gamma/\lambda.$$

Equations (3.117) predict that the scattered ray should be of greater wave-length than its parent primary ray, and that this increase in wave-length should be greater at large scattering angles. The wave-length change should however be the same for short wave-length as for long wave-length primary rays, and should be the same for all substances. According to eqs. (3.118) there should exist a type of β-ray with energy less than $h\nu$ by a factor of approximately $2\alpha \cos^2 \theta$. For all except very hard x-rays, these β-rays must thus possess much less energy than the photoelectrons described in Chap. VII. They should also always proceed at angles less than 90 degrees, and those at the smaller angles should have the greater energy. It follows from eqs. (3.119) that for each electron ejected at an angle θ there should be a photon of x-rays scattered in a definite direction ϕ. This is in sharp contrast with the classical electromagnetic theory, according to which the energy should be radiated in all directions. All of these predictions are subject to experimental test.

Measurements of the Change of Wave length

In Fig. III-46 the line M is calculated in each case from the theoretical formula for the change in wave-length. That it is not accidental that for carbon the agreement with the theory is so satisfactory is evident from the spectra shown in Fig. III-48, which shows similar spectra from many different scattering elements, obtained by Dr. Woo.

In Figs. III-49 and 50 are shown two beautiful series of photographic spectra obtained by Du Mond and Kirkpatrick.[125] They

[125] J. W. M. Du Mond and H. A. Kirkpatrick, Phys. Rev. **37**, 136; **38**, 1094 (1931).

show respectively spectra of the molybdenum K series scattered at three different angles and spectra of three different primary wavelengths scattered at about the same angle. In both series the scattering substance is graphite. The same kind of change in wave-length with scattering angle is evident in Fig. III–49 as that shown by the ionization spectra of Fig. III–46. Fig. III–50 exhibits in striking

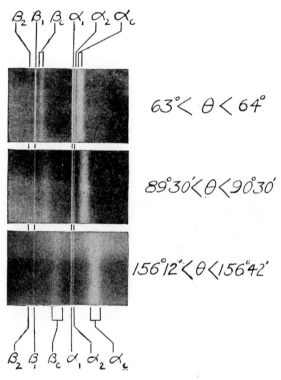

FIG. III–49. Multicrystal spectrograph spectra of molybdenum K lines scattered by carbon at three different angles. (Du Mond and Kirkpatrick.)

fashion the independence of $\delta\lambda$ from the primary wave-length, as predicted by eq. (3.117).[126]

[126] Among those who have published experiments showing the type of spectrum described above are: A. H. Compton, Bulletin National Research Council, No. 20, p. 15 (1922); Phys. Rev. **21**, 207, 483 and 715 (1923); **22**, 409 (1923); Phil. Mag. **46**, 897 (1923). A. H. Compton and Y. H. Woo, Proc. Nat. Acad. **10**, 271 (1924). A. H. Compton and J. A. Bearden, Proc. Nat. Acad. **11**, 117 (1925). P. A. Ross, Proc. Nat. Acad. **9**, 246 (1923); **10**, 304 (1924); Phys. Rev. **22**, 524 (1923). P. A. Ross and D. L.

In order to make an exact test of the wave-length equation, it is not only necessary to measure precisely the change in wave-length,

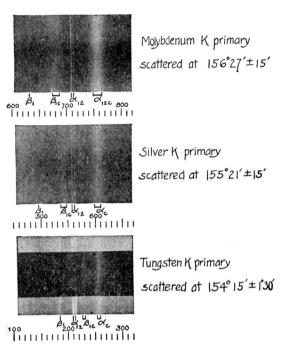

Molybdenum K primary
scattered at $156°27'±15'$

Silver K primary
scattered at $155°21'±15'$

Tungsten K primary
scattered at $154°15'±1°30'$

FIG. III–50. Spectra of x-rays of three different wave-lengths scattered by carbon at about 155 degrees. The scale indicates the wave-length in X.U. (1 X.U. = 10^{-11} cm. (Du Mond and Kirkpatrick.)

Webster, Proc. Nat. Acad. **11**, 56 (1925). B. Davis, Paper before the A. A. A. S. Dec. 28, 1923. J. A. Becker, Proc. Nat. Acad. **10**, 342 (1924). A. Müller, cf. W. H. and W. L. Bragg, X-Rays and Crystal Structure (1924) p. 297. M. de Broglie, Comptes Rendus, **178**, 908 (1924). A. Dauvillier, Comptes Rendus, **178**, 2076 (1924). M. de Broglie and A. Dauvillier, ibid. **179**, 11 (1924); J. de Physique, 6, 369 (1925). S. K. Allison and W. Duane, Proc. Nat. Acad. **11**, 25 (1925); Phys. Rev. **26**, 300 (1925). H. Kallman and H. Mark, Naturwiss. **13**, 297 (1925). Y. H. Woo, Proc. Nat. Acad. **11**, 123 (1925). H. M. Sharp, Phys. Rev. **26**, 691 (1925). J. W. M. Du Mond, Phys. Rev. **33**, 643 (1929); N. S. Gingrich, Phys. Rev. **36**, 1050 (1930); F. L. Nutting, Phys. Rev. **36**, 1267 (1930); J. A. Bearden, Phys. Rev. **35**, 1427 (1930).

During the period 1923–1924, a series of experiments performed at Harvard, chiefly by G. L. Clark, W. Duane, and W. W. Stifler, failed to show the change in wavelength here described, but seemed to show a different effect called "tertiary radiation." This effect was finally traced to spurious radiation, and the phenomenon above described was completely confirmed (cf. S. K. Allison and W. Duane, loc. cit.).

but also to scatter the x-rays at a definite and known angle ϕ. Perhaps the best experiment of this character is that of Gingrich,[127] in which the rays were scattered almost directly backward, at an effective angle of 161° 25'. Thus not only was $\delta\lambda$ a maximum, but the value of vers ϕ was near a maximum and could change only slowly with variations in ϕ. This gave resolving power which was much higher than is usual in spectra of scattered x-rays. Fig. III–51 shows a spectrum thus obtained. Not only the unmodified line but also the modified line is resolved into the α_1 and the α_2 components.

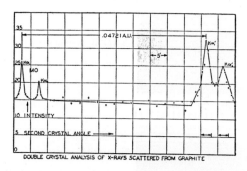

FIG. III–51. Double crystal spectrometer spectrum of scattered x-rays. (Gingrich.)

Measurements made to the peaks of the lines gave the result (in terms of $d_{\text{calcite}} = 3.029$ A),

$$\delta\lambda_{161°} = 0.04721 \pm 0.00003 \text{ A.}$$

It follows that

$$h/mc_{\text{expt}} = 0.02424 \pm 0.00004 \text{ A,} \qquad (3.120)$$

the additional probable error being due to the uncertainty in the angle of scattering.

From Birge's most probable values[128] of e, h and e/m it follows that $h/mc = 0.02415$ A. In view of the uncertainty of the atomic constants, this agreement must be considered very satisfactory.

[127] N. L. Gingrich, Phys. Rev. **36**, 1050 (1930). Notable precision measurements of this change in wave-length have also been made by Kallman and Mark, Sharp, Nutting, Du Mond and Kirkpatrick, and Bearden, all *loc. cit.*

In a very recent paper, P. A. Ross and P. Kirkpatrick (Phys. Rev. **45**, 223 (1934)) give without details an experimental value of h/mc by this method, 0.0238 ± 0.00003 A, which is inconsistent with Gingrich's value. The measurements of the other investigators just quoted seem to support Gingrich's higher value. The results of the further experiments promised by Ross and Kirkpatrick will be awaited with interest.

[128] R. T. Birge, Phys. Rev. **40**, 319 (1932).

The Unmodified Line

The simple theory outlined above accounts only for the existence of the line whose wave-length is modified. This is because we have considered only the interaction between quanta and electrons that are free. If an electron is so firmly bound within the atom that the impulse imparted by the quantum is insufficient to eject it, the atom in its final condition has the same energy as in the beginning, so that no energy is removed from the quantum. For the light atoms, in which all the electrons are loosely bound, the modified line should thus be relatively intense, whereas for the heavy atoms, in which most of the electrons are firmly held, the unmodified ray should have the greater energy. This is precisely what is shown by the figures reproduced above.

From this explanation of the unmodified line it would also follow that for ordinary light, for which the impulse imparted by a photon is far too small to eject even the most loosely bound electron, all the energy should lie in the unmodified line.[129]   On the other hand for γ-rays the impulse would be so great that almost every electron would be ejected, so that nearly all the scattered rays should be modified. This agrees exactly with Ross's observation that the light rays scattered by paraffin are unmodified,[130] and Compton's observation that there is no detectable scattered γ-radiation having the original wave-length.[131]

14. *Recoil Electrons Ejected by X-rays* [132]

The photon theory of the process of scattering with change in wave-length predicts that a corpuscular radiation should accompany

[129] Though the *momentum* of the light photon is insufficient to eject the electron, its energy is adequate to transfer the electron to a higher energy level. If a part of the energy of the photon is thus spent, the rest should appear as a scattered photon whose frequency is given by

$$h\nu - h\nu' = W_f - W_i,$$

or $$\delta\nu = (W_f - W_i)/h,$$

where W_f and W_i are the final and initial states of the atom. Light scattered with such a change in frequency was first observed by C. V. Raman (Indian J. of Physics 2, 387, (1928)), and has been the subject of many investigations since that time.

[130] P. A. Ross, Science, 57, 614 (1923).

[131] A. H. Compton, Phil. Mag. 41, 760 (1921).

[132] An exhaustive treatment of the experimental work on this subject may be found in Kirchner, Allgemeine Physik der Röntgenstrahlen, Akademische Verlagsgesellschaft M.B.H., Leipzig (1930), (Vol. 24, Handbuch der Physik). The present treatment was suggested in part by that of Kirchner.

the phenomenon. This will be made up of electrons which have rebounded from the impact of the photons and hence are called " recoil " electrons. At the time the theory was proposed, such a corpuscular radiation was not recognized, although indirect evidence suggested[133] that the secondary beta rays ejected from matter by hard gamma rays are mostly of this type. Within a few months of their prediction, however, two investigators, C. T. R. Wilson[134] at Cambridge, and W. Bothe[135] at Charlottenburg independently announced their discovery.

In the Wilson cloud chamber these electrons produce tracks which at ordinary x-ray tube voltages (around 100,000 volts) are short compared to the photo-electron tracks, which are produced by electrons to which the entire energy of a photon has been transmitted. It is seen also that the recoil electron tracks always disclose a component of the velocity in the forward direction of the x-ray beam. This is not true of all photo-electron tracks. (Cf. Sec. 11, Chap. VII.) The recoil tracks often have a typical appearance resembling that of a comma, with the tail of the comma originating in or near the x-ray beam and the thicker head pointing in the forward direction. C. T. R. Wilson named them " fish tracks " and they are often thus referred to. Further examination of the tracks discloses that those which start directly forward are usually longer than those beginning at an angle with the x-ray beam. Some of these properties are exhibited in the photographs of Fig. III–52, which represent the passage of x-rays of about 0.13 A through argon gas.

The qualitative properties of the fish tracks referred to in the preceding paragraph are in agreement with the predicted behaviour of recoil electrons according to the photon theory of scattering. One of the most convincing reasons for associating these short tracks with x-ray scattering comes from a study of their abundance relative to the number of photo-electron tracks observed. Assuming that the fish tracks are associated with scattering, and that a number N_r of them have been counted, we should have on the same films N_p photo-electron tracks, where

$$N_r/N_p = \sigma/\tau.$$

Here σ is the absorption coefficient due to scattering and τ that due

[133] A. H. Compton, Bull. Nat. Res. Counc. U.S.A. 20, 27 (1922).
[134] C. T. R. Wilson, Proc. Roy. Soc. Lond. A 104, 1 (1923).
[135] W. Bothe, Zeitschr. f. Physik 16, 319 (1923).

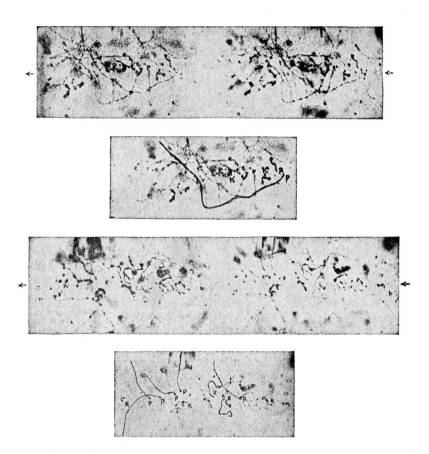

Fig. III–52. Photo-electron and recoil electron tracks produced by passage of c.13 A x-rays through argon. The first and third films from the top are stereoscopic pictures; twofold enlargements of the original. The second and fourth serve to point out significant tracks in the first and third. In order to call attention to certain interesting tracks in the unretouched stereoscopic pictures, these tracks have been drawn in on the orienting films.

$R \sim$ recoil electron

$P \sim$ photo-electron

$K \sim$ recoil electron associated with an Auger electron from internal conversion of the $K\alpha$ radiation.

The letters are placed at the beginnings of the tracks. The direction of the x-ray beam is from right to left. (After Kirchner.)

to true absorption. Due to the fact that τ increases as λ^3, while the variation of σ with λ is much less rapid, the number of R (recoil) tracks relative to that of P (photo-electron) tracks should increase

TABLE III-3

RELATIVE NUMBERS OF R AND P TRACKS ACCORDING TO COMPTON AND SIMON

Effective Wave-length	Total Tracks	N_r	N_p	N_r/N_p	σ/τ
0.71 A	58	5	49	0.10	0.27
0.44	24	10	11	0.9	1.2
0.29	46	33	12	2.7	3.8
0.20	84	74	8	9	10
0.17	73	68	4	17	17
0.13	79	72	1	72	32

rapidly as the wave-length diminishes. Table III–3 represents the results of counts of R and P tracks by Compton and Simon[136] and in Table III–4 is shown the result of similar counts by Nuttall and Williams.[137] The values of σ/τ are estimated from the experiments

TABLE III-4

RELATIVE NUMBERS OF R AND P TRACKS ACCORDING TO NUTALL AND WILLIAMS

Scattering Gas	λ in Angstroms	N_r	N_p	N_r/N_p	σ/τ
Oxygen.......... {	0.709	26	205	0.127	0.174
	0.614	129	608	0.212	0.268
	0.545	109	358	0.305	0.383
Nitrogen......... {	0.614	223	722	0.309	0.400
	0.545	109	202	0.540	0.572
Argon........... {	0.614	7	209	0.033	0.030
	0.545	4	139	0.029	0.043
Air............. {	0.57	153	454	0.337	0.372
	0.35	139	83	1.67	1.57
200 H_2 + 2.3 O_2.....	0.614	28	11	2.5	2.9
200 H_2 + 1.5 O_2.....	0.614	73	21	3.5	4.4

[136] A. H. Compton and A. W. Simon, Phys. Rev. **25**, 309 (1925).
[137] J. M. Nuttall and E. J. Williams, Phil. Mag. **1**, 1217 (1926).
[138] C. W. Hewlett, Phys. Rev. **17**, 284 (1921).

of Hewlett,[138] and it is seen that within the rather large experimental error due to the finite number of counts there is good agreement. Ikeuti[139] has counted 1500 such tracks using the $K\alpha$ radiation of tungsten of wave-length 0.21 A in air, and found $N_r/N_p = 11$, which agrees with the absorption coefficient ratio $\sigma/\tau = 11$ found by Hewlett.

The photon theory of scattering also predicts *the energies of the recoil electrons*. From eq. (3.118) we have

$$E_{\text{kin}} = h\nu \frac{2\alpha \cos^2 \theta}{(1 + \alpha)^2 - \alpha^2 \cos^2 \theta}$$

where

$$\alpha \equiv h\nu/mc^2,$$

ν is the frequency of the incident x-ray beam, and θ is the angle made by the recoiling electron with the forward direction of propagation of the beam. The maximum kinetic energy is obtained when the recoiling electron starts off in the forward direction of the beam, i.e., $\theta = 0$, and thus

$$(E_{\text{kin}})_{\text{max.}} = mc^2 \frac{2\alpha^2}{1 + 2\alpha}. \tag{3.121}$$

This shows that for the lower frequencies, the maximum kinetic energy increases as the square of the frequency, but at higher frequencies the increase is less rapid.

Measurements of the energies of recoil electrons have been carried out by three methods. One of these is the calculation of the energy from the observed range in the Wilson cloud chamber. Such estimates were made by C. T. R. Wilson in his discovery of the fish tracks, but as Compton and Hubbard[140] have pointed out, the results are necessarily very rough due in part to the inhomogeneity of the x-rays used. In Table III–5 are given results on the maximum range of recoil electrons as observed by Compton and Simon.[136] They used filtered general radiation from an x-ray tube operated from 21 to 111 kv.

Analogous observations have been made by Ikeuti[139] using radiation of the wave-length of tungsten $K\alpha$, 0.21 A, selected from the general radiation by reflection from a rock-salt crystal. He found that the maximum range of the fish tracks in air was between 0.33

[139] H. Ikeuti, Compt. rend. 180, 1257 (1925).
[140] A. H. Compton and J. C. Hubbard, Phys. Rev. 23, 439 (1924).

TABLE III-5

MAXIMUM ENERGIES OF RECOIL ELECTRONS ACCORDING TO COMPTON AND SIMON

Tube Voltage in Kv.	Effective Wave-length	Observed Maximum Range	Observed $(E_{kin})_{max}$ in Kv.	Calculated $(E_{kin})_{max}$ in Kv.
21	0.71 A	0 mm.	0	0.93
34	0.44	0	0	2.8
52	0.29	2.5	10.5	6.1
74	0.20	6	16	12
88	0.17	9	20	16
111	0.13	24	32	26

and 0.37 cm., whereas that computed from eq. (3.121) and Wilson's connection between kinetic energy and range is about 0.33 cm., according to Kirchner.[141]

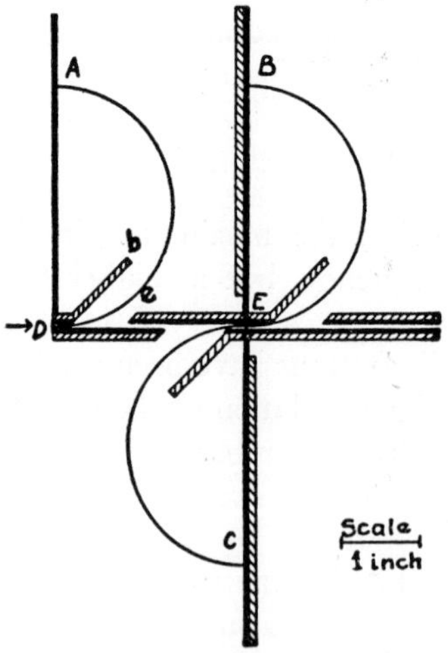

FIG. III-53. Arrangement of aluminium foil scatterers (at D and E) and photographic plates (at A, B, and C) in the investigation of recoil electrons from aluminium by magnetic deviation, according to Bless.

Early measurements of the range of the recoil electrons were made by Bothe,[142] using an ionization method. If the ionization is measured as a function of pressure in a chamber of small dimensions, a break in the ionization versus pressure curve will occur when the range of the recoil electrons is sufficiently large, so that they reach the walls of the chamber before all their energy is expended in the production of gaseous ions. Bothe made estimates of the energies of the recoil electrons from such measurements and found fair agreement with the theory.

Bless[143] has made a much more precise measurement of the maximum energy of the recoil electrons from aluminium by deviating them in a magnetic field. Figure III-53 shows

[141] F. Kirchner, Handbuch der Physik, Vol. 24, p. 299.
[142] W. Bothe, Zeitschr. f. Physik 20, 237 (1923).
[143] A. A. Bless, Phys. Rev. 30, 871 (1927).

the arrangement of the photographic plates. The lines of force of the magnetic field are perpendicular to the plane of the figure. At D and E aluminium foils were placed. Results obtained with Mo $K\alpha$, $\lambda = 0.71$ A, as the primary radiation are shown in Fig. III–54. In these films the kinetic energy of the electrons increases from left to right. The two upper films were obtained at positions A and B of Fig. III–53, and film B, especially, exhibits a well defined maximum of kinetic energy. It is significant that the film placed at C shows

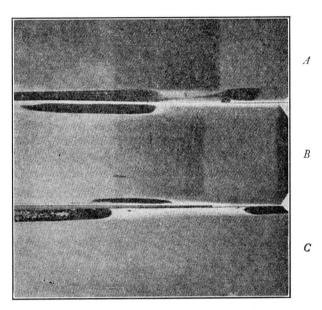

A

B

C

Fig. III–54. Magnetic spectra of recoil electrons from aluminium, ejected by x-rays of wave-length 0.71 A. The letters refer to the positions of the films as indicated in Fig. III–53.

no trace of a magnetic spectrum. Electrons reaching this film would have to have a component of their velocity in the backwards direction of the x-ray beam, and their absence lends support to the contention that the observed effects are due to recoil electrons. All of the exposures of Bless were made at a wave-length of 0.71 A except one, which was obtained at 0.48 A. The results of Bless are given in Table III–6. The agreement here is satisfactory.

According to the theory of scattering with change of wave-length, *the energy of the recoil electrons should vary with the angle of recoil* from

TABLE III-6

COMPARISON OF THE EXPERIMENTAL VALUES OF THE ENERGY IN KILOVOLTS OF THE
SCATTERED ELECTRONS WITH THE VALUES CALCULATED FROM EQ. (3-121)

Film	Effective Wave-length in A	$(E_{kin})_{max}$ in Kv., Observed	$(E_{kin})_{max}$ in Kv., Calculated
1	0.48	2.57	2.34
2		1.18	
3		1.28	
4		1.02	
5	0.71	1.16	1.10
6		1.15	
7		1.10	
8		1.10	

the direct beam, in contrast to the photo-electron energies, which are independent of angle. In the cloud chamber experiments of Compton and Simon, estimates of the ranges of the recoil electrons emitted at various angles with the x-ray beam were made, and qualitative agreement with the theory shown. Table III-7 gives some results of Kirchner on this point.[144] In his experiments the expansion chamber was filled with argon, and the filtered x-ray beam had an effective wave-length of 0.13 A. Although the number of tracks counted was not sufficient to give precise numerical values it is clear that the ranges diminish at the larger scattering angles.

Some information about the most probable angle of emission can be obtained from Table III-7, from which it is seen that more tracks were counted between 30° and 60° of the x-ray beam than at other angles. A similar result was obtained by Compton and Simon, although in neither case was the number of tracks counted sufficient to establish this result with satisfactory precision.

The effect of polarized x-rays on the scattering with change of wave-length has been studied by Kirchner.[145] This is an interesting problem because of the difficulty in including polarization phenomena in a purely corpuscular theory of light. Kirchner scattered x-rays

[144] F. Kirchner, Annalen der Physik 83, 969 (1927).
[145] F. Kirchner, Physikal. Zeitschr. 27, 385, 799 (1926); Ann. der Physik 81, 113 (1926).

TABLE III-7

RANGES OF RECOIL ELECTRONS IN ARGON AT VARIOUS ANGLES TO THE X-RAY BEAM
AT 0.13 A, AFTER KIRCHNER

Recoil Angle	Number of Scattered Electrons Having a Range				
θ	3 mm.	3–6 mm.	6–9 mm.	9–12 mm.	12 mm.
0°–15°	..	4	6	7	11
15°–30°	2	8	16	11	1
30°–45°	1	14	10	1	1
45°–60°	3	9	4	..	2
60°–75°	4	4	2		
75°–90°	12	4			

from a tube operated at 130 to 150 kv. from a paraffin block, and passed the radiation scattered at 90° to the direct beam through a Wilson cloud chamber. The camera was placed so that its axis was along the scattered x-rays and hence the photographic plates showed the projection of the tracks on a plane perpendicular to the direction of propagation of the beam producing the recoil electrons. The result of the experiment indicated that the most probable direction of ejection was perpendicular to the plane of the electric vector, in sharp contrast to the behaviour of ejected photo-electrons. It is difficult to explain this result from the electromagnetic theory, since this only supplies a force on the electron in the direction of the electric vector, and a small force (radiation pressure) in the direction of propagation of the x-ray beam.

Very little has been done on *the effect of binding energy in the atom on the recoil process.* Kirchner[146] has shown that with a wave-length of 0.13 A in the primary beam, the probability of ejection of an argon K shell electron as a recoil electron is the same as that of any other electron in the argon atom. This result was obtained by counting the number of Auger electron tracks (cf. Chap. VII, Sec. 2) associated with recoil tracks. Each Auger track means that the recoil electron came from the K level, for the production of the K state is a necessary preliminary to an internal conversion giving rise to an Auger electron. Such internal conversions are known to take place in roughly 90 per cent of K ionized argon atoms. Of 124 recoil tracks, Kirchner noted

[146] F. Kirchner, Annalen der Physik **83**, 969 (1927).

that 10 had associated Auger tracks. The fraction of the 124 electrons which came from the K shell was therefore

$$\frac{10}{124} \times \frac{100}{90} = 9 \text{ per cent,}$$

which is to be compared to 2/18, or 11 per cent which is the fraction of the total electron population of an argon atom which is in the K shell.

To summarize, it may be stated that though highly precise experiments on the properties of the recoil electrons have not as yet been performed, their qualitative properties leave no doubt of their existence and general agreement with the photon theory of scattering with change of wave-length.

15. Directed Quanta vs. Spreading Waves

We thus find that the wave-length of the scattered rays is what it should be if a quantum of radiation bounced from an electron, just as one billiard ball bounces from another. Not only this, but we actually observe the recoiling billiard ball, or electron, from which the quantum has bounced, and we find that it moves just as it should if a quantum had bumped into it. The obvious conclusion would be that x-rays, and so also light, consist of discrete units, proceeding in definite directions, each unit possessing the energy $h\nu$ and the corresponding momentum h/λ.

Waves vs. Conservation of Energy and Momentum.—If we wish to avoid this conclusion, and to retain the idea that energy proceeds in all directions from a radiating electron, we are presented with an alternative which is perhaps even more radical, namely, that when dealing with the interactions between radiation and electrons, the principles of the conservation of energy and momentum must be abandoned. If the energy radiated by an electron striking the target of an x-ray tube is distributed in all directions, only a very small fraction of it will fall upon any particular electron in the scattering material. But this minute fraction of the original radiated energy is sufficient to cause the ejection of a recoil electron with a considerable fraction of the energy of the initial cathode particle. Thus on the spherical wave hypothesis, when a recoil electron is ejected, it appears with many times as much energy as it receives from the incident radiation. In the corresponding case of the photo-electric effect, the suggestion has been made that energy is gradually accumulated and stored in the atom from which the photo-electron is ejected. In the present case this view is even more difficult to defend than in the case of the photo-electric effect, for here the loosely bound electrons, and apparently even free electrons as well, would have to be able to store up energy as readily as those tightly bound within the atom.

The lack of conservation of momentum on the spherical wave view is even more clearly evident than is the sudden appearance of energy. For just as in the case of the energy received by the scattering electron, so also the impulse received by the electron from the incident radiation is on the wave theory insignificant. We find, however, that a recoil electron moves with a velocity comparable with that of light, suddenly acquiring a momentum in the forward direction which is incomparably greater than the impulse it receives from the incident ray on the usual wave theory. To retain the conservation of momentum, we might suppose that the remaining part of the atom recoils with a momentum equal and opposite to that of the scattering electron. But the experiments indicate that the momentum may be equally readily acquired whether the electron is loosely or tightly bound. It is thus clear that the momentum acquired depends only upon the scattering electron and the radiation and has nothing to do with the remaining part of the atom. According to the spherical wave hypothesis, therefore, the electron does not receive an impulse as great as it is found to acquire.

If this work on the scattering of x-rays and the accompanying recoil electrons is correct, we must therefore choose between the familiar hypothesis that electromagnetic radiation consists of spreading waves, on the one hand, and the principles of the conservation of energy and momentum on the other. We cannot retain both.

The success of the applications of the conservation principles that have been made in this chapter to the problem of the scattering of radiation, inclines one to a choice of these principles even at the great cost of losing the spreading wave theory of radiation. Bohr, Kramers and Slater,[147] however, have shown that both these scattering phenomena and the photo-electric effect may be reconciled with the view that radiation proceeds in spherical waves if the conservation of energy and momentum are interpreted as statistical principles.

[147] N. Bohr, H. A. Kramers and J. C. Slater, Phil. Mag. 47, 785 (1924); Zeits. f. Phys. 24, 69 (1924).

Scattering of Photons by Individual Electrons

The essential feature of this suggestion of Bohr, Kramers and Slater as applied to the present problem is the hypothesis that spherical electromagnetic waves are scattered by " virtual oscillators," one such oscillator corresponding to each electron in the scattering medium. These virtual oscillators scatter the radiation in spherical waves in a manner similar to that demanded by the classical theory; but to account for the change of wave-length, they are supposed to scatter as if moving with such a velocity that the Doppler effect will give the same effect as that predicted by the quantum theory. The radiation pressure, which on the classical theory would be uniformly distributed over all the scattering electrons, appears on this view as the momentum of a few recoil electrons. For no individual electron is the momentum conserved; but the momentum of all the recoil electrons is (over a long period of time) equal to the impulse imparted to the whole scattering block by the pressure of the radiation. Similarly the difference between the energy spent on the virtual oscillators and that reappearing as scattered rays does not appear uniformly distributed among all the electrons, but rather as the kinetic energy of a small number of " recoil " electrons. Thus the energy, like the momentum, is conserved only statistically.

On this view, therefore, the radiation is continually being scattered, but only occasionally is a recoil electron emitted. This is in sharp contrast with the radiation quantum theory developed above, according to which a recoil electron appears every time a quantum is scattered. A crucial test between the two points of view is possible if one can detect pairs of individual recoil electrons and individual photons of scattered x-rays. For on the quantum view a beta ray resulting from the scattered x-ray should appear at the same instant as the recoil electron, whereas on the statistical view there should be no correlation between the time of production of the recoil electrons and the secondary beta rays due to the scattered radiation.

This experiment was devised and brilliantly performed by Bothe and Geiger.[148] X-rays were passed through hydrogen gas, and the resulting recoil electrons and scattered rays were detected by means

[148] W. Bothe and H. Geiger, Zeits. f. Phys. 26, 44 (1924); 32, 639 (1925); Naturwissenschaften, 13, 440 (1925).

A similar experiment, but with less definite results, has been performed also by R. D. Bennett, Proc. Nat. Acad. 11, 601 (1925); cf. also A. H. Compton, Proc. Nat. Acad. 11, 303 (1925).

of two different point counters, arranged as shown in Fig. III–55. Nothing was placed over the entrance to the chamber for counting the recoil electrons, but a window of thin platinum prevented recoil electrons from entering the chamber for counting the scattered photons (" $h\nu$ counter"). Of course not every photon entering the second counter will be noticed, for its detection depends upon the production of a β-ray. It was found that there were about 10 recoil electrons for every scattered photon that recorded itself.

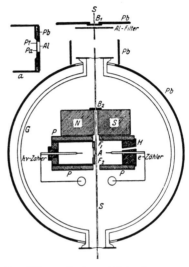

The impulses from the counting chambers were recorded on a moving photographic film, as shown in Fig. III–56. Here the upper record is that of the recoil electron counter, and the lower one that of the photon counter. The successive vertical lines represent intervals of 0.001 second. In this picture are shown A, an

Fig. III–55. Bothe and Geiger's arrangement for observing coincident scattered photons and recoil electrons. Hydrogen gas at A scatters the x-rays. Recoil electrons are detected by the "e Zähler," and photons by the "hν Zähler."

accurately simultaneous emission of electron and photon, and B, a recoil electron for which no associated scattered photon was recorded. In observations over a total period of over five hours, 66 such coincidences were observed. Bothe and Geiger calculate that on the

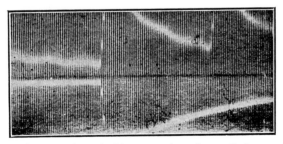

Fig. III–56. Record showing coincident reception of a recoil electron (above) and a photon (below). (Bothe and Geiger.)

statistical theory of Bohr, Kramers and Slater the chance is only 1 in 400,000 that so many coincidences should have occurred.

We have found from the cloud expansion experiments that on the average there are about as many recoil electrons as there are scattered quanta. Combining this result with that of Bothe and Geiger's experiment, we see that there is a quantum of scattered x-rays associated with each recoil electron.[149] This is directly contrary to the suggestion made by Bohr, Kramers and Slater.

Scattered X-rays as Photons

Important information regarding the nature of the radiation quantum associated with the recoil electron may be obtained by studying the relation between the direction of ejection of the recoil electron and the direction in which the associated quantum proceeds. According to eq. (3.119) we should have the definite relation

$$\tan \tfrac{1}{2}\phi = - \; 1/(1 + \alpha) \tan \theta. \qquad (3.122)$$

On the photon theory, therefore, if the scattered ray produces a beta ray, the direction ϕ in which the ray appears should be related to the angle θ of the recoiling electron by the same expression. But according to any form of the spreading wave theory, including that of Bohr, Kramers and Slater, the scattered rays may produce effects in any direction whatever, and there should be no correlation between the directions in which the recoil electrons proceed and the directions in which the secondary beta rays are ejected by the scattered x-rays.

This test has been made by means of a Wilson cloud expansion apparatus,[150] in the manner shown diagrammatically in Fig. I–34. Each recoil electron produces a visible track, and occasionally a secondary track is produced by the scattered x-ray, as in Fig. III–57. When but one recoil electron appears on the same plate with the track due to the scattered rays, it is possible to tell at once whether the angles satisfy eq. (3.122).

By the device of placing thin lead diaphragms in the expansion chamber, the probability that a scattered quantum would produce a beta ray inside the expansion chamber was made as great as 1 in 50.

[149] In Table III–3 we see that especially for the longer waves, N_R/N_P is somewhat less than σ/τ, i.e., the number of recoil electrons is slightly less than the number of scattered quanta. This is probably due in part to the fact that for the unmodified scattered rays no recoil electrons should appear.

[150] This experiment was suggested by W. F. G. Swann, and performed by A. W. Simon and A. H. C., Proc. Nat. Acad. Sci. 11, 303 (1925); Phys. Rev. 26, 289 (1925).

On the last 850 plates, 38 show both recoil tracks and secondary beta ray tracks.   In 18 of these cases the observed angle ϕ is within 20 degrees of the angle calculated from the measured value of θ, while the other 20 tracks are distributed at random angles.   This ratio 18 : 20 is about that to be expected for the ratio of the rays scattered by the part of the air from which the recoil tracks could be measured to the stray rays from various sources.

Figure III–58 shows graphically how the secondary beta rays are concentrated near the angle calculated from the direction of ejection of the recoil electrons.[151]   The fact that so many of the secondary tracks occur at angles for which Δ is less than 20° means that eq.

FIG. III–57.   Recoil electron and β-ray due to associated scattered x-ray showing predicted coordination of angles.   Lower figure, original photograph; upper figure, retouched.   (Compton and Simon.)

[151] When only one recoil electron and one secondary electron appeared on a photograph, the procedure was to record first the angle θ at which the track of the recoil electron begins.   Then the angle ϕ between the incident ray and the line joining the origin of the recoil track and the origin of the secondary track was noted.   The difference between this angle and the angle ϕ calculated from θ by eq. (3.122) was called Δ, and this value of Δ was assigned a weight of unity.   When a number n of recoil tracks appeared on the same plate with a secondary track, the value of Δ was thus determined for each recoil track separately, and assigned a weight of $1/n$.   Following this procedure there are values of Δ which are distributed approximately at random between o and 180° due to the $n - 1$ recoil electrons which are not associated with the secondary track.   This is in addition to the random values of Δ resulting from the presence of stray x-rays.   Plates on which more than three recoil tracks appeared were discarded.

(3.122) holds for each individual scattering event within experimental error. There is only about 1 chance in 250 that this agreement is accidental.

Since the only known effect of x-rays is the production of beta rays, and since the meaning of energy is the ability to produce an effect, this result means that there is scattered x-ray energy associated with each recoil electron sufficient to produce a beta ray and proceeding in a direction determined at the moment of ejection of the

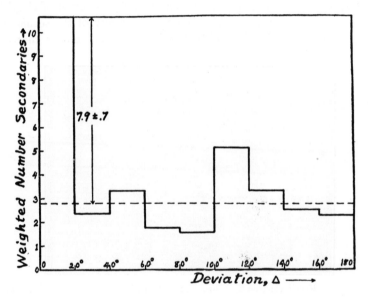

FIG. III–58. The predominance of secondaries near Δ = 0 means experimental agreement with photon theory relation between angles of scattering and recoil.

recoil electron. In other words, *the scattered x-rays proceed in directed quanta of radiant energy.*

Since other experiments show that these scattered x-rays can be diffracted by crystals, and are thus subject to the usual laws of interference, there is no reason to suppose that other forms of radiant energy have an essentially different structure. It thus becomes highly probable that all electro-magnetic radiation is constituted of discrete quanta proceeding in definite directions.

This result, like that of Bothe and Geiger, is irreconcilable with Bohr, Kramers, and Slater's hypothesis of the statistical production of recoil and photo-electrons. On the other hand, we see that eqs. (3.117), (3.118) and (3.119) are completely verified.

Unless the experiments we have been considering have been affected by improbably large experimental errors, there seems to be no escape from the conclusion that the fundamental assumptions on which the photon theory of scattering are based are valid. To be specific, (1) that the incident x-ray beam is divisible into discrete units possessing energy $h\nu$ and momentum $h\nu/c$, and that these units, or photons, may be scattered one at a time in definite directions by individual electrons, and (2) that when a photon is scattered by an electron, energy and momentum are conserved in the process.

16. The Uncertainty Principle

An important consequence of this evidence that radiation acts like particles, combined with the equally good proof that it has the characteristics of waves, is that there is a definite limit placed upon the precision of prediction of the future actions of an object as based upon observations made with any form of light. The existence of this natural limit was noted by Bohr and Heisenberg,[152] and has led to the formulation of the " Principle of Uncertainty." The experiments just described, together with those showing diffraction of electrons and atoms described briefly in Chap. I, may be considered as the experimental basis for this principle.

The manner in which the photon character of light implies such as uncertainty is made evident by Heisenberg's imagined experiment with the " gamma ray microscope." We assume a particle moving without friction and under no force, hence with steady, uniform motion, from time t_1 to t_2, as pictured in Fig. III–59. At instants t_1 and t_2 it is observed with a cross-hair microscope, and the distance traveled is accurately noted. Its momentum is then

$$p = mv = m\frac{q_2 - q_1}{t_2 - t_1},$$

where the q's are the distances measured from an arbitrary origin. Since the time and distance between points 1 and 2 can be made as great as desired, there is no limit to the precision with which this velocity and momentum can be determined. There is, however, a

[152] Cf. W. Heisenberg, "The Physical Principles of the Quantum Theory, Univ. of Chicago Press, 1930, for a thorough discussion of the bases for this principle and its consequences.

limit imposed by the resolving power of the microscope on the precision with which the position of the particle at time t_2 can be observed. This limit is approximately

$$\delta q = \lambda/\alpha \qquad (3.123)$$

where λ is the wave-length of the light with which the particle is illuminated and α is the angular aperture of the microscope objective. In order to determine the position as precisely as possible the wavelength will thus ideally be made as short as possible. Hence the use of the " gamma-ray microscope."

In order that the particle may be observed, however, radiation must enter the microscope objective, resulting in a recoil of the particle from the emitted ray. In order to make this effect as small

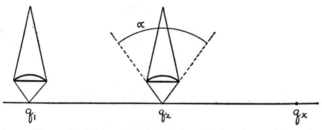

Fig. III–59. Illustrating the uncertainty of prediction from observations with Heisenberg's "gamma-ray microscope."

as possible, we shall use the minimum amount of light, namely one photon. Due to the angular aperture of the microscope lens, the direction of emission of this photon is uncertain through the range α. There results an uncertainty in the impulse of recoil applied to the particle along the q axis of amount

$$\delta p = \frac{h\alpha}{\lambda}, \qquad (3.124)$$

where h/λ is the momentum of the emitted photon. The product of the uncertainties in the position and the momentum is thus approximately

$$\delta q \delta p = h. \qquad (3.125)$$

This is Heisenberg's uncertainty formula.

It will be seen that the uncertainty of this product is independent of the wave-length, and is thus the same whatever type of radiation

THE UNCERTAINTY PRINCIPLE 229

is used. For shorter wave-lengths the position is made more accurate, but the momentum is less definite. For longer wave-lengths the position cannot be determined with precision.

It may be noted further that though the position of the particle might be determined from the microscope's diffraction pattern more closely than is suggested by the value $\delta q \sim \lambda/\alpha$, such a diffraction pattern implies the use of many photons of light. If only one photon is used, the position where it will appear in the diffraction pattern is uncertain by approximately the amount given by this equation. If more photons are used in order to determine the diffraction pattern with greater precision, it can be shown that the uncertainty in the momentum increases at the same rate that the uncertainty in the position decreases.

It is evident that in order to predict with definiteness the future position of the particle, it is necessary to know with precision both the position and velocity at an initial instant. As this is not known, definite prediction of the future position is impossible. The precision of such predictions increases rapidly, however, with the mass of the particle, since the uncertainty in velocity is $\delta p/m$. Thus for objects which are large enough to be handled in the laboratory, the uncertainty represented by this relation is inappreciable. A simple calculation will show, however, that for a moving electron the uncertainty is relatively great. In fact, if the electron is confined to the first Bohr orbit, the possible differences in momentum are so small that its angular position in the orbit is completely indeterminate.[153]

May there not, however, be some means of detecting moving particles which will not introduce uncertainties of the type just considered? It is evident that its position cannot be determined without the use of some material object which will be affected by the presence of the particle. To make the reaction on the particle as small as possible, we should use a very small portion of matter as the detector. If this detector is an electron, such as a beta ray from radium with which the particle might be impregnated, there will be a recoil from the beta ray. The uncertainty in momentum due to this recoil may

---

[153] In this case let p = angular momentum and q = angular position. The maximum possible uncertainty in p for the first Bohr orbit is then $\delta p = h/2\pi$. It follows from (3.125) that $\delta q = 2\pi$, the whole circumference of the orbit! For higher quantum states, $\delta p = nh/2\pi$ and $\delta q = 2\pi/n$. When n becomes large, δq becomes relatively definite, corresponding to the classical electron theory.

be reduced by allowing the electron to pass through a diaphragm of small aperture so that the uncertainty in its direction will be small. We are limited, however, in the smallness of this aperture by the fact that the moving electron has a wave-length given by de Broglie's wave-length equation (2.17),

$$\lambda = h/p,$$

so that diffraction must occur at the slit. The uncertainty in the position is, in fact, expressible in terms of λ just as before, and so, also, is the uncertainty in the momentum. Thus again the product of the two uncertainties is equal to h.

Since according to de Broglie's theory this relation between the wave-length and the momentum is universally applicable, it follows that there should be no way of avoiding the uncertainty of the type just described. Insofar as experiments with light, x-rays, electrons, hydrogen and helium atoms, etc., have verified de Broglie's relation, we may consider the uncertainty relation as experimentally confirmed.

Uncertainty Principle from de Broglie's Wave Mechanics

Let us assume two infinite wave trains of wave-length λ and $\lambda + \delta\lambda$ corresponding to particles with momentum $p = h/\lambda$ and $p - \delta p = h/(\lambda + \delta\lambda)$. The resulting wave train will have minima which will be separated by a number of waves equal to $\lambda/\delta\lambda$, that is at a distance $\lambda^2/\delta\lambda$ apart. If then the energy is associated with one of these wave groups of length $\lambda^2/\delta\lambda$, and if we suppose that this energy is carried by a moving particle somewhere within this train, the uncertainty in position of the particle is $\delta q = \lambda^2/\delta\lambda$, while its uncertainty in momentum is $\delta p = \delta(h/\lambda) = h\delta\lambda/\lambda^2$. Thus

$$\delta q \delta p = h, \tag{3.125}$$

as before. The uncertainty principle is thus much more general than the former deduction might seem to imply.

Uncertainties in Large Scale and Small Scale Events

The uncertainty represented by this relation is, as we have seen, of especial importance when applied to small scale events, especially to those of atomic and sub-atomic dimensions. It is worth noting, however, that under some conditions these uncertainties extend to large scale phenomena. A Geiger-Müller counter may be used, for example, to count the photo-electrons ejected by x-rays that have been diffracted by a ruled grating. Whether a photon will appear in the first or second order of the spectrum is uncertain due to considerations such as those that have just been advanced. If one such counter is placed to receive rays diffracted in the first order and another in the second order, repetition of the experiment of diffracting individual photons under identical initial conditions will not always give impulses in the same counter. That is, under identical initial conditions, as far as physical tests can show, we do not necessarily get the same results. It would only be as the average of a very large number of tries that the *probability* of diffraction in the first and second orders could be determined with precision.

It is with considerations of this kind in mind that Heisenberg writes,[154] " Resolution of the paradoxes of atomic physics can be accomplished only by further renunciation of old and cherished ideas. Most important of these is the idea that natural phenomena obey exact laws—the principle of causality. In fact, our ordinary description of nature, and the idea of exact laws, rests on the assumption that it is possible to observe phenomena without appreciably influencing them. . . . There exist no infinitesimals by the aid of which an observation might be made without appreciable perturbation."

Any action, on however large a scale, which depends at some stage upon an event so small as to be subject to Heisenberg uncertainty, will itself be uncertain to the same degree. Thus the Geiger counter may operate through an amplifier an electrical device of any desired magnitude, and the result will reflect the uncertainty of the photon's diffraction. It is because most large-scale events are the statistical averages of many small ones that they become relatively precise. The fact that there is a close analogy between a highly amplified physical action and the reaction of a living organism to a minute nerve current has led to questions regarding the role of causality in living matter which cannot be discussed here.

D. WAVE MECHANICS THEORY OF X-RAY SCATTERING

17. *Change in Wave-length of Scattered X-rays*

Schrödinger has shown[155] how a simple application of de Broglie's form of wave-mechanics leads to precisely the same result for the change in wave-length of scattered x-rays as that derived on the

[154] W. Heisenberg, *loc. cit.*, p. 62.
[155] E. Schrödinger, Ann. der Phys. 82, 257 (1927).

theory of impact between particles. Although this mechanical theory doubtless gives a more adequate picture of the cause of the wave-length change, it is nevertheless illuminating to present also the wave-mechanical view.

Let us change our coordinates in such a way that the conditions before and after impact of photon and electron are symmetrical. In place of Fig. III–47 we have in our new coordinates the condition shown in Fig. III–60. If we confine our discussion to the case for which $v \ll c$, where v is the velocity of the electron's recoil in the fixed coordinates, then the required velocity of the moving coordi-

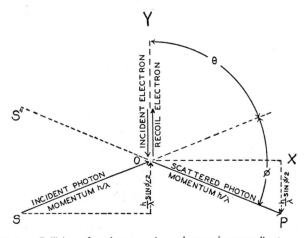

Fig. III–60. Collision of a photon and an electron in normalized coordinates.

nates is $\frac{1}{2}v$. At impact, the momentum of the electron then changes from $-mv/2$ to $+mv/2$, as expressed in the moving system, while the Y component of the photon's momentum changes from $+ (h/\lambda) \sin (\phi/2)$ to $- (h/\lambda) \sin (\phi/2)$. The condition for momentum conservation is thus

$$- \frac{mv}{2} + \frac{h}{\lambda} \sin \frac{\phi}{2} = \frac{mv}{2} - \frac{h}{\lambda} \sin \frac{\phi}{2},$$

or

$$2 \frac{h}{\lambda} \sin \frac{\phi}{2} = mv. \qquad (3.126)$$

The energy remains unchanged after impact.

If now, following de Broglie and Schrödinger, we represent the incident electron by a continuous train of ψ waves of length $\Lambda = h/(mv/2)$ moving along $-Y$, and the recoil electron by a similar train of the same wave-length moving along $+Y$, the two trains together will form standing waves for which the electric charge density is proportional to $\psi_{\text{inc}}\psi_{\text{rec}}^{*}$, and for which the distance from node to node is $\frac{1}{2}\Lambda = h/mv$. The de Broglie waves representing the electron thus form a Bragg grating of grating space $d = h/mv$. This grating will diffract the incident x-ray waves according to the usual equation

$$n\lambda = 2d \sin (\phi/2)$$

or

$$\lambda = 2 \frac{h}{mv} \sin \frac{\phi}{2}. \qquad (3.127)$$

Here n can have only the value 1, since the charge density is distributed along Y according to a sine function of period d, which according to the results developed in detail in Chap. VI gives zero intensity of reflection except in the first order. Thus eq. (3.127) becomes exactly equivalent to the momentum eq. (3.126).

If we now transform back to the fixed coordinates, our grating of stationary de Broglie waves is receding from O with a velocity $v/2$. Treating the grating as a mirror, this is equivalent to receiving the light from a virtual image of the source S'' which recedes from S with velocity v. According to Doppler's principle, a wave-length λ emitted from S'' would reach P with a value,

$$\lambda' = \lambda \left(1 + \frac{v}{c} \sin \frac{\phi}{2} \right), \qquad (3.128)$$

an increase in wave-length of

$$\delta\lambda = \frac{v}{c} \lambda \sin \frac{\phi}{2}. \qquad (3.129)$$

Substituting the value of v from eq. (3.126), this becomes

$$\delta\lambda = \frac{2h}{mc} \sin^2 \frac{\phi}{2},$$

$$= \frac{h}{mc} \text{vers } \phi, \qquad (3.130)$$

which is identical with the result (3.117) obtained from the photon theory.

18. *Intensity of Scattering from Free Electrons*

Since in the normalized coordinate system of Fig. III–60 there is no change in wave-length of the scattered x-rays, we may reasonably expect also no change in intensity. That there can be no intensity change in these coordinates depending upon the first or other odd power of v/c follows from the fact that the velocity is of opposite sign for the incident and the recoil motion of the electron, and in any average of the scattering from the initial and final states of motion such odd order effects must vanish. We may, therefore, rely to the

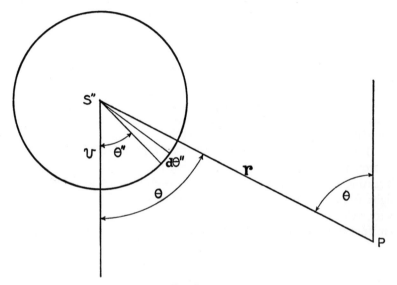

Fig. III–61.

first order of v/c on the results of a calculation of the intensity of scattering based upon the assumption that in these normalized co-ordinates it is the same as from an electron at rest. A more rigorous calculation by Klein and Nishina[156] shows that the result thus obtained is not reliable to higher powers of v/c.

To calculate the intensity in the fixed coordinates, we note as above that the scattering will be like reflection from a Bragg grating receding with velocity $v/2$ along the Y axis. The radiation reaching P will thus be as from the source S'', receding from S with a velocity

[156] O. Klein and Y. Nishina, Zeits. f. Phys. **52**, 853 (1928); cf. below, eq. (3.139).

$v = \beta c$. Draw about S'' (Fig. III-61) a sphere moving with it at velocity v. A photon ejected between θ'' and $\theta'' + d\theta''$ in these coordinates will then proceed to P between θ and $\theta + d\theta$ in the fixed coordinates. It can be shown[157] that to the first power of β the following relations hold:

$$\left. \begin{aligned} d\theta'' &= d\theta/(1 + \beta \cos \theta) \\ \sin \theta'' &= \sin \theta/(1 + \beta \cos \theta). \end{aligned} \right\} \qquad (3.131)$$

The probability that a photon emitted by S'' will come within the range $d\theta''$ is, however,

$$\begin{aligned} P_{\theta''}d\theta'' = P_\theta d\theta &= \tfrac{1}{2} \sin \theta'' d\theta'' \\ &= \frac{1}{2} \frac{\sin \theta d\theta}{(1 + \beta \cos \theta)^2}. \end{aligned} \qquad (3.132)$$

If $h\nu$ is the energy of the photon emitted from S'', its energy as observed at P will be, according to eq. (3.128),

$$\begin{aligned} h\nu' &= h\nu/(1 + \beta \sin \tfrac{1}{2}\phi) \\ &= h\nu/(1 + \beta \cos \theta). \end{aligned} \qquad (3.133)$$

Thus for each photon emitted from S'' the probable energy striking P within the angle $d\theta$ is

$$h\nu' P_\theta d\theta = \frac{h\nu}{2} \frac{\sin \theta d\theta}{(1 + \beta \cos \theta)^3}. \qquad (3.134)$$

If the source S'' were at rest, the corresponding intensity would be

$$h\nu_0 P_{0\theta} d\theta = \frac{h\nu}{2} \sin \theta d\theta. \qquad (3.135)$$

Thus the ratio of the scattering by the recoiling electron to that by an electron at rest is the ratio of (3.134) to (3.135), i.e.,

$$\left. \begin{aligned} I/I_0 &= (1 + \beta \cos \theta)^{-3} \\ &= (\nu'/\nu)^3 \end{aligned} \right\} \qquad (3.136)$$

where I_0 represents Thomson's value of I_e as given by eq. (3.04).

---

[157] Cf. Appendix I, eq. (31).

A comparison of eqs. (3.129) and (3.130) gives, since $\lambda = c/\nu$,

$$\beta = \frac{v}{c} = \frac{h\nu}{mc^2} 2 \sin \frac{\phi}{2}$$

$$= 2\alpha \sin \frac{\phi}{2}$$

where $\alpha \equiv h\nu/mc^2$. Thus

$$\beta \cos \theta = \beta \sin \frac{\phi}{2} = 2\alpha \sin^2 \frac{\phi}{2}$$

$$= \alpha \text{ vers } \phi,$$

whence eq. (3.136) may be written in the form,

$$I/I_0 = (1 + \alpha \text{ vers } \phi)^{-3}, \qquad (3.137)$$

which can be compared directly with the experiments.

This result was first derived by a somewhat similar argument by Breit,[158] and has been confirmed by different types of quantum mechanical calculations by Dirac,[159] Gordon,[160] and Schrödinger.[161] A less rigid derivation along rather similar lines led Compton[162] to the following formula, which has been used in many of the earlier discussions of the subject,

$$I/I_0 = 1 + \frac{2\alpha(1 + \alpha) \text{ vers}^2 \phi}{(1 + \cos^2 \phi)(1 + \alpha \text{ vers } \phi)^5}. \qquad (3.138)$$

Klein-Nishina Formula.—The form of wave-mechanics developed by Schrödinger, and used throughout in this book, except where specifically noted, is subject to the limitation that it is not invariant with Lorentz transformations. This is the same fault which makes it necessary to replace Newtonian mechanics with relativity mechanics when dealing with such high velocities that terms in β^2 become significant. For this reason deductions such as eq. (3.136), however rigorously derived from Schrödinger's theory, are unreliable to powers of β higher than the first. A type of quantum mechanics has, how-

---

[158] G. Breit, Phys. Rev. **27**, 362 (1926).

[159] P. A. M. Dirac, Proc. Roy. Soc. **111**, 405 (1926).

[160] W. Gordon, Zeits. f. Phys. **40**, 117 (1926).

[161] E. Schrödinger, Ann. der Phys. **82**, 257 (1927).

[162] A. H. Compton, Phys. Rev. **21**, 491 (1923). A discussion of other early formulas is given in X-rays and Electrons, pp. 296–305.

ever, been developed by Dirac,[163] which is invariant with Lorentz transformations, and which should accordingly be valid for all velocities. By its use Klein and Nishina[164] have shown that the intensity of the scattering by a free electron should be given by,

$$\frac{I}{I_0} = (1 + \alpha \text{ vers } \phi)^{-3} \left[1 + \frac{\alpha^2 \text{ vers}^2 \phi}{(1 + \cos^2 \phi)(1 + \alpha \text{ vers } \phi)} \right]. \quad (3.139)$$

This expression differs from that of Breit and Dirac (3.137) by an additional term proportional to α^2, *i.e.*, also to β^2, where β is the recoil velocity of the electron.

It is noteworthy that this additional term represents rays which are almost completely unpolarized.[165] It originates from the fact that according to Dirac's quantum mechanics the electron has some of the properties of a magnetic doublet (associated with its spin). When traversed by an electromagnetic wave of sufficiently high frequency, this doublet emits radiation of zero intensity in the forward direction and maximum intensity backwards (proportional to vers$^2 \phi$), which appears to have no exact analogue in classical electron theory.[166]

<hr>

[163] P. A. M. Dirac, Proc. Roy. Soc. **114**, 710 (1927); **117**, 610 (1928); **126**, 360 (1930).

[164] O. Klein and Y. Nishina, Zeits. f. Phys. **52**, 853 (1929). Cf. also I. Waller, Zeits. f. Phys. **61**, 837 (1930), who has derived the same formula in a different manner.

[165] Cf. Klein and Nishina, *loc. cit.* p. 867, and Y. Nishina, Zeits. f. Phys. **52**, 869 (1929).

[166] According to classical theory, an electron which has angular momentum $\sqrt{\frac{3}{4}} h/2\pi$ and magnetic moment $\sqrt{\frac{3}{4}}(h/2\pi)(e/mc)$, which gives the same results in line spectra as those required by Dirac's theory (cf. e.g., L. Pauling and S. Goudsmit " The Structure of Line Spectra " 1930, p. 54), should scatter additional radiation because of the precession of the electron's magnetic axis in the magnetic field of the electromagnetic wave. If the magnetic axes of the electrons are initially oriented at random, the intensity of the scattering of unpolarized x-rays by a single electronic magnetic doublet may be shown to be

$$I_m' = I_e \alpha^2 \frac{\frac{1}{2}(3 - \cos^2 \phi)}{1 + \cos^2 \phi}, \quad (3.140)$$

where I_e is the scattering due to the electron's electric charge.

This radiation I_m' acts as if it were incoherent with that represented by I_e, due to the electron's charge, for it is the two intensities rather than the amplitudes which are added. Though both components have the same frequency, the phase of the wave contributed by the magnetic doublet has an equal chance to be in the same or the opposite phase as the wave due to the electric charge. Thus on averaging the intensi-

19. Scattering from Bound Electrons[167]

According to the quantum theory, scattering of radiation occurs when an atom passes from one stationary state to another.[168] If $E_k = E_1, E_2, E_3 \ldots$ is the initial state of the atom, and $E_l = E_1, E_2, E_3 \ldots$ is its final state, the change in the atom's energy is

ties from different electrons, all first power terms due to added amplitudes disappear, and only the squared terms due to the added intensities remain.

The intensity due to the electron's magnetic moment as expressed by Klein and Nishina's formula is, to the same power of α,

$$I_m'' = I_e \alpha^2 \frac{(1 - \cos \phi)^2}{1 + \cos^2 \phi}. \tag{3.141}$$

On the wave mechanics theory this radiation is incoherent with I_e, because it represents transitions from one magnetic state of the electron to another, which, if there is any permanent magnetic field present, represents a change in energy and hence of frequency.

Thus the scattered rays represented by I_m' and I_m'' are both incoherent with the electrically scattered rays, they are of the same order of magnitude, vary with the frequency (through $\alpha = h\nu/mc^2$) in the same manner, and show closely similar features regarding polarization. In spite of this close correspondence, however, the difference in variation with ϕ is fundamental. There seems to be no way of obtaining I_m proportional to $(1 - \cos \phi)^2$ without considering the electron to be acted on simultaneously by a plane incident wave and a plane scattered wave of the same intensity propagated in the direction ϕ. Such a concept takes us at once out of classical and into quantum mechanics.

The use of such superposed trains of plane waves in wave-mechanics is illustrated, for example, in Schrödinger's treatment of the problem of x-ray scattering as described above, and is discussed in other connections by C. Eckart, Phys. Rev. 34, 167 (1929) and by G. Breit, Jour. Opt. Soc. Am. 14, 374 (1927).

[167] Cf. A. Sommerfeld, " Wave-Mechanics " (1929), p. 213, for a simple and excellent presentation of the fundamental principles of the wave-mechanical treatment of this problem.

[168] Cf. A. Smekal, Naturwiss. 11, 873 (1923), who first predicted the occurrence of such transitions associated with scattering.

According to the dispersion theory of H. A. Kramers and W. Heisenberg (Zeits. f. Phys. 31, 684 (1925)) which is confirmed by a thorough wave-mechanical study (cf. e.g., I. Waller, Zeits. f. Phys. 61, 837 (1930)) the atom may be more accurately thought of as being excited first from state k to an intermediate state s, representing absorption of energy, followed immediately by a transfer from state s to the final state l when the energy is radiated. Thus scattering becomes a process of absorption and emission similar to fluorescence. The time interval during which the energy is held by the atom in the scattering process is however so very small that polarization and coherence are not affected.

Since the energy concerned is determined solely by the initial and final states, for most purposes the existence of the intermediate state can be neglected.

$\delta E = E_l - E_k$. By an extension of Bohr's frequency principle, the frequency of the scattered ray was given by Smekal as,

$$h\nu' = h\nu + \delta E. \qquad (3.142)$$

If the atom is initially in an excited state, transitions to both higher or lower energy states are possible, so that δE may be either positive or negative, i.e.,

$$h\nu' = h\nu \pm |\delta E|. \qquad (3.143)$$

This corresponds to the classical case of scattering by an electron which is already vibrating with a frequency ν_0, in which case the scattered wave may be analyzed into two components of frequency

$$\nu' = \nu \pm \nu_0. \qquad (3.144)$$

If, however, the atom is initially in its ground state, transitions are possible only to the same or higher energy states, whence

$$h\nu' = h\nu \quad \text{or} \quad h\nu - |\delta E|, \qquad (3.145)$$

i.e., the frequency is either unchanged or is less than that of the incident ray.

Scattered radiation of unchanged frequency, i.e., for which $l = k$, constitutes the coherent radiation, which obeys the classical laws of interference. Radiation whose frequency is changed corresponding to transitions between states for which the electron is retained by the atom $(E < 0)$ was discovered in the visible region by Raman,[169] and is known as Raman scattering. The existence of such radiation as a part of scattered x-rays, though frequently suspected, has never been established.[170] It is probably too weak to be detected.[171]

[169] C. V. Raman, Indian Jour. of Physics **2**, 387 (1928). A good review of the extensive work that has recently been done on the Raman effect is given by R. W. Wood, " Physical Optics " (Macmillan, 1934) p. 444.

[170] The " tertiary radiation " of Clark and Duane, discussed briefly in the footnote to p. 209, was supposed to have a wave-length given approximately by this relation. Similarly, Davis and Mitchell (Phys. Rev. **32**, 331, 1928) and Davis and Purks (Phys. Rev. **34**, 1, 1929) observed faint lines that were ascribed to scattering accompanied by transitions from K to L levels in carbon and other light elements. More careful tests by J. A. Bearden, Phys. Rev. **36**, 791 (1930); N. S. Gingrich, *ibid.*, p. 1050; Du Mond and Kirkpatrick, *ibid.*, **37**, 136 (1931), and others have failed to confirm their presence.

[171] That such transitions should be possible in the x-ray region was shown by A. H. Compton (Phys. Rev. **24**, 168 (1924)). The final level l must, however, be unoccupied by an electron and in the normal atom the only unoccupied levels are those near the surface of the atom. These have an energy range so small compared with the energy of the photon that the chance of the electron's being captured here is very small (cf. A. Carelli, Zeits. f. Phys. **61**, 632 (1930)).

The scattered radiation of decreased frequency which is experimentally observed in the x-ray region is that for which $E_l < 0$, corresponding to a recoil electron ejected from the atom. Equation (3.145) does not define the magnitude of the frequency change in this process, except within the limits

$$0 < \delta\nu < h\nu \qquad (3.146)$$

imposed by the possible range of δE. We should thus expect the modified scattered rays to show a continuous spectrum. When, however, momentum considerations are included, this continuous spectrum will be found to have a maximum at the wave-length given by the photon formula (3.117). This prediction is in accord with the experimental observation of a broad modified line (cf. Fig. III–50).

a. *Conservation of Momentum in Wave Mechanics*

If in Schrödinger's wave equation (2.20) we use for V the potential energy of the electron in the combined electric field of the nucleus and electromagnetic field of the incident wave, Wentzel[172] has shown that for an atom with a single electron initially in the ground state k, the electric moment corresponding to eq. (2.28) becomes

$$M_q = \frac{1}{4\pi^2}\frac{e^2}{mv^2}E_0\cos\left(2\pi\nu't\right)\int\int\int q\,\frac{\partial}{\partial y}(\psi_k\psi_l{}^*)\cos\left(k_1\,a\cos\alpha\right)d\tau. \quad (3.147)$$

Here E_0 is the amplitude of the electric vector of the incident wave, assumed to be along the Y axis, which may have any orientation perpendicular to the direction of propagation X. The frequency $\nu' = \nu - \Delta\nu$ is that of the scattered wave, $\Delta\nu$ being the change in frequency. q is the arbitrary coordinate along which the electric moment is evaluated. The quantity[173]

$$k_1 \equiv \frac{4\pi}{\lambda}\sin\frac{\phi}{2}.$$

Thus, as will be seen from Fig. III–62, $(k_1 a \cos\alpha)$ is the phase differ-

[172] G. Wentzel, Zeits. f. Phys. **43**, 1 (1927). See A. Sommerfeld, "Wave Mechanics" p. 215, for a simplified derivation of this expression.

[173] This definition of k is a close approximation. Its exact form would be

$$k_1 \equiv 2\pi\left(\frac{u'}{\lambda'} - \frac{u}{\lambda}\right),$$

where u' and u are unit vectors in the direction of the scattered ray and the primary ray respectively. The expression used in the text is equivalent to this if $\lambda' = \lambda$.

ence between light scattered from the volume element $d\tau$ as compared with that from O. This phase term or " retardation " is necessary to give the effective value of the moment of this volume element as observed at P, since the wave-length considered is comparable with the atomic dimensions. Assuming that the atom is initially in the normal state

$$\psi_k = (\text{const.})e^{-k_2 a}. \qquad (3.148)$$

where

$$k_2 = \frac{1}{a_0} = \frac{2\pi}{h}\sqrt{2mE_k},$$

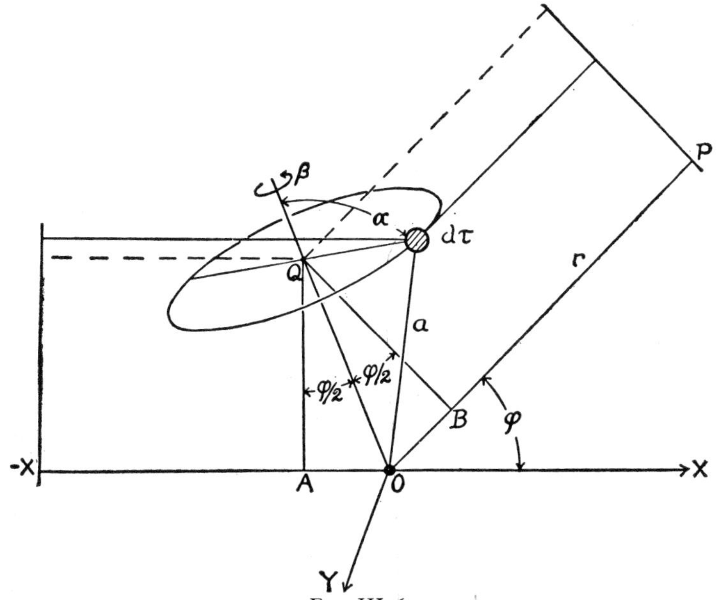

Fig. III-62.

a_0 being the radius of the first Bohr orbit ($h^2/4\pi^2 me^2$ for hydrogen). Similarly assuming that the final state l is that of an electron recoiling freely with energy $E_l = \frac{1}{2}mv^2$ and momentum $\sqrt{2mE_l}$,

$$\psi_l^* = (\text{const.}) f(\alpha, \beta) \frac{1}{a} e^{\pm ik_3 a},$$

where

$$k_3 = \frac{2\pi}{h}\sqrt{2mE_l},$$

and α and β are the angles defining the volume element (Fig. III-62).

Wentzel evaluates the volume integral with a result which may be expressed thus,

$$M_q = (\text{const.}) \frac{e^2}{m\nu^2} \frac{E_0 \cos (2\pi\nu't)}{(k_1 - k_3)^2 + k_2^2}. \tag{3.149}$$

According to eq. (2.01') the electric vector of the scattered radiation is proportional to $\ddot{M}_q$, i.e.,

$$E' = (\text{const.}) \frac{e^2\nu'^2}{m\nu^2} \frac{E_0 \cos (2\pi\nu't)}{(k_1 - k_3)^2 + k_2^2}. \tag{3.150}$$

Since the intensities of the scattered rays and the primary rays are proportional respectively to E'^2 and $E_0{}^2$, to the approximation that $\nu' = \nu$,

$$\frac{I'}{I} = \frac{\text{const.}}{[(k_1 - k_3)^2 + k_2{}^2]^2}. \tag{3.151}$$

Now note that

$$(k_2/k_3)^2 = E_k/E_l.$$

For the case of a loosely bound electron this quantity will be small, and we have approximately,

$$I'/I = (\text{const.})/(k_1 - k_3)^4. \tag{3.152}$$

This expression has an infinitely sharp maximum at $k_1 = k_3$, i.e.,

$$\frac{4\pi}{\lambda} \sin \frac{\phi}{2} = \frac{2\pi}{h} \sqrt{2mE_l},$$

or

$$\frac{2h}{\lambda} \sin \frac{\phi}{2} = mv, \tag{3.153}$$

which is exactly the equation (3.126) which we have used to express the conservation of momentum between the photon and the recoiling electron. Thus if the binding energy of the scattering electron is small, there is a sharp maximum of scattered x-rays near the angle required to conserve the momentum for a free electron. It follows that for a loosely bound electron the photon formula for the change in wave-length of scattered x-rays (eq. (3.117)) should hold rigorously when applied to the intensity maximum in the spectrum of the scattered line.[174]

---

[174] Cf. Sommerfeld and Wentzel in the papers cited. This conclusion is contrary to that drawn by P. A. Ross and P. Kirkpatrick (Phys. Rev. **45**, 223 (1934)) from a consideration of the momentum imparted to the atom as the electron is being removed.

b. *Width of the Modified Line*

Equation (3.151) shows that the maximum of the modified line becomes sharper as k_2 becomes less.   It will be noted, however, that k_2 is proportional to the momentum of the electron within the atom. Thus if the momentum of the electron before scattering is comparable with its momentum after scattering (k_2 comparable with k_3), the maximum spreads out just as in the familar case of a resonance maximum with a damping term.   The width of the modified line can be calculated from eq. (3.151) by giving k_2 and k_1 fixed values, and calculating I'/I as a function of k_3.   Since k_3 is proportional to $\sqrt{E_l}$, we have also, assuming for the moment that $E_k \ll E_l$, that k_3 is also proportional to $\sqrt{\delta\nu}$, since to a first approximation $\delta\nu = E_l/h$.   In this manner Wentzel shows that

$$\frac{\Delta\nu}{\delta\nu} \sim \frac{k_2}{k_3} = \sqrt{\frac{E_k}{E_l}} \sim \frac{p_k}{p_l} \sim \sqrt{\frac{\nu_k}{\delta\nu}}. \qquad (3.154)$$

Here $\Delta\nu$ is the frequency width of the modified line; $\delta\nu$ is its decrease in frequency, $\nu - \nu'$; p_k and p_l are respectively the momenta of the electron within the atom and when recoiling; and $\nu_k = E_k/h$.

These equations indicate that a prominent modified line is to be expected only from those electrons whose binding energy is relatively small.   Thus in the case of the Mo$K\alpha$ line (0.71 A) scattered at 90 degrees, E_l corresponds to 560 volts.   For hydrogen, for which $E_k = 13.5$ volts, we should have $\Delta\nu/\delta\nu \sim 0.16$.   If we use 350 volts for E_k for the carbon K electrons, we have $\Delta\nu/\delta\nu \sim 0.8$.   This means that only the valence electrons can give a distinct line for this primary wave-length.   Of course, with shorter wave-lengths, more of the electrons would become effective.   There is thus no reason to expect a marked increase in the width of the modified line with large atomic numbers, for the more tightly bound electrons either produce no modified line at all, or give rise to so broad a band as to be undetectable.   This result is in accord with Woo's spectra (Fig. III–48), which show no obvious change in width with atomic number.

We should, however, anticipate a relative sharpening of the modified line with larger values of E_l.   Such an effect is clearly shown[175] in Du Mond and Kirkpatrick's spectra, Fig. III–50, which compare

[175] Wentzel (*loc. cit.*) notes the same phenomenon in similar spectra by M. de Broglie and A. Dauvillier, in which the effects with copper and silver anticathodes were compared.

the scattered lines for different primary wave-lengths. Similarly their photographs in Fig. III–49 agree well with the predictions of eq. (3.154), according to which for constant ν_k the relative width $\Delta\lambda/\delta\lambda$ is proportional to $1/\sqrt{\delta\nu}$, while the absolute width $\Delta\delta$ is directly proportional to $\sqrt{\delta\nu}$. Quantitative width measurements of these spectra emphasize the satisfactory character of this agreement.[176]

c. *Motion of Electrons within the Atom*

A clearer concept of the physical origin of the breadth of the modified line comes from a purely corpuscular theory, in which the photon collides with an electron which is in normal motion within the atom just before the impact. This theory has been developed by Jauncey,[177] and gives results which correspond closely with those later found by Wentzel, as described above. According to Jauncey's theory the conservation of energy and of momentum is represented by the following equations (neglecting v^2/c^2),

$$\tfrac{1}{2}mv^2 + h\nu = \tfrac{1}{2}mv'^2 + h\nu' \tag{3.155}$$

$$mv + \frac{h\nu}{c}j = mv' + \frac{h\nu}{c}j'. \tag{3.156}$$

In these equations the kinetic energy is that of the electron immediately before and immediately after the collision (unprimed and primed quantities respectively). The second is a vector equation where j is a unit vector in the direction of the primary photon and j' is a unit vector in the direction of scattering. The potential energy does not appear in these equations, but the condition is imposed that if the final kinetic energy $\tfrac{1}{2}mv'^2$ is less than $|E_k|$, the work required to remove the electron, the corresponding ray will be unchanged in wave-length.[178] It will be seen that if the initial velocity of the

---

[176] Cf. J. W. M. Du Mond and 'H. A. Kirkpatrick, Phys. Rev. **37**, 136 and **38**, 1094 (1931). The qualitative aspects of this phenomenon have been recognized since the earliest spectra of scattered x-rays were made. Cf. e.g., A. H. Compton, Phys. Rev. **22**, 409 (1923), and S. K. Allison and W. Duane, Phys. Rev. **26**, 300 (1925).

[177] G. E. M. Jauncey, Phys. Rev. **25**, 314 and 723 (1925). Cf. also A. H. Compton, Phys. Rev. **24**, 168 (1924), and J. W. M. Du Mond, Phys. Rev. **33**, 643 (1929).

[178] This limitation does not agree exactly with the deductions from Wentzel's wave-mechanics theory, according to which if $\tfrac{1}{2}mv'^2 < |E_k|$ the intensity of the modified line falls to a low value but remains appreciable for all values of $E_k < h\nu$. This latter limit agrees also with the findings of Compton (*loc. cit.*) from a more general form of photon theory.

electron is zero, these equations become identical with eqs. (3.114), (3.115) and (3.116).

Jauncey shows that if v is large compared with v', the resulting change in wave-length must lie within the range

$$\lambda' - \lambda = \frac{h}{mc} \text{ vers } \phi \pm \lambda \frac{v}{c} \sqrt{2 \text{ vers } \phi}. \qquad (3.157)$$

Thus if, as in the last section, we call $\Delta\lambda$ the width of the modified line and $\delta\lambda$ the mean wave-length change, we have

$$\Delta\lambda = 2\lambda \frac{v}{c} \sqrt{2 \text{ vers } \phi}, \qquad (3.158)$$

and

$$\frac{\Delta\lambda}{\delta\lambda} = \frac{\Delta\nu}{\delta\nu} \sim \frac{mv}{h/\lambda} \sim \frac{\sqrt{E_k}}{\sqrt{E_i}},$$

which is the result reached in eq. (3.154) from wave mechanics. In the present case, however, all possible values of $\lambda' - \lambda$ as given by (3.157) are equally probable. Thus for electrons with a definite initial speed the shape of the modified line should be rectangular.

In calculating the scattering from atoms, Jauncey used the contemporary Bohr theory according to which the K electrons revolve in circular orbits with constant speed, while the other electrons are in either circular orbits or elliptical orbits of differing ellipticities. On this basis he predicted widths that were in qualitative agreement with experiment.[179]

Du Mond (loc. cit.) has extended this theory in two ways. Starting with eq. (3.158), he has calculated the shape of the modified lines from various kinds of substances using electron velocities calculated from the more recent forms of quantum theory. He has also shown how the observed shape of the modified line may be analyzed to find the distribution of electron velocities required to produce the line. The latter procedure constitutes much the most direct method yet devised for determining the motions of electrons within atoms.[180]

[179] Cf. X-rays and Electrons, p. 287 for a more complete discussion of this theory.

[180] A complete summary of this work is given by J. W. M. Du Mond in Rev. Mod. Phys. 5, 1 (1933). See also Jauncey, Phys. Rev. 46, 667 (1934).

The height y of the modified line at a wave-length l from its center is given by Du Mond as (see Fig. III–63)

$$y = k \int_{l}^{\infty} \frac{1}{l} \, \Phi\left(\frac{l}{2\lambda^*}\right) dl, \qquad (3.159)$$

where $\Phi(\beta)d\beta$ is the probability that the electron which scatters the photon will have a speed between $v = \beta c$ and $v + dv$; λ^* is defined by the expression (to the first power of v/c),

$$\lambda^* = \lambda\sqrt{\tfrac{1}{2} \text{ vers } \phi};$$

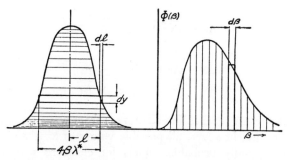

Fig. III–63. Illustrating the relation between spectral intensity distribution in the modified line (left) and population of electron speed states (right). Each elementary rectangle on the left is equal to one on the right. (DuMond.)

and k is an arbitrary constant. On the other hand, the velocity distribution is given by

$$\Phi(\beta) = K l \, dy/dl, \qquad (3.160)$$

where K is another arbitrary constant.

In Fig. III–64 are shown I, the observed spectral line when rays from a molybdenum target are scattered by beryllium; II, the shape of the modified line calculated from eq. (3.159) when $\Phi(\beta)$ is calculated from a free atom of the wave-mechanics type; V, the shape due to a Bohr Sommerfeld atom (Jauncey's theory); III, the shape assuming that the two outer electrons of the Be atom have the motions appropriate to conduction electrons according to Sommerfeld's theory of metallic conduction; and IV, the shape supposing the two conduction electrons per atom act as " free " electrons with the velocities ascribed by classical kinetic theory. It is evident that the experiments rule out cases IV and V, whereas III gives best

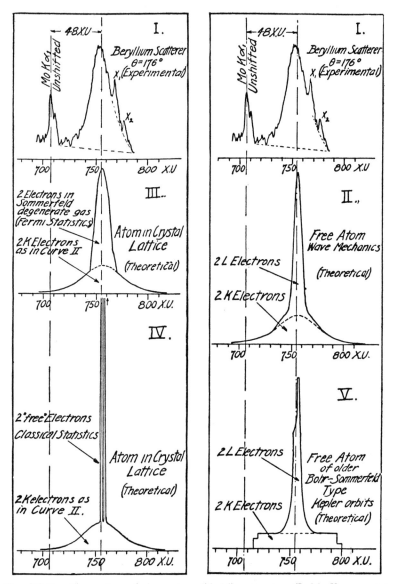

FIG. III–64. Comparison of observed modified line structure (I. Mo $K\alpha$ rays scattered from Be) with theoretical structures calculated on various assumptions. (DuMond.)

agreement with the observed curve.   Because of other factors, such
as the angular range of ϕ through which the rays were scattered,
may have contributed appreciably to the observed width, the agreement between I and III may be considered as rather satisfactory.

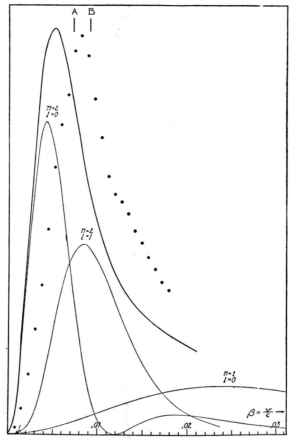

Fɪɢ. III–65.   Comparison of the momentum distribution calculated for a free carbon
atom with that calculated from the experimental breadth of a modified line. (DuMond.)

Figure III–65 shows in the experimental points the velocity distribution $\Phi(\beta)$ in graphite as obtained by applying eq. (3.160) to
the third of Du Mond and Kirkpatrick's spectra shown in Fig. III–49.
Compared with it is the velocity distribution calculated for the wave-
mechanics carbon atom.   The close similarity in shape is evident

The fact that the "observed" velocities are somewhat higher may indicate that in the solid the valence electrons move faster than in free carbon atoms. Thus lines A and B show the calculated positions of the peaks for two alternative assumptions regarding the motion of the valence electrons as conduction electrons. On the other hand, some other recent experiments, such as those of Gingrich and Bearden referred to above, show modified lines with somewhat sharper peaks than found by Du Mond and his collaborators. This would shift the "observed" velocity maximum of Fig. III–65 over toward the "calculated" maximum. The net result is that considering the combined uncertainties of both the experiments and the theory, this figure shows as good agreement as can be expected.

It thus appears that we have a rather direct experimental measure of the velocities of electrons in atoms, and the velocities observed are in satisfactory agreement with those deduced from the wave-mechanics theory of the atom. This result is the counterpart of that from the diffraction of x-rays, which as we have seen enables us to find the spatial distribution of the electrons in atoms. In later chapters we shall see how their energies can also be determined with high precision. It need hardly be added that these measurements of position and momentum are not made on individual electrons, but are statistical in character.

d. *Polarization of the Scattered Rays from Bound Electrons*

If a term which is roughly of the order of magnitude of q/λ' is neglected as compared with 1, that is for wave-lengths that are large compared with the Bohr orbits corresponding to the atomic energy levels, it can be shown[181] that eq. (3.147) reduces to

$$M_y = -\frac{1}{4\pi^2}\frac{e^2}{m\nu^2}E_0 \cos(2\pi\nu't) \int\int\int (\psi_k\psi_l{}^*) \cos(k_1 a \cos \alpha)d\tau$$

$$M_x = M_y = 0. \tag{3.161}$$

The effective electric moment of the scattering atom is thus in the direction of the electric vector E_0 of the incident wave. This is the same as for the Thomson theory of scattering developed early in the chapter, and means that the resulting radiation is polarized just as on the classical theory. The neglected term also has been shown

---

[181] Cf. Sommerfeld and Wentzel in the papers quoted for justification of this approximation.

by Dirac[182] to represent rays polarized in the same manner. Thus except for the electron spin term introduced by Klein and Nishina's relativity formula, the polarization according to wave-mechanics should be exactly that predicted by the simple classical theory.

The experiments by Compton and Hagenow quoted on page 120, as well as similar ones with longer waves by Kallmann and Mark[183] and with shorter waves by Barrett and Bearden[184] are in complete accord with this prediction. Further work on polarization of very short x-rays is, however, much to be desired, in order to test Nishina's prediction of an unpolarized component proportional to ν^2. As noted on p. 238, if the electron has a magnetic moment, such an unpolarized component should exist, though experiments adequate to detect its presence seem not to have been performed.

Intensity of Scattering from Bound Electrons

Making use of eq. (2.29), we have for the intensity of the radiation from an electric doublet,

$$I' = \frac{c}{8\pi} E'^2 = \frac{c}{8\pi} \frac{\sin^2 \theta}{r^2 c^4} \sum_l \left(\frac{d^2 M_{kl}}{dt^2}\right)^2, \qquad (3.162)$$

where θ is the angle between E and r, and the summation is taken over all the possible states l to which the atom may be excited. If for M we use, following Wentzel, the value given by the simplified formula (3.161), we have

$$\ddot{M}_{kl} \equiv \frac{d^2 M_{kl}}{dt^2}$$

$$= \frac{e^2 \nu'^2}{m\nu^2} E_0 \cos (2\pi\nu't) \int \int \int (\psi_k \psi_l{}^*) \cos (k_1 a \cos \alpha) d\tau. \qquad (3.163)$$

For a free electron traversed by the same electromagnetic wave, we should have,

$$\ddot{M}_e = e \frac{d^2 y}{dt^2} = \frac{e^2}{m} E_0 \cos 2\pi\nu t.$$

[182] P. A. M. Dirac, Proc. Roy. Soc. **111**, 405 (1926).
[183] H. Kallmann and H. Mark, Zeits. f. Phys. **36**, 120 (1926).
[184] C. S. Barrett and J. A. Bearden, Phys. Rev. **29**, 352 (1927).

With the further approximation that $\nu' = \nu$, we have then

$$\dot{M}_{kl} = \dot{M}_e \int \int \int (\psi_k \psi_i{}^*) \cos (k_1 a \cos \alpha) d\tau.$$

Thus

$$I' = I_e \sum_l \left[\int \int \int (\psi_k \psi_i{}^*) \cos (k_1 a \cos \alpha) d\tau \right]^2, \qquad (3.164)$$

where

$$I_e = \frac{c}{8\pi} \frac{\sin^2 \theta}{r^2 c^4} \dot{M}_e{}^2$$

is the classical scattering from an electron. Wentzel has calculated the sum of these squared integrals, using the complete system of proper functions ψ_l, and finds for the total simply 1. Thus to the degree of approximation used, the scattering by the bound electron is

$$I' = I_e, \qquad (3.165)$$

exactly that calculated classically for a free electron.

For long waves and small scattering angles, for which k_1 approaches zero, $M_{kl} = 0$ or 1 according as $l \neq k$ or $l = k$. In this case the sum consists of the single term $l = k$, which represents no change in wave-length. For larger values of k_1, other terms are significant, which being of different frequency are incoherent with the unmodified line. These transitions represent the modified line.

As we have seen, for high frequencies the scattered intensity is less than I_e by the factor $(\nu'/\nu)^3$. This factor does not appear in eq. (3.165) because of the approximation of dropping the factor $(\nu'/\nu)^2$ which appears in (3.163). If this factor is retained, the instantaneous intensity is changed by the factor $(\nu'/\nu)^4$. The duration of each wave received by the observer is, however, increased by the ratio ν/ν', so that the energy received per wave, and hence the average intensity for the complete wave train, is less by the factor $(\nu'/\nu)^3$. This was shown in eq. (3.136) for the scattering by free electrons. We now find that the same intensity factor applies to the incoherent rays from bound electrons, though our calculation is still incomplete due to the approximations made in reaching eq. (3.163). This result was originally postulated by Compton[185] from analogy with the free electron case, and has been confirmed by experiment.[186]

[185] A. H. Compton, Phys. Rev. 35, 932 (1930).
[186] Cf. e.g., Y. H. Woo, Proc. Nat. Acad. Sci. 17, 473 (1931).

Ratio of Coherent to Incoherent Scattering

Since for the ray of unchanged frequency $l = k$, we have for this ray simply,

$$\ddot{M}_{kk} = \ddot{M}_e \int \int \int (\psi_k \psi_k^*) \cos (k_1 a \cos \alpha) d\tau. \qquad (3.166)$$

Using the value

$$\psi_k = \sqrt{\frac{k_2^3}{\pi}} e^{-k_2 a}$$

(cf. eq. (3.148)), this integral can be immediately solved, giving

$$\ddot{M}_{kk} = \ddot{M}_e \left(1 + \frac{k_1^2}{4k_2^2} \right)^{-2}, \qquad (3.167)$$

which may be put in the form of either

$$\ddot{M}_{kk} = \ddot{M}_e \left(1 + \frac{E_l}{4 |E_k|} \right)^{-2}, \qquad (3.168)$$

or

$$= \ddot{M}_e \left(1 + \frac{\pi a_0}{\lambda} \sin \frac{\phi}{2} \right)^{-2}. \qquad (3.169)$$

The intensity of the undisplaced line, being proportional to $\ddot{M}_{kk}^2$, thus decreases for larger ratios of the recoil energy to the binding energy (3.168), and with the ratio of the effective ψ_k radius to the wave-length. The first statement is essentially the same as that resulting from Jauncey's photon theory of the unmodified line (p. 244), whereas the second relates this ratio to interference.

For comparison with experiment it is necessary to develop the corresponding theory for an atom with many electrons. Following Wentzel in his second paper,[187] we note that in this case the atom's scattering moment is the geometric resultant of the electric moments of all the electrons, that is

$$M = \sum_k \sum_l M_{kl}, \qquad (3.170)$$

where the first summation is taken over all the electrons in their normal states k.

For the *unmodified scattering* we then have in place of (3.166)

$$\sum \ddot{M}_{kk} = \ddot{M} \sum \int \int \int (\psi_k \psi_k^*) \cos (k_1 a \cos \alpha) \, d\tau, \qquad (3.171)$$

[187] Zeits. f. Phys. **43**, 781 (1927).

and the corresponding intensity is

$$I_{unm} = I_e \left[\Sigma \int \int \int (\psi_k \psi_k^*) \cos (k_1 a \cos \alpha) d\tau \right]^2. \qquad (3.172)$$

It will be seen that eq. (3.171) corresponds to our earlier formula (3.28) which is the interference factor that takes account of the phase differences between the rays scattered from various parts of the atom. The correspondence is exact if $\psi_k \psi_k^* = u(a)$, the volume density of electricity at a distance a from the atomic center. Thus the $I_{\text{unmodified}}$ is the same as the I_{coherent} of the classical treatment.

It will be useful to write

$$f_{kk} \equiv \int \int \int (\psi_k \psi_k^*) \cos (k_1 a \cos \alpha) d\tau, \qquad (3.173)$$

where f_{kk} is identical with the *electronic structure factor f* of eq. (3.26), though more generally defined, since no assumption is made here regarding the spherical symmetry of the atom.

In calculating the intensity of the *modified scattering*, we note that in the sum (3.170) those terms for which $l \neq k$ represent rays whose frequency differs from the primary frequency. For these incoherent rays it is, therefore, necessary to add up separately the intensity due to each component. Since according to eqs. (3.164) and (3.165) the total intensity due to each individual electron by itself would be I_e, the modified or incoherent intensity due to each electron is $I_e(1 - f_{kk}^2)$. The modified intensity from the whole atom is then simply,

$$I_{\text{mod}} = I_e \Sigma (1 - f_{kk}^2) = I_e(Z - \Sigma f_{kk}^2). \qquad (3.174)$$

This is precisely the second term of Woo's classically derived equation (3.35) which was there also ascribed to incoherent scattering.

The *total scattered intensity* is thus, according to Wentzel's theory, the sum of expressions (3.172) and (3.174),

$$I' = I_e \{ (\Sigma f_{kk})^2 + Z - \Sigma f_{kk}^2 \}, \qquad (3.175)$$

which is exactly the equation (3.36) derived from classical theory. The present theory has the merit, however, of giving this result uniquely, whereas on the classical theory several alternative expressions appeared to be possible.

As has already been noted, a factor $(\nu'/\nu)^3$ has been omitted from the formula for I_{mod}, having been lost in one of the approximations.

A more recent analysis by Waller[188] and Waller and Hartree,[189] shows also that if the electron spin is taken into account, some of the k to l transitions included in Wentzel's expression are forbidden by Pauli's exclusion principle, further reducing the strength of the modified ray. The complete expression for the modified ray, according to present theory would thus be

$$I_{\text{mod}} = I_e R \left\{ Z - \Sigma f_{kk}^2 - \underset{k \neq l}{\Sigma \Sigma} f_{kl}^2 + Z I_m \right\}, \qquad (3.176)$$

where R is the factor $(\nu'/\nu)^3$, and the terms are arranged in order of importance. Waller's correction appears in the third term, in which the sum is to be taken only over those transitions for which the electron spin is the same for the k state and the l state. Ordinarily this correction is negligible, but may in an extreme case amount to about 10 per cent of the incoherent scattering. The term $Z I_m$, on the other hand, represents the second term in the brackets of Klein and Nishina's equation (3.139), which is a further relativity correction. As we have seen, this term is negligible for ordinary x-ray wave-lengths.

The tests cited earlier in the chapter show that both eqs. (3.172) and (3.174) are in good agreement with experiment. Some very recent work by Harvey, Williams and Jauncey[190] on the diffuse scattering of x-rays by a single crystal of sodium fluoride have however supplied a more critical test for the incoherent scattering. From eqs. (3.103) and (3.106) this diffuse scattering may be written

$$S_c = \frac{F^2}{Z} (1 - e^{-4M}) + \frac{I_{\text{mod}}}{Z I_a}. \qquad (3.177)$$

The first term, representing the unmodified scattering due to the thermal motion of the atoms in the lattice, is relatively small for NaF crystals, so that most of the scattered radiation is of the modified type. Figure III–66 shows a comparison of their observed intensity with that calculated from (3.177), using in case I,

$$I_{\text{mod}} = I_e R Z (1 - f^2),$$

as in eq. (3.34); in case II,

$$I_{\text{mod}} = I_e R (Z - \Sigma f_{kk}^2),$$

[188] I. Waller, Phil. Mag. **4**, 1228 (1927); Zeits. f. Phys. **41**, 213 (1928).
[189] I. Waller and D. R. Hartree, Proc. Roy. Soc. **124**, 119 (1929).
[190] G. G. Harvey, P. S. Williams and G. E. M. Jauncey, Phys. Rev. **46**, 365 (1934).

as in eqs. (3.38) and (3.174); and in case III,

$$I_{\mathrm{mod}} = I_e R(Z - \Sigma f_{kk}{}^2 - \underset{k \neq l}{\Sigma \Sigma} f_{kl}{}^2),$$

as in eq. (3.176). They consider the agreement with the last calculation to be as good as can be expected in view of the uncertainties of experiment and calculation, whereas the other two formulas though not far wrong, show departures greater than the experimental errors.

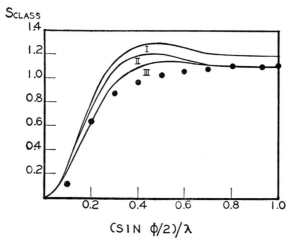

Fig. III–66. Diffuse scattering per electron from NaF crystal compared with that calculated on different theories of incoherent scattering. Curve III is computed from Waller's theory. (Harvey, Williams, and Jauncey.)

20. *Experiments with Very Short Waves*

For wave-lengths so short that the effect of recoil on intensity becomes marked, the effects of interference become small, especially for scattering by light elements. We may in this case, therefore, use the formulas of Breit-Dirac (3.137) or Klein and Nishina (3.139) which apply to free electrons.

Direct tests of the *scattering as a function of angle* are rather difficult, because the rays scattered at different angles are of different wave-lengths, and ionize the gas in the ionization chamber with different efficiencies. The correction for this effect in the x-ray region is of the same order of magnitude as the differences between the predictions of the classical and the quantum theories. Thus although a correction can be made, it is difficult to obtain a really reliable test. In the gamma ray region this difficulty is not so serious because the ionization by gamma rays does not vary as rapidly with wavelength.

Measurements have, however, been made in the x-ray region by Dessauer and Herz,[191] Friedrich and Goldhaber,[192] and Chylinski,[193] which are designed to test this point. Friedrich and Goldhaber's curve, shown in Fig. III-67 as plotted by Kirchner,[194] is typical of these measurements. It represents rays of effective wavelength 0.14 A, scattered by water. The agreement of the experimental points with the curve based on Breit-Dirac's formula is as

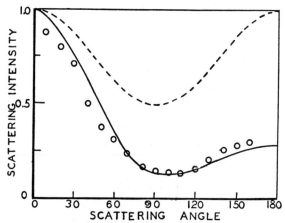

FIG. III-67. Directional distribution of x-rays of wave-length 0.14 A, scattered by water as compared with Breit-Dirac theory (solid curve) and classical theory (broken curve), according to Friedrich and Goldhaber.

good as can be expected. For this wave-length the difference between this and Klein-Nishina's formula is negligible.

In the gamma ray region, Fig. III-4 shows in the lower curve some early measurements by Compton,[195] which as will be seen fit the curve based on the Breit-Dirac formula very well if the wavelength is assumed to be 0.017 A, a value which is however considerably higher than present estimates for the hard γ-rays from RaC.

[191] F. Dessauer and R. Herz, Zeits. f. Phys. **27**, 56 (1924).
[192] W. Friedrich and G. Goldhaber, Zeits. f. Phys. **44**, 700 (1927)
[193] S. Chylinski, Phys. Rev. **42**, 153 (1932).
[194] F. Kirchner, " Physik der Röntgenstrahlen," p. 497.
[195] A. H. Compton, Phil. Mag. **41**, 749 (1921).

More recent experiments by Chao[196] support rather the formula of Klein and Nishina. His measurements of the scattering of the hard γ-rays from thorium C by aluminium are compared in Table III-8 with the theoretical calculations from Klein and Nishina and

TABLE III-8

INTENSITY OF SCATTERING OF γ-RAYS (λ = 0.005 A) FROM ALUMINIUM
AT DIFFERENT ANGLES

	35°	55°	90°	135°
Experiment..........	1.00	.509	.259	.185
K-N theory.........	1.00	.493	.249	.180
B-D theory.........	1.00	.295	.061	.037

from Breit and Dirac. The agreement is very much better with the former theory. This result must not be given too much weight since for a sufficiently greater assumed wave-length the latter theory would have been given the better fit, and the effective wave-length is hard to determine reliably. However, the result does give strong support to Klein and Nishina's equation.

Measurements of the absorption due to scattering give the best test as yet made of these formulas. If I_ϕ is the intensity of the rays scattered at an angle ϕ with the primary beam, the total number of scattered quanta is clearly,

$$n_s = \int_0^\pi \frac{1}{h\nu'} I_\phi \cdot 2\pi r^2 \sin \phi d\phi. \qquad (3.178)$$

But each of these quanta represents the removal of energy $h\nu$ from the primary beam. The scattering absorption coefficient, or fraction of the incident energy which is scattered is, therefore,

$$\sigma = \frac{n_s h\nu}{I} = \int_0^\pi \frac{I_\phi}{I} \frac{\nu}{\nu'} 2\pi r^2 \sin \phi d\phi. \qquad (3.179)$$

Substituting

$$\nu/\nu' = (1 - \alpha \operatorname{vers} \phi),$$

[196] C. Y. Chao, Phys. Rev. 36, 1519 (1930); Science Reports National Tsing Hua University, 1, 159 (1932).

and taking I_ϕ from Breit-Dirac's equation (3.137), eq. (3.179) gives on integration,

$$\sigma = \sigma_0 \cdot \frac{3}{4} \frac{1 + \alpha}{\alpha^3} \left\{ \frac{2\alpha(1 + \alpha)}{1 + 2\alpha} - \log(1 + 2\alpha) \right\}, \qquad (3.180)$$

where σ_0 is the classical scattering by a single electron, $(8\pi/3)e^4/m^2c^4$. For Klein-Nishina's formula (3.139), we get in the same way

$$\sigma = \sigma_0 \cdot \frac{3}{4} \left[\frac{1 + \alpha}{\alpha^3} \left\{ \frac{2\alpha(1 + \alpha)}{1 + 2\alpha} - \log(1 + 2\alpha) \right\} \right.$$
$$\left. + \frac{1}{2\alpha} \log(1 + 2\alpha) - \frac{1 + 3\alpha}{(1 + 2\alpha)^2} \right]. \qquad (3.181)$$

Using Compton's value of I_ϕ from eq. (3.138), integration yields the simple formula,

$$\sigma = \sigma_0/(1 + 2\alpha). \qquad (3.182)$$

The last formula differs from the other two only in terms of α^2 and higher, and is practically indistinguishable from that of Breit-Dirac throughout the x-ray region.

A very good experimental test of these formulas is afforded by recent experiments in the hard x-ray region by Read and Lauritsen,[197] combined with Chao's experiments[198] with gamma rays.[199]

Using potentials up to the unusual value of a million volts, Read and Lauritsen selected the desired wave-lengths by reflection from a rock-salt crystal and measured the absorption in carbon and aluminium. Chao used the filtered γ-rays from thorium C, whose wave-length as estimated from the speeds of secondary β-rays is 0.0047 A. These rays were scattered from aluminium at such angles that, with the increase in wave-length due to scattering, values of λ from 0.007 to 0.047 A were obtained.[200] Their absorption was in turn measured in aluminium. The results of these remarkable experiments are plotted in Fig. III–68. There will be seen wide departures of the data not only from the predictions of the classical theory, but also, especially at the shorter wave-lengths, from the Breit-Dirac theory.

---

[197] J. Read and C. C. Lauritsen, Phys. Rev. **45**, 433 (1934).

[198] C. Y. Chao, *loc. cit.*

[199] Other experiments leading to the same conclusion are described in X-rays and Electrons, p. 306.

[200] Cf. A. H. Compton, Phil. Mag. **41**, 760 (1921), and X-rays and Electrons, p. 183 for introduction of this technique.

Throughout the wave-length range investigated, the Klein-Nishina formula is completely verified.[201]

These experiments may be considered as confirming the introduction of the relativity or spin term in the formula for scattered x-rays. Thus the scattering of x-rays, like studies of line spectra, requires the assumption that the electron is magnetized.

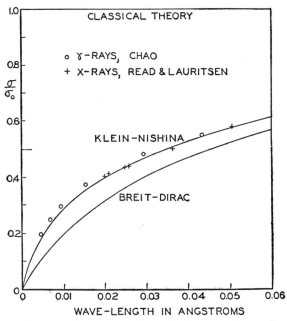

Fɪɢ. III–68.   Absorption due to scattering in aluminium.   Circles, Chao's measurements with γ-rays; crosses, Read and Lauritsen's data with x-rays; showing confirmation of Klein and Nishina's theory.

True absorption due to scattering.—We commonly distinguish between the two components τ and σ which enter into the total absorption μ of a beam of x-rays by calling τ the " true " absorption, and

[201] It must not be inferred from this that extrapolation of the Klein-Nishina formula to still shorter wave-lengths is, therefore, justified.   The experiments of Chao, Meitner and others show that for γ-ray wave-lengths additional types of absorption appear. These are presumably due to the nucleus.   It follows that the formulas discussed here cannot be applied with confidence to such short waves as those for example associated with cosmic rays.

σ the " scattering " absorption. It is, however, a distinctive feature of the quantum theory of scattering that a part of the energy removed from the primary beam is truly absorbed. We refer to that part of the energy of the primary photon which is spent in producing the recoil electrons.

The magnitude of this true absorption due to scattering can be easily calculated. If $2\pi r^2 I_\phi \sin\phi \, d\phi$ is the energy per second scattered between ϕ and $\phi + d\phi$, we have seen above (eq. (3.179)) that the energy removed from the primary beam to produce these scattered rays is

$$\frac{\nu}{\nu'} \cdot 2\pi r^2 I_\phi \sin\phi \, d\phi.$$

The difference between these two quantities,

$$\left(\frac{\nu}{\nu'} - 1\right) \cdot 2\pi r^2 I_\phi \sin\phi \, d\phi,$$

is therefore the energy spent in setting in motion the recoil electrons associated with these scattered rays. The coefficient of true absorption due to scattering is thus,

$$\sigma_a = \int_0^\pi \left(\frac{\nu}{\nu'} - 1\right) \cdot 2\pi r^2 I_\phi \sin\phi \, d\phi$$

$$= 2\pi r^2 \alpha \int_0^\pi I_\phi \text{ vers } \phi \sin\phi \, d\phi. \tag{3.183}$$

Similarly the coefficient of true scattering may be defined as

$$\sigma_s = 2\pi r^2 \int_0^\pi I_\phi \sin\phi \, d\phi. \tag{3.184}$$

If we use the value of I_ϕ given by eq. (3.138), we obtain from (3.183),

$$\sigma_a = \sigma_0 \cdot \frac{\alpha}{(1 + 2\alpha)^2}, \tag{3.185}$$

and from (3.184)

$$\sigma_s = \sigma_0 \frac{1 + \alpha}{(1 + 2\alpha)^2}. \tag{3.186}$$

The values of σ_a and σ_s calculated from the other quantum formulas for I_ϕ lead to much more complicated expressions, which are, however, the same to the first order of α.

When the quantum theory of scattering was proposed, no such true absorption had been found associated with scattering in the case of x-rays. Ishino had, however, demonstrated the existence of true absorption in the case of γ-rays,[202] and there was a strong tendency to associate this true absorption with the scattering.[203] The discovery of recoil electrons associated with the scattered rays requires the existence of such true absorption for both x-rays and γ-rays.

An experimental test of eq. (3.185) in the x-ray region has been made by Fricke and Glasser,[204] by a study of the ionization produced in small ionization chambers by the recoil electrons. They have determined the ratio of the photo-electric absorption τ to the scattering true absorption σ_a for two different wave-lengths, and for various materials. The second column of Table III–9 gives their results for

TABLE III–9

RATIO OF PHOTOELECTRIC TO SCATTERING TRUE ABSORPTION BY CARBON

(Fricke and Glasser)

λ, A. U., (Effective)	$\dfrac{\tau}{\sigma_a}$ Obs.	$\dfrac{\tau}{\rho}\begin{cases}\text{Hewlett}\\\text{Allen}\end{cases}$	$\dfrac{\sigma_a}{\rho}$ (Eq. 9.47)	$\dfrac{\tau}{\sigma_a}$ Calc.
0.180	.28	.0065	.0170	.38
0.115	.094	.00172	.0202	.085

carbon. The agreement with the values in the last column, which they calculate from eq. (3.185) with the help of Hewlett's and Allen's absorption data, is rather satisfactory.

Perhaps the best test of this scattering absorption is, however, the measurements of the recoil electrons. The experiments described in Sec. 14, which show that the number and energy of these particles is in close accord with the theoretical predictions, imply that the energy absorbed to produce the recoil electrons must also agree with the theory.

[202] M. Ishino, Phil. Mag. **33**, 140 (1917).

[203] Cf. e.g., A. H. Compton, Bulletin Nat. Res. Coun. No. 20, p. 45 (1922). The connection between the true absorption and the scattering of γ-rays had been emphasized earlier by E. Rutherford.

[204] H. Fricke and O. Glasser, Zeits. f. Phys. **29**, 374 (1924).

21. Summary

Our investigation of x-ray scattering from the standpoint of the hypothesis of photons thus gives results in complete accord with experiment. Similarly, our study based on the classical wave theory has enabled us to account for the chief features of diffraction of x-rays and their polarization. We have seen how the wave mechanics brings these two conceptions into a unified whole. It was in the study of the quantum features of x-ray scattering that the experimental basis for Heisenberg's principle of uncertainty was first laid. The intimate overlapping of the classical and quantum features of x-ray scattering have thus made it an unusually valuable field of study for clarifying our ideas of the fundamentals of atomic physics.

CHAPTER IV

DISPERSION THEORY APPLIED TO X-RAYS

1. *Introduction*

The term " dispersion " was introduced into physics in a purely qualitative way, to describe the action of a prism on a beam of light containing different wave-lengths, for instance, sunlight. After passage through the prism, the various colors are spread out or dispersed into a spectrum. In a slightly different sense of the word, we speak of the " dispersion " of an optical instrument, meaning in general the separation produced in two dispersed beams per unit difference in wave-length. In the case of a prism and optical light, we often speak of the dispersion as $d\theta/d\lambda$, where $d\theta$ is the angular separation of corresponding points on the diffraction patterns due to two wave-lengths differing by $d\lambda$. When dealing with the photographic registration of a spectrum, we often speak of the dispersion in a reciprocal sense, that is, the number of wave-length units (angstroms) per unit distance (millimeter) along the photographic plate.

It has been found possible to attribute the dispersing power of a prism to a change in the refractive index of its material with wave-length. The refractive index of a substance for a certain wave-length is a quantity whose accurate measurement is comparatively simple. Even with x-rays, where the effects produced by the index of refraction are decidedly second order phenomena, the technique has been rapidly improved until measurements of the unit decrement of the index accurate to 0.5 per cent can readily be made. In view of this important physical quantity, the term " dispersion theory " has come to represent for the most part theoretical attempts to explain the variation of refractive index with wave-length, although it is also applied to the wave-length dependence of other optical properties.

The index of refraction of ordinary transparent media for visible light increases as the wave-length decreases, that is, in a prism the violet is the more refrangible end of the spectrum. This is now called " normal " dispersion, for in 1862 Leroux[1] discovered " anomalous " dispersion in a prism filled with iodine vapor, in which the red light is bent more than the blue, and the index of refraction decreases as the wave-length decreases. It was soon discovered that such anomalous dispersion occurred if the incident light had a frequency very near to an absorption or emission frequency characteristic of the substance. This discovery provided a strong indication of the assumptions necessary for a successful theory of dispersion, namely, that such a theory must deal with the propagation of radiation through a medium consisting of oscillators having their own natural frequencies. Evidence that such ideas were in the minds of physicists at that time, and ready for development, is shown in the following statement by Stokes,[2] concerning the origin of fluorescence, written in 1852. " Nothing seems more natural than to suppose that the incident vibrations of the luminiferous aether produce vibratory movements along the ultimate molecules of sensitive substances, and that the molecules in turn, swinging on their own account, produce vibrations in the luminiferous aether, and thus cause the sensation of light. The periodic times of these vibrations depend on the periods in which the molecules are disposed to swing, not upon the periodic time of the incident vibrations." The ideas expressed here are the basis of dispersion theory as we know it today, except that we do not now speak so confidently of the ether, and have identified the " ultimate molecules," except in the far infra-red, with the electrons in the substance.

The first steps from which modern dispersion theory can be directly traced seem to have been made by Maxwell[3] in 1869, who derived the equation of propagation of a disturbance through a medium composed of ether " loaded " with oscillators having a characteristic frequency. Three years later Sellmeier[4] independently gave a similar treatment. Both these derivations neglected the damping of the oscillators, which it is necessary to consider in order that the refractive index be calculated as finite when the frequency

[1] Leroux, F. P., Comptes Rendus 55, 126 (1862).

[2] Stokes, Sir G. G., Phil. Trans. p. 463 (1852). Quoted in " History of the Theories of Aether and Electricity," by E. T. Whittaker. Longmans Green, Lond. 1910, p. 291.

[3] Maxwell, J. C., Cambridge Calendar 1869; republished by Lord Rayleigh, Phil. Mag. 48, 151 (1899).

[4] Sellmeier, W., Ann. der Physik 145, 399; 520 (1872).

of the incident radiation corresponds to a natural frequency of the oscillators.

With the discovery of the electron at the close of the nineteenth century, and the subsequent development of electron theory, the foundations of modern dispersion theory were laid. Lorentz[5] has given a theory which explains the behaviour of the index of refraction in the optical region, and gives quantitative agreement with refractive indices for x-rays in regions not too close to critical absorption limits.

In this chapter we will develop equations similar to those obtained by Lorentz, keeping in mind, however, that we are dealing with the refraction of x-rays. We will show that this theory predicts an absorption curve for x-rays which is widely different from that experimentally obtained, and how, in the effort to remove this discrepancy, a new theory of x-ray dispersion has been developed. The type of modification of the absorption theory necessary for the x-ray region was realized by A. H. Compton[6] in 1922. The assumption of " virtual " oscillators in the atom was formally introduced as a method of developing dispersion theory by Kramers[7] in 1924. The actual application of these ideas to the variation of the index of refraction with wave-length in the x-ray region was made by Kallmann and Mark[8] and by Kronig.[9] Other writers who have developed various aspects of the theory are Bothe,[10] Prins,[11] and Waller.[12]

2. The Differential Equation for the Free, Damped Oscillations of an Electron

In the chapter on the production of x-rays, we have seen that the classical theory attempted to account for the general x-radiation by the emission of a pulse of electromagnetic radiation as an electron was suddenly stopped in the target of an x-ray tube. This single pulse, when analyzed into a spectrum by a crystal, for instance,

[5] Lorentz, H. A. The Theory of Electrons. G. E. Stechert, N. Y., 1923.
[6] Compton, A. H., Bull. Nat. Res. Counc. U.S.A. 4, Pt. 2, No. 20 (1922).
[7] Kramers, H. A., Nature 113, 673; 114, 310 (1924).
[8] Kallmann and Mark, Naturwiss. 14, 648 (1926), Ann. d. Physik 82, 385 (1927).
[9] Kronig, R. de L., J. Opt. Soc. Am. 12, 547 (1926) and Phys. Rev. 27, 797 (1926).
[10] Bothe, Zs. f. Physik 40, 653 (1927).
[11] Prins, J. A., Zs. f. Physik 40, 653 (1928).
[12] Waller, I., Zs. f. Physik 61, 837 (1930).

would show some intensity at all wave-lengths. On the other hand
the presence of sharp characteristic lines in the x-ray spectrum means,
from the classical standpoint, the emission of long wave-trains from
some oscillating mechanism in the target. The actual wave-length
breadth of the $K\alpha$ lines of molybdenum has been measured,[13] and
the full width of the peak at half maximum found to be 0.294 X. U.,
or $\Delta\lambda/\lambda = 4.2 \times 10^{-4}$. The fact that these lines are not infinitely
narrow means that the wave-train is not infinitely long, or more
precisely, on the classical theory, does not have constant amplitude
throughout its length. A decrease in the amplitude of successive
waves emitted by the assumed oscillators could come from a damping
of the oscillators, and assuming that these are electrons, we will now
proceed to find out what form this damping factor may have.

A vibrating electron is accelerated, and an accelerated electron
radiates electromagnetic energy. This radiated energy must come
from the potential and kinetic energy in the vibratory motion, and
will therefore result in a decrease in the amplitude. In eq. (2.04)
of Chap. II we have seen that the rate of loss of energy by an accelerated electron is given by

$$\frac{dw}{dt} = -\frac{2e^2a^2}{3c^3},\qquad(4.01)$$

where w is the energy content of the electron, t is the time, e, the
electronic charge, a the acceleration, and c the velocity of the electromagnetic waves. In setting up the differential equation of motion
of the electron, we must express the loss of energy specified in the
preceding equation by considering what retarding force acting on the
electron would produce the effect. Let us write the acceleration as
the first time derivative of the velocity, and then set down the expression giving us the energy emitted in a time interval $t_2 - t_1$. This
is[14]

$$\int_{t_1}^{t_2} \frac{dw}{dt}\, dt = -\frac{2e^2}{3c^3}\int_{t_1}^{t_2} \left(\frac{dv}{dt}\right)^2 dt,\qquad(4.02)$$

in which v represents the velocity of the electron. We wish to introduce the quantity F into these equations, where F represents the

[13] Allison, S. K., and Williams, J. H., Phys. Rev. 35, 149 (1930).

[14] Abraham, M., Theorie der Elektrizität, B. G. Teubner, Leipzig (1908), vol. 2,
p. 64, et seg.

force equivalent of the electromagnetic damping. The quotient dw/dt has the dimensions of power, or of force x velocity, so that we may introduce F into the equations by writing Fv instead of dw/dt on the left hand side of eq. (4.02). The right hand side of eq. (4.02) may be integrated by parts, with the result

$$\int \left(\frac{dv}{dt}\right)^2 dt = v\frac{dv}{dt} - \int v\frac{d^2v}{dt^2}\,dt.$$

Making these changes in eq. (4.02) gives us the following:

$$\int_{t_1}^{t_2} Fv\,dt = -\frac{2e^2}{3c^3}\left[v\frac{dv}{dt} - \int v\frac{d^2v}{dt^2}\,dt\right]_{t_1}^{t_2}. \qquad (4.03)$$

As long as the motion of the electron is a vibratory one, instants must recur at which the acceleration is zero. In certain types of damping this does not occur when the electron is passing through the center of force, but since the acceleration must alternately assume positive and negative values, there must always be a time at which it is zero. We may, therefore, always find such values of t_1 and t_2 in the limits of our integration that the first term in the brackets on the right hand side of eq. (4.03) is zero, leaving effectively

$$\int_{t_1}^{t_2} Fv\,dt = \frac{2e^2}{3c^3}\int_{t_1}^{t_2} v\frac{d^2v}{dt^2}\,dt. \qquad (4.04)$$

By inspection and comparison of the expressions of the preceding equation, it is clear that

$$F = \frac{2e^2}{3c^3}\frac{d^2v}{dt^2}. \qquad (4.05)$$

This last expression gives us the force equivalent to the electromagnetic damping.

Let us now consider the unforced oscillations of the electron, that is, those executed in the absence of an impressed alternating electromagnetic field such as a light wave. In this case there are two forces acting on the electron, the so-called restoring force and the damping force just discussed. We shall assume that the restoring force F_r is proportional to the first power of the displacement ξ of the electron from a rest position, and write[15]

$$F_r = - mk_0^2c^2\xi, \tag{4.06}$$

where m is the electronic mass, c the velocity of light, and $k_0 = 2\pi\nu_0/c$, where ν_0 is the frequency of the undamped oscillations. We may now use Newton's second law of motion, with the forces of eqs. (4.05) and (4.06), and write the equation of motion of the electron as follows:

$$- mk_0^2c^2\xi + \frac{2e^2}{3c^3}\frac{d^2v}{dt^2} = m\frac{dv}{dt}. \tag{4.07}$$

If we make the displacement the only dependent variable in the equation, and express time derivatives by dots over the quantity differentiated, eq. (4.07) becomes

$$\ddot{\xi} - \frac{2e^2}{3mc^3}\dddot{\xi} + k_0^2c^2\xi = 0. \tag{4.08}$$

An outstanding feature of this equation which governs the free, damped, oscillations of an electron is that it involves the third time derivative of the displacement.

3. A Classical Estimate of the Width of Spectrum Lines

Since the effect of the electromagnetic damping is to decrease the amplitude of the motion as time goes on, we are led to expect a solution of eq. (4.08) having the following form:

$$\xi = \xi_0 e^{-bt} \cos(\omega_0 t - \theta). \tag{4.09}$$

Here ξ_0 is the amplitude at the time $t = 0$, and $\omega_0 = k_0c = 2\pi\nu_0$. We wish to find an expression for the damping factor b in terms of

---

[15] Eq. (4.06) may be justified as follows. Due to the assumption that the force is proportional to the displacement, the undamped motion will be linear simple harmonic motion; which may be represented by

$$\xi = R \cos 2\pi\nu_0 t,$$

where R is the amplitude. The restoring force will be

$$F_r = m\frac{d^2\xi}{dt^2}$$

and by differentiation we find

$$F_r = - 4\pi^2 m\nu_0^2 R \cos 2\pi\nu_0 t = - mk_0^2c^2\xi,$$

which agrees with eq. (4.06).

fundamental physical constants by substitution of this solution in eq. (4.08). We shall do this under the assumption that $b \ll \omega_0$, which means that the decrease of amplitude is gradual. In performing the necessary differentiations, it is very convenient to express ξ as the real part of a complex number. We see that the right hand member of eq. (4.09) is the real part of the following:

$$\xi = \xi_0 e^{-bt} e^{i(\omega_0 t - \theta)} = \xi_0 e^{-i\theta} e^{i(\omega_0 - b)t}. \tag{4.10}$$

If we now calculate $\dot{\xi}$ and $\ddot{\xi}$ from eq. (4.10), and substitute in eq. (4.08), we obtain

$$(i\omega_0 - b)^2 - \alpha(i\omega_0 - b)^3 + \omega_0^2 = 0, \tag{4.11}$$

where

$$\alpha = \frac{2e^2}{3mc^3} \doteq 6.3 \times 10^{-23}.$$

If now in eq. (4.11) we drop terms in b higher than the first power, we obtain

$$i\omega_0^3 \alpha - b(2i\omega_0 + 3\omega_0^2 \alpha) = 0.$$

The value of α is so small, that even in the x-ray region the second term in the coefficient of b in the preceding equation is negligible, so that we obtain the following value of b:

$$b = \frac{e^2 \omega_0^2}{3mc^3}. \tag{4.12}$$

Let us now consider the radiation scattered by this oscillator. Let an observer be stationed at a great distance ρ from the oscillator, and let the angle between the direction of motion of the electron and the line joining the center of oscillation to the observer's position be ϕ. If E is the strength of the electric field at the observer's position, we have seen in the chapter on the production of x-rays that

$$E = \frac{\ddot{\xi} e \sin \phi}{\rho c^2}. \tag{4.13}$$

θ can be set equal to zero in eq. (4.10) without loss of generality, and remembering that b is a small quantity compared to ω_0, we may write

$$\ddot{\xi} = -\xi_0 \omega_0^2 e^{-bt} e^{i\omega_0 t}$$

In this expression, the time t is measured at the electron's position; the field E actually travels with the finite velocity c. We express the time lag involved by replacing t in the previous expressions by $(t - \rho/c)$, and measuring time at the observer's position. We thus obtain the following expression for the intensity of the electric field at the observer's position

$$E = -\frac{e\xi_o\omega_o^2 \sin \phi}{\rho c^2} e^{-b(t - \rho/c)} e^{i\omega_o(t - \rho/c)}$$

For the present, we may consider the observer's position fixed, and concentrate our interest on the effect of the damping factor. With this in mind we may simplify the preceding equation to read

$$E = E_o e^{-bt} e^{i\omega_o(t - \rho/c)}, \tag{4.14}$$

where E_o is a constant.

The length of time required for the amplitude of the field oscillations to decrease to $1/e$ of their initial value will be $1/b$. During this time the front of the disturbance has traveled a distance c/b, so that the number of waves in this part of the wave train is $c/b\lambda_o$. We thus arrive at the following formulae:

Length of wave train (to amplitude E_o/e) $\dfrac{3mc^2}{4\pi^2e^2}\lambda_o^2$ (4.15)

Number of waves in train (to amplitude E_o/e) $\dfrac{3mc^2}{4\pi^2e^2}\lambda_o$ (4.16)

Effective time of oscillation $\dfrac{3mc^3}{4\pi^2e^2\nu_o^2}$ (4.17)

The values of some of these quantities for typical regions in the spectrum are shown in Table IV–1.

TABLE IV–1

DAMPING OF WAVES DUE TO RADIATION

Wave-length in A.U.	Effective Number of Waves	Effective Time	Effective Length
0.01 (hard γ-rays).........	27	9×10^{-20} sec.	2.7×10^{-9} cm.
0.50 (x-rays).............	1350	2.3×10^{-16}	6.8×10^{-6}
5000 (light).............	1.35×10^7	2.3×10^{-8}	6.8×10^2

The preceding discussion shows that a damped electronic oscillator according to the classical theory will emit a wave train of constantly decreasing amplitude. We will now investigate the spectrum of this wave train as revealed by some diffraction mechanism, in other words, we will deduce the shape and width of a spectrum line.[16] Since the wave-train to be analyzed harmonically extends from o to ∞, we must apply Fourier's integral to the problem. A standard form of Fourier's integral[17] is as follows:

$$F(t) = \frac{1}{\pi} \int_0^\infty d\omega \int_{-\infty}^\infty F(\tau) \cos \omega(t - \tau) d\tau. \qquad (4.18)$$

In our problem, $F(t)$ represents the wave-train under consideration, and is given by the right hand member of eq. (4.14). τ represents a "running coordinate" which disappears after the integration is completed. Equation (4.18) is somewhat simplified if the trigonometric function is expressed as the real part of a complex quantity. With this understanding we may write

$$F(t) = \frac{1}{\pi} \int_0^\infty d\omega \int_{-\infty}^\infty F(\tau) e^{i\omega(t-\tau)} d\tau, \qquad (4.19)$$

which simplifies to

$$F(t) = \frac{1}{\pi} \int_0^\infty e^{i\omega t} \phi(\omega) d\omega, \qquad (4.20)$$

where

$$\phi(\omega) = \int_{-\infty}^\infty F(\tau) e^{-i\omega\tau} d\tau. \qquad (4.21)$$

If we count time beginning when the disturbance reaches the observer as $t = $ o, the $F(t)$ with which we have to deal is defined as follows:

$$-\infty < t < o \qquad F(t) = o$$

$$o < t < \infty \qquad F(t) = E_o e^{-bt} e^{i\omega_0(t - \rho/c)}$$

---

[16] The derivation given here was suggested by that of Mandersloot, W. C., Jahrb. der Radioakt. und Elektron. **13**, 16 (1916). The problem has also been treated by Jauncey, G. E. M., Phys. Rev. **19**, 68 (1922).

[17] Cf. Byerly, W. E., An Elementary Treatise on Fourier Series; Mellor, J. W., Higher Mathematics, p. 479.

Therefore in calculating $\phi(\omega)$ from (4.21) we have

$$\phi(\omega) = E_0 \int_0^\infty e^{-b\tau} e^{i\omega_0(\tau - \rho/c)} e^{-i\omega\tau}\, d\tau$$

$$= E_0 \left\{ \frac{1}{i(\omega - \omega_0) + b} \right\} e^{-i\omega_0\rho/c}. \qquad (4.22)$$

So that from eq. (4.20) we may write

$$F(t) = \frac{1}{\pi} E_0 e^{-i\omega_0\rho/c} \int_0^\infty \frac{e^{i\omega t}}{i(\omega - \omega_0) + b}\, d\omega. \qquad (4.23)$$

The right hand member of eq. (4.23) may be thought of as a series of cosine waves of all frequencies from o to ∞, represented by

$$\frac{1}{\pi} E_0 \left[\frac{1}{i(\omega - \omega_0) + b} \right] e^{i(\omega t - \omega_0\rho/c)}. \qquad (4.24)$$

We proceed to find the amplitudes of these waves. To do this we must put eq. (4.24) in such a form that the coefficient of the exponential part is entirely real. This may be accomplished by multiplying numerator and denominator of the expression in brackets by $\{i(\omega - \omega_0) - b\}$ and then using the well known relation between the algebraic and exponential form of a complex number. Equation (4.24) then becomes

$$\frac{1}{\pi} E_0 \frac{1}{\sqrt{b^2 + (\omega - \omega_0)^2}} \exp\left\{ i\left(\omega t - \frac{\omega_0\rho}{c} + \tan^{-1}\frac{\omega - \omega_0}{b} \right) \right\}. \qquad (4.25)$$

The amplitude of a wave of frequency $\omega/2\pi$ is the coefficient of the exponential part of (4.25), and since the intensity is proportional to the square of the amplitude

$$I_\omega \sim \frac{E_0^2}{\pi^2} \frac{1}{b^2 + (\omega - \omega_0)^2}. \qquad (4.26)$$

where I_ω is the intensity at a frequency $\omega/2\pi$. This function has a maximum at $\omega = \omega_0$ and if we use as our measure of intensity the ratio of I_ω to the maximum value of I, we get

$$\frac{I_\omega}{I_{\max}} = \frac{1}{1 + \{(\omega - \omega_0)/b\}^2}. \qquad (4.27)$$

This is the classical expression for the shape of a spectrum line. By setting it equal to $\frac{1}{2}$, we may deduce the half width of the curve at half maximum in frequency units (w_ν) and in wave-length units (w_λ); Fig. IV-1. The results are

$$w_\nu = \frac{2\pi e^2 \nu_0{}^2}{3mc^3}.$$ (4.28)

$$w_\lambda = \frac{2\pi e^2}{3mc^2}.$$ (4.29)

The wave-length width is independent of wave-length, and on calculation comes out to be 5.9×10^{-13} cm., or 0.059 X. U.

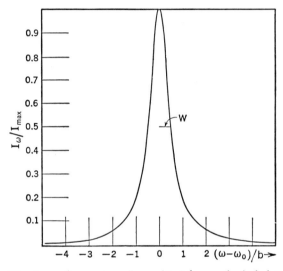

Fig. IV-1. The shape of a spectrum line emitted from a classical electronic simple harmonic oscillator with electromagnetic damping, according to eq. (4.27). Eqs. (4.28) and (4.29) refer to the half width at half maximum of this curve.

In the x-ray region the Doppler effect due to the thermal motion of the atoms in the target can give no appreciable contribution to the observed width, due to the fact that the Doppler broadening is inversely proportional to the frequency, and is already small in the optical region. In measuring the width of the Mo $K\alpha$ lines with the double spectrometer, Allison and Williams[18] showed that the width was independent of voltage, at least between 25 and 50 kilovolts. This lends support to the view that these lines are not accompanied

[18] Phys. Rev. **35,** 1476 (1930).

by close satellites representing higher stages of excitation of the atom. The observed half width at half maximum of Mo $K\alpha_1$ was 0.147 X. U., about 2.5 times that calculated from eq. (4.29). The theory here outlined therefore gives the correct order of magnitude of the width.

Of course a great body of evidence exists to show that any classical theory such as that proposed here is incapable of adequate treatment of problems concerning the origin of spectrum lines. We need only to call attention to the fact that we have assumed that the line is radiated by a simple harmonic electronic oscillator. Such simple harmonic oscillations can only radiate one frequency, and the number of such oscillators which it is necessary to assume in order to explain the large numbers of spectrum lines produced by a given atomic species is in conflict with our knowledge of the number of electrons per atom. On the other hand, if we treat a multiply periodic oscillator, we find that the frequency depends on the energy content, and no such thing as a sharp spectrum line could be radiated.

A qualitative disagreement of a suggestive type between the above classical theory and experiment is furnished by comparison of the experiments quoted above with those of Williams,[19] who measured the widths of the uranium L series lines. The wave-lengths of the Mo $K\alpha_1$ and U $L\beta_3$ lines are almost identical, being 707.8 and 708.4 X. U. respectively. The U $L\beta_3$ line is much the wider, having a half width at half maximum of 0.382 X. U. This shows clearly that the widths are dependent on the properties of the initial and final states in the transition producing the line.

Recent calculations of the intrinsic shapes and widths of spectrum lines have been made by Weisskopf and Wigner,[20] and by Hoyt,[21] using the wave mechanics. The results show that to a first approximation the shape of a line should be given by eq. (4.27), but that the damping factor b depends on quantities associated with the initial and final states of the transition.

4. *The Forced, Damped Oscillations of an Electron, and the Dielectric Constant of the Medium*

In the classical theory, the scattered radiation of unchanged wave-length is produced by the forced oscillations of the electrons in the

---

[19] Williams, J. H. Phys. Rev. **37**, 1431 (1931).
[20] Zs. f. Phys. **63**, 54 (1930).
[21] Phys. Rev. **36**, 860 (1930).

scattering material. These oscillations, after the transients have died down, take on the frequency of the impressed wave, and the electron scatters a wave of the same frequency. The interaction between the waves and the oscillator is small unless the frequency of the waves is very near to the natural frequency of the oscillator, where the absorption mounts to very high values.

Equation (4.08) gives us the oscillations of the electron in the absence of an impressed alternating electric field. In the corresponding expression for the forced oscillations we must include the force exerted by the field on the electron. Let the incident plane waves of wave-length $2\pi/k$ be traveling in the positive direction of the x-axis, and be represented by

$$E = e^{ik(ct - x)},$$

in which we have assumed unit incident amplitude. Let us further agree that the symbol e represents the charge on the electron in magnitude only, that is, $e = 4.77 \times 10^{-10}$ esu. We must therefore write the force exerted by the field E upon the electron as $-eE$, due to the intrinsically negative electronic charge. Addition of this force[22] to eq. (4.08) gives us

$$\ddot{\xi} - \frac{2e^2\dddot{\xi}}{3mc^3} + k_q^2c^2\xi = -\frac{e}{m}e^{ik(ct - x)}. \tag{4.30}$$

In this[23] and subsequent equations, we will use the subscript q instead of o to indicate a natural frequency of the atom, and in the x-ray case, q may refer to the K, L, M, etc., limits.

[22] In a general treatment of dispersion theory, it is necessary to take account of the forces exerted on the electronic oscillator by adjacent electrons in the medium, so that the E of the oncoming wave is not necessarily the E which acts on the oscillator. (Cf. e.g. Page, Introduction to Theoretical Physics, Van Nostrand (1929), page 467 et seq.) It may be shown that this consideration leads to an equation similar to eq. (4.35), and of the form

$$\kappa_q = 1 + \frac{4\pi n_0 e^2}{mc^2(k_q^2 - k^2) - \frac{4}{3}\pi n_q e^2 + \frac{2}{3}e^2 ik^3}$$

where n_q is the number of electrons per unit volume having the characteristic frequency $k_q c/2\pi$. In the x-ray region it may be shown that the term $4\pi n_q e^2/3$ is negligible in comparison with other terms in the denominator.

[23] This equation appears in a treatment of x-ray refraction by Darwin, Phil. Mag. **27**, 675 (1914).

When a steady state has been reached, we may expect a solution of this equation of the form

$$\xi = \alpha e^{ik(ct - x)}. \qquad (4.31)$$

The constant α can be determined by differentiation of eq. (4.31) and substitution in eq. (4.30), leading to the result

$$\xi = - \frac{e e^{ik(ct - x)}}{mc^2(k_q{}^2 - k^2) + 2e^2ik^3/3}. \qquad (4.32)$$

ξ is the displacement of the electron from its position of rest, and is thus connected with the polarization of the medium. The polariza-

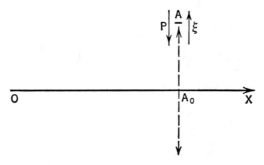

F1G. IV–2. If we suppose that the effect of the electric component of an electromagnetic wave moving along OX is to displace the electron originally at A_0 to a point A, then, due to the intrinsically negative electronic charge, the induced polarization P is in the opposite direction to the displacement ξ.

tion is defined as the electric moment per unit volume, which thus becomes the total charge of one sign times the separation of charge. The polarization P is a directed quantity, and its direction is that of the electric moment of the dipoles produced in the medium. The direction of an electric moment is such that its positive sense is that of a line drawn from the negative charge to the positive. In Fig. IV–2 let A_0 represent the rest position of the electron, and let A be the position of the electron when it has a displacement $+ \xi$; the electric moment is directed from A toward A_0 because of the negative charge of the electron. It is therefore proportional to $-\xi$, and if n_q is the number of electrons per unit volume of the characteristic frequency $k_q c/2\pi$, the polarization produced by them will be

$$P_q = - n_q e \xi. \qquad (4.33)$$

The negative sign enters here due to our convention that the symbol e represents the electronic charge in numerical value only.

We will now calculate the dielectric constant κ from the polarization of the medium by using the well-known relation[24]

$$\kappa = 1 + 4\pi P/E. \tag{4.34}$$

Combination of the preceding three equations leads to the expression

$$\kappa_q = 1 + \frac{4\pi n_q e^2}{mc^2(k_q^2 - k^2) + 2e^2 i k^3/3}. \tag{4.35}$$

In this equation κ_q is the contribution to the dielectric constant from electrons of the type q.

5. Significance of the Complex Dielectric Constant

In eq. (4.35) we see that the dielectric constant is a complex quantity, and in this section we will endeavor to give a physical interpretation to its real and its imaginary parts. Let us represent the complex dielectric constant in the following way

$$\kappa = 1 - 2\delta - 2i\beta \tag{4.36}$$

and express δ and β in terms of the quantities appearing in eq. (4.35). If the numerator and denominator of the fraction appearing in the right hand member of this equation are multiplied by the complex conjugate of the denominator, the expression may be thrown into a form in which it may readily be compared with eq. (4.36). It then appears that

$$\delta_q = - \frac{2\pi n_q e^2 mc^2(k_q^2 - k^2)}{m^2 c^4(k_q^2 - k^2)^2 + 4e^4 k^6/9}. \tag{4.37}$$

$$\beta_q = \frac{4\pi n_q e^4 k^3}{3\{m^2 c^4(k_q^2 - k^2)^2 + 4e^4 k^6/9\}} \tag{4.38}$$

In discussing the physical meaning of the complex nature of the dielectric constant, we will use the celebrated relation deduced by Maxwell between the phase velocity of the waves in the medium and the dielectric constant, which is

$$v = c/\sqrt{\kappa}, \tag{4.39}$$

---

[24] This relation is derived in any moderately advanced text on electricity and magnetism, e.g. Page, Introduction to Theoretical Physics, p. 330.

We see at once that if the dielectric constant is complex, the phase velocity v is also. Instead of directly discussing the complex phase velocity, we will discuss its reciprocal,[25] which we will call the complex wave slowness, S_c. We will have

$$S_c = \frac{I}{c}(I - 2\delta - 2i\beta)^{1/2}.$$

In all cases in which the theory being developed here has been applied to experiment, δ and β are small quantities usually of the order of 10^{-6}. We will anticipate this result in the process of taking the square root of κ, and write approximately

$$S_c = \frac{I}{c}(I - \delta - i\beta) = S - iS_i. \tag{4.40}$$

In general the equation of a wave moving through the medium may be written

$$E = Ae^{i\omega(t-x/v)} = Ae^{i\omega(t-S_c x)}$$

where $\omega = 2\pi\nu$, ν being the frequency, and v is the phase velocity. Putting in the real and imaginary parts of the complex wave slowness from eq. (4.40), we obtain

$$E = Ae^{i\omega[t-(S-iS_i)x]} = Ae^{-\omega S_i x}e^{i\omega(t-Sx)} \tag{4.41}$$

We see now that the complex nature of the dielectric constant, and hence of the phase velocity, introduces an absorption coefficient ωS_i into the wave equation, and that the waves diminish in amplitude as they pass through the medium. If A_x is the amplitude after penetrating a distance x,

$$A_x = A_0 e^{-2\pi c S_i x/\lambda} \tag{4.42}$$

In order to find the connection between cS_i and the ordinary linear absorption coefficient which we will call μ_l, we must express the rate of decrease of intensity, which is proportional to the square of that of the amplitude. Thus

$$I_x = I_0 e^{-4\pi\beta x/\lambda}$$

and

$$\beta = \frac{\lambda}{4\pi}\mu_l. \tag{4.43a}$$

[25] Page, L., Introduction to Theoretical Physics, Van Nostrand (1929), page 468.

We have thus shown that the real part of the complex dielectric constant is related to the phase velocity of waves in the medium, whereas the imaginary part has to do with their absorption.

6. The Index of Refraction

Since the index of refraction is the ratio of the phase velocities in vacuum and in the medium, or c/v, it will appear in this theory as a complex number, called the complex index of refraction μ_c, where

$$\mu_c = \mu - i\mu_i = 1 - \delta - i\beta \qquad (4.43b)$$

The real index of refraction, which is the ratio of the real phase velocities, is $1 - \delta$. We shall call δ the unit decrement of the refractive index, and consider its value. An expression for δ has been given as eq. (4.37). The term $4e^4k^6/9$ which appears in the denominator of this expression is due to the electromagnetic damping, and we shall show that except in regions where k is very near k_q this term is negligible. This can be shown by a sample numerical calculation. Consider, for instance, the refraction of x-rays of wave-length $2\pi \times 10^{-9}$ cm. by a glass prism. The shortest x-ray wave-length characteristic of the glass will be the K limit of calcium, which we may take as $\pi \times 10^{-8}$ cm. Using these values we find

$$\tfrac{4}{9} e^4 k^6 = 2.3 \times 10^{16},$$

$$m^2 c^4 (k_q{}^2 - k^2)^2 = 6.1 \times 10^{23},$$

showing that unless k is extremely near k_q, the damping term may be omitted. If this is done, eq. 4.37 becomes

$$\delta_q = -\frac{2\pi n_q e^2}{mc^2(k_q{}^2 - k^2)} = \frac{n_q e^2}{2\pi m(\nu^2 - \nu_q{}^2)}. \qquad (4.44)$$

If the medium contains electrons of various natural frequencies ν_q, and n_q is the number of electrons per cubic centimeter of natural frequency ν_q, the formula becomes

$$\delta = \sum_q \delta_q = \frac{e^2}{2\pi m} \sum_q \frac{n_q}{\nu^2 - \nu_q{}^2}. \qquad (4.45)$$

In many cases, index of refraction measurements have been made at wave-lengths so much shorter than any critical absorption wave-length of the medium that for any ν_q, $\nu^2 \gg \nu_q{}^2$. Here eq. (4.45) becomes

$$\delta = \frac{ne^2}{2\pi m \nu^2} = \frac{ne^2\lambda^2}{2\pi mc^2}, \qquad (4.46)$$

where n is the total number of electrons per cubic centimeter.

7. Experimental Methods for Measuring the Refractive Index

At the present time there are four principal methods of measuring the index of refraction for x-rays, which we shall now briefly describe.[26]

(1) *Variation of apparent wave-length with order in the crystalline diffraction of x-ray lines.*—In the chapter on accurate measurement of x-ray wave-lengths it is shown that if the uncorrected Bragg formula is used to compute the wave-length from the observed glancing angle, the values thus calculated will depend on the order of reflection. Conversely, through accurate measurement of the Bragg angle at various orders, it is possible to compute the unit decrement of the refractive index from the equation

$$\delta = \frac{\lambda_1 - \lambda_2}{\bar{\lambda}} \frac{n_2{}^2}{n_2{}^2 - n_1{}^2} \sin^2 \theta_1, \qquad (4.47)$$

where λ_1 and λ_2 are the apparent wave-lengths in the orders n_1 and n_2, θ_1 is the observed glancing angle for the order n_1 and $\bar{\lambda}$ is the mean of λ_1 and λ_2. This method was the first to yield quantitative information on x-ray refractive indices. In 1919 Stenstrom[27] measured the variation of the apparent wave-length of $MoL\beta_1$ and other lines when reflected in various orders from sugar crystals. He found positive values of δ, using eq. 4.47, and thus showed that the refractive index was less than unity, as predicted by the theory.

---

[26] These methods are discussed in the following:

Siegbahn, Spektroskopie der Röntgenstrahlen, 2nd Ed., Julius Springer, Berlin (1931).

Larsson, Diss. Uppsala (1929).

[27] Stenström, W., Diss. Lund, 1919.

Duane and Patterson, Phys. Rev. **16**, 532 (1920).

Larsson, Ark. Mat. Astr. o. Fys. Uppsala **19A**, 14 (1925).

Kellström, Z. Physik. **41**, 516 (1927).

Larsson, Phil. Mag. **3**, 1136 (1927).

Enger, Z. Phys. **46**, 826 (1928).

Bergqvist, Z. Phys. **66**, 494 (1930).

Compton, A. H., Rev. Sci. Instr. **2**, 365 (1931).

The variations with order observed by this method are however very small, and for accurate measurements of δ this method has been superseded by the third to be described in this section.

(2) *Determination of the limiting angle of total reflection.*—Since the index of refraction is less than unity, if x-rays strike a polished surface at a sufficiently small glancing angle they are totally reflected, as we have seen in the introductory chapter. According to elementary theory, there is a maximum glancing angle beyond which total reflection does not occur, and if this critical glancing angle θ_c can be measured,

$$\delta = \tfrac{1}{2}\theta_c^2. \tag{4.48}$$

If the intensity of reflection of a beam of monochromatic x-rays of small divergence is plotted against glancing angle, an estimate of θ_c may be obtained from the rapid diminution of the reflecting power in this region. Refractive indices were first measured in this way by A. H. Compton in 1922, and since that time many others have used the same procedure.[28] It has been found, however, that in a more complete theory of the variation of intensity near the critical angle, the effect of the absorption of the x-rays in the medium must be taken into account. We shall discuss this effect in Sec. 12 of this chapter, and give there a list of references to papers on total reflection in which this effect has been studied. If the absorption is considerable, there will not be a sharp critical angle, and the experi-

---

[28] Compton, A. H., Bull. Nat. Res. Counc. U.S.A. **20**, 48 (1922), Phil. Mag. **45**, 1121 (1923).

Davis and Terrill, Proc. Nat. Acad. Sci., U.S.A. **8**, 357 (1922).

Siegbahn and Lundquist, Fysik. Tidskrift **21**, 170 (1923).

Wolfers, Compt. rend. **177**, 32 (1923).

Kirkpatrick, Nature **113**, 98 (1924).

Stauss, Nature **114**, 88 (1924).

Carrara, N. Cimento **1**, 107 (1924).

de Broglie, M. and Thibaud, J., Compt. rend. **181**, 1034 (1925).

Doan, Phil. Mag. **4**, 100 (1926).

Linnik and Lashkareff, Z. Physik **38**, 659 (1926).

Edwards, Phys. Rev. **30**, 91 (1927).

Forster, Naturwiss. **15**, 969 (1927).

Dershem, Phys. Rev. **31**, 1117 (1928).

Lashkareff and Hertzrücken, Z. Phys. **52**, 739 (1928).

Thibaud, J. Phys. et le Radium **10**, 8 (1929).

Dershem, Phys. Rev. **35**, 128 (1930).

Kellermann, K. Ann. Phys. **4**, 185 (1930).

Smith, Phys. Rev. **40**, 156 (1932).

ment will not give an accurate value of δ unless some consideration of the absorption is included in the treatment of the results. This method is therefore not in general capable of a precision comparable to that of the next two methods to be described.

(3) *The crystal wedge method.*—This method was devised by Bergen Davis in 1924, and since that time has been applied by several experimenters.[29]   An artificial plane polished face is cut on the crystal so that the angle between the face and the reflecting planes of the crystal is very nearly the Bragg angle for the wave-length used. As we see from Fig. IV–3, under these circumstances either the incident ray enters or the diffracted ray leaves the crystal at a small

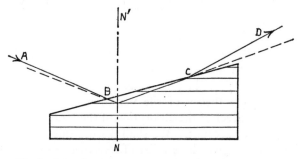

FIG. IV–3. The horizontal lines in this figure represent the direction of the atomic planes in a crystal.   An artificial face in the direction BC has been cut on the crystal. Due to the effect of refraction, mainly at C, the incident ray AB does not make the same angle with the normal NN' as does the ray leaving the crystal, CD.

angle with its face.   The ray is therefore changed in direction due to refraction much more than would be the case if the face of the crystal were parallel to the cleavage planes.   The incident ray AB makes a different angle with the normal NN' to the crystal planes than does the diffracted ray CD; in other words, there is lack of symmetry of the incident and diffracted rays about this normal, in contrast to the usual case in which the crystal surface is a natural one, parallel to the cleavage planes.   This lack of symmetry can be detected by rotation of either the crystal or the source and detector of the rays about NN'; in either case it will be found that a rotation different

[29] Davis and Hatley, Phys. Rev. **23**, 290 (1924).
von Nardroff, Phys. Rev. **24**, i.e., 143 (1924).
Hatley, Phys. Rev. **24**, 486 (1924).
Larsson, Diss. Uppsala, 1929.

from 180° is required to obtain reflection.   From this difference and the known angle made by the cleavage planes with the artificial surface, the index of refraction may be computed.   This method is one of high accuracy due to the precision with which the glancing angle in crystalline diffraction may be measured.

(4) *The prismatic deviation method.*—By analogy with optics, the early experimenters[30] with x-rays attempted to detect refraction by passing the radiation through prisms, but up to 1924 the results were all negative.   In this year, Larsson, Siegbahn, and Waller[31] first

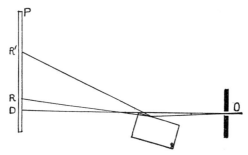

Fɪɢ. IV-4.   Refraction of x-rays by a right-angled prism.   *OD* represents the direct beam, which is partly cut off by the angle of the prism, which projects into it.   The ray reaching the photographic plate *P* at *R'* has been totally reflected, and the ray reaching *R* has been refracted.

demonstrated such a prismatic deviation.   By this time considerable information was available on x-ray refractive indices from other sources, and the optimum design of the apparatus could be calculated with some certainty.   Figure IV-4 shows the experimental arrangement in a schematic manner.   The deviation of the refracted beam from the direct beam is greatest when the glancing angle on the prism is very near the critical angle for total reflection.   Hence some of the

[30] Winkelmann and Straubel, Wied. Ann. **59**, 324 (1896).
    Walter, B., Naturwiss. Rdsch. **11**, 322 (1896).
    Gouy, Compt. rend. **122**, 1197 (1896); **123**, 43 (1896).
    Barkla, Phil. Mag. **31**, 257 (1916).
    Webster and Clark, Phys. Rev. **8**, 528 (1916).
    Keene, Phil. Mag. **32**, 603 (1916).
[31] Larsson, Siegbahn, and Waller, Naturwiss. **52**, 1212 (1924).
    Davis and Slack, Phys. Rev. **27**, 18 (1926).
    Larsson, Diss. Uppsala (1929).
    Stauss, Phys. Rev. **36**, 1101 (1930), J. O. S. A. **20**, 616 (1930).
    Bearden, Phys. Rev. **39**, 1 (1932).

softer components of the beam are totally reflected instead of being refracted. The refracted beam is spread out into a spectrum, and line spectra of x-rays have been obtained by this method, although the resolving power is not very great. Davis and Slack obtained their measurements by placing the prism between the crystals of a double spectrometer, and observing the shift of the maximum of the rocking curve on the second crystal. Stauss showed that by varying the arrangement of Fig. IV–4 so that the x-ray beam entered the prism (really a right-angled block) almost normally to one of its faces and made an internal glancing angle on the refracting face almost equal to the critical angle for total reflection, the refracted beam becomes less divergent than the incident one. Bearden has used this method and the standard one of Fig. IV–4 in an attempt to measure refractive indices with sufficient accuracy to obtain an independent value of the wave-lengths of x-ray lines.

In comparing the results of index of refraction determinations by these three methods with calculations from the Lorentz dispersion theory, we will in this section only make comparisons in wave-length regions so far removed from the characteristic wave-lengths of the dispersing medium that in eq. (4.45), $\nu_q^2 \ll \nu^2$, leaving us only eq. (4.46). A few of the results are shown in Table IV–2.

TABLE IV–2

SOME OBSERVED VALUES OF δ COMPARED WITH CALCULATIONS FROM EQ. 4.46

λ	Substance	$\delta \times 10^6$ Eq. 4.46	$\delta \times 10^6$ Obs.	Observer		Method
0.52 A.	Glass †	0.9	0.9	Compton,	1922	Reflection
0.631	Glass	1.43	1.22 ±.15	L. S. & W.,*	1924	Prism
0.708	Calcite	1.84	2.03 ±.09	Hatley,	1924	Wedge
0.708	Calcite	1.84	2.001±.009	Pardue,	1932	Prism
1.279	Glass	5.2	4.2	Compton,	1922	Reflection
1.279	Silver	19.8	21.5	Compton,	1922	Reflection
1.389	Glass	6.65	6.65 ±.05	L. S. & W.,	1924	Prism
1.537	Glass	8.14	8.12 ±.05	L. S. & W.,	1924	Prism
1.537	Glycerine	4.34	4.41	Smith,	1932	Reflection
1.537	Water	3.53	3.69	Smith,	1932	Reflection
1.750	Glass	10.5	10.0 ±.4	L. S. & W.,	1924	Prism
1.933	Glass	12.8	12.4 ±.4	L. S. & W.,	1924	Prism

* L. S. & W. = Larsson, Siegbahn, and Waller.
† The density of the glass was 2.55.

The opinion of most of the experimenters who have measured δ in regions in which eq. (4.46) may be expected to apply is that the dispersion theory is confirmed by their results within the limit of error. Pardue, however, is of the opinion that the value of δ found for calcite in his work does not agree with the theory. He also looked for and found no evidence of a dependence of δ on direction through the crystal, which of course occurs prominently with visible light in the well known double refraction. This is to be expected, because the anisotropically bound electrons giving rise to the optical double

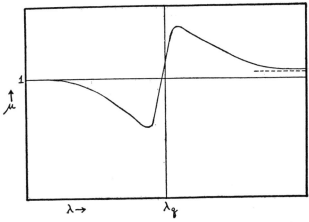

FIG. IV-5. This purely qualitative figure represents some features of the Lorentz theory of the change of the index of refraction μ with wave-length in the x-ray region. These are quantitatively expressed in eqs. (4.45), (4.49), and (4.50). The extent of the region in which the value of μ crosses unity is greatly exaggerated in this figure with respect to the rest of this curve. It is assumed that every electron in the medium has only one natural frequency, ν_q.

refraction are so lightly held in comparison to the x-ray frequencies that they behave essentially as free electrons. With the possible exception of calcite we may say, then, that the Lorentz dispersion theory gives satisfactory results when compared with experiment in regions in which the natural electronic frequencies of the medium may be neglected.

8. *Absorption of X-rays and the Dispersion Theory*

We will now consider the dispersion theory in the neighborhood of the natural frequencies of the electrons in the medium. In the interpretation of the theory, we shall for the moment assume that the natural frequency of the K electrons, for instance, is that of the K absorption limit. This important point will be more fully discussed later. If we use eq. (4.44) in approaching the region $\nu = \nu_q$ from the high frequency side, δ becomes larger, and eventually would go to infinity at $\nu = \nu_q$. Here, however, the approximation used in eq. (4.44) becomes invalid, and we must return to eq. (4.37), in

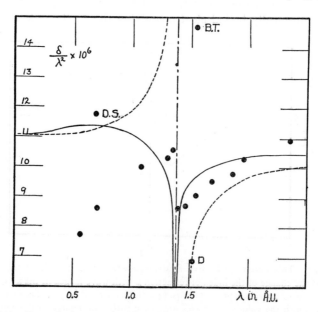

Fɪɢ. IV–6.   Data obtained on the index of refraction of copper for x-rays by various observers.   D.S. = Davis and Slack (1926); B.T. = M. de Broglie and Thibaud (1925); D. = Doan (1927). The remaining points are by Forster (1928). The dotted curve is predicted by the Lorentz dispersion theory; the solid one by the more recent theory of Kramers, Kallmann, and Mark. From A. Larsson, Thesis, Uppsala, 1929.

which the damping term causes δ to remain finite. This behavior is shown in Fig. IV–5. For short wave-lengths, the refractive index μ approaches unity, that is, δ approaches zero. At $\nu = \nu_q$ it may be shown from eq. (4.37) that if the medium only contains one kind of electron having critical frequency ν_q,

$$\mu = \frac{1}{\sqrt{2}}\sqrt{1 + \sqrt{1 + (3n_q\lambda_q{}^3/4\pi^2)^2}}. \qquad (4.49)$$

At frequencies small with respect to ν_q, with the same restriction, we have

$$\mu = 1 + \frac{n_q e^2 \lambda_q{}^2}{2\pi m c^2}. \qquad (4.50)$$

In 1929, Larsson[32] reviewed the experimental evidence then existing on the values of δ in regions in which ν_q cannot be neglected. Figure IV-6, showing the data on copper, is typical. In addition to the data in this figure, it may be mentioned that von Nardroff[33] measured the values of δ for pyrites, using wave-lengths near the K absorption limit of iron. With n_K calculated on the assumption of 2 K electrons per atom in eq. (4.45), he found good agreement with the theory. It is seen that the data on copper are inconclusive, however, with values by Forster[28] lying far below the theoretical curve on the short wave-length side of the limit, whereas the value by Doan[28] is in good agreement. In calcite, the results of Dershem[28] indicated that an anomaly in the δ/λ^2 curve of quite a different type than that expected by eq. (4.45) takes place at the K limit of calcium, but his values did not check quantitatively the Lorenz formula even at considerable distances from the limit. Before the experimental evidence became reliable enough in this region to be decisive, a revised theory of x-ray dispersion made its appearance, and we shall see how it came into being by a study of the predictions of the Lorentz theory as to absorption.

We have shown in eq. (4.43a) that the linear absorption coefficient μ_l in the dispersing medium is related to the imaginary part of the complex refractive index. From eqs. (4.43a) and (4.38) it results that

$$\mu_l{}^q = \frac{8\pi n_q e^4 k^4}{3\{m^2 c^4 (k_q{}^2 - k^2)^2 + 4e^4 k^6/9\}}. \qquad (4.51)$$

In this expression $\mu_l{}^q$ is the contribution to the linear absorption coefficient from electrons of the type q. In order to discuss this equation and the following theory, we will change the notation slightly, using the variable ω instead of k by the relation $\omega = kc$, and introducing the quantity η, defined by

$$\eta = \frac{2e^2 \omega^2}{3mc^3}. \qquad (4.52)$$

[32] Larsson, Diss. Uppsala (1929).
[33] Nardroff, R. von, Phys. Rev. 24, 143 (1924).

Making these changes in eq. (4.51), we obtain

$$\mu_l{}^q = \frac{4\pi n_q e^2}{mc} \frac{\eta \omega^2}{(\omega_q{}^2 - \omega^2)^2 + \eta^2 \omega^2}. \qquad (4.53)$$

In studying this function, it is easier to get an idea of its shape by plotting not μ_l directly, but to consider that the interesting region will be that in which ω is very near ω_q, that is, the region of the resonance frequency. Now in this immediate region, all the ω's in eq. (4.53) may be set equal to ω_q's except in the parentheses in the denominator. By this procedure we obtain

$$\phi = \frac{1}{1 + \{2(\omega - \omega_q)/\eta\}^2} \qquad (4.54)$$

in which

$$\phi = \frac{\omega_q{}^2}{6\pi n_q c^2} \mu_l{}^q \qquad (4.55)$$

By a comparison of eq. (4.52) (with $\omega = \omega_q$ in this narrow region) with eq. (4.12) we see that $\eta = 2b$, and hence the right-hand members of eq. (4.54) and eq. (4.27) are identical. Thus the Lorentz theory predicts an absorption coefficient variation in the region of the characteristic frequency of the same nature as the shape of a spectrum line.

The type of absorption predicted by eq. (4.54), however, is not observed in the x-ray region. In the first place, selective absorption of an x-ray emission line does not take place, in remarkable contrast to the absorption of radiation of the wave-length of the D lines by sodium vapor. The K electrons appear to respond not at all to frequencies less than the K critical absorption frequency. If the frequency of the incident radiation is increased, absorption begins suddenly when the frequency corresponds to the K limit, and at higher frequencies the absorption coefficient falls off approximately as ν^{-3}. This behavior is indicated in Fig. IV–7, where the Lorentz absorption and the observed absorption near a critical frequency are contrasted. This large qualitative discrepancy between theory and experiment shows that a radical change in the theory is necessary, and we are driven to remodel the theory in a highly formal manner, assuming a distribution of " virtual " oscillators which will explain the observed absorption.

Let us consider a frequency interval $d\omega/2\pi$ on the high-frequency side of the q absorption limit, near a frequency $\omega/2\pi$. We will explain the absorption of this frequency by the electrons associated with the critical absorption frequency $\omega_q/2\pi$ by assigning a set of virtual oscillators of characteristic frequency $\omega_j/2\pi$ to the atom, where ω_j may have any value from ω_q to ∞. Some of these virtual oscillators will lie near the incident frequency $\omega/2\pi$ and contribute to its absorption. If z_q is the number of electrons per atom associated with the q critical absorption frequency, the number or

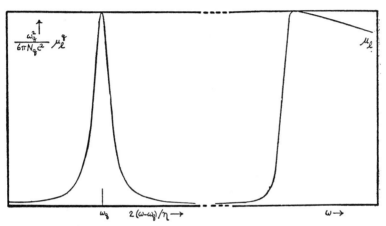

Fig. IV–7. The left-hand curve of this figure shows the variation of a quantity proportional to the contribution to the linear absorption coefficient from electrons of the type q with frequency in a region of critical absorption eq. (4.54), according to the Lorentz dispersion theory. The right-hand curve shows the shape of a typical x-ray absorption limit in a qualitative way. Aside from the difference in shape of the theoretical and observed curves, it should be remembered that the observed discontinuities always occur at frequencies higher than that associated with the emitted line.

strength of the virtual oscillators assigned to frequency $\omega_j/2\pi$ will be determined by [33a]

$$z_q = \int_{\omega_q}^{\infty} f(\omega_j)\,d\omega_j, \tag{4.56}$$

where $f(\omega_j)$ is the distribution function in question.

If now we write eq. (4.53) in a form applicable to the q limit, we see that n_q represents the number of q electrons per cubic centi-

[33a] We will here adopt the elementary view-point that the sum of the number of virtual oscillators assigned to a level is the same as the electron population of that level as given by the Pauli exclusion principle. This point is discussed later in Chap. VII, Sec. 9, in the light of the dispersion theory of Kramers and of Ladenburg.

meter. If then in this expression we replace n_q by z_q, we see that it is applicable to the contribution to the atomic absorption coefficient from the q electrons, which contribution we will call $\mu_a{}^q$. Thus we have

$$\mu_a{}^q = \frac{8\pi}{3}\left(\frac{e^2}{m}\right)^2\left(\frac{\omega}{c}\right)^4\frac{z_q}{(\omega_q{}^2 - \omega^2)^2 + \eta^2\omega^2} \qquad (4.57)$$

and

$$\mu_a{}^q = \frac{8\pi}{3}\left(\frac{e^2}{m}\right)^2\left(\frac{\omega}{c}\right)^4\int_{\omega_q}^{\infty}\frac{f(\omega_j)d\omega_j}{(\omega_j{}^2 - \omega^2)^2 + \eta^2\omega^2}. \qquad (4.58)$$

We will evaluate this integral in the region where $\omega > \omega_q$, in which the virtual oscillators corresponding to the q electrons have characteristic frequencies. Since the term $\eta^2\omega^2$ in the denominator is small, only small values of $(\omega_j{}^2 - \omega^2)^2$ will contribute effectively to the integral. This means that only those virtual oscillators having characteristic frequencies very near to the frequency of the incident radiation will be effective in its absorption. This consideration allows us to make some useful and legitimate approximations in the evaluation. We only need to discriminate between ω and ω_j in terms involving the difference of these quantities; furthermore, we can neglect the variation of $f(\omega_j)$ over the narrow region in which effective contributions to the integral are found, and merely use $f(\omega)$. We may, with these points in mind, re-write eq. (4.58) as follows:

$$\mu_a{}^q = \frac{8\pi}{3}\left(\frac{e^2}{m}\right)^2\left(\frac{\omega}{c}\right)^4 f(\omega)\frac{1}{4\omega^2}\int_{\omega_q}^{\infty}\frac{d\omega_j}{(\omega_j - \omega)^2 + \eta^2/4} \qquad (4.59)$$

The integral in the preceding expression gives

$$\frac{2}{\eta}\left[\tan^{-1}\frac{2(\omega_j - \omega)}{\eta}\right]_{\omega_q}^{\infty} = \frac{2}{\eta}\left[\tan^{-1}\infty - \tan^{-1}\frac{2(\omega_q - \omega)}{\eta}\right]. \qquad (4.60)$$

Due to the smallness of η, the term $2(\omega_q - \omega)/\eta$ will be a very large negative number unless an incident frequency is under investigation which is within the width of a spectrum line from the critical absorption limit at ω_q. If we exclude this small region, we may set $\tan^{-1}2(\omega_q - \omega)/\eta = -\pi/2$, so that the expressions in eq. (4.60) reduce to simply $2\pi/\eta$, and the result of the integration of (4.59) is

$$\mu_a{}^q = \frac{4\pi^2e^4\omega^2}{3m^2c^4\eta}f(\omega). \qquad (4.61)$$

If we now introduce the value of η from eq. (4.52), we obtain

$$\mu_a{}^q = \frac{2\pi^2 e^2}{mc} f(\omega).$$ (4.62)

Before proceeding directly to an expression for $f(\omega)$ in terms of fundamental physical constants, we will now obtain an expression for the contribution of the q electrons to the atomic absorption coefficient in terms of z_q. Combining eqs. (4.62) and (4.56); remembering that we have shown that the numerical values of ω and ω_j are for our present purposes the same, we find

$$\int_{\omega_q}^{\infty} \mu_a{}^q d\omega = \frac{2\pi^2 e^2}{mc} z_q.$$ (4.63)

From the preceding relation we see that by an evaluation of the integral, by graphical integration of experimental data on atomic absorption coefficients or otherwise, values of z_q may be computed. The results thus obtained are not in entirely satisfactory agreement with the numbers of electrons associated with the various energy levels according to the periodic system, the number of dispersion electrons in general being less than that required by the Pauli exclusion principle for the completion of the shell. This matter will be more completely discussed in the treatment of the absorption of x-rays.

We will now introduce into our equations what we will consider simply as an experimental fact, namely that the absorption by ejection of photo-electrons varies as the cube of the wave-length. Thus we may write

$$\mu_a{}^q = k_q/\omega^3,$$ (4.64)

where k_q is a constant pertaining to the absorption by the q level of the atom. Putting this expression in eq. (4.63), and performing the indicated integration, we obtain

$$\mu_a{}^q = \frac{4\pi^2 e^2}{mc} \frac{\omega_q{}^2}{\omega^3} z_q.$$ (4.65)

This is a general law of absorption, derived in a semi-empirical manner, in that we have arbitrarily introduced the dependence on the cube of the wave-length. Summed over the various atomic levels, and expressed in terms of wave-lengths, this formula may be written

$$\mu_a = \frac{2\pi e^2}{mc^2} \lambda^3 \sum_q \frac{z_q}{\lambda_q{}^2} = 1.76 \times 10^{-20} \lambda^3 \sum_q \frac{z_q}{\lambda_q{}^2}. \tag{4.66}$$

In this and in the subsequent eq. (4.67), λ is to be expressed in angstrom units.

In 1924 Jauncey,[34] in a survey of the data on the absorption of x-rays found that in a rather rough fashion, the behavior of the atomic absorption coefficient is expressed by

$$\mu_a = 1.71 \times 10^{-20} \lambda^3 \sum_q \frac{z_q}{\lambda_q{}^2}. \tag{4.67}$$

The close agreement between the empirically determined constant and the constant of eq. (4.66) gives us confidence that the theory has something fundamentally correct about it. However Jauncey's formula does not represent the experimental data in all its details with satisfactory accuracy, and hence we cannot be entirely satisfied about the theory.

At present we are especially interested in the distribution function $f(\omega_j)$, as expressed in terms of z_q. We can obtain this by a combination of eqs. (4.65) and (4.62), giving

$$f(\omega_j) = \frac{2\omega_q{}^2 z_q}{\omega_j{}^3}. \tag{4.68}$$

In this expression we have again introduced the subscript j, because in the following treatment of the index of refraction it will be necessary to distinguish between ω_j, the frequency characteristic of one of the virtual oscillators (times 2π), and ω, referring to the incident radiation.

9. The Kramers–Kallmann–Mark Theory of the Refractive Index

In the last section we have revised the expression given us in the dispersion theory so that it gives an absorption curve of the type experimentally encountered in x-rays. We will now put this revised expression into our formula for the complex refractive index, which we have seen involves absorption. The result will be a new formula

[34] Jauncey, G. E. M., Phil. Mag. 48, 81 (1924). The experimental test of eq. (4.66) is discussed in A. H. Compton, X-rays and Electrons, Van Nostrand (1926), pp. 203–204.

for the real refractive index, and a new shape for the dispersion curve in regions of critical absorption. From eqs. (4.43), (4.37), (4.38) and (4.52), we obtain

$$\mu_c^q = 1 + \frac{2\pi e^2 n_q}{m} \frac{1}{\omega_q^2 - \omega^2 + i\eta\omega}, \qquad (4.69)$$

in which μ_c^q is the contribution to the complex refractive index from electrons of the type q in the medium. According to our revised theory, we now have to replace each electron of the type q by a distribution of virtual oscillators according to eq. (4.68), varying in frequency from ν_q to ∞. The distribution per electron will be given by $f(\omega_j)/z_q$, and using this to replace unity in the numerator of the fraction in eq. (4.69), we obtain

$$\mu_c^q = 1 + \frac{4\pi e^2 n_q \omega_q^2}{m} \int_{\omega_q}^{\infty} \frac{d\omega_j}{\omega_j^3(\omega_j^2 - \omega^2 + i\eta\omega)}. \qquad (4.71)$$

This expression may be integrated,[35] giving as a result

$$\mu_c^q = 1 + \frac{4\pi e^2}{m} n_q \omega_q^2 \left[\frac{1}{2\omega(i\eta - \omega)} \left\{ \frac{1}{\omega_q^2} + \frac{1}{\omega(i\eta - \omega)} \ln \frac{\omega_q^2}{\omega_q^2 - \omega^2 + i\eta\omega} \right\} \right] \qquad (4.72)$$

in which the symbol ln signifies logarithm to the base e. By straightforward algebraic processes, and the introduction of the new symbols

$$x = \omega/\omega_q \quad \text{and} \quad \gamma = \eta/\omega_q \qquad (4.73)$$

we obtain

$$\delta_q + i\beta_q = \frac{2\pi e^2 n_q}{m\omega_q^2} \frac{ln(1 - x^2 + ix\gamma) + (x^2 - ix\gamma)}{(x^2 - ix\gamma)^2} \qquad (4.74)$$

In order to find the expressions for δ_q and β_q it is necessary to separate the real and imaginary parts of the right-hand member of the preceding equation. When we do this we find that the resulting expressions are different for the cases $x < 1$ and $x > 1$, because of the complex nature of the argument of the logarithm. This means that there are different formulae for the long and short wave-length sides of the critical absorption wave-length λ_q. We shall give the resulting equations for δ_q and β_q in their complete form, as tabulated by Glocker and Schäfer, and in a form given by Prins[36] in which the higher powers of the damping constant γ are neglected.

[35] For instance, Peirce A Short Table of Integrals No. 80, p. 11.
[36] Glocker and Schäfer, Zs. f. Physik **73**, 289 (1931).
Prins, Zs. f. Physik **47**, 479 (1928).

On the long wave-length side of the q limit, where $x < 1$, we have

$$\delta_q = \frac{2\pi e^2 n_q}{m\omega_q^2}\left[\frac{1}{(x^2 + \gamma^2)^2 x^2}\left\{\tfrac{1}{2}(x^2 - \gamma^2)ln[(1 - x^2)^2 + \gamma^2 x^2]\right.\right.$$
$$\left.\left. - 2\gamma x \tan^{-1}\frac{\gamma x}{1 - x^2} + x^2(x^2 + \gamma^2)\right\}\right]. \quad (4.75)$$

Equation (4.75) is valid in the region $x \leqq 1$; an approximation which loses its validity as x approaches 1 is the following:

$$\delta_q = \frac{2\pi e^2 n_q}{m\omega_q^2}\frac{1}{x^2}\left(1 + \frac{ln(1 - x^2)}{x^2}\right). \quad (4.76)$$

Similarly, in this region, eq. (4.77) gives a value of β good in the region $x \leqq 1$, whereas eq. (4.78) cannot be applied close to

$$\beta_q = \frac{2\pi e^2 n_q}{m\omega_q^2}\left[\frac{1}{(x^2 + \gamma^2)^2 x^2}\left\{\gamma x ln[(1 - x^2)^2 + \gamma^2 x^2]\right.\right.$$
$$\left.\left. + (x^2 - \gamma^2)\tan^{-1}\frac{\gamma x}{1 - x^2} + \gamma x(x^2 + \gamma^2)\right\}\right], \quad (4.77)$$

the critical absorption limit.

$$\beta_q = \frac{2\pi e^2 n_q}{m\omega_q^2}\frac{\gamma}{x^3}\left(\frac{2 - x^2}{1 - x^2} + \frac{2ln(1 - x^2)}{x^2}\right). \quad (4.78)$$

On the short wave-length side of the q limit, where $x > 1$,

$$\delta_q = \frac{2\pi e^2 n_q}{m\omega_q^2}\left[\frac{1}{(x^2 + \gamma^2)^2 x^2}\left\{\frac{x^2 - \gamma^2}{2}ln[(x^2 - 1)^2 + \gamma^2 x^2]\right.\right.$$
$$\left.\left. + 2\gamma x \tan^{-1}\frac{\gamma x}{x^2 - 1} + x^2(x^2 + \gamma^2) - 2\pi\gamma x\right\}\right], \quad (4.79)$$

or, if x is not too close to the limit,

$$\delta_q = \frac{2\pi e^2 n_q}{m\omega_q^2}\frac{1}{x^2}\left\{1 + \frac{ln(x^2 - 1)}{x^2} - \frac{2\pi\gamma}{x^3}\right\}. \quad (4.80)$$

The following eqs. (4.81) and (4.82) apply to the value of β_q on

$$\beta_q = \frac{2\pi e^2 n_q}{m\omega_q^2}\left[\frac{1}{x^2(x^2 + \gamma^2)^2}\left\{\gamma x ln[(x^2 - 1)^2 + \gamma^2 x^2]\right.\right.$$
$$\left.\left. - (x^2 - \gamma^2)\tan^{-1}\frac{\gamma x}{x^2 - 1} + \gamma x(x^2 + \gamma^2) + \pi(x^2 - \gamma^2)\right\}\right], \quad (4.81)$$

the short wave-length side of the limit. The values of δ_q and β_q,

$$\beta_q = \frac{2\pi e^2 n_q}{m\omega_q^2} \frac{1}{x^2}\left[\frac{\pi}{x^2} + \frac{\gamma}{x}\left\{\frac{x^2 - 2}{x^2 - 1} + \frac{2\ln(x^2 - 1)}{x^2}\right\}\right], \qquad (4.82)$$

applicable in the case where $x = 1$, and the incident wave-length coincides with the critical absorption wave-length, are found by setting $x = 1$ in eqs. (4.75) and (4.77).

10. *Comparison of the Expressions for the Refractive Index with Experiment*

The expressions given in the last section for δ_q will reduce to the same formulae as were obtained from the Lorentz dispersion theory if the incident wave-length is sufficiently far removed from a critical absorption wave-length of the medium.   For instance, if in eq. (4.80) we consider a very small value of x, we approach as near as we please to eq. (4.46).   Thus, any experiments designed to distinguish between the theories must be performed near a critical absorption limit of the medium.   In this section we shall discuss only one such set of experiments, namely, those performed by Larsson on calcite near the K critical absorption limit of calcium.

Larsson has compared his experiments with theoretical equations in which the damping term is neglected.   Let us suppose that all the perturbations which cause the value of δ to differ from that of eq. (4.46) are caused by the K electrons of calcium.   With this in mind, we may write, from eq. (4.45)

$$\frac{\delta}{\lambda^2} = \frac{e^2}{2\pi mc^2} \frac{N\rho}{M}\left[\frac{z_K \lambda_K^2}{\lambda_K^2 - \lambda^2} + Z_M - z_K\right]. \qquad (4.83)$$

In this expression we have

N = Avogadro number   = 6.064×10^{23}
ρ = density of calcite   = 2.710 g/cc.
M = molecular weight of calcite   = 100.07
z_K = number of K electrons in calcium   = 2
λ_K = wave-length of calcium K limit   = 3.0643 A. U.
Z_M = number of electrons per molecule of $CaCO_3$ = 50

Using these numerical values, and arranging the constant so that λ is expressed in angstroms, we have for eq. (4.83)

$$\frac{\delta}{\lambda^2} = 7.32 \times 10^{-8}\left(48 + \frac{18.78}{9.390 - \lambda^2}\right) \qquad (4.84)$$

Turning now to the revised dispersion theory, on the long wave-length side of the K limit of calcium, we have, by eq. (4.76)

$$\frac{\delta}{\lambda^2} = \frac{e^2}{2\pi mc^2} \frac{N\rho}{M} \left[Z_M + z_K \frac{\lambda^2}{\lambda_K^2} \ln \left(1 - \frac{\lambda_K^2}{\lambda^2} \right) \right] \qquad (4.85)$$

or numerically,

$$\frac{\delta}{\lambda^2} = 7.32 \times 10^{-8} \left[50 + \frac{2\lambda^2}{9.390} \ln \left(1 - \frac{9.390}{\lambda^2} \right) \right] \qquad (4.86)$$

On the short wave-length side of the limit, since we are neglecting the damping, we merely reverse the signs of the quantities in the argument of the logarithm in eq. (4.86).

The experiments were performed with the crystal wedge method previously discussed, using emission lines having wave-lengths in the desired region. Table IV–3, taken from Larsson's dissertation, shows the results.

TABLE IV–3

δ Values for $CaCO_3$

Line	λ (X. U.)	$\delta \times 10^6$	$\delta/\lambda^2 \times 10^6$ (λ in A)
CuKα_1	1537.4	8.80	3.72
FeKα_1	1932.1	13.89	3.72
VaKα_1	2498.4	22.37	3.59
TiKβ_1	2509.0	23.26	3.70
ScKβ_1	2773.9	27.05	3.51
ILβ_1	2930.9	28.54	3.32
ScKβ_1	3025.0	29.34	3.21
TeLβ_4	3040.0	28.67	3.10
TeLβ_1	3070.0	30.18	3.20
CaKβ_1	3083.4	32.02	3.37
SbLβ_1	3218.4	35.98	3.47
SnLβ_1	3377.9	39.57	3.47
K Kβ_1	3446.8	41.87	3.52
K Kα_1	3733.7	49.19	3.53

A graphical comparison of the results with eqs. (4.86) and (4.84) is shown in Fig. IV–8. It is clear that the unmodified Lorentz formula is inadequate to represent the experimental facts. Although the modified theory gives qualitatively the correct shape of the curve, there are minor quantitative discrepancies, notably on the long wave-length side of the limit. Near the limit, we cannot expect perfect agreement, due to the fact that we have neglected the damping constant, which becomes important in this region. A better fit between experiment and theory may be obtained by letting z_K differ from 2. Evidence has been obtained[37] from various sources that instead of 2, a value of z_K from 1.3 to 1.7 gives better agreement with

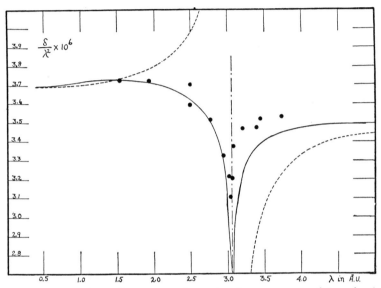

Fig. IV–8. The solid circles represent the results of measurements of the refractive index of calcite for x-rays in the region of the K absorption limit of calcium. The solid curve represents the prediction of the theory of Kramers, Kallmann, and Mark; the dotted curve, the older Lorentz dispersion theory. Both theoretical curves are plotted neglecting damping. From Larsson, Thesis, Uppsala, 1929.

experiment. A theoretical discussion of this effect has been given by Kronig and Kramers.[38]

A second feature in which the two dispersion theories differ is that the newer theory predicts a slight maximum in the δ/λ^2 against λ curve at a wave-length approximately half that of the critical absorption limit. No such maximum should exist on the older

[37] Compton, X-rays and Electrons (1926), p. 202.
    Houstoun, R. A., Phil. Mag. 2, 512 (1926).
    Prins, Zs. f. Phys. 47, 479 (1928).
[38] Kronig and Kramers, Zs. f. Phys. 48, 174 (1928).

theory, the curve merely rising very slowly in this region due to the anomalous effect of the absorption limit. Larsson has searched for this maximum in the refraction of quartz, which he investigated by means of a prism, and has found evidence of its existence.

It may thus be said that, as an improvement, the revised dispersion theory gives qualitatively the correct shape of the x-ray dispersion curve, whereas the older theory does not. There are, however, minor disagreements between this theory and experiments which are to a great extent removed in the wave-mechanical dispersion theory discussed in Sec. 13 of this chapter.

11. *Variation of Atomic Structure Factors in Regions of Anomalous Dispersion*

By the atomic structure factor we mean the ratio of the amplitude of the wave scattered in a certain direction from an atom to that which would be scattered classically in that direction from the same incident beam by a free, undamped electron. This classical scattering from a free electron is often called "J. J. Thomson scattering." The equation of motion of the electron in this case is a special case of eq. (4.30), in which the accelerations due to damping and to the restoring force are neglected, leaving merely

$$a = \ddot{\xi} = - eE/m.$$

Using this expression in eq. (4.01), we find that the rate of loss of energy from an electron according to this simple type of scattering is

$$\frac{dw}{dt} = - \frac{2e^4E^2}{3m^2c^3}. \tag{4.87}$$

Let us now consider scattering from an atom in which there are bound electrons, whose vibrations are electromagnetically damped. The electromagnetic wave scattered from this atom at any point will be the resultant of waves scattered from its constituent electrons. Unless the point at which the wave is observed lies in the direction of the incident beam, the waves scattered from the individual electrons will contain phase factors due to the fact that all the electrons are not located at the same point, and hence the path lengths from the various oscillators to a wave front in the diffracted beam are not identical. We are not interested in this effect in the present section, and will confine our attention at first to scattering in the forward direction, in which this disturbing element does not appear. In this direction, then, if all the electrons reacted in the same way to the incident beam, we would expect the phases of all the waves to be the same, and hence the amplitude of the resultant wave to be simply Z times the amplitude scattered by a single electron, where Z is the number of electrons per atom. But the purpose of the discussion in this section is to show that if some of the electrons in the atom have natural frequencies which cannot be neglected in comparison with the incident frequency, phase changes will be introduced even in the forward direction.

We may find the acceleration of an electron executing forced, damped oscillations by differentiation of eq. (4.31) which gives the displacement. This gives

$$a = \ddot{\xi} = - k^2 c^2 \xi = - \omega^2 \xi,$$

in which ξ is a complex quantity. Now from eq. (4.01) we may write:

$$\frac{dw}{dt} = - \frac{2\omega^4}{3c^3} \left| \xi e \right|^2 = - \frac{2\omega^4}{3c^3} \left| p \right|^2 . \tag{4.88}$$

In this expression p is the electric moment of the dipole resulting from the displacement of a single electron. Since we are only concerned with the square of this moment, we need not introduce the negative sign, as was done in eq. (4.33). In treating the radiation of energy from an entire atom, we sum up the moments of all the constituent electrons, writing instead of eq. (4.88):

$$\frac{dW}{dt} = - \frac{2\omega^4}{3c^3} \left| \sum_q z_q p_q \right|^2 . \tag{4.89}$$

The polarization of the medium, which will in this case be a complex quantity P, will be given by

$$P = n_a \sum_q z_q p_q,$$

where n_a is the number of atoms per cc. From eq. (4.34) we can write for the dielectric constant

$$\kappa = 1 + \frac{4\pi}{E} n_a \sum z_q p_q.$$

In taking the square root of this quantity to obtain the refractive index, we remember that it differs only very slightly from unity, and thus from eq. (4.34) we have

$$\delta + i\beta = n_a \sum_q z_q(\delta_q + i\beta_q) = - \frac{2\pi n_a}{E} \sum_q z_q p_q.$$

We now see a connection between the rate of radiation from the atom and the complex refractive index, which from eq. (4.89) is

$$\frac{dW}{dt} = - \frac{\omega^4 E^2}{6\pi^2 c^3} \left| \sum_q z_q(\delta_q + i\beta_q) \right|^2. \tag{4.90}$$

In order to obtain the ratio of the rate of scattering of energy by the atom to that from a single electron, we must divide the right hand member of eq. (4.90) by the value in eq. (4.87). This leaves us an energy ratio which by definition is equal to $f_0{}^2$, where f_0 is the atomic structure factor at scattering angle zero.[38a]   Thus

$$f_0{}^2 = \frac{m^2 \omega^4}{4\pi^2 e^4} \left| \sum_q z_q(\delta_q + i\beta_q) \right|^2, \tag{4.91}$$

in which δ_q and β_q may be obtained from eqs. (4.75) to (4.82). In most cases thus far studied, the electrons in the atom may be divided into two groups, one of which comprises the K electrons and produces the anomalous effects, the other, all the remaining electrons which scatter in the J. J. Thomson fashion. With this subdivision in mind, we may write

$$f_0 = \frac{2\pi mc^2}{e^2 \lambda^2} \left| z_K(\delta_K + i\beta_K) + (Z_M - z_K) \frac{e^2 \lambda^2}{2\pi mc^2} \right|.$$

In this expression, the δ value of the $(Z_M - z_K)$ electrons which are scattering normally has been written in from eq. (4.46). A form of the preceding equation more directly suitable for calculation is

$$f_0 = \frac{2\pi mc^2}{e^2 \lambda^2} \left[\left\{ z_K \delta_K + (Z_M - z_K) \frac{e^2 \lambda^2}{2\pi mc^2} \right\}^2 + z_K{}^2 \beta_K{}^2 \right]^{1/2}. \tag{4.92}$$

The dashed curve of Fig. IV–9 shows the prediction of eq. (4.92) for the variation of the atomic structure factor of iron in the region of the anomalous dispersion due to the K limit. The solid curve shows the prediction of a wave-mechanical treatment of the atomic

---

[38a] In Chap. III the atomic structure factor is denoted by F. f is used here and in all other chapters of the book.

structure factor by Hönl[39] which is mentioned in Sec. 13 of this chapter. The principal difference in this newer treatment is seen to lie on the long wave-length side of the limit and is largely due to the fact that in the wave-mechanical treatment z_K is not equal to the electron population of the K level as given by the Pauli exclusion principle, but is approximately 1.32 for iron, instead of 2.

The form of the curve predicted by the Kramers-Kallmann-Mark dispersion theory may be changed somewhat if γ is treated as an adjustable constant rather than a value to be rigorously calculated

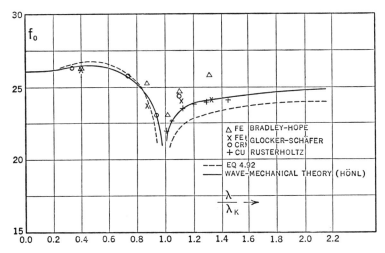

Fig. IV-9. Theory and experiment on the atomic structure factor of 26Fe. The chromium and copper points are reduced to the iron diagram. (After Hönl.) The shape of the Kramers-Kallmann-Mark curve on the short wave-length side of the limit may be somewhat influenced by varying the value of γ.

from theory. The fact that the width of spectrum lines in the x-ray region is not that predicted by the classical theory may be taken to indicate that the actual damping is not that classically predicted, but is in general greater. Accordingly γ has often been used as a constant to be determined directly from experiment, and we shall discuss two methods by which this may be done. By a combination of eqs. (4.29), (4.52) and (4.73), we may obtain

$$\gamma = 2w_\lambda/\lambda.$$

39 H. Hönl, Annalen der Physik 18, 625 (1933).

If we take the half width at half maximum (w_λ) of Mo $K\alpha_1$ as 0.15 X. U., and its wave-length as 708 X. U., we obtain $\gamma = 4 \times 10^{-4}$ which gives a rough idea of a possible value of the damping to use in the x-ray region.

Another estimate of γ may be based on the lowest value of δ/λ^2 obtained by Larsson at the K limit. By setting $x = 1$ in eq. (4.75), we obtain

$$\left(\frac{\delta}{\lambda^2}\right)_K = \frac{e^2 n_K}{2\pi m c^2}\left[\frac{(1 - \gamma^2)\ln\gamma - \gamma\pi + 1 + \gamma^2}{(1 + \gamma^2)^2}\right]$$

By subtracting the contributions to the observed δ due to the electrons in the medium whose natural frequencies can be neglected, $(\delta/\lambda^2)_K$ may be obtained. γ may then be calculated from the preceding expression. A quantity of the order of magnitude 1×10^{-3} is obtained from Larsson's data by this method. In Fig. IV-9 the Kramers-Kallmann-Mark curve is calculated with $\gamma = 0$, which does not differ appreciably from the curve calculated for $\gamma = 1 \times 10^{-3}$ except in the immediate neighborhood of the K limit.

Evidence of the change of the atomic structure factor in the region of anomalous dispersion was obtained in 1925 in an ingenious experiment devised by Mark and Szilard.[40] In this experiment the reflection of x-rays from the (111) planes of a RbBr crystal was studied at various wave-lengths. In most regions of the spectrum, the first order (111) reflection, computed on the basis of a simple translatory cubic lattice, is absent in KCl and RbBr, appearing however in NaCl. This is due to the fact that the electronic population of the Rb and Br ions, for instance, is the same, and the waves reflected from these alternate planes suffer complete destructive interference in this order. But Mark and Szilard found that this order appears if the line Sr $K\alpha_1$ is used as the primary wave-length. Sr $K\alpha_1$ has the wave-length 873.45 X. U., whereas the K limits of Rb and Br are at 814.10 and 918.09 X. U. respectively. Thus the Sr $K\alpha_1$ line lies on the short wave-length side of the Br limit, but on the long wave-length side of the Rb limit, and the appearance of a diffracted beam at this wave-length shows clearly that between the two limits the atomic structure factors of Rb and Br are not the same.

In studying the intensity of reflection of x-rays from powdered

---

[40] Mark and Szilard, Zs. f. Physik **33**, 688 (1925).

crystals containing Ni, Cu, and Fe, Wyckoff and Armstrong[41] have found that as the wave-length used approaches the K limit of these scatterers from the short wave-length side, the atomic structure factors decrease, and increase again after the limit is passsed, in qualitative agreement with the theory. Effects closely connected with the one under discussion here have been observed by Coster, Knol, and Prins[42] in the reflection of x-rays from crystals of ZnS. A change of the atomic structure factor of Zn in the region of its K limit was involved, although the primary purpose of the experiments was to detect the hemihedral character of the ZnS structure by taking reflections from two opposite (111) faces.

Glocker and Schäfer[43a] have investigated the behaviour of the atomic structure factor of iron near the FeK absorption limit. Their results at first indicated a pronounced lack of agreement between theory and experiment on the short wave-length side of the K limit, and indicated that the reduction in the value of the atomic structure factor due to anomalous dispersion varies with scattering angle. The experiments have, however, been reconsidered by Schäfer,[43b] and he has found that a re-calculation of the correction for absorption in the powdered crystals used is necessary. The correction may depend on the particle size in a complicated manner if the wave-length used is on the short wave-length side of a critical absorption limit where the absorption is high. When this effect is corrected for, the atomic structure factor curve is found to be lowered by the same amount at all scattering angles, and the discrepancy between theory and experiment on the short wave-length side òf the limit disappears. Fig. IV-9 shows the results for Fe and Cr, the latter being reduced to the Fe scale. The constant decrement in the atomic structure factor at all angles measured is considered to apply to the factor at $0°$ scattering angle, or f_0.

Rüsterholz[43c] has studied the atomic structure factor of copper near the CuK limit and these results are indicated on Fig. IV-9.

Coster and Knol have estimated the atomic structure factor in

[41] Armstrong, Phys. Rev. **34**, 931 (1929).

   Wyckoff, Phys. Rev. **35**, 583 (1930) and **36**, 1116 (1930).

[42] Coster, Knol, and Prins, Zs. f. Physik **63**, 345 (1930).

[43a] Glocker and Schäfer, Zeitschr. f. Physik **73**, 289 (1931).

[43b] K. Schäfer, Zeitschr. f. Physik **86**, 739 (1933).

[43c] A. Rüsterholz, Helv. Physica Acta IV, No. 2, 68 (1931); Zeitschr. f. Physik **82**, 538 (1933).

regions near critical absorption and at angles greater than zero by the following reasoning. Let us divide the atomic structure factor into two parts

$$f = f_K + f_R,$$

in which f_K represents the contribution to the atomic structure factor from the K electrons (outside of regions of anomalous dispersion this is put equal to 1.3) and f_R the contributions from all the other electrons of the atom. The K electrons are very much closer to the nucleus than any others; we will therefore assume that f_K does not vary with scattering angle, for if both K electrons were located at the same point this would be strictly true. Coster and Knol[44] therefore ascribe all the variation of f with scattering angle to a variation of f_R, and this variation can easily be obtained from experimental data far from any anomalous region by subtraction of 1.3 from the f values as a function of $\sin \theta/\lambda$. This may be then used in the anomalous region, for we have no reason to expect that any electrons except the K electrons will behave anomalously near the K critical absorption limit.

Coster and Knol[45] have used this idea in interpreting the results of Bradley and Hope[46] on the atomic structure factor of iron near the K absorption limit. Since the f_K varies little with $\sin \theta/\lambda$, while f_R falls off rapidly as this quantity increases, the maximum effect of the anomalous behavior of the K electrons on f is observed at large glancing angles for a given wave-length, although as has been previously stated, the decrement in the atomic structure factor is approximately independent of angle. Points obtained by Bradley and Hope are shown in Fig. IV–9.

From Fig. IV–9 it is seen that all the observed points, with the possible exception of some of those by Bradley and Hope on the long wave-length side of the limit, are in good agreement with the theory, and indicate that the value of z_K, as predicted by the Kramers-Heisenberg dispersion formula, which was later incorporated into the wave-mechanical treatment of dispersion, is less than 2, and that the wave-mechanical value of 1.3 for Fe is approximately correct. These questions are again referred to in Sec. 13 of this chapter and Sec. 9 of Chapter VII.

[44] Coster and Knol, Z. f. Physik 75, 340 (1932).
[45] Coster and Knol, Proc. Roy. Soc. Lond. A. 139, 459 (1933).
[46] Bradley and Hope, Proc. Roy. Soc. Lond. A. 136, 272 (1932).

12. *The Effect of Absorption on the Intensity of Reflection of X-Rays Near the Critical Angle for Total Reflection.*

We have seen previously that from an elementary viewpoint, x-rays incident upon a medium in which their refractive index is less than unity should be totally reflected providing the glancing angle θ is less than $\sqrt{2\delta}$. If the glancing angle in a given experiment is increased, beginning with a value in the range in which total reflection can take place, there is a very rapid diminution in intensity of the reflected beam near the region $\theta_c = \sqrt{2\delta}$; provided the absorption of the x-rays in the reflecting material can be neglected. For highly absorbed radiation, however, nothing in the nature of a limiting angle appears. We shall show how Fresnel's equations can be applied to this problem. These equations are derived in the standard textbooks on electromagnetic theory and the theory of optics.[47]

Consider x-rays incident on medium 2 from medium 1, and let the subscripts 2 and 1 refer to these media, respectively. We will first consider the reflection of radiation which is polarized so that its electric vector lies perpendicular to the plane of incidence. This type of polarization we will denote by the subscript σ, using the subscript π for the type in which the electric vector lies in the plane of incidence. It is known that the plane of polarization, as defined in optics, means the plane in which the vibrations of the magnetic force are executed, hence the present case is one in which the plane of polarization coincides with the plane of incidence. In a theory sufficiently general to explain the effect under consideration, the amplitudes of the incident and reflected waves may conveniently be expressed as complex quantities. Let E_σ be the complex amplitude of the electric component of the incident radiation, and R_σ the complex amplitude of the electric component of the reflected radiation. It is then shown that a result in accordance with Maxwell's equations and the conditions of continuity at the interface of the two media is:

$$\frac{R_\sigma}{E_\sigma} = \frac{\cos \phi_1 - \sqrt{\frac{\kappa_2 \mu_1}{\kappa_1 \mu_2}} \cos \phi_2}{\cos \phi_1 + \sqrt{\frac{\kappa_2 \mu_1}{\kappa_1 \mu_2}} \cos \phi_2}. \tag{4.93}$$

[47] Drude, The Theory of Optics, Eng. Trans., Longmans Green (1902). Eqs. 23, p. 282, and the discussions on p. 295 and in Chap. IV, p. 358, are applicable.

Jeans, Electricity and Magnetism, IV Ed., Cambridge Univ. Press (1920). Eq. (4.93) of this section is taken from eq. 564, p. 541.

In this expression, ϕ_1 and ϕ_2 are the optical angles of incidence and refraction respectively and κ is the dielectric constant. μ is the magnetic permeability of the medium. The above equation is one of those commonly referred to as Fresnel's equations for reflection and refraction.

It is known that for frequencies as low as those in the optical region, μ is always unity,[48] even for iron, so that we can set both μ_1 and μ_2 equal to 1. If medium 1 be air, of negligible density compared to medium 2, we can set $\kappa_1 = 1$, as is apparent from eq. (4.35). Thus for our problem eq. (4.93) may be written

$$\frac{R_\sigma}{E_\sigma} = \frac{\cos \phi_1 - \sqrt{\kappa_2} \cos \phi_2}{\cos \phi_1 + \sqrt{\kappa_2} \cos \phi_2}. \qquad (4.94)$$

The preceding equation has been developed in a very general way, and it is valid whether or not total reflection takes place. When total reflection occurs, $\sin \phi_2$ becomes greater than 1 and hence $\cos \phi_2$ becomes imaginary. In this case we can write

$$\cos \phi_2 = \sqrt{1 - (\sin^2 \phi_1)/\kappa_2} = \sqrt{1 - (1 - \sin^2 \theta)/\kappa_2} ,$$

using the definition of the index of refraction as the ratio of the sines of the incident and refracted angles, and introducing the glancing angle θ instead of the optical angle of incidence. Substituting these expressions in eq. (4.94) and dropping the subscript on κ since we are concerned with the dielectric constant in the second medium alone, we obtain

$$\frac{R_\sigma}{E_\sigma} = \frac{\sin \theta - [\kappa - 1 + \sin^2 \theta]^{1/2}}{\sin \theta + [\kappa - 1 + \sin^2 \theta]^{1/2}}. \qquad (4.95)$$

Now in Sec. 5 of this chapter, we have shown that where in the elementary theory the dielectric constant appears, there appears in the present treatment a complex dielectric constant, which differs from unity only by small amounts. This is connected with the complex index of refraction in the following manner

$$\kappa = \mu_c^2 = (1 - \delta - i\beta)^2$$

and from a theoretical viewpoint δ and β are to be obtained from summations of eqs. (4.75) to (4.82). The theoretical connection between β and the linear absorption coefficient for intensities is given in eq. (4.43). The effect of absorption on the intensity of reflection

[48] This is discussed in Drude Theory of Optics, Eng. Trans. (1902), p. 452.

may therefore be computed by inserting a complex dielectric constant in eq. (4.95).

It may be well to remark that in the region of total reflection, the quantity $(\kappa - 1 + \sin^2 \theta)^{\frac{1}{2}}$ is complex even if the imaginary part of the complex dielectric constant is neglected. This of course means that there is a change of phase in reflection in this region, and it may furthermore be deduced that the wave which enters the medium penetrates it only to the extent of a depth comparable with the order of magnitude of one wave-length. We can in any case proceed to calculate the intensity ratio by multiplying the amplitude ratio by its complex conjugate. The treatment given here follows that of Dershem and Schein.[49] In the derivation of the following formulae, δ and β are treated as small quantities, and their squares and products neglected with respect to their first powers. Also θ has been set equal to sin θ, since the glancing angles involved are small. With these substitutions and simplifications, we obtain

$$\frac{R_\sigma}{E_\sigma} = \frac{\theta - (\theta^2 - 2\delta - 2i\beta)^{\frac{1}{2}}}{\theta + (\theta^2 - 2\delta - 2i\beta)^{\frac{1}{2}}}. \qquad (4.96)$$

If we now set

$$a - ib = (\theta^2 - 2\delta - 2i\beta)^{\frac{1}{2}},$$

we may find the value of a and b by expanding the radical on the right-hand side of the equation by usual methods. This gives

$$a = \frac{1}{\sqrt{2}} \sqrt{\sqrt{(\theta^2 - 2\delta)^2 + 4\beta^2} + \theta^2 - 2\delta},$$

$$b = \frac{1}{\sqrt{2}} \sqrt{\sqrt{(\theta^2 - 2\delta)^2 + 4\beta^2} - \theta^2 + 2\delta}. \qquad (4.97)$$

[49] The following references are to papers in which special attention has been paid to the phenomenon in question.

Forster, Helv. Phys. Acta. **1**, 18 (1928).

Prins, Z. Physik **47**, 479 (1928).

Schon, Z. Physik **58**, 165 (1929).

Jentzsch, Physik. Zeitschr. **30**, 268 (1929).

Valouch, J. de Physique et le Rad. **10**, 109 (1929), **1**, 261 (1930).

Thibaud, J. de Physique et le Rad. **1**, 37 (1930).

Kiessig, Ann. Phys. **10**, 715 (1931).

Nahring, Physik. Zeitschr. **31**, 401, 799 (1930); **32**, 179 (1931).

Dershem and Schein, Phys. Rev. **37**, 1246 (1931).

Pardue, Phys. Rev. **39**, 1 (1932).

If I_0 represent the intensity of the incident beam, and I that of the reflected beam, we have

$$\frac{I}{I_0} = \left|\frac{R_\sigma}{E_\sigma}\right|^2 = \frac{(\theta - a)^2 + b^2}{(\theta + a)^2 + b^2} \tag{4.98}$$

The numerical values of a and b may be readily found by substitution of those for θ, δ, and β in eqs. (4.97).

In the case of the component polarized in such a way that the

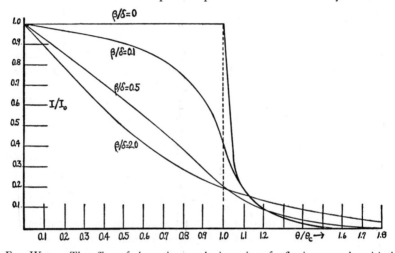

FIG. IV–10. The effect of absorption on the intensity of reflection near the critical angle θ_c. These are theoretical curves, calculated from an equation similar to eq. (4.98). (After Nahring.)

electric vector lies in the plane of incidence, the electromagnetic theory gives instead of eq. (4.94),

$$\frac{R_\pi}{E_\pi} = \frac{\sqrt{\kappa}\cos\phi_1 - \cos\phi_2}{\sqrt{\kappa}\cos\phi_1 + \cos\phi_2}.$$

Treatment of this expression in the same way as above leads to the result

$$\frac{I}{I_0} = \frac{(\theta - 2\delta\theta - a)^2 + (b - 2\beta\theta)^2}{(\theta - 2\delta\theta + a)^2 + (b + 2\beta\theta)^2}$$

in which a and b have the values given in eq. (4.97). For the small glancing angles at which the equations are applied, however, the difference between the intensity of reflection of the σ- and π- components is negligible, and we can use eq. (4.98) for an unpolarized beam.

Equations similar to these have been developed by other investigators. The effect of various values of the index of absorption, β, upon the reflection curve is shown in Fig. IV–10, taken from Nähring. In this figure, values of θ/θ_c are plotted as abscissae, where θ_c is obtained from eq. (4.48). The various curves are for different values

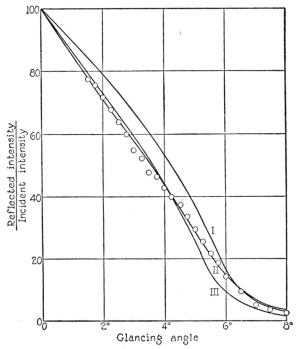

Fig. IV–11. The results of Dershem and Schein on the intensity of reflection of $C\ K\alpha$ from quartz, compared with theoretical curves computed from various values of δ and β.

of β/δ. Since for a given medium, β increases approximately as λ^4 (see eq. (4.43)) and δ as λ^2, it is clear that the ratio β/δ will rapidly increase as longer wave-lengths are used. Obviously for long wave-lengths the method of total reflection will not yield a sharp critical angle, and hence, without consideration of the absorption, a value of δ. Various experimenters have shown, however, that the theory developed above accounts in a satisfactory manner for the observed intensity of reflection of x-rays. Fig. IV–11 shows the result obtained by Dershem and Schein for the reflection of the $K\alpha$ line of carbon, 44.5 A from a quartz mirror. The value of δ used in the calculation was obtained by the application of eq. (4.46), since the wavelength used lies above the K limits of silicon and oxygen, and well below their L limits. The K electrons of oxygen and silicon were not counted in computing n. Instead of calculating β from eqs. (4.75)–(4.82), the linear absorption coefficient was obtained directly from previous experiments of the authors, and β computed by eq. (4.43). Curve I was plotted with $\delta = 4.8 \times 10^{-3}$ and $\beta = 1.68 \times 10^{-3}$, the latter value being indicated by the absorption experiments. Curve II, giving a good fit to the experimental points, is plotted with the values $\delta = 4.8 \times 10^{-3}$ and $\beta = 2.5 \times 10^{-3}$. Curve III shows an attempt to fit the data by leaving β at 1.68×10^{-3}, the value obtained by experiment, and changing δ to 4.0×10^{-3}. The agreement between calculated and observed values is not improved by this change in δ. It seems that the correct value of β to be used in the calculations is somewhat higher than that which results from measurements of the linear absorption coefficient. This conclusion has also been reached by Edwards, who reflected x-rays of wave-length 0.69 A from glass, silver, and platinum. Thibaud has reflected soft x-rays from a glass grating, and found a variation of the type discussed here. Nähring has found that x-rays of various wave-lengths from 1.242 to 2.285 A when reflected from a polished silver mirror give intensities which as a function of the glancing angle agree with the Fresnel equations. We must conclude with Dershem and Schein that in spite of minor discrepancies between theory and experiment, it is remarkable that formulas developed for the optical region before anything was known of x-rays or quantum absorption phenomena should yield results so nearly in accord with experiment when extended to this region where the wave-lengths are over one hundred times shorter.

13. *The Wave-Mechanical Treatment of X-ray Dispersion Theory.*

There are at least two points in which the treatment of dispersion given in this chapter needs reconsideration, if a complete theory of the phenomena is desired. One of these is the empirical introduction of the λ^3 law of absorption into the Kramers-Kallman-Mark dispersion theory. Experiment shows that such a simple absorption law is not always adequate, and any complete theory of the interaction of x-rays with matter must necessarily include a theory of the varia-

tion of the absorption coefficient with wave-length.   Another point
is the value of the integral of eq. (4.56), or the total number of virtual
oscillators to be assigned to an atomic level.   Experiment shows that
in the case of the K and L levels this number is less than the electron
population of the level, whereas in the Kramers-Kallmann-Mark
theory it is set equal to 2 and 8 for the K and L levels respectively.

Both of these considerations are intimately connected with the
problems of x-ray absorption, and the discussion here must be considered in connection with Secs. 9 and 10 of Chapter VII.   The direct
application of these ideas to x-ray dispersion theory has been made
by Hönl.[50]   He has based his treatment of the refractive index on
Sugiura's[51] calculation of the oscillator strengths corresponding to
transitions from quantized configurations in hydrogen to configurations of positive total energy, belonging to the continuous spectrum.
By making approximations corresponding to the screening and relativity effects which take place in the x-ray levels of the heavier atoms,
Hönl calculates a distribution function per electron for the K electrons, which in terms of ω is

$$f_H(\omega_j) = \frac{2^7 e^{-4}}{9} \frac{2\pi}{\omega_K} \left\{ \frac{4}{(1 - \Delta_K)^2} \left(\frac{\omega_K}{\omega_j}\right)^3 - \frac{1}{(1 - \Delta_K)^3} \left(\frac{\omega_K}{\omega_j}\right)^4 \right\}, \quad (4.99)$$

where

$$\Delta_K = \frac{(Z - s)^2 + \frac{1}{4}\alpha^2(Z - s)^4 \ldots - h\nu_K/Rhc}{(Z - s)^2}. \quad (4.100)$$

In these expressions ω_K is $2\pi\nu_K$, where ν_K is the K critical absorption
frequency, and ω_j has the same relation to the frequency ν_j of a
virtual oscillator. s is the appropriate screening constant for the K
level, and α is the fine structure constant, or $2\pi e^2/hc$. R is the
Rydberg constant in cm.$^{-1}$ and c is the velocity of light.

Let us now turn to eq. (4.71), which gives us an expression for
the contribution to the complex index of refraction from electrons
of the type q, in terms of the frequency distribution of the virtual
oscillators corresponding to these electrons.   From eq. (4.68) we see
that

$$\mu_c^q = 1 + \frac{2\pi e^2}{m} \int_{\omega_q}^{\infty} f(\omega_j) \frac{1}{\omega_j^2 - \omega^2 + i\eta\omega} d\omega_j. \quad (4.101)$$

In Sec. 8 of this chapter, eq. (4.56), we have defined our function $f(\omega_j)$

[50] H. Hönl, Zeitschr. f Physik 84, 1 (1933).   Annalen der Physik 5, 18, 42 (1933).
[51] Y. Sugiura, Journal de Physique 8, 113 (1928).

so as to represent the distribution of virtual oscillators for the total number of electrons in the q shell. The function $f_H(\omega_j)$ of eq. (4.99) represents the distribution per electron. For the two K electrons we may then write

$$1 - \delta_K - i\beta_K = \mu_c{}^K = 1 + 2\,\frac{2\pi e^2}{m} \int_{\omega_K}^{\infty} f_H(\omega_j)\,\frac{1}{\omega_j{}^2 - \omega^2 + i\eta\omega}\,d\omega_j. \quad (4.102)$$

This expression, neglecting the damping term involving η, leads to

$$\delta_K = \frac{n_a e^2}{2\pi m \nu^2}\,\frac{2^7 e^{-4}}{9}\left\{\frac{4}{(1-\Delta_K)^2}\left(1 + x^2 ln\left|1 - x^{-2}\right|\right)\right.$$

$$\left. - \frac{1}{(1-\Delta_K)^3}\left(\frac{2}{3} + 2x^2 + x^3 ln\left|\frac{1-x}{1+x}\right|\right)\right\}, \quad (4.103)$$

in which

$$x = \nu_K/\nu$$

and n_a is the number of atoms per unit volume which contain the K electrons in question. The corresponding expression for the absorptive index β is

$$\beta_K = \frac{n_a e^2}{2\pi m \nu^2}\,\frac{2^7 e^{-4}}{9}\left\{\frac{4x^2}{(1-\Delta_K)^2} - \frac{x^3}{(1-\Delta_K)^3}\right\} \text{ for } x \leqq 1$$

$$= 0 \text{ for } x > 1. \quad (4.104)$$

The extent of the agreement of eq. (4.103) with the experiments on the refractive index is shown in Fig. IV–12. It is seen that the agreement of the newer theory with experiment is clearly better than that of the old on the long wave-length side of the limit.

Hönl has also given a very complete discussion of the wave-mechanical treatment of the variation of the atomic structure factor with wave-length in regions of anomalous dispersion. This treatment is an improvement on the elementary considerations which were used to obtain eq. (4.92) in the same way in which the treatment culminating in eq. (4.103) is an improvement on the Kramers-Kallmann-Mark theory of the refractive index. In addition to the elementary theory the more complete theory of Hönl gives a method of estimating the decrement in the atomic structure factor in regions of anomalous dispersion as a function of scattering angle. A complete treatment of the interaction of an electromagnetic wave with an atom of finite extent containing oscillators of various natural frequencies must begin with a formula giving the electric moment induced in an atom, and the expression must be sufficiently general to include both the effect of finite extent (phase shifts due to difference in phase of the exciting radiation in various parts of the atom) and the influence of the natural frequencies (resonance effects shifting the phases of the oscillators with respect to that of the incident wave). Such a formula has been proposed by Waller[52] as a generalization

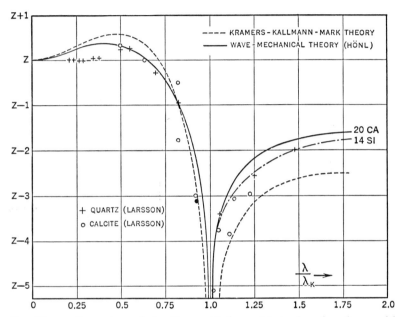

Fig. IV-12. Comparison of the Kramers-Kallmann-Mark dispersion theory with the wave-mechanical dispersion theory and the experiments of Larsson on the refractive index of x-rays in quartz and calcite. Values of $(2\pi mc^2\delta)/n_a e^2\lambda^2$ are plotted as ordinates. (From Hönl.)

of the Kramers-Heisenberg[53] equation. Hönl succeeded in developing that part of the Waller formula which deals with the anomalous dispersion into a very rapidly converging series by the use of spherical harmonics. The successive terms represent scattering by a dipole, quadrupole, octopole, etc. The calculations have been carried out only for the K shell and only the results of the dipole approximation

[52] I. Waller, Zeitschr. f. Physik **51**, 213 (1928).
[53] H. A. Kramers and W. Heisenberg, Zeitschr. f. Physik **31**, 681 (1925).

are reported. This is sufficient, however, at the present stage of accuracy of the experiments. The calculations are made neglecting the effects of electron spin, relativity, and radiation damping, and are limited therefore to the region $h\nu \ll mc^2$, that is, $\lambda \gg 0.024$ A. Let Δf be the decrement of the atomic structure factor due to the K electrons, obtained from

$$\Delta f = f - f_{\text{exp}}.$$

Here f is the value of the atomic structure factor calculated from a theoretical atomic model from purely geometrical grounds, that is, assuming some $U(r)$ in eq. (6.96), Chapter VI, and neglecting any resonance effects between the incident frequency and any natural frequency of the atom. f_{exp} is the observed value in a region of anomalous dispersion of the K electrons. Hönl shows that all the effects observable experimentally from the K shell will be given by

$$\Delta f = -\frac{2^7 e^{-4}}{9} (4Q_2' - Q_3')$$

where

$$Q_n'(x) = -\frac{x^n}{(1 - \Delta)^n} \int_x^\infty \left(\frac{1}{\zeta - 1} + \frac{1}{\zeta + 1} \right) \frac{d\zeta}{\zeta^n}$$

and $x = \nu_K/\nu = \lambda/\lambda_K$. The value of Δ is given by

$$\Delta = \frac{(Z - s)^2 - h\nu_K/Rhc}{(Z - s)^2},$$

and is identical with that in eq. (7.58), Chap. VII. A dependence of Δf on the atomic number comes in through Δ, and the wave-length dependence through x. Δf is for all experimental purposes independent of scattering angle, since we are dealing with the K electrons.

The variation of the atomic structure factor for 26Fe to be expected from Hönl's results has been shown in Fig. IV–9. Collected values of Δf for the K electrons of 26Fe, 42Mo, and 74W, calculated by Hönl, are shown in Table IV–4. The values of Δ for 26Fe, 42Mo, and 74W are 0.212, 0.182, and 0.143 respectively. In this table the values of Δf at $x = \infty$ are the oscillator strengths of the K levels and agree with those of Table VII–17, Chapter VII.

TABLE IV-4

HÖNL'S CALCULATED VALUES OF THE STRUCTURE FACTOR DECREMENT Δf
AT VARIOUS WAVE-LENGTHS

(a) Short Wave-length Side of the Limit

$x = \lambda/\lambda_K$	0.2	0.5	0.667	0.75	0.9	0.95
26Fe	−0.17	−0.30	−0.03	0.28	1.47	2.40
42Mo	−0.16	−0.26	0.01	0.31	1.48	2.32
74W	−0.15	−0.25	0.01	0.30	1.40	2.18

(b) Long Wave-length Side of the Limit

$x = \lambda/\lambda_K$	1.05	1.11	1.2	1.33	1.5	2.0	∞
26Fe	3.30	2.60	2.20	1.90	1.73	1.51	1.32
42Mo	3.08	2.44	2.06	1.77	1.61	1.43	1.24
74W	2.85	2.26	1.91	1.65	1.49	1.31	1.15

CHAPTER V

THE STUDY OF CRYSTAL STRUCTURE BY MEANS OF X-RAYS [1]

1. *Introduction; Distinguishing Properties of Crystals*

A single crystal may be defined as a solid object of uniform chemical composition, which, as it occurs in nature, or is formed in the laboratory by solidification of the liquid, precipitation from solution, or by other analogous methods, is bounded by plane surfaces, the interrelations of which exhibit a typical symmetry. Common crystals which have long been recognized are ice, quartz, calcite, and rock salt. These substances also undoubtedly attracted attention due to their transparency, but transparency is not at all a necessary property of crystals. Many solid objects are aggregates of minute crystals packed together in a more or less random fashion. This is true of the metals and alloys as we commonly see them. Very few truly amorphous or non-crystalline solid substances are known. Glass if properly annealed is a close approach to a truly non-crystalline body. In addition to being bounded by plane surfaces crystals are distinguished from amorphous material by the property of anisotropy. For instance, the following properties of a crystal depend in magnitude on the direction through the crystal in which they are measured: temperature expansion coefficient, linear compressibility, index of refraction for light, electrical conductivity, heat conductivity, velocity of sound.

From a study of the external symmetry of crystals as exhibited by their forms, from measurements of the angles between typical plane faces which remain invariant from specimen to specimen,

---

[1] The following books deal with the study of crystal structures by means of x-rays:

Bragg, W. H., and Bragg, W. L., X-rays and Crystal Structure. G. Bell, Lond. (1915) (and subsequent editions).

Ewald, P. P., Kristalle und Röntgenstrahlen. J. Springer, Berlin, 1923. Handb. der Physik, 2nd Ed., Vol. 23 (1933).

Wyckoff, R. W. G., The Structure of Crystals. Chem. Cat. Co., N. Y., 1931.

The method of approach to many topics in this chapter has been influenced by a study of Wyckoff's book. The derivation of Laue's equations parallels that of Ewald.

from observation of the phenomenon of cleavage, in which some crystals tend to fracture along perfectly definite directions, and from many other observations, investigators have long been convinced that the atoms or molecules of which crystals are built are not oriented at random like sand grains in a sand pile, but are packed together with the greatest order and regularity. A very fundamental problem in the study of crystals is to determine, if possible, this internal order, and to interpret from it the external and macroscopic properties of crystals.

The fundamental discovery of Laue[2] that x-rays are diffracted from crystals at one stroke laid the foundation for a domain of physics, the spectroscopy of x-rays, and for the new science of crystal structure, which draws support from physics, chemistry, and crystallography. This chapter is intended to present a brief account of the methods used in the study of crystal structure, but the material presented here will be far from adequate for the training of those who wish to conduct researches in this field.

2. The External Symmetry of Crystals[3]

By the external symmetry of crystals is meant those symmetry characteristics which can be detected by the methods available to crystallographers before the advent of x-ray diffraction. Some of these methods have been mentioned in the preceding section of this chapter; in addition to these are studies of the optical properties of the crystal, such as the variation of the refractive index with direction, and the double refraction of optically active crystals. Again, if parts of the crystal surface are dissolved in some solvent, so-called etch figures are formed, which in their symmetry properties disclose some of the external symmetry of the crystal.

The results of the study of thousands of crystal forms by such methods have revealed that these external symmetry properties can be expressed in terms of three fundamental elements of symmetry, whose definitions will now be given.

(1) *The plane of symmetry.*—If a figure has a plane of symmetry, a point in the figure will have a mirror image in this

[2] Friedrich, W., Knipping, P., and v. Laue, M. Sitzb. math.-phys. Klasse Bayer. Akad. Wiss. München. 303 (1912).

[3] An invaluable collection of data on the external symmetry of crystals is that of Groth, Chemische Krystallographie, Leipzig (1906) 5 vols.

plane. In other words, if a perpendicular is dropped from this point to the plane, and extended an equal distance through it, the perpendicular will terminate in an equivalent point.

(2) *The center of symmetry.*—If a figure has a center of symmetry at some point, a line drawn to this center from a point of the figure and extended an equal distance beyond the center terminates in an equivalent point.

(3) *The n-fold axis of symmetry.*—If a figure has an *n*-fold axis of symmetry, a rotation of the figure around the axis through the angle $2\pi/n$ superimposes equivalent points.

The terms reflection, inversion, and rotation are applied to the operations suggested in the definitions of the plane of symmetry,

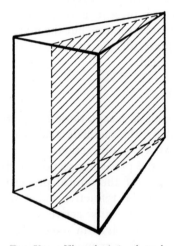

FIG. V–1. The shaded plane is a plane of symmetry in the right prism whose cross-section is an isosceles triangle.

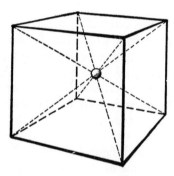

FIG. V–2. The center of a cube is a center of symmetry.

center of symmetry, and axis of symmetry respectively. Every object has an infinite number of one-fold axes of symmetry, since this simply means superposition after a 360° rotation. In crystals, in addition to the one-fold axes, only 2-, 3-, 4-, and 6-fold axes have been found. This limitation of the number of kinds of axes is of cardinal importance in crystal symmetry. Figures V–1, V–2, and V–3 show examples of the elements of symmetry.

Derived or composite symmetry properties may arise from

successive applications of the symmetry operations.   Thus an n-fold
rotary reflection results from a rotation of
$2\pi/n$ radians about the rotation axis, followed by reflection in a plane of symmetry
perpendicular to that axis.   This is illustrated by the assemblage of points in Fig.
V–4.   After rotation of this group of points
90° about the Z-axis and reflection in the
XY plane, it is indistinguishable from its
original form.   Another composite symmetry
property of importance is the n-fold rotary
inversion, in which a rotation of $2\pi/n$
radians is succeeded by an inversion through
a center of symmetry on the axis of rotation.   The order in which the elements are
applied is immaterial, both in the rotary
inversion and rotary reflection.

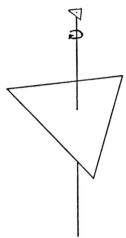

Fig. V–3.   The equilat-
eral triangle has a three-
fold rotation axis of symmetry perpendicular to
its plane and passing
through its center.

These symmetry properties are not entirely independent, for the existence of two
of them may be equivalent to the existence
of a third.   Thus a 2-fold rotation axis along
the Z direction and a center of symmetry
at the origin imply a plane of symmetry lying in the XY plane.

Every crystal is characterized by one or more simple or com-

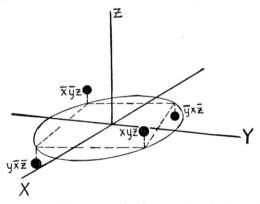

Fig. V–4.   A point group formed by a fourfold rotation-reflection axis along the Z
direction, the reflection taking place in the XY plane.   If the point group is rotated
90° around the Z axis and then reflected in the XY plane it becomes indistinguishable
from its original form.

posite elements of symmetry. Let us suppose that the locations of the symmetry elements appropriate to some crystal are specified with respect to a system of coordinates. The operation of these elements upon a general point of coordinates xyz will produce a group of equivalent points. If the coordinates of the points in this so-called point group are given, they constitute an adequate description of the symmetry elements which produced the group. Thus the points of Fig. V–4 constitute a point group arising from a 4-fold rotation reflection axis.

There are 32 point groups, that is, 32 different combinations of the symmetry elements about a point in space are possible. Each

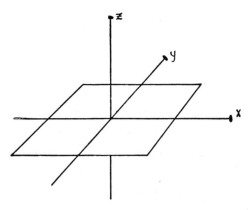

Fig. V–5. The elements of symmetry of a point group representing holohedry of the orthorhombic system. Twofold rotation axes coincide with the X, Y, and Z axes, and the XY plane is a plane of symmetry.

of these point groups has the external symmetry characteristics of a crystal class, and no crystals are known which do not fit into one of these classes. A complete description of the point groups and a nomenclature for them may be found in many of the numerous textbooks on crystallography or crystal structure.[4] Figure V–5 shows the elements of symmetry of a point group which has the external symmetry of the crystal class called holohedry of the ortho-rhombic system. Here we have three 2-fold rotation axes at right angles, and a plane of symmetry, taken as the XY plane, which contains two of the rotation axes. These symmetry elements will

[4] For instance, Wyckoff, loc. cit.

produce the following equivalent points[5] from a point whose coordinates are xyz:

$$x y z \quad x y \bar{z} \quad \bar{x} y \bar{z} \quad \bar{x} \bar{y} \bar{z} \quad \bar{x} y z \quad x \bar{y} \bar{z} \quad \bar{x} \bar{y} z \quad x \bar{y} \bar{z}$$

These eight points will lie at the corners of a rectangular parallelopiped whose three dimensions are in general different. The elements
already given require in addition that the ZY and ZX planes be
planes of symmetry. The common crystal barite, or heavy spar,
belongs to this class.

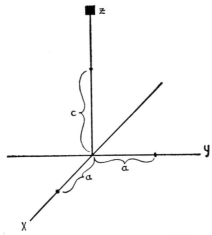

Fig. V–6. The appropriate axes for a point group having as its sole element of
symmetry a fourfold axis. The axis is placed along the Z axis of rectangular coordinates, with a unit distance c, which is different from the unit distance a along the
X and Y axes.

3. The Crystallographic Axes

The symmetry requirements of the point groups suggest certain
axial systems and ratios of unit distances along these axes which are
best adapted for description of the group. Let us consider a point
group which has as its one element of symmetry a 4-fold axis, Fig.
V–6. Here we see that the three coordinate axes are best chosen
at right angles. Let the 4-fold axis lie along the Z direction. Then
if a point lies on the X axis at unit distance from the origin, operation
of the symmetry element will produce an equivalent point on the

---

[5] It is uniform practice in writing coordinates to put a minus sign over the symbol
to which it applies.

Y axis, at the same distance from the origin. Thus the same unit distance is called for along the X and Y axes, but if the symmetry of the group is not to be exceeded, there will be a different unit distance along Z. The ratio of the unit distance along Z to that along X or Y is called the axial ratio. The axes here described are known as the tetragonal axes. The 32 point groups call for six or seven axial systems. Two of the seven systems are closely related (the rhombohedral and hexagonal systems) and are by some authors grouped under one system.

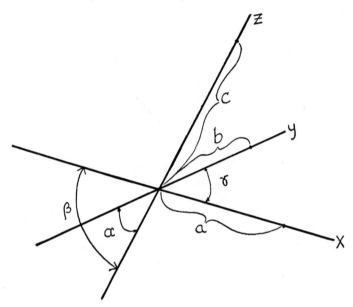

FIG. V–7. The triclinic axes and unit distances. All the inter-axial angles and the unit distances are different.

The most general crystallographic axes, the triclinic, are shown in Fig. V–7. The remaining axial systems can be expressed as special cases of the triclinic, and are so tabulated in Table V–1.

The planes which appear as faces of a crystal may be defined in terms of their intercepts upon the crystallographic axes. These intercepts are given in terms of the unit lengths on the various axes when used to locate a plane. Three numbers, called Miller indices, are customarily given to represent these intercepts. They are not the intercepts themselves, but are the lowest three integers

TABLE V-1

THE CRYSTALLOGRAPHIC SYSTEMS AS SPECIAL CASES OF FIG. V-7

System	Special Conditions	
Triclinic	No special conditions	
Monoclinic	$\beta \neq \alpha = \gamma = 90°$;	$a \neq b \neq c$
Orthorhombic	$\alpha = \beta = \gamma = 90°$;	$a \neq b \neq c$
Tetragonal	$\alpha = \beta = \gamma = 90°$;	$a = b \neq c$
Cubic	$\alpha = \beta = \gamma = 90°$;	$a = b = c$
Rhombohedral	$\alpha = \beta = \gamma \neq 90°$;	$a = b = c$
Hexagonal	$\beta = \alpha = 90°, \gamma = 120°$;	$a = b \neq c$

having the same ratios as the reciprocals of the intercepts. Thus if the intercepts of a plane upon the orthorhombic axes, for instance, are $2a/3$, $2b/5$, $\frac{1}{2}c$, the Miller indices of the plane will be (354). In general the Miller indices are represented by (hkl), corresponding to the X, Y, and Z intercepts respectively. If a plane is parallel to one of the axes, the corresponding Miller index is zero.

We now come to a law which expresses the result of thousands of crystallographic measurements, called the law of rational indices. It may be stated as follows: it is always possible to find a set of axes and axial ratios for any crystal such that the Miller indices of any natural face are small integers. The assumption that no exceptions to this rule are possible is fundamental to the theories of crystal structure.

4. The Internal Symmetry of Crystals; the Space Lattices

Speculations as to the internal arrangements of the structural units of crystals which would build up the observed external characteristics were first guided by a study of the phenomenon of cleavage. In 1784 Haüy[6] examined the cleavage of various habits of the crystal calcite, that is, different specimens of the substance in which certain faces were more prominently displayed than in others, hence superficially appearing to be quite distinct. He found that on cleavage he was always able to split out a rhombohedron from all these forms, and he theorized that the unit of structure of calcite was a minute rhombohedron, which repeated throughout space, built up the macroscopic whole. Haüy's theory, in which the form of the unit was determined by cleavage, is now obsolete

[6] Haüy, Abbé Réné Just, Essai d'une théorie sur la structure des cristaux, Paris, 1784.

because crystals are known having no cleavage, also crystals like fluorspar cleave into octahedrons which cannot be packed together to fill up space. Nevertheless, the fundamental idea of a structural unit, the same for all habits of a crystal class, has persisted. Such a unit may be an atom, a molecule, or a group of molecules.

We will first consider the patterns by which these units are distributed in space. These are called the space lattices, and are three dimensional point nets. Each point of a space lattice is a reference

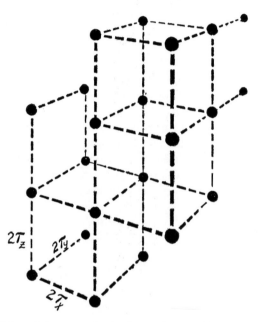

Fig. V–8a.   A fragment of a simple translatory cubic space lattice.

point corresponding to one of the structural units. If the structural unit is a single kind of atom, one atom at each point of the space lattice would build up the entire structure.

An important property of a lattice is its set of so-called primitive translations. These are the coordinates of adjacent points relative to an arbitrarily selected point in the lattice. The simplest of the space lattices, and for a long time the only ones postulated, are the so-called simple translatory lattices. A portion of the simple translatory cubic lattice is shown in Fig. V–8a. The axes of reference of the lattice and the unit lengths along the axes are those of the cubic system of crystals. If we call the distance between adjacent lattice points along the X axis $2\tau_x$, then the primitive translations of this lattice are

$$2\tau_x,0,0 \qquad 0,2\tau_y,0 \qquad 0,0,2\tau_z$$

in which

$$\tau_x = \tau_y = \tau_z.$$

Similar simple translatory lattices can be built up using the crystallographic axes of all the crystal systems.

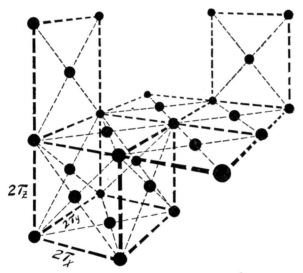

Fig. V–8b.   A fragment of a face-centered cubic lattice.

There are, however, more complicated lattices which may exist without violating the external symmetry of crystals. There are two more lattices applicable to the cubic system, namely, the so-called face-centered and body-centered lattices. Figure V–8b shows a portion of a face-centered cubic lattice. If $2\tau_x$ is the distance between adjacent lattice points along the X direction, the primitive translations of this lattice are

$$\tau_x,0,\tau_z \qquad 0,\tau_y,\tau_z \qquad \tau_x,\tau_y,0$$

where as before,

$$\tau_x = \tau_y = \tau_z.$$

The body-centered cubic lattice, a portion of which is shown in Fig. V–8c, has the primitive translations

$$2\tau_x,0,0 \qquad 0,2\tau_y,0 \qquad 0,0,2\tau_z \qquad \tau_x,\tau_y,\tau_z.$$

Lattices whose variations from the simple translatory lattice are analogous to those discussed above exist for all the crystal systems except the triclinic, which has only one lattice. There are 14 space lattices, and each one of these has the highest symmetry compatible with the axes on which it is built. In other words, each space

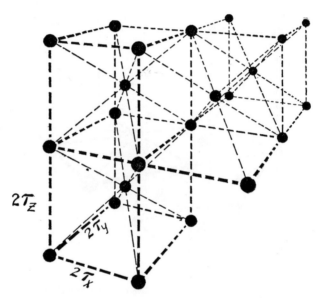

FIG. V–8c.   A fragment of a body-centered cubic lattice.

lattice has the symmetry of the most symmetrical point group assigned to its axes.

5. *The Space Groups and the Unit Cell*

We have seen that the internal structure of a crystal can be thought of as a repetition of some fundamental group along the points of a space lattice. What is the nature of the group which is thus repeated? Some crystals are known in which this group is simply one atom, and the crystal is built by placing atoms of the substance at the points of the space lattice. These constitute the simplest known crystals and are the solid forms of some of the elements.

The internal structure of single crystals of copper, for instance, is built up of copper atoms arranged at the lattice points of the face-centered cubic lattice of Fig. V–8*b*. If the atoms of copper in the crystal, either due to their shape, or to their effective shape which is influenced by their thermal motions, are spherically symmetrical, then the crystal as a whole must exhibit the highest symmetry compatible with the cubic axes. It is known that twenty-one elements crystallize with this structure.

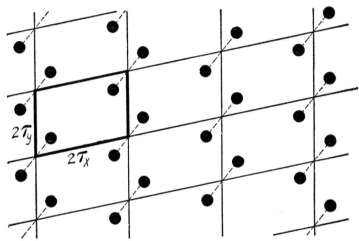

Fig. V–9. A two-dimensional space group formed by repeating a point group consisting of a center of symmetry along a two-dimensional lattice. The centers of symmetry coincide with the lattice points.

Fourteen elements are known to crystallize so that their internal structure consists of single atoms placed at the lattice points of the body-centered cubic lattice. The most stable modification of iron at room temperature is built up in this way.

No examples are known in which identical atoms are placed at the lattice points of the simple translatory cubic lattice. A possible explanation for this is that such an arrangement does not give as close a packing of spheres as does either of the other two cubic lattices.

More complicated structures may be built by placing a point group at each lattice point. Such structures are in general called space groups. This procedure gives the possibility of producing structures of lower symmetry than is evidenced by the lattice itself. A portion of a very simple two-dimensional space group is shown in Fig. V–9. The point group which is repeated over the plane lattice consists of a center of symmetry, and thus each lattice point is such a center. The equivalent points of this point group, repeated over the lattice, constitute the space group. In this way the simpler space groups are constructed.

When we extend the point groups out into space by repetition along the lattices, we, however, introduce a new possible symmetry

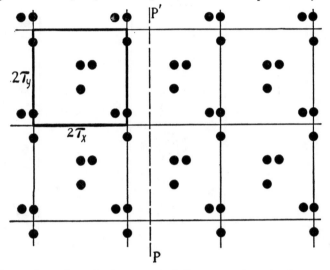

Fig. V–10. A two-dimensional space group built on a two-dimensional space-centered lattice. PP' is the trace of a glide plane of symmetry, of translation τ_y.

element, the translation. By moving a point group from one lattice point to the next we cause it to coincide completely with the group already there. To the observer of the external symmetry of the crystal, who cannot detect translations of atomic dimensions, such an operation appears quite analogous to the other symmetry operations previously discussed. Composite internal symmetry elements combining the translation with reflection or rotation are called glide planes or screw axes respectively.

Figure V–10 shows a two-dimensional space group built upon the two-dimensional projection of a body-centered lattice. The line PP' is the trace of a glide plane of symmetry. The translation associated with the glide plane is of length τ_y. If the pattern to the right of PP' is shifted up or down a distance τ_y, PP' becomes the trace of an ordinary plane of symmetry, and if the pattern were on atomic dimensions the observer would conclude that only the simpler symmetry existed. The existence of such translational symmetry elements greatly increases the number of space groups having the external symmetry of a given point group. Thus there are ten possible space groups having external symmetry equivalent to the highest possible in the cubic system, and 230 in all corresponding to the 32 point groups.[7]

A space group may be described by giving the lattice on which it is built and the location of its symmetry elements with respect to a lattice point. Another method of description is to give the coordinates of the equivalent points lying within the so-called unit cell of the group. The unit cell can be defined as the smallest volume from which the entire space group can be built by repetition along the lattice axes. In space groups built on simple translatory axes, the unit cell is a parallelopiped bounded by edges of lengths $2\tau_x$, $2\tau_y$, $2\tau_z$, and hence having corners in adjacent lattice points. Such a two-dimensional unit cell is heavily outlined in Fig. V–9. In space groups built on one of the more complex lattices, the unit cell contains lattice points on its sides or within it. This is illustrated by the cell outlined in Fig. V–10.

The conventional method of giving the location of equivalent points in the unit cell is to give the coordinates with respect to the origin in terms of the length of side of the cell. In a crystal of molybdenum the points of a body-centered cubic lattice are occupied by molybdenum atoms. The unit cell is shown in Fig. V–11. X-ray measurements have shown the length of side of this unit (a_0) to be 3.14×10^{-8} cm. The cell contains two atoms of molybdenum, since each of the eight corners is shared among eight adjacent cells. The cell may be formally described by giving the coordinates of the two molybdenum atoms, which are

$$\text{OOO} \qquad \tfrac{1}{2}\tfrac{1}{2}\tfrac{1}{2}.$$

[7] The 230 space groups were deduced independently, and by different methods by:

Federov, E., Z. Krist. **24**, 209 (1895). This work had appeared in Russian several years previously.

Schoenflies, A., Kristallsysteme und Krystallstruktur, Leipzig (1891).

Barlow, W., Z. Krist. **23**, 1 (1894).

A simplified derivation has been given by Hermann, C., Z. Krist. **68**, 257 (1928).

These coordinates are to be applied to each corner of the unit cell in turn, drawing in those atoms, which then fall within the unit. Figure V–12 shows the unit cell of a metallic crystal whose atoms lie at the points of a face-centered cubic lattice. There are four atoms in the unit cell, and their coordinates are

$$000 \qquad \tfrac{1}{2}\tfrac{1}{2}0 \qquad \tfrac{1}{2}0\tfrac{1}{2} \qquad 0\tfrac{1}{2}\tfrac{1}{2}.$$

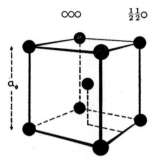 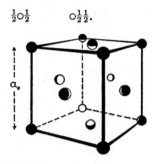

FIG. V–11. The unit cell of a crystalline element with atoms at the points of a body-centered cubic lattice.

FIG. V–12. The unit cell of a crystalline element with atoms at the points of a face-centered cubic lattice.

6. The Importance of Space Group Theory in the Deduction of the Structure of Crystals

The results of the theory of space groups permit the tabulation of the coordinates of equivalent points in the unit cell. For instance, there exists a space group having the external symmetry of holohedry of the cubic system (the highest cubic symmetry) which if its unit cell contains an atom at a general position, xyz, must contain in all 192 identical atoms equivalent to it whose coordinates can be written down from theory alone. Later in this chapter we shall show how x-ray methods can determine the size of the unit cell and the number of atoms or molecules in it. This can usually be accomplished even when it is impossible to go further and find the exact locations of the atoms in the cell. Now it is often found that the number of atoms of one kind in the unit cell is small, considerably smaller than corresponds to the number permitted by space group theory when the atoms lie in general positions. Thus there are only four molecules of sodium chloride in the unit cell, and hence four sodium atoms.

From the standpoint of space group theory the number of equivalent positions in the unit cell may be greatly reduced if the atoms occupy, not general positions, but special positions with regard to the symmetry elements. Thus atoms may lie on symmetry planes, or rotation axes, or in centers of symmetry. In the same space group mentioned previously in this section, the number of equivalent points may be reduced from 192 to 16 if the points lie at such special positions. Thus it frequently happens that the atoms in the unit cell occupy these special positions, and a knowledge of them will greatly reduce the labor of testing out all conceivable arrangements. The special positions of equivalent points have been tabulated by Wyckoff, and by Astbury and Yardley.[8]

In the simplest crystal types, such as the crystals of many of the elements, and of the alkali halides, the external symmetry is so high, and the number of atoms or molecules in the unit cell so small, that application of the space group theory to the deduction of the structure is putting this powerful tool to a trivial use. The atoms lie in such highly specialized positions that trials of a few structures suggested by intuitive notions of symmetry almost invariably have succeeded in establishing the correct one. Thus the structures of rock-salt, potassium chloride, diamond, and even calcite have been deduced without recourse to space group theory. But in the analysis of more complicated crystals of lower symmetry types it has become essential to utilize the results of the theory, and it is just such crystals which await analysis, most of the simpler ones having been done. Once the number of molecules in the unit cell and the space group are known, the theory lays before the investigator a finite number of possible arrangements from which the correct one is to be selected. The coordinates of the permitted positions may contain one or more unknown parameters which must be evaluated. It is this last step which is by far the most difficult, and often impossible. The theory of space groups has, however, greatly shortened the first stages in the analysis of a crystal.

7. *The Diffraction of X-rays by Crystals; Development of Laue's Equations*

In Chapter I of this book we have given a very elementary derivation of Bragg's law from consideration of the reflection of an x-ray beam from a set of parallel planes, and the interference of

---

[8] Wyckoff, R. W. G., The Analytical Expression of the Results of the Theory of Space Groups. Carnegie Inst. Wash. Publ. 2nd Ed. (1930).
Astbury, W. T. and Yardley, K., Phil. Trans. 224A, 221 (1924).

reflected beams from successive planes. We can learn a great deal about the interaction of x-rays and crystals by developing Bragg's equation in an entirely different manner. We will study the interaction of x-rays with a structure composed of scattering units (atoms) placed at the lattice points of a simple translatory cubic lattice. Thus the diffracting structure will be that of Fig. V-8a. Although as has been previously stated, no known crystal has exactly such a structure, it will be shown that the results of such an investigation are readily extended to structures actually known to exist.

We may consider this three-dimensional structure as built up from what we shall call one-dimensional point gratings, meaning the

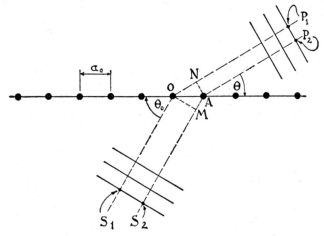

Fig. V-13.   Diffraction of plane waves by a one-dimensional point grating.

regular array of points, spaced a_0 apart, met with along the X, Y, and Z directions. Let us consider the diffraction effects from a single one-dimensional point grating. Let plane, monochromatic x-rays be incident upon it, causing the electrons in the atoms at the lattice points to scatter coherently secondary x-rays in all directions. In Fig. V-13 the parallel wave-fronts are represented as coming up from below. Let the rays S_1O and S_2A represent distances in the oncoming beam, and OP_1 and AP_2 distances in the scattered radiation. There will be a maximum of intensity in the direction of OP_1 and AP_2 in case the following relation holds true,

$$S_1OP_1 - S_2AP_2 = m_1\lambda,$$ (5.01)

where m_1 is an integer, and λ is the wave-length of the radiation.
From Fig. V–13 we see the following relations:

$$S_1OP_1 - S_2AP_2 = NO - MA = a_0 \cos \theta - a_0 \cos \theta_0. \quad (5.02)$$

The equation giving the angle from the grating at which a maximum
of diffracted intensity is to be expected is then

$$m_1\lambda = a_0 (\cos \theta - \cos \theta_0). \quad (5.03)$$

It is of interest to note that eq. (5.03) predicts that for a given
value of a_0, no diffracted maxima (zero order excepted) can occur

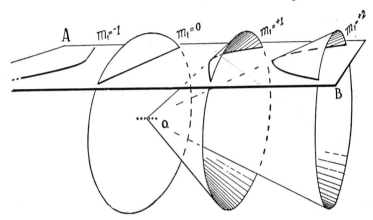

FIG. V–14. Diffraction pattern formed with monochromatic radiation on plane AB
by a one-dimensional point grating at O. The radiation is incident on the grating
directly from below

for wave-lengths longer than $2a_0$. This is because the maximum
value of the term in parentheses in the equation is 2. Thus there
is a maximum wave-length for the grating, depending upon its
spacing.

The atoms along the one dimensional grating scatter secondary
radiation in all directions, hence the three-dimensional representation of the diffraction pattern may be obtained by rotation about
the line of the grating. The diffraction maxima thus lie along cones
whose mutual axis is the line of the grating. We shall illustrate, in
Fig. V–14, the appearance of the spectra of various orders on a
plane parallel to the line of the grating, situated at a distance from
it great in comparison to the length of the grating. It has also been
assumed in Fig. V–14 that the incident radiation comes from directly

below the grating, that is, $\theta_0 = \pi/2$ in eq. (5.03) and $\cos \theta_0 = 0$. The spectrum of zero order appears as a straight line upon this plane, the other orders, of the same wave-length, appear as hyperbolae.

If the incident radiation is not monochromatic, but contains many wave-lengths, there are many cones for every order outside the zeroth order, and for white or general radiation, radiation will reach every part of the plane AB. The orders will also overlap, and any point on the plane may receive radiations of wave-length λ, $\lambda/2$, $\lambda/3$, etc.

We will now consider the spectrum from a two-dimensional grating, made up of linear gratings of the kind previously discussed placed at right angles in a plane. Such a two-dimensional array of

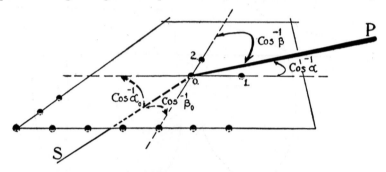

Fig. V–15. Diffraction of plane waves by a two-dimensional point grating.

points is shown in Fig. V–15. The parameter a_0 is the same for both linear gratings, since we are building on a simple translatory cubic lattice. In Fig. V–15 SO is a normal to the oncoming wave fronts and its direction cosines with respect to the two component gratings are α_0 and β_0. Let α and β be the direction cosines of the line OP, which has a direction in which constructive interference takes place between the wavelets scattered by every atom in the grating. Then by analogy with eq. (5.03) we see that the conditions to be fulfilled for a maximum in the diffraction pattern are

$$m_1\lambda = a_0(\alpha - \alpha_0)\Big|$$
$$m_2\lambda = a_0(\beta - \beta_0)\Big|, \qquad (5.04)$$

where m_1 and m_2 are two integers, not necessarily equal. Eqs. (5.04) mean that along the direction OP the path differences in the radiation scattered from atoms whose coordinates in terms of a_0

and with respect to any arbitrarily chosen lattice point as origins
are (1,0) and (0,1), are respectively $m_1\lambda$ and $m_2\lambda$.

Figure V–16 represents the spectrum produced with monochromatic incident radiation in an arrangement similar to that of
Fig. V–14. The two-dimensional grating is to be placed in the
position of the one-dimensional of the figure, its plane normal to
the plane of the illustration, and radiation incident on it from below.
The hyperbolae of Fig. V–16 represent the linear spectra of the
component gratings for various values of m_1 and m_2. The intersection points of these hyperbolae are the actual maxima observed.

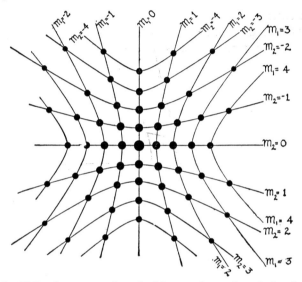

Fig. V–16. Diffraction pattern formed with monochromatic radiation from a two-
dimensional grating situated as in Fig. V–14.

Each maximum may be characterized by two integers, giving the
values of m_1 and m_2 in the component linear grating spectra. It
is instructive to notice that in adding the second linear grating at
right angles to the first, we have reduced the dimensions of the spectra
from lines to points.

It is interesting to note what happens if, leaving the direction
of the incident radiation fixed, we remove the monochromatic
restriction, and illuminate the two-dimensional grating with white
or general radiation. In discussion of this case we shall borrow
the terms " red " and " blue " from visible light, using them entirely

in a general sense to mean longer or shorter wave-lengths, respectively. In Fig. V–17 the curves marked m_1 show the intersections of the cones of order m_1 for two different wave-lengths with the plane on which the spectrum is taken. The blue curve will lie nearer the spot of order numbers (o, o) than the red, as may be seen from eq. (5.03). The same is true for the hyperbolae from the spectrum of order m_2 from the other component grating. Let us suppose that two blue hyperbolae intersect at the point B. Here there will be an intensity maximum in the diffraction pattern for radiation of that wave-length. The same holds for the point R, where two red hyperbolae intersect. Between the points R and B will be a

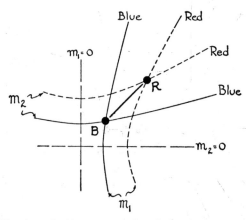

FIG. V–17. Diffraction of white or general radiation by a two-dimensional point grating.

line on which diffraction maxima of intermediate color will appear, so that a " rainbow " will be formed, radiating away from the direction of prolongation of the direct beam (spot of order (o,o)), with its blue end nearer the center. Such rainbows can be seen by looking at an arc light through a fine mesh handkerchief, which is essentially a two-dimensional grating of the kind under discussion.

We now come to the problem of a three-dimensional grating, built of component one-dimensional gratings of equal interval a_0 along the X, Y, and Z directions. Let α_0, β_0, γ_0 be the direction cosines of the incident radiation with respect to these axes, and α, β, γ, the corresponding quantities for a line in the direction of a maximum in the scattered radiation. Then the condition for constructive interference for the waves scattered from every atom in the array is that there be a solution of the following simultaneous equations, known as Laue's equations:

$$\left.\begin{aligned} m_1\lambda &= a_0(\alpha - \alpha_0) \\ m_2\lambda &= a_0(\beta - \beta_0) \\ m_3\lambda &= a_0(\gamma - \gamma_0) \end{aligned}\right\} . \tag{5.05}$$

Figure V–18 is illustrative of the conditions in general in an arrangement similar to that of Fig. V–15. In the present case the three-

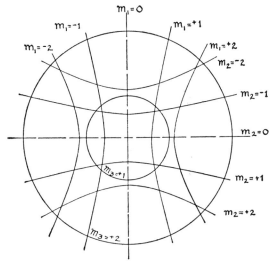

Fig. V–18.   There are in general no common intersections of the loci of the diffraction maxima of the three component linear gratings in a three-dimensional point grating, hence in general no Laue spots appear with monochromatic x-rays.

dimensional grating is to replace the one-dimensional one of the illustration, with one of its axes (the Z axis) vertical, so that the wave-fronts of the oncoming monochromatic radiation are perpendicular to it. The axes of the diffraction cones from the component gratings parallel to the Z axis are vertical, and their sections by the plane AB are therefore circles, as shown in Fig. V–18. The appearance of a maximum in the diffraction pattern would correspond to a common intersection of two hyperbolae and a circle. It is clear that, in general, such an intersection cannot take place, therefore in general there is no monochromatic diffraction pattern at all produced for a given value of α_0, β_0, and γ_0.

Let us now consider what happens if, keeping the direction cosines of the incident beam constant, we replace the monochromatic incident beam by white radiation, containing a large number of wave-lengths. The production of Laue spots under these conditions is illustrated in Fig. V–19. As before, the component curves marked R are due to a red wave-length in the spectrum. At point R, two red curves intersect, and if we were dealing with a two-dimensional grating, an interference maximum would result. But since the circular red curve does not pass through this point, we get only destructive interference and no maximum. The same may be said

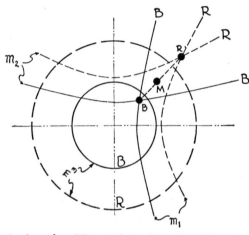

Fig. V–19. Production of a diffracted beam by a three-dimensional grating with white radiation.

about the point B, where two blue hyperbolae intersect. Let us consider the state of affairs along the line BR. If no third dimension was in the grating, a spectrum would be spread out along BR, containing wave-lengths between B and R as in Fig. V–17. In general, these intermediate wave-lengths will also be suppressed by destructive interference, but in the region between the two circles, there necessarily must be some point M at which the intersecting circle is of the same wave-length as that corresponding to the point of intersection on the two-dimensional line spectrum BR. Here, then, and only at one point, and for a single wave-length, a Laue spot will appear.

For this reason, a Laue photograph, in which the crystal is held stationary with respect to the incident beam of x-rays, is always taken with general x-radiation, otherwise practically no spots would appear. If the crystal is rotated, however, special values of α_0, β_0, γ_0 may be found at which monochromatic x-rays may be diffracted, and diffracted beams flash out.

Laue's equations may be solved in a form readily adapted to the interpretation of a Laue photograph. Such photographs are prepared by the method schematically shown in Fig. V–20. The incident pencil of x-rays is collimated by passage through two slits, and in the figure we may imagine it to be parallel to one of the principal axes of the crystal. 2θ is the angle between a diffracted beam and the direction of the direct beam. This may be easily

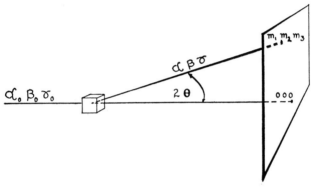

Fig. V–20. Schematic illustration of the production of a Laue photograph.

measured by measuring the distance on the photographic plate from the Laue spot of order numbers ($m_1m_2m_3$) to the central spot (ooo) and the distance from the plate to the crystal. Therefore a solution of eqs. (5.05) in which this angle appears rather than the direction cosines themselves will be experimentally practicable. We will use the following well-known relations between any three direction cosines

$$\alpha_0^2 + \beta_0^2 + \gamma_0^2 = \alpha^2 + \beta^2 + \gamma^2 = 1, \tag{5.06}$$

$$\cos 2\theta = \alpha\alpha_0 + \beta\beta_0 + \gamma\gamma_0. \tag{5.07}$$

By solving eqs. (5.05) for $(\alpha - \alpha_0)$, $(\beta - \beta_0)$, and $(\gamma - \gamma_0)$, respectively, squaring these solutions, and adding the three squared equations, we obtain the following expressions:

$$\lambda^2(m_1^2 + m_2^2 + m_3^2) = 2a_0^2(1 - \cos 2\theta)$$
$$= 4a_0^2 \sin^2 \theta.$$

Solving this last equation for sin θ gives the desired expression,

$$2a_0 \sin \theta = \lambda\sqrt{m_1^2 + m_2^2 + m_3^2}. \qquad (5.08)$$

8. Bragg's Interpretation of Laue's Equations

We shall now show that eq. (5.08) may readily be interpreted according to Bragg's method, that is, the diffracted beam forming the maximum may be considered to come from the reflection of the radiation by a set of planes in the crystal. In order to do this, we must first define the idea of a plane of reflection somewhat more sharply than is usually the case. Figure V–21 represents a plane wave front, S, moving toward a plane, AB, on which we assume a reflected wave is built up, of which P is a wave-front. The ordinary

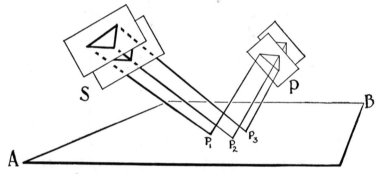

FIG. V–21.   Reflection of a plane wave S into a plane wave P by a reflection plane AB.

laws of reflection, namely, that the angles of incidence and reflection are equal, and that the incident beam, the reflected beam, and the normal to the reflecting plane at the point of incidence lie in a plane, can also be expressed as follows:

$$SP_1P = SP_2P = SP_3P \ldots \qquad (5.09)$$

in which P_1, P_2, etc., are the intersections of normals from the incident and reflected waves with the plane AB. We may thus state that a reflecting plane is one which converts an oncoming wave, S, into a reflected wave, P, in such a manner that the distances SP_1P, SP_2P, etc., are all equal.

In Fig. V–22 let us consider a plane wave from below advancing toward a crystal along the normal characterized by α_0, β_0, γ_0. A diffracted beam is formed along the direction characterized by

α, β, γ, and has the ordinal numbers $(m_1 m_2 m_3)$. These integral ordinal numbers mean that the following path-difference equations hold true

$$SAP - SOP = m_1\lambda \left.\right\}$$
$$SBP - SOP = m_2\lambda \left.\right\}.$$
$$SCP - SOP = m_3\lambda \left.\right\}$$

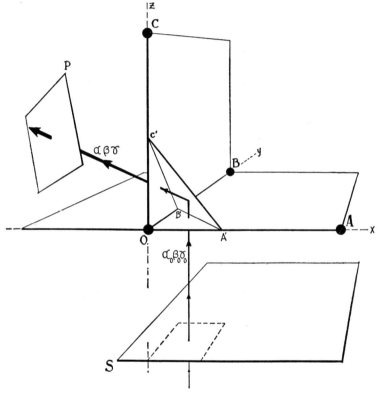

FIG. V-22. The formation of the diffracted maximum along the direction $\alpha\beta\gamma$ may be considered as due to reflection of $\alpha_0\beta_0\gamma_0$ in plane $A'B'C'$, and analysis shows that the Miller indices of plane $A'B'C'$ will be integral.

If these path differences were all equal, we could consider, by the previous definition, that the diffracted beam of wave-front P had been formed from S by reflection from a plane passing through points A, B, and C. But in general, of course, m_1, m_2, and m_3 are not equal. Even though this be the case, we yet can easily find a plane at which all the path lengths from S to P will be the same. A little consideration will show that such a plane will intercept the X, Y, and Z axes of Fig. V–22 at the points A', B', and C', where

$$\left.\begin{array}{l} OA' = OA/m_1 \\ OB' = OB/m_2 \\ OC' = OC/m_3 \end{array}\right\}. \tag{5.10}$$

When the location of the points $A'B'C'$ on the coordinate axes have been defined by eqs. (5.10), it is true that the distances $SA'P$, $SB'P$, $SC'P$, measured along the normals to the incident and diffracted waves, are equal, and hence the geometrical requirements for reflection from plane $A'B'C'$ are fulfilled.

What are the Miller indices of plane $A'B'C'$? From the definition of Miller indices in Sec. 3 of this chapter we see that we must express the intercepts of the plane in terms of the unit lengths along the axes, which in this case are all equal to a_0. Thus the intercepts in these terms are $1/m_1$, $1/m_2$, and $1/m_3$. The reciprocals of these intercepts are then m_1, m_2, and m_3. But these are not necessarily the smallest integers having this ratio, since nothing in the diffraction theory prevents the order numbers from having a common integral divisor. If such a divisor exists, we call it N, and write

$$\left.\begin{array}{l} h = m_1/N \\ k = m_2/N \\ l = m_3/N \end{array}\right\}. \tag{5.11}$$

These Miller indices will be integral numbers, and hence, by the law of rational indices, discussed in Sec. 3 of this chapter, if the numbers are small, the plane $A'B'C'$ will be parallel to an important possible crystal face. Substitution of eqs. (5.11) in (5.08) gives

$$2a_0 \sin \theta = N\lambda\sqrt{h^2 + k^2 + l^2}. \tag{5.12}$$

In order to put eq. (5.12) into the form of Bragg's law we must introduce the interplanar spacing D, which may be treated as follows. We will here adopt a procedure slightly more general than necessary for the immediate purpose by not restricting our derivation to a grating composed of atoms at the points of a simple translatory cubic lattice. We will retain the cubic axes, but consider the case in which there is an atom j in the crystal, at a general position. In Fig. V–23 plane $A'B'C'$ passes through the origin, and is a plane of a set of parallel planes defined by the Miller indices (hkl). Now from analytic geometry, if a plane has intercepts at points u, v, w, on the X, Y, Z axes, respectively, it has the equation

$$x/u + y/v + z/w = 1. \tag{5.13}$$

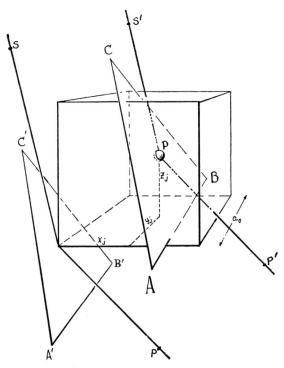

FIG. V–23. Plane ABC has integral Miller indices (hkl) and passes through an atom at $x_jy_jz_j$ in the unit cell. The perpendicular distance from the point $x_jy_jz_j$ to a plane parallel to ABC through the origin is given by eq. (5.19). The difference in phase in the contribution to the scattered radiation from atoms in plane ABC and in plane $A'B'C'$ enters into the crystal structure factor.

One of the planes of the set parallel to $A'B'C'$ (this plane does not appear in Fig. V–23) has intercepts at a_0/h, a_0/k, a_0/l, from the definition of Miller indices, and substitution of these intercepts in eq. (5.13) gives as the equation of this plane

$$hx + ky + lz - a_0 = 0. \tag{5.14}$$

From this it is easily seen that the equation of plane $A'B'C'$, passing through the origin, is

$$hx + ky + lz = 0. \tag{5.15}$$

Now we consider the atom j at point P in the crystal, of coordinates $x_j y_j z_j$, and a plane through P parallel to $A'B'C'$, which plane we shall call ABC. We want the perpendicular distance from plane ABC to plane $A'B'C'$. It is well to state at present that this is not, in general, equal to the d in Bragg's formula, even though the atom j may lie within the unit cell one of whose corners is at the origin. In this latter case, the distance in question may be an integral multiple of the d which appears in Bragg's law for these (hkl) planes. This will appear more clearly when we consider the structure of rock salt.

Since the point $x_j y_j z_j$ lies in the plane ABC, we will attain our result by using the expression from analytic geometry giving the perpendicular distance from a point to a plane. The perpendicular distance from a point of coordinates $x_p y_p z_p$ to a plane of equation

$$A_1 x + A_2 y + A_3 z + A_4 = 0 \tag{5.16}$$

is given by P, where P is obtained from

$$P = \frac{A_1 x_p + A_2 y_p + A_3 z_p + A_4}{\sqrt{A_1^2 + A_2^2 + A_3^2}}. \tag{5.17}$$

Now if we adopt the conventional manner of giving the coordinates of the atom in the unit cell, as described in Sec. 5 of this chapter, the actual distances represented by our $x_j y_j z_j$ are

$$\left.\begin{aligned} x_p &= a_0 x_j \\ y_p &= a_0 y_j \\ z_p &= a_0 z_j \end{aligned}\right\}. \tag{5.18}$$

The appropriate values of A_1, etc., may be seen from a comparison of eqs. (5.16) and (5.15). Thus the expression for P_j becomes

$$P_j = \frac{a_0(hx_j + ky_j + lz_j)}{\sqrt{h^2 + k^2 + l^2}}. \tag{5.19}$$

We will use eq. (5.19) in this general form later, in the development of the expression for the crystal structure factor but for the present purpose we will return to our special case of a grating built of diffracting centers at the points of a simple translatory cubic lattice. In this case, the coordinates of any atom in the crystal, expressed in terms of the unit lengths, are three integral numbers, if the origin is chosen coincident with one atom. Let these three numbers for some atom in the crystal be pqr. Then eq. (5.19) becomes

$$P_j = \frac{a_0(hp + kq + lr)}{\sqrt{h^2 + k^2 + l^2}}. \tag{5.20}$$

Now a plane parallel to those specified by the indices (hkl) passes through every atom in the crystal, and each one of these planes is identical in its areal density of atoms. If the atom at pqr is located far from the origin, eq. (5.20) will give us a perpendicular distance much greater than the minimum distance between identical planes, which is what we seek for the Bragg law. We are interested then in the minimum value of $|(hp + kq + lr)|$ where h, k, l, p, q, r are integers, positive or negative. Now for any three integers h, k, l it is possible to find three integers p, q, r such that

$$|(hp + kq + lr)| = 1. \tag{5.21}$$

Hence the minimum value of P_j, which we shall call D, is for a set of diffracting points placed on a simple translatory cubic lattice given by

$$D = a_0/\sqrt{h^2 + k^2 + l^2}. \tag{5.22}$$

where a_0 is the lattice interval. Combination of eqs. (5.22) and (5.12) gives the Bragg law

$$N\lambda = 2D \sin \theta. \tag{5.23}$$

We have used capital letters for N and D in eq. (5.23) because the equation, as derived, deals with orders and grating spaces deduced from simple translatory cubic lattices. In the next section we will bring out the distinction between these quantities and the observed n's and d's in rock salt. In actual practice, Bragg's law, eq. (5.23), is easier to use than eq. (5.12) or (5.08). The present derivation of the law clarifies many points not made clear in the elementary derivation usually presented. The truly three-dimensional nature of the diffracting apparatus is emphasized, and the progressive restriction of the diffraction phenomena as more dimensions are added to the grating is shown.

Through the Bragg law we can see how to extend the treatment to more complicated crystals. Thus whether or not the crystallographic axes are cubic, the concept of the perpendicular distance between like planes is easily visualized. Each Laue spot may be considered as a colored reflection from a set of crystal planes.

The derivation must even in its present form be considered elementary, however, because it only locates the maxima of the diffraction, telling us nothing about the intensity, or the wave-length breadth of the maxima. These extremely important questions will be dealt with under the chapter on intensity of reflection of x-rays from crystals.

9. Evidence for the Structure of Rock Salt; the Crystal Structure Factor

The first crystal structure to be determined with the new x-ray method of attack was that of rock salt or sodium chloride.[9] This pioneer work was distinguished from all subsequent researches in crystal structure by the fact that prior to the solution of the problem, the wave-lengths of x-ray lines were unknown. Thus until the relatively recent work on the diffraction of x-rays by ruled gratings, the basis for the correctness of our knowledge of x-ray wave-lengths was identical with the evidence for the correctness of the rock salt structure. Because of the simplicity of the structure and the uniqueness of the problem, a description of the analysis does not afford a good example of the way in which the much more complicated crystals being worked on today are attacked. A brief mention of the typical steps in a modern crystal analysis will be given at the end of this chapter.

It is obvious from the symmetry properties of the crystal that it belongs in the cubic system, and although for a time the etch figure data seemed to show that it does not belong to the highest symmetry class of the cubic system, there is now no doubt that this is the case.[10] The crystal was mounted on the axis of a Bragg ionization spectrometer, and radiation from a tube with a rhodium target fell upon it. The spectra obtained as the glancing angle of the radiation on the (100), (110), and (111) faces was increased are shown in the lower part of Fig. V–24. The two strong lines which appear in various orders in the spectra are the $K\alpha$ lines of rhodium. If we call the order which first appears as we increase the glancing angle

[9] Bragg, W. H., Proc. Roy. Soc. Lond. **A89**, 246 (1913).

[10] Herzfeld, K. and Hettich, A., Z. Physik **38**, 1; **40**, 327 (1922).

Lowry, T. M. and Vernon, M. A., Trans. Faraday Soc. **25**, 286 (1929).

the first order, we obtain the ratios between the sines of the angles
for the first orders from the three planes indicated in Table V-2.

TABLE V-2

OBSERVED VALUES OF SIN θ_1 IN THE REFLECTION OF $RhK\alpha_1$
FROM ROCK SALT

Plane	sin θ_1	$\dfrac{(\sin \theta_1)_{hkl}}{(\sin \theta_1)_{100}}$
100	0.1087	1
110	0.1538	$\sqrt{2}$
111	0.0942	$\frac{1}{2}\sqrt{3}$

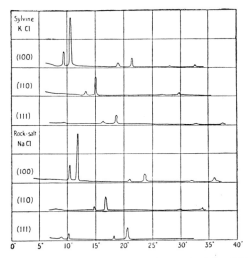

FIG. V-24. Spectra obtained from prominent planes of sylvine (KCl) and rock salt
(NaCl) with the ionization spectrometer. (After Bragg.)

We can calculate the sine ratios we would expect to observe if the
crystal were built up of identical diffracting units at the lattice points
of a simple translatory cubic lattice by the formulae developed in the
preceding section. Thus we can calculate values of D from eq.
(5.22), and use them in (5.23), putting $N = 1$ for the first order.
We then obtain the predicted values of Table V-3.

The definite disagreement between Table V-3 and Table V-2
for the (111) plane shows that the structure cannot be the simple
one postulated. A further investigation of the crystal shows that
all planes in which hkl are all odd show this anomalous behavior.

TABLE V-3

PREDICTED SINE RATIOS FOR A SIMPLE TRANSLATORY CUBIC LATTICE

Plane	D (Eq. 5.22)	$\dfrac{(\sin \theta_1)_{hkl}}{(\sin \theta_1)_{100}}$
100	a_0	1
110	$a_0/\sqrt{2}$	$\sqrt{2}$
111	$a_0/\sqrt{3}$	$\sqrt{3}$

Figure V–25 shows a structure for rock salt proposed by the Braggs to fit the data obtained, and this structure is now conceded to be correct. The figure shows the unit cell. The location of the atoms in it may be formally described as follows:

$$4 \text{ Na atoms at} \quad 000 \quad \tfrac{1}{2}\tfrac{1}{2}0 \quad 0\tfrac{1}{2}\tfrac{1}{2} \quad \tfrac{1}{2}0\tfrac{1}{2} \Big\}$$
$$4 \text{ Cl atoms at} \quad \tfrac{1}{2}\tfrac{1}{2}\tfrac{1}{2} \quad \tfrac{1}{2}00 \quad 0\tfrac{1}{2}0 \quad 00\tfrac{1}{2} \Big\} \qquad (5.24)$$

The atomic population of successive planes parallel to the (100),

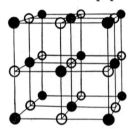

FIG. V–25. The unit cell of rock salt. The full circles show the location of sodium centers; the open ones, chlorine centers.

(110), and (111) planes of correct or true sodium chloride are shown in Fig. V–26a. The observed interplanar distances d will be the distances between planes of identical atomic population or, in other words, scattering power. Thus from the postulated structure we can calculate the expected sine ratios as in Table V–4.

It is seen that the calculated sine ratios of Table V–4 agree with those observed as in Table V–2, and in fact a more complete investigation shows a complete agreement, for all types of planes, between observed and calculated sine ratios, if we adopt the unit cell of Fig. V–25.

TABLE V-4

SINE RATIOS FOR SODIUM CHLORIDE CALCULATED FROM FIG. V–25

Plane	d	$\dfrac{(\sin \theta_1)_{hkl}}{(\sin \theta_1)_{100}} = \dfrac{d_{100}}{d_{hkl}}$
100	$a_0/2$	1
110	$a_0/2\sqrt{2}$	$\sqrt{2}$
111	$a_0/\sqrt{3}$	$\tfrac{1}{2}\sqrt{3}$

The question now arises: is this agreement sufficient to establish the correctness of the assumed structure? The answer is that the discussion so far given is insufficient to establish the structure, because from the theory of space groups we can write down at least one other arrangement of 4 molecules of NaCl in a cubic unit cell which would give exactly the same sine ratios as those observed, and in fact would give a Laue photograph the spots of which would coincide exactly with those of a photograph of sodium chloride taken under

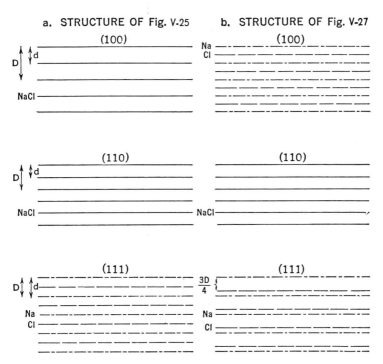

a. STRUCTURE OF Fig. V-25   b. STRUCTURE OF Fig. V-27

FIG. V–26. The succession of planes parallel to the (100), (110), and (111) planes, in (a) true rock salt, and (b) a hypothetical rock salt built on the cubic zinc sulfide structure.

the same conditions. This arrangement would not, however, have the highest symmetry of the cubic system, whereas this high symmetry is actually possessed by NaCl. This is an illustration of the fact that in general a Laue photograph may have higher symmetry than is actually present in the crystal. For purposes of illustration we will examine this alternative structure, which we shall call pseudo sodium chloride, and show how it may be eliminated from consideration. Figure V–27 shows the unit cell of this structure, the atoms in which would be located as follows:

$$\left.\begin{array}{llllll}
4\ \text{Na} & \text{atoms at} & 000 & \tfrac{1}{2}\tfrac{1}{2}0 & \tfrac{1}{2}0\tfrac{1}{2} & 0\tfrac{1}{2}\tfrac{1}{2} \\[4pt]
4\ \text{Cl} & \text{atoms at} & \tfrac{1}{4}\tfrac{1}{4}\tfrac{1}{4} & \tfrac{3}{4}\tfrac{3}{4}\tfrac{1}{4} & \tfrac{3}{4}\tfrac{1}{4}\tfrac{3}{4} & \tfrac{1}{4}\tfrac{3}{4}\tfrac{3}{4}
\end{array}\right\} \qquad (5.25)$$

This structure actually occurs as the zinc sulfide arrangement, if we think of the Na atoms as replaced by Zn and the Cl by S. Figure V–26b shows the atomic population of successive planes in this

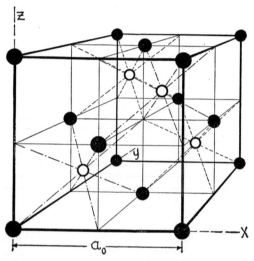

Fig. V–27. "Pseudo sodium chloride." With sodium centers at full circles and chlorine centers at open circles, and with $a_0 = 5.628$ A, a crystal built on this unit cell would give a Laue photograph the positions of whose spots would be identical with a photograph obtained from true sodium chloride, built on the structure of Fig. V–25.

pseudo sodium chloride, and it is seen that the d values would be the same as those of true sodium chloride.

A discussion of the intensities in the diffraction pattern is essential before the pseudo sodium chloride structure can be eliminated as a possible one. It can be seen in a general way that the intensities will be different from the two structures; for instance in Fig. V–26 it is seen that the sodium planes parallel to (100) in pseudo sodium chloride have chlorine planes exactly between them. These will interfere to some extent with the first order reflection, but strengthen the second order. Thus intensity effects quite different than from the true sodium chloride structure are to be expected.

We shall study the intensity effects in a preliminary way in this section, merely learning enough about them to tell one structure from the other. This will be done by a derivation of the so-called " crystal structure factor." This factor occurs in the amplitude of the wave scattered at a given angle from the incident beam by the unit cell of the crystal. The wave-trains scattered by each atom in the unit cell superimpose their displacements at a given external point (i.e., in a Laue spot) but phase differences between wave-trains scattered from atoms at various locations in the unit will in general prevent the amplitude of the scattered wave from being the algebraic sum of the component amplitudes. It is with this effect that the crystal structure factor deals. In order to develop it we have to introduce a symbol for the amplitude scattered from a single atom.

The atomic structure factor for an atom j, which we shall represent by f_j, can be defined as the ratio of the amplitude of the wave scattered by the atom at a given angle to the amplitude of the wave which would, under the same conditions, be scattered by a single electron according to the J. J. Thomson formula. Now if the incident wave-length is far from any critical absorption wave-length of the atom, the amplitude scattered at scattering angle zero, that is, in the forward direction, would be the algebraic sum of the amplitudes scattered (we may suppose according to J. J. Thomson's formula) from the various electrons, thus here $f_j = Z_j$, where Z_j is the number of extra-nuclear electrons of the atom j. For all other scattering angles, f_j is less than Z_j, due to interference between various electrons in the atom. It is not essential for this derivation to discuss the atomic structure values further.

In Fig. V–23 SS' represent points on an advancing plane wave front, and PP' lie on a plane wave formed after diffraction in the unit cell. Let ABC be a plane so located that the diffracted wave may be considered to have arisen from it by reflection. $A'B'C'$ is a plane parallel to ABC through the origin of coordinates. Let the type of atom in the plane through the origin[11] be denoted by the subscript 1, that in plane ABC by subscript 2.

In Sec. 1 of Chap. VI we will derive the expression for the wave

---

[11] If the unit cell of the crystal is such that no atoms are located at the corners, we may consider the reflection from the plane through the origin as giving a reference path distance, to which the others are compared, and since only differences enter, the result will be the same.

scattered from an atomic plane. At present we do not need to consider the precise form of this equation, but will only call attention to certain factors which it contains. Let Y_1 be the expression for the scattered wave from plane $A'B'C'$, containing atoms of type 1. Then

$$Y_1 \sim f_1 e^{ik(ct - \rho_1)}, \tag{5.26}$$

where $k = 2\pi/\lambda$, c is the velocity of light, t the time, and ρ_1 the distance measured along the wave-normals from some arbitrary wave-front in the incident radiation to a wave-front at the point of observation, which lies in the direction of the reflected wave. The corresponding expression for the wave diffracted from plane ABC, containing atoms of type 2, will be

$$Y_2 \sim f_2 e^{ik(ct - \rho_2)}. \tag{5.27}$$

The combined wave-motion will be

$$Y_1 + Y_2 \sim (f_1 + f_2 e^{ik\Delta\rho_2}) e^{ik(ct - \rho_1)}, \tag{5.28}$$

where

$$\rho_1 - \rho_2 = \Delta\rho_2. \tag{5.29}$$

In general, if there are many atoms in the unit cell, the diffracted wave may be written

$$Y = \Sigma Y_j \sim F e^{ik(ct - \rho_1)}, \tag{5.30}$$

where

$$F = \Sigma f_j e^{ik\Delta\rho_j}. \tag{5.31}$$

The F which appears in eqs. (5.30) and (5.31) is known as the crystal structure factor.[11a]

In order to get the formula for F in a form more suitable for calculation, we will express $\Delta\rho_j$ in terms of the Miller indices of the planes and the coordinates of the atom j in the unit cell. These path differences $\Delta\rho_j$ are easily expressed in terms of the length of the perpendicular between the plane ABC and the plane $A'B'C'$ (Fig. V–28). This distance we have already obtained in eq. (5.19).

[11a] The representation of the crystal structure factor by the symbol F and the atomic structure factor by f is used in all chapters of this book except Chap. III. In Chap. III f stands for an electronic structure factor, which is not considered outside that chapter, and F is used for the atomic structure factor. The crystal structure factor is not discussed in Chap. III.

We now wish to express $\Delta\rho_j$ in terms of P_j. The situation is shown in the two-dimensional Fig. V–28 from which it is clear that

$$\Delta\rho_j = 2P_j \sin \theta. \tag{5.32}$$

Substitution for P_j from eq. (5.19), and for $\sin \theta$ from (5.23) gives

$$\Delta\rho_j = N\lambda(hx_j + ky_j + lz_j) \tag{5.33}$$

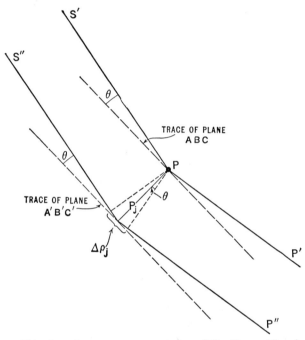

Fig. V–28. This plane figure represents a section of Fig. V–23. The plane of this figure includes the ray $S'PP'$, and, hence, by the laws of reflection, the normal to plane ABC at P.

so that eq. (5.31) for the crystal structure factor may be written

$$F = \sum_j f_j e^{2\pi Ni(hx_j + ky_j + lz_j)}. \tag{5.34}$$

This expression is widely used in crystal structure work. It has been derived here for a cubic unit cell, but it may readily be shown that it is valid for any unit cell, providing the coordinates of the atoms are given according to the accepted conventions. We see that in general the crystal structure factor is a complex number, and we know that every complex number can be expressed in the form $a + bi$. The appropriate values of a and b may be found by expressing the right-hand member of eq. (5.34) in trigonometric terms. Equation (5.30) shows us that the complex expression for the diffracted wave may be represented by

$$(a + bi)e^{ik(ct-p_1)} = \sqrt{a^2 + b^2}\,e^{ik\{ct-p_1+(1/k)\text{ arc tan }b/a\}} \qquad (5.35)$$

Since the physical wave motion is proportional to the real part of the expressions in eq. (5.35), it follows that A, the amplitude of the diffracted wave, is proportional to $\sqrt{a^2 + b^2}$, or symbolically, to $|F|$. Hence we have

$$A \sim |F| = \sqrt{[\Sigma f_i \cos 2\pi N(hx_i + ky_i + lz_i)]^2}$$
$$\overline{+ [\Sigma f_i \sin 2\pi N(hx_i + ky_i + lz_i)]^2}. \qquad (5.36)$$

Let us now return to our problem, which is the distinction between the true sodium chloride structure, and that given as pseudo sodium chloride. This will afford a good example of the use of eq. (5.36), which will now be applied to the (100) planes of true sodium chloride. The calculation of F_{100} may be made from the trigonometric form of eq. (5.34), into which the coordinates as given in (5.24) are to be substituted. We get

$$F_{100} = f_{\text{Na}}\left[\cos 2\pi N(0) + \cos 2\pi N(\tfrac{1}{2}) + \cos 2\pi N(0) + \cos 2\pi N(\tfrac{1}{2})\right]$$
$$+ if_{\text{Na}}\left[\sin 2\pi N(0) + \sin 2\pi N(\tfrac{1}{2}) + \sin 2\pi N(0) + \sin 2\pi N(\tfrac{1}{2})\right]$$
$$+ f_{\text{Cl}}\left[\cos 2\pi N(\tfrac{1}{2}) + \cos 2\pi N(\tfrac{1}{2}) + \cos 2\pi N(0) + \cos 2\pi N(0)\right]$$
$$+ if_{\text{Cl}}[0],$$

or
$$F_{100} = 2(1 + \cos \pi N)(f_{\text{Cl}} + f_{\text{Na}}). \qquad (5.37)$$

It is seen that this F factor is entirely real. It may be shown that this is always the case when the unit cell contains a center of symmetry at the origin. Table V–5 shows F values calculated from eq. (5.34) for the true NaCl structure of (5.24) and the pseudo structure of (5.25). It will be sufficient for our purpose here to get qualitative indications of how the intensity will vary with N for the reflections from a given set of planes. The intensity will depend on $|F|^2$, but for convenience we will in Table V–6 give the values of $\tfrac{1}{4}|F|$.

TABLE V-5

CALCULATED F VALUES FOR TWO PROPOSED NaCl UNIT CELLS

Plane	F for True NaCl	F for Pseudo NaCl
(100)	$2(f_{Na} + f_{Cl})(1 + \cos \pi N)$	$4f_{Cl} \cos \pi N \cos \tfrac{1}{2}\pi N + 2f_{Na}(1 + \cos \pi N)$
(110)	$2(f_{Na} + f_{Cl})(1 + \cos \pi N)$	$2(f_{Na} + f_{Cl})(1 + \cos \pi N)$
(111)	$4f_{Na} + f_{Cl}(\cos 3\pi N + 3 \cos \pi N)$	$4[f_{Na} + f_{Cl} (\cos \tfrac{3}{2}\pi N + i \sin \tfrac{3}{2}\pi N)]$

TABLE V-6

VALUES OF $\tfrac{1}{4}|F|$ FOR TWO PROPOSED NaCl UNIT CELLS

N	True NaCl (100) $\tfrac{1}{4}\|F\|$	n	(110) $\tfrac{1}{4}\|F\|$	n	(111) $\tfrac{1}{4}\|F\|$	n	Pseudo NaCl (100) $\tfrac{1}{4}\|F\|$	n	(110) $\tfrac{1}{4}\|F\|$	n	(111) $\tfrac{1}{4}\|F\|$	n
1	0		0		$f_{Na} - f_{Cl}$	1	0		0		$\sqrt{f_{Na}^2 + f_{Cl}^2}$	1
2	$f_{Na} + f_{Cl}$	1	$f_{Na} + f_{Cl}$	1	$f_{Na} + f_{Cl}$	2	$f_{Na} - f_{Cl}$	1	$f_{Na} + f_{Cl}$	1	$f_{Na} - f_{Cl}$	2
3	0		0		$f_{Na} - f_{Cl}$	3	0		0		$\sqrt{f_{Na}^2 + f_{Cl}^2}$	3
4	$f_{Na} + f_{Cl}$	2	$f_{Na} + f_{Cl}$	2	$f_{Na} + f_{Cl}$	4	$f_{Na} + f_{Cl}$	2	$f_{Na} + f_{Cl}$	2	$f_{Na} + f_{Cl}$	4

In Table V-6 a distinction is drawn between the order N, computed for a crystal made of diffracting centers at the points of a simple translatory lattice, and the order n, recognized by spectroscopists. Thus in NaCl reflections from the (100) planes, the first order, that is, the one appearing nearest the direct beam, has $N = 2$, since the order for $N = 1$ has zero intensity. In the subsequent discussion we will refer to orders by their n, instead of their N values.

As far as we can see from the table, on either structure, the intensity of the first and second orders from the (110) planes should be the same. Instead, as the lower half of Fig. V-24 shows, the second order is much weaker than the first. This is primarily due to the fact that the atomic structure factors f_{Na} and f_{Cl} are themselves functions of the scattering angle, and fall off rapidly as this increases, especially in the smaller angle ranges. This decrease in the atomic structure factors is superimposed on all the calculations of Table V-6. But for pseudo NaCl this decline as observed in the

(100) spectra should be quite different from what it is in the (110) since the absolute value of the crystal structure factor for the first order from (100) is the difference instead of the sum of the two atomic factors. On the contrary, the data show the same type of decline, agreeing with the calculations based on the true unit. A more striking case is the second order from (111), which on the pseudo unit should be relatively weak with respect to the first, whereas actually the second order is observed to be stronger than the first, agreeing with the F values from the true unit. Even qualitative agreements of this kind, when carried out for many reflections, are sufficient to exclude all other structures except the true unit. It is hoped that this treatment has emphasized the fact that even in the simplest of structures, it is necessary to show agreements of a qualitative kind between calculated and observed intensities. In the complicated crystals being analyzed today the final check on any postulated structure is always a detailed agreement of this kind.

Once the correct structure of NaCl was established, it was a simple matter to calculate approximate x-ray wave-lengths. The length of side of the unit cell, a_0, is the edge of a cube having the density of rock salt and containing four molecules of NaCl and is found to be 5.63×10^{-8} cm. d for the first order from (100) is $\frac{1}{2}a_0$ (Table V-4), and $n = 1$; hence substitution of the value of $\sin \theta$ from Table V-2 in $n\lambda = 2d \sin \theta$ gives the wave-length of the $K\alpha_1$ line of rhodium as 6.12×10^{-9} cm. These calculations will be treated in more detail in the chapter on the accurate measurement of x-ray wave-lengths.

The upper part of Fig. V-24 shows spectra obtained from sylvine, or solid KCl. The great chemical similarity between this compound and sodium chloride leads one to expect that the two crystals will be built in the same way, and this is actually the case. On inspection of the KCl spectra, we see, however, that apparently this is not so, for all the planes have a regular decline of intensity with order, and the weak first order from (111), which appears in NaCl at unexpectedly small glancing angles, is entirely absent in KCl. This is due to a peculiarity of the KCl crystal, namely, that the atomic structure factors f_K and f_{Cl} are identical within the limits of error of the intensity measurements. K and Cl undoubtedly occur in the crystal in ionic form, and these two ions have the same number of electrons. Hence we can understand the KCl spectra from Table V-6 for true sodium chloride if we write 0 for $|F|$ everywhere the difference of the atomic factors appears. Because of this peculiarity, the spectra of KCl agree with those calculated from identical diffracting centers at the points of a simple translatory cubic lattice, and the crystal represents one of the very few examples of this simplest of all structures.

10. *Important Methods in the Analysis of Crystal Structure; Conclusion*

In this section we will give brief mention to some important methods of investigating crystal structure that are in use to-day. The first of these is the oldest, namely, the method of the Laue photograph. A schematic arrangement for the production of these photographs has been indicated in Fig. V–20, and we have previously shown that in order to obtain more than a few chance spots, general radiation must be used. This is commonly obtained from an x-ray tube having a tungsten target, and operated between 50 and 60 kilovolts. Under these circumstances the white radiation has a short wave-length limit around 0.22 A, and is intense between 0.3 and 0.5 A.

In case a crystal is being investigated on which crystallographic data are not available, valuable information as to the crystal symmetry may be obtained from the symmetry of the Laue diffraction pattern. All crystals will appear to have a center of symmetry, however, whether or not such a center actually exists. As we have seen, the Laue photographs from NaCl, which has such a center, and ZnS, which has not, may be identical in the location of their spots, if reduced to the same scale.

We will not discuss here the detailed procedures which have been worked out for indexing Laue photographs, that is, for finding the Miller indices of the planes producing each spot. This problem is essentially the same as that confronting the crystallographers in giving indices to crystal faces, and methods have been devised for doing this by projecting the normals to the planes on various surfaces.[12] When the operation has been completed, it is possible to assign to each spot three integers, which represent the indices of the planes producing it.

The advantages of the Laue photograph method are due to the fact that it is an easy method of obtaining qualitative data on the

[12] Wyckoff, R. W. G., The Structure of Crystals. Chem. Cat. Co., New York (1931), Chap. VI.

reflections from a large number of crystal planes. The time necessary to investigate an equal number of reflections with the ionization spectrometer would be prohibitive. Due to this fact, a very important function of the Laue photograph is that it affords a very good method of finding out whether a postulated unit cell for the crystal is large enough. Let us illustrate for a cubic crystal; and suppose that we have studied reflections from a few simple faces by the Bragg method, for instance, and have set up a unit cell which satisfies the data obtained. Turning now to the Laue photograph, after indexing the spots and measuring values of $\sin \theta$, we can calculate values of $N\lambda$ for all the spots, if we wish, from a combination of eqs. (5.22) and (5.23) which gives

$$N\lambda = (2a_0 \sin \theta)/\sqrt{h^2 + k^2 + l^2}. \qquad (5.38)$$

Now if our choice of a_0 is too small, it is fairly certain that for some of the spots the value of $N\lambda$ will come out smaller than the calculated short wave-length limit of the spectrum, known from the operating voltage of the tube. Since no energy exists in the primary beam at such a wave-length, it is certain that a_0 must be increased. A proper choice of a_0 will give values of $N\lambda$ down to, but not below, the limit of the spectrum.

Very qualitative data on the intensity of the Laue spots can be obtained from visual inspection of the original negative. Complicating factors are the silver and bromine absorption limits in the photographic film, and the fact that different Laue beams traverse different crystal thicknesses. Nevertheless, if only a few parameters are needed to locate atoms in the unit cell, such rough data may be entirely sufficient. For the more complicated crystals now awaiting analysis, however, more accurate intensity information is needed than can be obtained by this method.

The method of the Braggs, in which reflections from crystal faces are examined in the ionization spectrometer, is of importance chiefly for the accuracy of the intensity measurements. Also the method is capable of yielding accurate values of $\sin \theta$, and hence of the dimensions of the unit cell. Its disadvantage is the time consumed in taking enough readings to get results from a considerable number of planes.

In the discussion of Laue's eqs. (5.05), we mentioned the fact that, in general, no reflections appear for monochromatic incident radiation if the orientation of the crystal with respect to the incident beam is unaltered. If the crystal is rotated, however, and a large range of $\alpha_0 \beta_0 \gamma_0$ values run through, orientations will result which give diffracted beams. This is often called the method of rotation photographs, and is a third procedure often used in crystal analysis. In some cases the crystal is merely rocked back and forth through an angular range in which reflections are likely to occur. In order to compare intensities, the angular rate of rock-

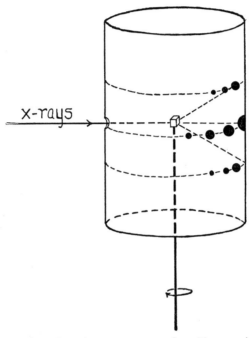

X-rays

Fig. V–29. Schematic design of an arrangement for taking rotation photographs in which the crystal turns completely through 360°.

ing must be constant, and cams specially designed for this purpose have been made. Other arrangements have been used where the crystal executes complete revolutions, in which case the spectra are registered on a cylindrical film surrounding the crystal. Such an arrangement is shown in Fig. V–29. The crystal is usually rotated about some important axis, in which case the reflections from all planes parallel to this axis lie in a plane normal to the axis and containing the direct beam. This plane cuts the cylindrical film in a circle, and when the film is unrolled the reflections will lie on a horizontal line containing the registration of the incident beam. Above and below this line are other so-called layer lines. Graphical methods of indexing the patterns produced have been worked out and made available to investigators.[13]

The fact that the wave-length of all the spots in a rotation photograph is known makes it possible to apply the Bragg Law, after θ values have been obtained from simple measurements on the film combined with a knowledge of the radius of the cylinder on which it was wound. This method, therefore, like the Bragg method, is very useful for suggesting possible dimensions of the unit cell. The method can be extended to great precision, as has been shown in x-ray spectroscopy by Siegbahn, but for crystal structure work sufficient accuracy may be attained without elaborate apparatus.

The rotation photograph may also detect a type of error which can creep into measurements with the ionization spectrometer. Let us suppose that the angular separation of two layer lines is small, and hence that close above or below the line of spots belonging to a given layer, spots of an adjacent layer appear. If such a crystal is being investigated with the ionization spectrometer and the opening of the ionization chamber is sufficiently large, spots actually lying on an adjacent layer line may be confused with the principal spectrum being investigated. On the photographic film, where the whole pattern is evident, such confusion is not likely to arise.[14]

The methods previously discussed have all assumed that single crystals of the substance of greater than microscopic dimensions are available. Laue photographs can be prepared from crystals whose edges are on the order of a millimeter long, but such crystals are difficult to orient. Powder photographs may be made from crystalline material in the form of microscopic particles.[15] If monochromatic x-rays are passed through such material, the entirely random orientations of the particles with respect to the beam means that some of them will be in a position to reflect the radiation from an important set of planes. The essentials for an arrangement suitable

[13] Bernal, J. D., Proc. Roy. Soc. Lond. A 113, 117 (1926).

[14] Such an effect is undoubtedly the explanation of certain so-called " X-peaks " or " anomalous " diffraction maxima observed from potassium iodide crystals with the ionization chamber. G. L. Clark and W. Duane, Proc. Nat. Acad. Sci. U.S.A. 9, 131 (1923).

[15] The method of powder photographs was independently developed by
Debye, P. and Scherrer, P., Phys. Z. 17, 277 (1916).
Hull, A. W., Phys. Rev. 10, 661 (1917).

for taking powder photographs are shown in Fig. V–30. The radiation used is made approximately monochromatic by an appropriate filter, zirconium oxide being used in case molybdenum radiation is available.   The diffracted maxima lie on cones co-axial with the direct beam, and if a photographic plate is mounted normal to the direct beam, concentric circles are registered upon it.   Usually a plate or film in the form of a rectangle long in its horizontal dimension is used, so that only arcs of the circles appear.

If the symmetry of the crystal is high, and the number of atoms or molecules in the unit cell small, the diffraction patterns are of sufficient simplicity so that powder photographs can be of great

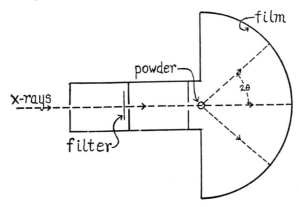

FIG. V–30. Schematic design of an arrangement for taking powder photographs. The filter produces approximately monochromatic radiation.

service in the analysis of the structure.   Thus in the case of the metals, where the above conditions are fulfilled in many cases, the powder photographs are often in themselves sufficient to establish the structure.   This is also true of the alloys, which have been investigated largely by this method.

Let us calculate what sort of a diagram should appear from a metal (Me) crystallized into a body-centered cubic lattice.   The structure of the cubic unit cell may be formally expressed as

$$2 \text{ Me atoms at} \qquad \text{ooo} \qquad \tfrac{1}{2}\tfrac{1}{2}\tfrac{1}{2}. \qquad (5.39)$$

The structure factor for planes of Miller indices (hkl) can be calculated from eq. (5.34), from which it results that

$$F_{hkl} = f_{\text{Me}}[\cos 2\pi N(\text{o} + \text{o} + \text{o}) + \cos 2\pi N(\tfrac{1}{2}h + \tfrac{1}{2}k + \tfrac{1}{2}l)],$$

or

$$F_{hkl} = f_{Me}[1 + \cos \pi N(h + k + l)]. \qquad (5.40)$$

From this we may deduce the following:

(1) If $(h + k + l)$ is even, $F_{hkl} = 2f_{Me}$ for any order.

(2) If $(h + k + l)$ is odd, then

(a) If N is odd, $F_{hkl} = 0,$

(b) If N is even, $F_{hkl} = 2f_{Me}.$

Thus in the application of eq. (5.23) odd values of N are omitted if calculations are being made on planes the sum of whose Miller indices is odd. With this restriction, values of θ from the following equation will be one-fourth of the angle of the cones on which the diffracted maxima lie.

$$\sin \theta = N\lambda(h^2 + k^2 + l^2)^{1/2}/2a_0. \qquad (5.41)$$

In estimating the intensities of the powder lines, a factor not previously mentioned must be taken into account. In eq. (5.38) it is clear that any permutations of the same three integers representing h, k, and l will lead to the same value of θ. Also negative values may be allowed, since the indices enter as their squares. Thus the same result would be obtained from the following planes: (100), (010), (001), ($\bar{1}$00), (0$\bar{1}$0), (00$\bar{1}$); making six possible permutations. If all three indices are different, and different from zero, there are 48 possible permutations. This number enters as a factor in the intensity of reflection, since in this general case 48 different crystal orientations can cooperate in giving the same powder line. We must also take account of the decline of the structure factor f_{Me} with increasing θ. This may be done for rough estimates by introducing a factor $1/\sin^2 \theta$, and to this approximation at small angles we can neglect polarization factors and factors due to different path lengths in the specimen. Thus if j is the number of permutations of positive and negative values of hkl possible, we may write roughly

$$\text{Intensity} \sim \frac{j}{N^2(h^2 + k^2 + l^2)}. \qquad (5.42)$$

Table V–7 gives data on the first eight powder lines observable from a body-centered cubic crystal composed of identical atoms.

TABLE V-7

LINES IN A BODY-CENTERED CUBIC POWDER PHOTOGRAPH

hkl	N	$(2a_0 \sin \theta)/\lambda$	j	Intensity
110	1	1.41	12	6.0
100	2	2.00	6	1.5
211	1	2.45	24	4.0
110	2	2.82	12	1.5
310	1	3.16	24	2.4
111	2	3.46	8	0.7
321	1	3.74	48	3.4
100	4	4.00	6	0.4

Figures V–31 and V–32 show the estimated intensities and the actual powder photograph obtained from molybdenum, which crystallizes in a body-centered cubic unit cell.

We have now mentioned four methods for the study of crystal structures. All these are used in laboratories well equipped for this work. Although each new crystal to be investigated presents fresh problems, it is possible to state in general what are the steps in a structure determination. The first of these is usually the determination of the unit cell dimensions, from rotation or ionization spectrometer data, substantiated from the Laue photograph, as mentioned above Next comes the selection of the proper space group, the first step in which is usually finding the lattice on which it is built. This may usually be done by noting omissions of reflections from certain orders of the simple translatory lattice. An example of this has just been mentioned in the body-centered cube, in which odd values of N when $(h + k + l)$ is odd are missing. The typical omissions of this type for the various space groups are known, and usually the selection of the proper one is not a matter of great difficulty. If the unit cell contains many atoms in general positions, then the real problem of the structure determination begins. The "parameters" or coordinates of these atoms in the unit cell must be found by checking

FIG. V-31. A photograph of the diffraction of radiation of wave-length 0.710 A (Mo Kα) by powdered molybdenum crystals.

against the observed intensities.   Here the investigator calls to his aid many general factors, such as probable ionic radius, grouping of the atoms into radicals, as in sulfates, carbonates, etc.   Often without such guides, the general problem would be too difficult, and the investigator can only try certain arrangements, which by analogy

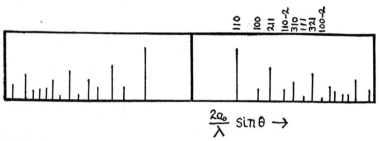

Fig. V–32.   The estimated intensities in the powder photograph of Fig. V–31 are shown by the heights of the vertical lines.   Compare the calculated values in column 5, Table V–7.

with other compounds already known, seem probable.   Once the correct arrangement is found, however, such a widespread agreement with intensities results that no doubt is left as to its validity.[15]

[15] The collected results of structure determinations on crystals may be found in:
    Wyckoff, R. W. G., The Structure of Crystals.   Chem. Cat. Co., New York, 2nd Ed. (1931).
    Strukturbericht, 1913–1928 (Ergänzungsband, Z. Krist.) Leipzig. Akad. Verlags. (1931) Editors: Ewald, P. P. and Hermann, C.

CHAPTER VI

The Intensity of Reflection of X-rays from Crystals

A. THE DIFFRACTION OF X-RAYS BY A PERFECT CRYSTAL

1. *Introduction*

In the chapter on crystal structure, we have studied the diffraction of x-rays by a crystal lattice, but we have in that treatment only attempted to locate the maxima in the diffraction pattern. In the present treatment we shall attempt to go much more deeply into the problem, and investigate such matters as the intensity of reflection, the shape of the intensity versus angle curve near a diffraction maximum, and the resolving power of the diffracting mechanism. These problems were first attacked in two remarkable papers by Darwin[1] in 1914. Darwin found the form of the diffraction pattern and calculated the coefficient of reflection, neglecting, however, the absorption in the crystal. Some mathematical aspects of the problem were of interest to Lamson[2] and to Gronwall.[3] Gronwall derived in a very elegant manner expressions which relate to the diffracted intensity from an infinite number of parallel planes, or from any finite number of planes. The physical interpretation of these results has been discussed by Allison,[4] and he has shown that the mathematical form of the result of Gronwall is the same as that of Darwin. Schlapp[5] has derived the result of Darwin in a more general manner, and given a solution which includes the total reflection of the radiation from the crystal at small glancing angles.

In 1917, Ewald,[6] unaware of the previous work of Darwin, studied the problem, and developed the " dynamical theory of x-ray interference." In this work he examined the diffraction pattern

[1] Darwin, C. G., Phil. Mag. **27**, 325; 675 (1914).

[2] Lamson, Phys. Rev. **17**, 624 (1921).

[3] Gronwall, Phys. Rev. **27**, 277 (1926).

[4] Allison, S. K., Phys. Rev. **29**, 375 (1927).

[5] Schlapp, R., Phil. Mag. **1**, 1009 (1926).

[6] Ewald, P. P., Ann. d. Phys. **54**, 519; 577 (1917), Zs. f. Physik **2**, 232 (1920); **30**, 1 (1924); Physik. Zeitschr. **26**, 29 (1925).

produced by a scattering mechanism consisting of electronic dipoles at the points of a crystal lattice. The results are essentially the same as those of Darwin. Lohr[7] has treated the problem of transmission and reflection of radiation in a medium in which there is a periodic variation in the density of the scattering material, and found that his more general treatment gives results agreeing with those of Ewald. Laue[8] has presented the work of Ewald in a somewhat revised form.

It has been mentioned that in the early work of Darwin, the absorption of the radiation in the crystal was neglected. This is also true in the considerations of Ewald. Prins[9] has pointed out that in view of the considerations advanced in the chapter on dispersion theory of x-rays in this book, the proper method to treat absorption is to insert into the equations what amounts to a complex refractive index. This procedure has of course been known for a long time in the theory of optics, but there was some hesitation in employing it in the x-ray region because it was known that the absorption is largely by photoelectric processes which are incoherent with the direct radiation, and have no exact explanation on the classical theory.

In the subsequent treatment we shall study the problem of reflection from a three dimensional crystal grating according to the modification of Darwin's treatment introduced by Prins. We shall then examine the special case of negligible absorption, corresponding to Darwin's original work, because the equations of Prins then reduce to expressions capable of being manipulated without too great labor. Furthermore calculations on a theory which neglects absorption give fair approximations to rigorous results in many cases of importance.

2. The Reflection from a Single Plane of Atoms

We shall first define what is meant by a perfect crystal. In view of results to be discussed later, many crystals are thought to be built up of a so-called mosaic of very small units, some 10^{-5} cm on a side. These units are roughly oriented in the direction of the cleavage planes of the crystal, but may be tilted some minutes or seconds of arc from that direction. Fig. VI–I gives a crude picture

[7] Lohr, E., Sitzber. Akad. Wiss. Wien, Math. Naturwiss. Klasse 2a 517 (1924).

[8] Laue, M. von, Ergebnisse der Exakten Naturwiss., Julius Springer, Berlin Bd. X, pp. 137–158 (1931).

[9] Prins, Zs. f. Physik 63, 477 (1930).

of the conception of a mosaic structure. Our calculations will be made for a crystal in which there is no distortion of this type, in fact, mathematically we will assume that all space below the XY plane is occupied by a single crystal. At first we will restrict the calculation to a crystal made up of only one kind of atom, so that each plane has the same reflecting power as all the others. Furthermore we shall assume that a uniform spacing exists, namely, that the planes are not staggered.

In the chapter on the study of crystal structure, we have shown that if the diffraction problem is attacked by considering the scattering from the component one-dimensional point arrays of the crystal, a result is reached which may also be interpreted on the concept of crystal planes. Because of the greater simplicity of this concept,

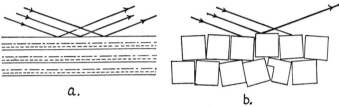

a.
b.

Fig. VI–1. This figure illustrates the incidence of a monochromatic, parallel, x-ray beam upon (a) a perfect crystal, and (b) a mosaic crystal. In case (a), when the glancing angle is within the diffraction pattern range, the entire incident beam is diffracted; in case (b) only a portion is diffracted, and if the crystal is rotated, other parts of the mosaic will make glancing angles within the diffraction pattern range, apparently increasing the width of the region in which diffraction takes place.

we shall use the idea of crystal planes in development of the diffraction problem, and first deduce an expression for the reflected wave from a single plane.

In Fig. VI–2, ψ is the glancing angle of the oncoming ray SO on the plane of atoms, supposedly coinciding with the XY plane of a set of Cartesian coordinates. We wish a mathematical expression for the incident radiation, assumed to consist of plane, monochromatic waves. A trigonometric form of the wave-equation, sufficiently general for the purpose, is[10]

$$T_0 = A \cos k \left[ct - (lx + my + nz) \right]. \qquad (6.01)$$

[10] This form of the wave-equation is discussed in many standard texts on the subject, for instance Jeans, The Mathematical Theory of Electricity and Magnetism, The University Press, Cambridge (1920), Sec. 591, page 534.

In this expression, T_0 may be taken to represent the instantaneous value of the electric (or magnetic) intensity due to the wave-motion, A is the amplitude, k is $2\pi/\lambda$, c the velocity of propagation, t the time, l, m, n, the direction cosines of the direction of propagation, and xyz the coordinates of a point at which the electric field is observed and the time measured. These direction cosines are the cosines of the angles between the positive direction of propagation and the positive directions of the X, Y, and Z axes respectively. In Fig. VI–2, the angle which the positive direction of the ray makes with the X axis is $-\psi$, hence $l = \cos(-\psi) = \cos\psi$. If we now choose

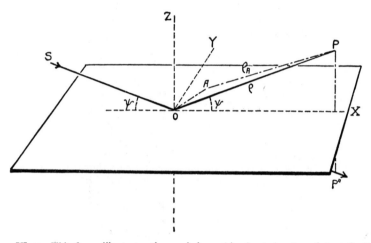

Fig. VI–2. This figure illustrates the symbols used in the derivation of the reflection from a single atomic plane. P and P'' are points on the reflected and transmitted beam, respectively. The plane of incidence is the XZ plane.

the Z axis and hence the XZ plane so that the plane contains the incident ray SO, then the angle made with the Y axis is 90° or, $m = 0$. The angle made with the positive Z axis is $-(90° + \psi)$, hence $n = \cos[-(90° + \psi)] = -\sin\psi$. Furthermore we will assume unit incident amplitude, and with the special values of the direction cosines applicable to the problem in mind, eq.(6.01) becomes

$$T_0 = \cos k[ct - (x\cos\psi - z\sin\psi)].$$

For the purposes of calculation we shall find it convenient to use the well-known device of representing the above trigonometric expression as the real part of a complex quantity. With this understanding, we may write the preceding equation as

$$T_0 = e^{ik[ct - (x \cos \psi - z \sin \psi)]}. \qquad (6.02)$$

We will now consider a point P so situated that it lies on the ray which would be reflected from SO according to the geometrical laws of reflection. This means that the coordinates of P are

$$(\alpha, o, \alpha \tan \psi) \qquad (6.03)$$

where α is the x-coordinate of P. The justification for this special choice of location for P is that physically we know that the greatest intensity will be in the direction which obeys the laws of reflection, and we can profitably study the intensity reflected by expressing in our equations only slight deviations in direction from the ray OP. If we let the distance OP equal ρ, we have the relations

$$\rho = \sqrt{\alpha^2(1 + \tan^2 \psi)} = \alpha \sec \psi. \qquad (6.04)$$

We will now consider the contributions to the radiation at P scattered by an atom at the position (x, y, o) on the scattering plane. This involves the expression for the wave scattered from an atom irradiated by the incident beam.

Let us first consider the wave scattered to P by an atom at the origin. Substitution of the coordinates (o, o, o) in eq. (6.02) gives us as the expression for the incident wave upon this atom

$$e^{ikct}.$$

We will now avoid the question of trying to calculate the scattered wave by writing it in the following manner. We will represent the amplitude of the scattered wave at unit distance by $f(2\psi, k)$, since the scattering angle is in this case 2ψ. It is well to note that $f(2\psi, k)$ introduced in this treatment is not the atomic structure factor as commonly defined, but is proportional to it. $f(2\psi, k)$ is the atomic structure factor multiplied by the scattering for a single free electron. Thus the wave scattered by this atom when it reaches the point P may be represented by

$$\rho^{-1} f(2\psi, k) e^{ik(ct - \rho)}.$$

We will now set up the expression for the wave reaching P from an atom at the more general position A (Fig. VI–2) of coordinates (x, y, o). The expression for the wave incident on such an atom is

$$e^{ik(ct - x \cos \psi)}$$

since $z = o$. The atom will scatter radiation in all directions, that arriving at P being represented by

$$\frac{f(2\psi, k)}{\rho_A} e^{ik(ct - x \cos \psi - \rho_A)}, \qquad (6.05)$$

where ρ_A is the distance AP. Now in writing the scattering angle as 2ψ in eq. (6.05) we have assumed that the point A is not far from the origin. We do this as a result of our physical knowledge that to a first approximation the radiation travels in straight lines, and we know that illumination may be cut off from P by removing a very small amount of reflecting material near the origin (Fresnel zones). For this reason, also, it is permissible to set $\rho_A = \rho$ outside the exponential expression in eq. (6.05). This is because the phase is enormously more sensitive to variations in ρ than is the amplitude factor. Thus if ρ changes by the small amount λ, the phase goes through a change of 2π, whereas the amplitude factor is decreased by the negligible factor $(1 - \lambda/\rho)$.

We will now expand the expression for the distance ρ_A in case the point A lies near the origin, and the distance $OP = \rho$ can be used as a reference length. Using the ordinary expression deduced in analytic geometry for the distance between two points in terms of their coordinates, and making use of eq. (6.04), we find

$$\rho_A = \sqrt{(\alpha - x)^2 + y^2 + \alpha^2 \tan^2 \psi} = \sqrt{\rho^2 + (x^2 + y^2 - 2\alpha x)}. \quad (6.06)$$

Since ρ is by far the largest quantity in the right-hand member of eq. (6.06), we may expand the radical by the binomial theorem and neglect powers of x and y higher than the second. This gives

$$\rho_A = \rho - x \cos \psi + (x^2 \sin^2 \psi + y^2)/2\rho. \qquad (6.07)$$

When this expression for ρ_A is substituted in eq. (6.05), it becomes

$$\frac{f(2\psi, k)}{\rho} e^{ik(ct - \rho)} e^{-ik(x^2 \sin^2 \psi + y^2)/2\rho}. \qquad (6.08)$$

Let M be the number of atoms per unit area on the plane, that is, in an area of amount $dxdy$ there are $Mdxdy$ atoms. Thus the total wave motion S, contributed by the plane at P, is

$$S = \frac{Mf(2\psi, k)}{\rho} e^{ik(ct-\rho)} \int_{-\infty}^{\infty} \int_{-\infty}^{\infty} e^{-ik(x^2 \sin^2 \psi + y^2)/2\rho} dy dx. \quad (6.09)$$

In extending the limits of integration to infinity, we of course assume that the crystal is not so minute that the diffraction pattern is affected by its finite size. The double integral in eq. (6.09) can be shown[11] to have the value

$$-\frac{2\pi i\rho}{k \sin \psi} = -\frac{i\lambda\rho}{\sin \psi}.$$

Substitution of this in eq. (6.09) gives the following result for S, the total reflected wave from the plane:

$$S = -\frac{i\lambda Mf(2\psi, k)}{\sin \psi} e^{(2\pi i/\lambda)(ct-\rho)} \quad (6.11)$$

Since the amplitude of this expression does not depend on ρ, we see that the scattered wavelets from the atoms in the plane have reconstructed themselves into a reflected, plane wave. The factor $-i$ in the amplitude of eq. (6.11) may be interpreted as a change of phase of $\frac{1}{4}\lambda$.

[11] Let Z be the double integral in question, and let $ik/2\rho = i\phi$. Then Z may be written

$$Z = \int_{-\infty}^{\infty} e^{-i\phi x^2 \sin^2 \psi} \left[\int_{-\infty}^{\infty} e^{-i\phi y^2} dy \right] dx.$$

The integral in brackets in this expression may be treated as follows:

$$\int_{-\infty}^{\infty} e^{-i\phi y^2} dy = 2 \left[\int_{0}^{\infty} \cos \phi y^2 dy - i \int_{0}^{\infty} \sin \phi y^2 dy \right].$$

These integrands are in the form $\cos u^2 du$ and $\sin u^2 du$ respectively, and can be integrated by ordinary methods. Cf. Peirce, A Short Table of Integrals, p. 63, No. 487, remembering that we are here integrating an even function, and the integral from $-\infty$ to ∞ is twice the integral from 0 to ∞. We find then

$$Z = \sqrt{\frac{\pi}{2\phi}} (1 - i) \int_{-\infty}^{\infty} e^{-i\phi x^2 \sin^2 \psi} dx$$

and treating the integral in this expression in exactly the same way, we obtain the result of eq. (6.10).

3. *The Transmitted Beam and the Complex Refractive Index*

We now seek an expression for the transmitted wave. Thus in Fig. VI–2 we seek an expression for the wave at P'' built up from the scattered wavelets from points $A(x, y, o)$. The process of finding an expression for this wave is exactly the same as that of developing eq. (6.11), with the exception that instead of $f(2\psi, k)$ as it appears in eq. (6.05), we will have $f(o, k)$, since in the forward direction the scattering angle is zero. If we let T represent the scattered wave at some point P'', where the distance OP'' in Fig. VI–2 is ρ, we have

$$T = -\frac{i\lambda M f(o, k)}{\sin \psi} e^{(2\pi i/\lambda)(ct - \rho)} \tag{6.12}$$

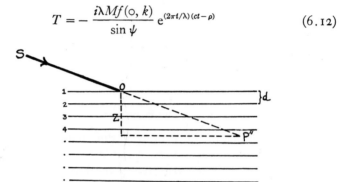

FIG. VI–3. This figure illustrates the method of numbering the crystal planes and the location of the point P'' within the crystal at which the expression for the transmitted wave is to be computed. The path of the radiation incident along SO is not along OP'', because of refraction.

For convenience in calculation we will now introduce two symbols, s and σ, defined by the following relations:

$$s \equiv \frac{M\lambda f(2\psi, k)}{\sin \psi}, \tag{6.13}$$

$$\sigma \equiv \frac{M\lambda f(o, k)}{\sin \psi}. \tag{6.14}$$

When these symbols are introduced into eqs. (6.11) and (6.12), we see that the scattered reflected and transmitted wave from a single plane of atoms may be represented by the following rules:

(1) The amplitude of the scattered wave in the forward direction from a single plane, measured at the origin ($\rho = 0$) is ($-i\sigma$) times the amplitude of the incident wave.

(2) The amplitude of the reflected wave from a single plane, measured at the origin, is ($-is$) times the amplitude of the incident wave.

We must now discuss the expression for the amplitude of the total transmitted wave. To obtain this we add the amplitude which the incident wave-motion T_0 would have at P'' to the amplitude of the scattered wave from the atomic plane at P''. We may here interpolate the following remarks. Due to the fact that energy is scattered in the reflected wave S, the energy of the total beam, at P'' must be less than the incident energy. Thus the principle of conservation of energy imposes a restriction on the amplitude of the scattered wave, requiring a change of phase in scattering such that the square of the modulus of the amplitude of the total transmitted wave at P'' must be less than unity. When we then write the amplitude of the total transmitted wave, measured at the origin (see rule 1 above), as

$$1 + (-i\sigma) = 1 - i\sigma, \qquad (6.14a)$$

the principle of conservation of energy requires that σ be complex, as we shall verify later.

Let us now consider a case in which the transmitted wave has penetrated r crystal planes, as in Fig. VI–3. Let OP'' be the distance reached from the origin. Then the wave at P'' may be expressed by

$$(1 - i\sigma)^r \, e^{(2\pi i/\lambda)(ct-\rho)}.$$

Since σ is a very small quantity compared to unity, the preceding expression may be written

$$e^{-ir\sigma} \, e^{(2\pi i/\lambda)(ct-\rho)} \qquad (6.15)$$

using the ordinary expansion of an exponential and neglecting higher powers of σ. If z is the vertical depth of penetration then ρ, the distance along the path of the radiation, is $z \operatorname{cosec} \psi$. At this point we will also introduce n_a, the number of atoms per cubic centimeter, and d, the interplanar distance. We have

$$n_a = M/d = Mr/z. \qquad (6.16)$$

Introduction of these new symbols into eq. (6.15) gives, after substituting for σ from eq. (6.14)

$$e^{-in_a\lambda f(o,k)\rho}\, e^{(2\pi i/\lambda)(ct-\rho)}. \qquad (6.17)$$

We will now show the connection between the quantities in eq. (6.17) and the index of refraction. From eq. (4.41), Chap. IV, we have a type form for the passage of a wave motion through an absorbing, refracting medium. It is

$$E = A\, e^{-\omega S_i x}\, e^{i\omega(t-Sx)},$$

where $-iS_i$ is the imaginary part of a quantity S_c called the complex wave slowness, which is the reciprocal of the complex wave velocity, and S is the real part of that quantity. x is the distance from some arbitrary zero measured along the direction of propagation of the wave and $\omega = 2\pi\nu$, where ν is the frequency of the wave motion. Now if we consider the first medium as air, in which the wave velocity is wholly real and equal to c, then we have the relation

$$\mu_c = cS_c = cS - icS_i.$$

In terms of the complex index of refraction μ_c, and λ instead of ω, eq. (4.41) may be expressed

$$E = A\, e^{-(2\pi ix/\lambda)\mu_c}\, e^{2\pi ict/\lambda}. \qquad (6.18)$$

If we now throw (6.17) into a form strictly comparable with the right-hand member of (6.18), we get

$$e^{-(2\pi\rho i/\lambda)(1 + n_a\lambda^2 f(o,\,k)/2\pi)}\, e^{2\pi ict/\lambda},$$

and from a comparison of these last two expressions, we see the following important relations:

$$\mu_c = 1 + \frac{n_a\lambda^2 f(o,\,k)}{2\pi}, \qquad (6.19)$$

or

$$\mu_c = 1 + \frac{\lambda \sin \psi}{2\pi d}\, \sigma. \qquad (6.20)$$

The significance of the imaginary part of the complex refractive index may be obtained from a consideration of eqs. (4.43a) and (4.43b) from which we see that if we represent μ_c as $1 - \delta - i\beta$, we have $\beta = (\lambda/4\pi)\mu_l$, where μ_l is the linear absorption coefficient for energy.

At this point we come to the consideration of an important and interesting assumption which differentiates the most recent treatment of this problem, due to Prins (1930), from the original solution by Darwin (1914). The question under consideration is how to deal with the incoherent secondary radiation. In building up the expression for the reflected wave motion from an atomic plane, we have assumed that the waves scattered from each atom can interfere, constructively. This implies, first, that they are of the same wavelength, and second, that they are scattered with the same phase shift from each atom. The first of these requirements we know to be untrue for a large part of the secondary radiation, namely the fluorescence radiation. In the x-ray region this is never of the same wave-length as the radiation which causes it. The second requirement is also probably not fulfilled for this type of secondary radiation. The first act of the incident beam in its production is to eject an electron from an atom in the plane; then, some time afterward, an electron falls into the vacancy created, giving rise to the fluorescence radiation. This lapse of time between excitation and emission is very likely a matter of probability. Thus the wave-motion is stopped by the act of ejection and started by the act of emission at an indeterminate later time. We describe this by saying that this type of the secondary radiation is incoherent with respect to the incident waves. The classical theory, in its original form as used by Darwin, is unable to cope with this incoherent radiation, and if we rigidly adhered to this limitation, we would consider μ_l as merely that part of the linear absorption coefficient due to classical, coherent scattering, which in general would only be a small part of the total linear absorption coefficient.

Darwin recognized this difficulty, and inserted into his equations a term obviously designed to take account of this incoherent loss of energy. Thus instead of (6.14a), Darwin wrote the amplitude of the total transmitted wave as

$$(1 - h - i\sigma)$$

in which h represented the incoherent losses. This h was later dropped in his treatment, and his final equations are applicable only in case this type of absorption is negligible.

The newer treatment includes all the absorption of whatever type in σ, and was attempted in view of the success of this method in dealing with the variation of atomic structure factors with wave-length, and the reflection of soft x-rays from polished surfaces, as discussed in Chap. IV.

From a comparison of eqs. (6.19), (6.20) and (4.43b), we obtain

$$- (\delta + i\beta) = \frac{n_a\lambda^2 f(0, k)}{2\pi} = \frac{\lambda \sin \psi}{2\pi d} \sigma. \qquad (6.21)$$

σ has to do with the amplitude factor in the transmitted wave. Let us define a complex number $(\Delta + ib)$ by analogy to $(\delta + i\beta)$, which will pertain to the reflected radiation from the plane. Let

$$\Delta + ib = (\delta + i\beta)\frac{f(2\psi, k)}{f(0, k)}. \qquad (6.22)$$

Then substitution from eqs. (6.13), (6.14), (6.16) and (6.22) enables us to write

$$- (\Delta + ib) = \frac{n_a\lambda^2 f(2\psi, k)}{2\pi} = \frac{\lambda \sin \psi}{2\pi d} s. \qquad (6.23)$$

4. Development and Solution of the Difference Equations

We now proceed to the treatment of reflection from an infinite number of atomic planes, composing a crystal. In order to evaluate properly the effect of multiple reflection within the crystal, we will devise a system of notation as follows:

Let T_r represent the total wave proceeding downward, measured on the Z axis ($x = y = 0$) at a point just above plane $r + 1$.

Let S_r represent the total wave proceeding upward, measured on the Z axis at a point just above plane $r + 1$.

Then T_0 is the incident wave on the crystal, measured at the origin, and S_0 is the total reflected wave from the entire crystal, also measured at the origin. We can build up difference equations connecting these quantities as follows. Consider an expression for S_0 (Fig. VI-4). Part of S_0 comes from the fraction of T_0 which is reflected at plane number one. Another part of S_0 comes from the fraction of S_1 which is transmitted upward through plane number one. Now S_1 represents the total wave just above the second plane, and when this plane wave has advanced so that it reaches the origin, it will have advanced normal to its wave-front a distance $d \sin \psi$, hence its phase will change by an amount $kd \sin \psi$, or the expression for the wave must be multiplied by

$$e^{-ikd \sin \psi},$$

so that we have

$$S_0 = - is T_0 + (1 - i\sigma)S_1 e^{-ikd \sin \psi}.$$

The general form of this last expression is seen to be

$$S_r = - is T_r + (1 - i\sigma)S_{r+1} e^{-ikd \sin \psi}. \qquad (6.24)$$

Another difference equation may be deduced by consideration of T_r. Part of T_r is due to the part of T_{r-1} transmitted by plane r. Another part of T_r is contributed by S_r which advances upward, is partially reflected downward by plane r, and thus turns in the direction of

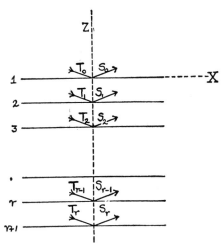

FIG. VI–4. This figure illustrates the notation used in Darwin's derivation of the difference equations whose solution leads to the expression for the diffracted intensity.

the transmitted beam T_r. The phase change due to distance traversed in this last process is $2kd \sin \psi$. Thus we obtain

$$T_r = (1 - i\sigma)T_{r-1} e^{-ikd \sin \psi} - is S_r e^{-2ikd \sin \psi}. \qquad (6.25)$$

A solution of eqs. (6.24) and (6.25) would consist in finding an expression for the ratio S_0/T_0 which would depend only on the constants relating to a single plane. We will first modify eq. (6.25) by making the left-hand member T_{r+1} instead of T_r and multiplying each term by exp $(ikd \sin \psi)$, giving

$$T_{r+1} e^{ikd \sin \psi} = (1 - i\sigma)T_r - is S_{r+1} e^{-ikd \sin \psi}.$$

We will now introduce the following symbols for convenience:

$$\phi \equiv e^{-tkd \sin \psi}, \quad t \equiv (1 - i\sigma), \quad \text{and} \quad a \equiv - is. \qquad (6.26)$$

With these modifications, our eqs. (6.24) and (6.25) become

$$\left.\begin{aligned}S_r &= aT_r + t\phi S_{r+1} \\ \phi^{-1}T_{r+1} &= tT_r + a\phi S_{r+1}\end{aligned}\right\}. \qquad (6.27)$$

We will now eliminate the symbol S from the equations. If we solve the second of the equations under (6.27) for S_{r+1}, we obtain

$$S_{r+1} = (\phi^{-1}T_{r+1} - tT_r)/a\phi. \qquad (6.28)$$

Substitution of eq. (6.28) in the first of eqs. (6.27) gives for S_r:

$$S_r = aT_r + t(\phi^{-1}T_{r+1} - tT_r)/a. \qquad (6.29)$$

We now decrease the subscripts in the second of the eqs. (6.27) by one unit, and solve for S_r, thus obtaining a second and independent expression for S_r. Equating these two expressions and rearranging gives the following:

$$\phi t(T_{r-1} + T_{r+1}) = T_r\{1 + \phi^2(t^2 - a^2)\}. \qquad (6.30)$$

We expect a solution for T_r of the form

$$T_r = T_0 x^r, \qquad (6.31)$$

that is, T_r is related to T_0 by a sort of absorption factor, depending on the number of planes traversed; the conservation of energy requiring that the real part of x shall be less than unity, otherwise the wave will increase in intensity as it traverses the crystal. Substitution of eq. (6.31) in (6.30) gives

$$\frac{1 + x^2}{x} = \frac{1 + \phi^2(t^2 - a^2)}{\phi t}. \qquad (6.32)$$

It will be shown that it is not necessary to proceed to a solution for x at this point. With our object in mind of obtaining an expression for S_0/T_0, let us substitute eq. (6.31) in (6.29), and then set $r = 0$. This procedure gives

$$\frac{S_0}{T_0} = a\left\{1 + \frac{xt}{a^2\phi} - \frac{t^2}{a^2}\right\}. \qquad (6.33)$$

By straightforward algebraic processes, without approximations, we may obtain from eqs. (6.33) and (6.32) the following:

$$\frac{S_0}{T_0} = \frac{a}{1 - \phi x t} = \frac{-is}{1 - x(1 - i\sigma)\,e^{-ikd\sin\psi}}. \qquad (6.34)$$

5. Limitation of the Solution to a Region Near the Bragg Angle

Although eq. (6.34) is a satisfactory solution of the difference equations, the variable ψ is involved in a very complicated manner, and the meaning of x is not physically clear. In order to put the solution into a form more easily handled, we will use our physical knowledge that all important values of ψ are located in a very small angular range about a glancing angle θ_0, defined by

$$\sin\theta_0 \equiv n\lambda/2d, \qquad (6.35)$$

in which λ is the wave-length in air. Now let us set

$$kd\sin\psi = kd\sin\theta_0 + \xi = (2\pi d\sin\theta_0)/\lambda + \xi, \qquad (6.36)$$

in which it is understood that ξ is a small quantity whose higher powers are negligible. From eq. (6.35) we see that this is equivalent to

$$kd\sin\psi = n\pi + \xi, \qquad (6.37)$$

and in view of this, that

$$e^{-ikd\sin\psi} = (-1)^n\,e^{-i\xi}. \qquad (6.38)$$

We now turn to an investigation of the quantity x which appears in eq. (6.34). If we replace the symbols ϕ, t, and a in eq. (6.32), by their equivalents given in eqs. (6.26), we may obtain, after an approximate calculation, in which s, σ, and ξ are treated as small quantities, the result

$$x + 1/x = (-1)^n\{2 + s^2 - (\sigma + \xi)^2\}. \qquad (6.39)$$

From the right-hand member of this last expression, we see that the value of $(x + 1/x)$ must be very nearly $(-1)^n 2$, which means that the value of x must be very nearly $(-1)^n$. This suggests that we may proceed by setting

$$x = (-1)^n(1 - \epsilon), \qquad (6.40)$$

where ϵ is a small quantity. Using this fact, we find that

$$x + 1/x = (-1)^n(2 + \epsilon^2).$$

Comparison of this expression with eq. (6.39) shows that

$$\epsilon^2 = s^2 - (\sigma + \xi)^2.$$

Putting this value in eq. (6.40) gives

$$x = (-1)^n \{1 \pm \sqrt{s^2 - (\sigma + \xi)^2}\}. \tag{6.41}$$

The ambiguity of the radical sign in this expression and those following is resolved by the fact that the real part of x must be less than unity.

We will now collect these expressions and give the solution in terms of experimentally measurable quantities. Putting eqs. (6.41) and (6.38) in eq. (6.34) gives, after rearrangement and an approximate calculation,

$$\frac{S_0}{T_0} = \frac{-s}{(\sigma + \xi) \pm \sqrt{(\sigma + \xi)^2 - s^2}}. \tag{6.42}$$

The final form of the solution is obtained by working out an expression for ξ in terms of angular deviations from θ_0. From eq. (6.35), making use of the fact that only those values of ψ which are very near θ_0 are important, we obtain

$$\xi = kd(\psi - \theta_0) \cos \theta_0. \tag{6.43}$$

In eqs. (6.21) and (6.23), which are expressions for s and σ, we may now replace ψ by θ_0, because these functions do not vary rapidly enough with angle to affect the result over the narrow angular range around θ_0 where appreciable intensity of reflection takes place. Since the wave motions S_0 and T_0 are both measured at the origin, the ratio S_0/T_0 represents the ratio of their complex amplitudes, and the intensity ratio will be proportional to $|S_0/T_0|^2$. If we represent the ratio of the intensity of the reflected beam to the intensity of the incident beam as $I(\psi - \theta_0)$, we find, from eq. (6.42)

$$I(\psi - \theta_0) = \left| \frac{\Delta + ib}{\left\{ (\psi - \theta_0) \cos \theta_0 \sin \theta_0 - (\delta + i\beta) \atop \pm \sqrt{\{(\psi - \theta_0) \cos \theta_0 \sin \theta_0 - (\delta + i\beta)\}^2 - (\Delta + ib)^2}} \right\}} \right|^2 . \tag{6.44}$$

If we wish to evaluate this expression from purely theoretical grounds, we are to calculate δ and β as the sums of quantities δ_q and β_q which may be calculated by eqs. (4.75) to (4.82), Chap. IV. The subscripts q indicate whether the electrons contributing a given term in the sum belong to the $K, L, M, \ldots$, etc., shells of the atom. The calculation of $(\Delta + ib)$ from purely theoretical grounds involves greater difficulties. The relation of this quantity to $(\delta + i\beta)$ is seen from eq. (6.22). In an actual calculation, it would be necessary to represent $(\Delta + ib)$ as a sum of terms arising from the individual electrons of the atom, as follows

$$\Delta + ib = \sum_q (\delta_q + i\beta_q) \frac{f_q(2\theta_0, k)}{f_q(0, k)} e^{-ik(\rho_q - \rho_0)}. \qquad (6.45)$$

The exponential term in the preceding expression represents the difference in path in the scattered wave from a single atom due to the fact that all the electrons are not located at a single point. The function $f_q(2\theta_0, k)$ refers to the amplitude scattered by an electron of the type q at the scattering angle $2\theta_0$. This will depend on the polarization of the incident radiation, and we shall have to distinguish between σ-polarization, in which the electric vector of the incident radiation is perpendicular to the plane of incidence, and π-polarization, in which the incident electric vector lies in the plane of incidence. We shall reserve discussion of the effect of polarization to a later section of this chapter. The calculation of the path differences $(\rho_q - \rho_0)$ involves some assumptions as to the distribution of electricity in the atom, and we must adopt some atom model or other. This is the problem of the calculation of atomic structure factors, and their variation with scattering angle, and is discussed elsewhere in this book.

Furthermore, we have assumed that the atoms lie in geometrically perfect planes, whereas if they are vibrating due to thermal motion, this is not the case. The temperature correction is to be made by multiplication of the expression for $(\Delta + ib)$, in eq. (6.45), by some temperature factor such as that derived first by Debye.[12]

6. *Calculation of the Diffraction Pattern for the Reflection of* Mo $K\alpha_1$ *from Calcite*

The many factors on which the quantity $(\Delta + ib)$ depends make a calculation of it based on fundamental assumptions concerning atomic structure and radiation very complicated. By proceeding in a semi-empirical manner, that is, by making use of other experimental results to give values of the quantities needed, we can, however, carry out a calculation which we have every reason to believe will give a result accurate to within a few per cent. We shall indicate

[12] Debye, P., Ann. d. Physik **43**, 49 (1914).

how the diffraction pattern due to a wave-length of 708 X. U. (Mo $K\alpha_1$) reflected from a calcite crystal in the first order, should appear. In this calculation we shall neglect the temperature effect.

In the first place, in applying eq. (6.44) to calcite, we must take account of the fact that calcite is a composite crystal, consisting of interlaced planes of Ca, C and O atoms. In such a case, one adopts the unit cell as a scattering unit instead of an atom. This means specifically that we must change our expression $(\Delta + ib)$, relating to the scattering power of a single atom, to an expression $D + iB$, applying to the scattering power of the unit cell. Thus

$$D + iB = \sum_j (\Delta + ib)_j e^{2\pi Ni(hx_j + ky_j + lz_j)}, \qquad (6.46)$$

where $(x_j y_j z_j)$ are the coordinates of the atom j in the unit cell, (hkl) are the Miller indices of the reflecting plane, and N is the order of reflection. This last expression is similar to eq. (5.34) of Chap. V, and examples are given there of calculation of the exponential term. The coordinates of the atomic positions in the unit cell of calcite have been determined, and may be found in text-books on crystal structure.[13]   They are:

$$2\text{Ca at } \tfrac{1}{4}\tfrac{1}{4}\tfrac{1}{4} \qquad \tfrac{3}{4}\tfrac{3}{4}\tfrac{3}{4}$$

$$2\text{C at } 000 \qquad \tfrac{1}{2}\tfrac{1}{2}\tfrac{1}{2}$$

$$6\text{O at } \tfrac{1}{4}\tfrac{3}{4}0 \qquad \tfrac{3}{4}0\tfrac{1}{4} \qquad 0\tfrac{1}{4}\tfrac{3}{4} \qquad \tfrac{1}{4}\tfrac{3}{4}\tfrac{1}{2} \qquad \tfrac{3}{4}\tfrac{1}{4}\tfrac{1}{4} \qquad \tfrac{1}{2}\tfrac{1}{4}\tfrac{3}{4}$$

This unit cell is not one which has its faces parallel to the cleavage planes of calcite, and hence the indices of these planes are not (100) in terms of this unit cell, but are (211). If these indices and the above coordinates are substituted in eq. (6.46), we obtain the following expansion; applicable in the first order, $(N = n = 1)$:

$$D + iB = 2(\delta + i\beta)_{\text{Ca}} \frac{f_{\text{Ca}}(2\theta_0, k)}{f_{\text{Ca}}(0, k)}$$

$$+ 2(\delta + i\beta)_{\text{C}} \frac{f_{\text{C}}(2\theta_0, k)}{f_{\text{C}}(0, k)} + 2(\delta + i\beta)_{\text{O}} \frac{f_{\text{O}}(2\theta_0, k)}{f_{\text{O}}(0, k)}. \qquad (6.47)$$

Let us now consider the calculation of the values of δ_j which go into the expressions $(\delta + i\beta)_j$. These δ_j's apply to the index of refraction of a substance built up of atoms of only one kind. In the present case, δ_{Ca}, for instance, applies to the index of refraction of a substance

[13] Wyckoff, R. W. G., The Structure of Crystals, Chem. Cat. Co., N. Y., 1931.

obtained by removing all the atoms from the unit cells of calcite except the one calcium atom in question. We will then calculate δ_{Ca} from eq. (4.46), since the wave-length is sufficiently far removed from the K critical absorption limit of calcium. n will now mean the number of electrons per unit volume in the substance described above, and will be 20 times the number of calcium atoms per unit volume. If V is the volume of the unit cell, and M the molecular weight of calcite, then $V = 2M/N\rho$, where N is the Avogadro number and ρ the density of calcite. Then $n = 20/V$, and from these considerations and eq. (4.46) we obtain

$$\delta_{Ca} = \frac{5N\rho e^2\lambda^2}{\pi m c^2 M}.$$

Using the value 2.71024 for the density of calcite, and calculating δ_O and δ_C in an analogous fashion, we find

$$\delta_{Ca} = 3.68 \times 10^{-7}$$
$$\delta_O = 1.47 \times 10^{-7}$$
$$\delta_C = 1.11 \times 10^{-7}$$

We may here note that the unit decrement of the index of refraction of calcite for this wave-length may be computed as follows:

$$\delta = 2\delta_{Ca} + 2\delta_C + 6\delta_O = 1.82 \times 10^{-6}.$$

We will now consider the values of the β_j's which appear in $(\Delta + i\beta)_j$. We obtain these values directly from the known linear absorption coefficients through eq. (4.43a), instead of using the theoretical expressions for β in eqs. (4.75) to (4.82). Column 2 of Table VI-1 contains values of the mass absorption coefficient, μ/ρ, taken from experimental data.[14]

TABLE VI-1

ABSORPTION OF Mo $K\alpha$ IN CALCITE

Absorber	μ/ρ	μ_l	β_j
Ca	20.2	10.95	6.16×10^{-9}
C	0.67	0.11	6.2×10^{-11}
O	1.00	0.22	1.24×10^{-10}

[14] A. H. Compton, X-rays and Electrons, Van Nostrand (1926), p. 182.

The linear coefficients in the third column of this table are calculated using the density of a substance containing only one of the atoms in question in the volume of a unit cell of calcite, as was done in the calculation of the δ_j's. The value of β for the absorption of Mo $K\alpha$ in calcite may be now calculated by the relation

$$\beta = 2\beta_{Ca} + 2\beta_C + 6\beta_O = 1.32 \times 10^{-8}.$$

We are now ready to discuss values of the ratios $f_j (2\theta_0, k)/f_j (o, k)$. The best approximations to these values may be obtained from tables of atomic structure factors, obtained from observations on powdered crystals, as will be explained later in this chapter.[15] These tables show the scattered amplitude from an atom in terms of the scattering of an electron as a function of $(\sin \theta)/\lambda$ only, which thus depends entirely on the order of reflection. There is some evidence that these ratios depend on λ in a more complicated way, especially near a critical absorption limit of the substance,[16] but for the present calculation this effect is neglected. If we wish to obtain $f_{Ca}(2\theta_0, k)/f_{Ca}(o, k)$, for instance, we must make some assumptions about the state of the calcium atoms in calcite, i.e., how many electrons are to be associated with each calcium center. We have already made the assumption of 20 electrons per calcium center in dealing with the calculation of δ_{Ca} and β_{Ca}, but the present considerations are more sensitive to the particular assumption made than in the previous case. This is due to the fact that the outlying electrons in the atom have a large effect on the angle variation of the atomic structure factor, due to their large distance from the nucleus, whereas their strength of binding is the only disturbing factor in δ. We shall assume each type of atom in $CaCO_3$ to possess its full quota of electrons as a neutral atom. This is not strictly true chemically, due to the ionic type of binding, but in spite of the previous statement, the difference between f values calculated on this and other assumptions is probably less than the error of measurement in the experimental tests of the result of the calculation. For Mo $K\alpha$ in the first order from the cleavage planes of calcite, $(\sin \theta)/\lambda = 0.165$, and from the previously mentioned tables we find the values in Table VI–2.

[15] James and Brindley, Phil. Mag. 12, 81 (1931).
    Pauling and Sherman, Zs. f. Krist. 81, 1 (1932).
[16] Glocker and Schäfer, Zs. f. Physik 73, 289 (1931).

TABLE VI-2

VALUES OF $f_j(2\theta_0,k)/f_j(0,k)$ FOR Mo $K\alpha$ FROM CALCITE IN THE FIRST ORDER

Atom	$f(2\theta_0,k)/f(0,k)$
Ca	$15.3/20 = 0.768$
C	$3.9/6 = 0.650$
O	$6.2/8 = 0.775$

Substitution of the values developed in the previous discussion in eq. (6.47) leads to the results

$$D + iB = 9.38 \times 10^{-7} + 9.74 \times 10^{-9}i$$

$$\delta + i\beta = 1.82 \times 10^{-6} + 1.32 \times 10^{-8}i$$

$$\theta_0 = 6° 42.'5,$$

and the equation of the diffraction pattern is

$$I(\psi-\theta_0) = \left| \left\{ \frac{D+iB}{(\psi-\theta_0)\sin\theta_0\cos\theta_0 - (\delta+i\beta)} \right\} \right|^2 . \quad (6.48)$$
$$\pm\sqrt{\{(\psi-\theta_0)\sin\theta_0\cos\theta_0 - (\delta+i\beta)\}^2 - (D+iB)^2}$$

Although this equation applies only to that component of the incident radiation polarized so that its electric vector lies perpendicular to the plane of incidence, the diffraction curve obtained from this equation differs only slightly from that of Fig. VI-5, which is calculated from the expression applicable to unpolarized radiation, as will be explained later. It is seen that according to the theory here developed, as high as 99% of the energy incident on the crystal in plane wave-fronts may be reflected, at the wave-length of Mo $K\alpha$ in the first order. The angular width at half maximum is 3.6 seconds of arc. A feature of the curve of some interest is that there is no ordinate about which it is symmetrical, although it is centered roughly about a glancing angle θ, where

$$\theta - \theta_0 = \delta \sec\theta_0 \csc\theta_0. \quad (6.49)$$

We shall see in the next section that if the effect of absorption is neglected, the diffraction pattern is actually symmetrical about an ordinate displaced toward larger angles by the amount indicated in eq. (6.49). To an approximation which becomes decreasingly valid as the absorption increases we may therefore call the shift represented in eq. (6.49) the correction to the Bragg angle due to the existence of the refractive index. The lack of symmetry referred to above becomes increasingly evident as the wave-length, and hence the absorption, increases. A diffraction pattern calculated from eq. (6.48) for wave-length 2.299 A is shown in Fig. VI–6.

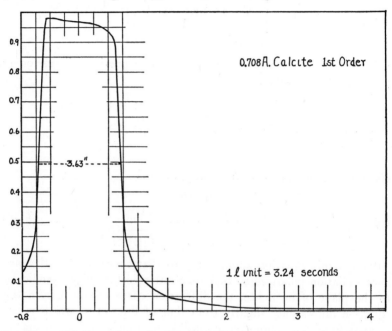

FIG. VI–5. This figure shows the theoretical diffraction pattern for the reflection of a parallel beam of unpolarized radiation of wave-length 0.708 A (Mo $K\alpha$) from a perfect calcite crystal in the first order from the cleavage face. The calculation was made from eqs. (6.54) and (6.50), with values of the constants as given in the text. At this glancing angle there is little difference between σ- and π-polarized components.

For purposes of calculation, it is very convenient to shift the angle from which deviations are measured from θ_0 to θ, and at the same time change the unit of angle used. The radian is such a large unit of angle compared to the very small angles in question that such a change is almost imperative. Let us introduce the variable l, defined by

$$l = (\psi - \theta)/(\theta - \theta_0) = \delta^{-1}(\psi - \theta_0) \sin \theta_0 \cos \theta_0 - 1. \quad (6.49a)$$

This means that the angular unit in which the deviations l are measured is $2\delta/\sin 2\theta_0$ radians. If the variable $(\psi - \theta_0)$ of eq. (6.48) is replaced by l, we may write

$$I'(l) = \left| \frac{\delta^{-1}(D + iB)}{l - i\beta\delta^{-1} \pm \sqrt{(l - i\beta\delta^{-1})^2 - \{(D + iB)\delta^{-1}\}^2}} \right|^2 . \quad (6.50)$$

The abscissae of Fig. VI-5 are in these l units.

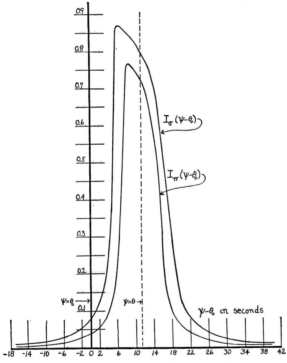

FIG. VI-6. These diffraction pattern curves refer to the reflection of a wave-length of 2.3 A from the cleavage face of a calcite crystal in the first order. The curves were calculated from eq. (6.48), using the experimental values $\delta = 19.21 \times 10^{-6}$; $\beta = 8.15 \times 10^{-7}$. The pattern for unpolarized radiation would be given by eq. (6.54), and thus would lie between the two curves shown.

7. *The Limiting Case of the General Solution in Which the Absorption is Zero; Darwin's Solution*

The mathematical form of eq. (6.48) is such that calculations based upon it are very tedious and difficult. We can learn a great deal about the diffraction pattern if we make the approximation that the absorption is negligible. In this way we can derive equations much more amenable to calculation which give roughly the desired information in the wave-length range below 1 A for calcite or other crystals of similar atomic constituents. Under these circumstances we drop entirely the term B in the quantity $D + iB$, leaving only

$$D = \sum_j \delta_j \frac{f_j(2\theta_0, k)}{f_j(0, k)} e^{2\pi N i(hx_j + ky_j + lz_j)}.$$

Under conditions in which the absorption can be neglected, it is also true that there is no anomalous dispersion, that is, the δ_j values are given by

$$\delta_j = \delta Z_j / Z,$$

where Z_j is the number of electrons in the atom j and Z is the total number of electrons in the unit cell ($Z = 100$ for calcite). Under these circumstances, also,

$$f_j(0, k) = Z_j \times \text{(amplitude scattered by a free electron)}$$

and

$$f_j(2\theta_0, k) = f_j \times \text{(amplitude scattered by a free electron)}$$

where f_j as it appears on the right-hand side of the preceding expression is the atomic scattering factor as it appears in eq. (5.34), Chap. V, for instance. After substitution of these values in the previous expression for D in this section, and realization that the expressions may be now simplified by the introduction of the crystal structure factor F from eq. (5.34), we obtain

$$D = \delta F Z^{-1}.$$

Thus in this approximation, eq. (6.50) becomes

$$I^D(l) = \left| \frac{F Z^{-1}}{l \pm \sqrt{l^2 - F^2 Z^{-2}}} \right|^2, \tag{6.51}$$

which is the result originally obtained by Darwin in 1914. We will now evaluate the formula in various ranges of l. It is seen by inspection that $I^D(l) = 1$ for $l = \pm F Z^{-1}$ or 0. In the region $-F Z^{-1} < l < F Z^{-1}$, the radical in eq. (6.51) is in general imaginary, but straightforward evaluation of the reflected intensity gives $I^D(l) = 1$ throughout this region. If we call this angular range through which there is 100 per cent reflection of the incident intensity $\Delta\theta$, we have

$$\Delta\theta = 2\delta FZ^{-1} \sec\theta_0 \csc\theta_0 = 4\delta FZ^{-1} \csc 2\theta_0. \quad (6.52)$$

We will now discuss the evaluation of $I^D(l)$ in regions where $|l| > |FZ^{-1}|$. In this range there are two possibilities, namely, (a) $l < -FZ^{-1}$ and (b) $l > FZ^{-1}$. We will first discuss possibility (a). Let $l = -(FZ^{-1} + q)$ where q is a real, positive quantity. Making this substitution in eq. (6.51) gives

$$I^D(l) = \left| \frac{FZ^{-1}}{-FZ^{-1} - q \pm q\sqrt{2FZ^{-1}/q + 1}} \right|^2.$$

Now since to give physical reality to our problem, $I^D(l) \leq 1$, we must have in the preceding equation

$$\left| -FZ^{-1} - q \pm q\sqrt{2FZ^{-1}/q + 1} \right| \geq FZ^{-1}.$$

Since q and FZ^{-1} are positive numbers, we have

$$\sqrt{2FZ^{-1}/q + 1} > 1,$$

which means that the negative sign must be used before the radical. In possibility (b), a similar argument shows that the positive sign must be used. The expressions for the reflected intensity in various ranges are summarized in Table VI–3.

TABLE VI–3

EVALUATION OF DARWIN'S FORMULA IN VARIOUS RANGES

Region	Eq. (6.51)
$l < -FZ^{-1}$	$\left(\dfrac{FZ^{-1}}{l - \sqrt{l^2 - F^2Z^{-2}}}\right)^2$
$-FZ^{-1} < l < FZ^{-1}$	1
$l > FZ^{-1}$	$\left(\dfrac{FZ^{-1}}{l + \sqrt{l^2 - F^2Z^{-2}}}\right)^2$

A plot of the function evaluated in Table VI–3 is shown in Fig. VI–7. The value of F, computed from eq. (5.34) and the data in Table VI–2, is 51.6. From eq. (6.52) the extent of the region of 100 per cent reflection is 3.3 seconds of arc, which we see is about equal to the width at half maximum of the curve predicted by the more general theory in which the absorption is included. It should be borne in mind that all the preceding calculations apply to polarization in which the electric vector is perpendicular to the plane of incidence. An idea of the steepness of the sides of the diffraction pattern curve of Darwin may be obtained from the fact that its

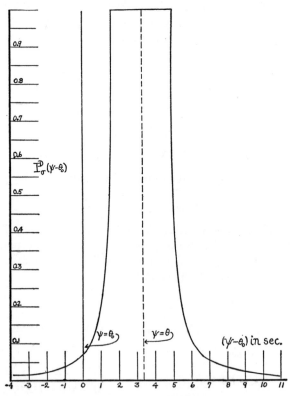

Fig. VI–7. Darwin's diffraction pattern for Mo $K\alpha$ from a perfect calcite crystal in the first order of the cleavage planes. Comparison of this figure with Fig. VI–5 shows the effect of neglecting the absorption of this wave-length in the crystal.

width at half maximum is only 6 per cent greater than the region of 100 per cent reflection.

8. The Effect of Polarization on the Diffraction Pattern

If the incident radiation is unpolarized, we can consider it as composed of two plane polarized constituents, one with its electric vector lying perpendicular to the plane of incidence (σ-polarization), and the other with its electric vector parallel to the plane of incidence (π-polarization). In eq. (6.48) the value of $(D + iB)$ will depend on the polarization, since this influences the amplitude scattered by a single electron to a given point. We shall have

$$(D + iB)_\pi = (D + iB)_\sigma \cos 2\theta_0, \qquad (6.53)$$

where $(D + iB)_\sigma$ is the value of the quantity $(D + iB)$ calculated by the methods of the preceding section, and applicable to σ-polarization. Each polarized component of the unpolarized incident beam will contain half the intensity, and each ordinate in the diffraction pattern will be the sum of the ordinates due to these two constituents; that is

$$I'(l) = \tfrac{1}{2}I_\sigma'(l) + \tfrac{1}{2}I_\pi'(l), \qquad (6.54)$$

where $I'(l)$ applies to the unpolarized pattern, and I_σ' and I_π' refer to expressions in which eq. (6.48) is adapted to the σ- and π-components by using the appropriate form of $(D + iB)$ from eq. (6.53).

In the special case of Darwin's formula, the diffraction pattern for an unpolarized beam is given by

$$I^D(l) = \frac{1}{2}\left[\left|\frac{FZ^{-1}}{l \pm \sqrt{l^2 - F^2 Z^{-2}}}\right|^2 + \left|\frac{FZ^{-1}\cos 2\theta_0}{l \pm \sqrt{l^2 - F^2 Z^{-2}\cos^2 2\theta_0}}\right|^2\right]. \qquad (6.54a)$$

In the case of π-polarization there is in Darwin's formula a region of 100 per cent reflection, but it is more restricted in angular range than is the σ-component, whose angular range is given by eq. (6.52). The angular range of 100 per cent reflection for the π-component is that of the σ-component multiplied by $\cos 2\theta_0$, or

$$\Delta\theta_\pi = 4\delta F Z^{-1} \cot 2\theta_0.$$

In the more general equation in which the absorption is taken account of, the maximum of the π-component diffraction pattern is not as high as that of the σ-component.

9. Qualitative Calculation of the Depth of Penetration into the Crystal

It is clear from the fact that for certain angles of incidence as high as 99 per cent of the incident intensity of the wave-length of Mo $K\alpha_1$ is reflected in the first order according to the present theory, that the radiation must be turned back before it has penetrated far enough into the crystal to make appreciable the effect of ordinary absorption. In this section we shall make a rough calculation of the depth of penetration predicted by the theory. This is of great importance in the determination of wave-lengths of x-ray lines by the photographic method, in which a correction must be made if the center of reflection is not over the axis of the instrument. In the solution of the difference equations appearing in the diffraction problem we assumed that the expression for the wave after having passed through r planes is related to the incident wave T_0 by

$$T_r = T_0 x^r.$$

The value of x may be obtained from eq. (6.41), which, due to the smallness of s, σ, and ξ with respect to unity, we may write

$$x = (-1)^n\, e^{\pm\sqrt{s^2-(\sigma+\xi)^2}}.$$

Putting this last expression in eq. (6.31), and squaring, to get the intensity ratio, we obtain

$$I_r/I_0 = (-1)^{2rn}\, e^{\pm 2r\sqrt{s^2-(\sigma+\xi)^2}}.$$

Now $(-1)^{2rn}$ is always 1, and $r = z/d$, where z is the vertical depth of penetration and d is the grating space. From the preceding expression we also see that the rate of decrease of intensity as the radiation passes into the crystal will vary with the glancing angle, since ξ appears in the exponential term and is defined by eq. (6.43). Since we are only making a rough calculation, we will calculate the penetration for a single glancing angle defined by

$$\psi = \theta_0 + \delta \sec \theta_0 \csc \theta_0.$$

It is seen from Fig. VI-5 that this angle will lie well within the diffraction pattern. The corresponding value of ξ may be found by substitution of this last expression in eq. (6.43). It is

$$\xi = \frac{2\pi d\, \delta}{\lambda \sin \theta_0}.$$

Let us now limit ourselves to the special case of Darwin's solution, which will certainly give the correct order of magnitude of the penetration. Dropping terms arising from the absorption, and using eq. (6.21), we find that for these special considerations, $\sigma + \xi = 0$. From this discussion it results that we may write

$$I_r/I_0 = e^{\pm 2zs/d}.$$

Now in the evaluation of s for a composite crystal like calcite, as discussed in Sec. 6, we must use the quantity $(D + iB)$, related to the scattered wave from the entire unit cell of the crystal, instead of $(\Delta + ib)$, relating to the scattering from a single atom. Applying this, and dropping B's to conform to Darwin's solution, we find from eq. (6.23)

$$S = - \, \delta F Z^{-1} \frac{2\pi d}{\lambda \sin \theta_0}.$$

In order that the intensity may decrease as we go deeper into the crystal we must have a real negative exponent in the expression for I_r/I_0, and since in the present simplified case, s is entirely real, we get

$$I_r/I_0 = e^{-(4\pi \delta F/Z\lambda \sin \theta_0)z}.$$

We will call the absorption coefficient indicated by the preceding expression the primary extinction coefficient μ_e, where

$$\mu_e = \frac{4\pi \delta F}{Z\lambda \sin \theta_0}. \tag{6.55}$$

Computation of μ_e using values developed in Sec. 6 of this chapter leads to the result $\mu_e = 1.4 \times 10^4$. From the value of β for Mo $K\alpha$ and calcite obtained there, it may be shown that the ordinary linear absorption coefficient, μ_l, is about 2.3×10^1. Since this applies to the absorption along the path of the rays and μ_e applies to the vertical depth, μ_l must be multiplied by the factor cosec θ_0 for comparison with μ_e. This gives 2.0×10^2 as the ordinary linear absorption coefficient effective in the vertical direction in first order reflection. Thus there is a 70-fold increase in the absorption coefficient when the glancing angle is such that a diffracted maximum may form. It may be further shown that when constructive interference occurs in the first order, the intensity of the transmitted beam is reduced to one-half its initial value after penetration to a depth of 5×10^{-5} cm., whereas if only ordinary absorption were effective, the corresponding depth would be about 3×10^{-3} cm. Equation (6.55) applies to the extinction of the σ-polarized component. In order to express the extinction of the π-polarized radiation, the expression in eq. (6.55) must be multiplied by the factor cos $2\theta_0$. In higher orders of reflection, the penetration is greater, and the distinction between the ordinary absorption and the extinction rapidly disappears.

We must remember that we have calculated the extinction only for a particular glancing angle, lying in the center of the diffraction pattern, if Darwin's equations are used. The extinction is greatest at the smaller glancing angle end of the region of 100 per cent reflection, and decreases as we proceed toward the larger glancing angle end of this range. We can now see a physical reason for the asymmetry of the diffraction pattern predicted by the more general theory in which the absorption is included. At the larger glancing angle end of the region, where the penetration is deepest, the effect of absorption lowers the reflected intensity more than at the small angle end; hence the lack of symmetry.

10. *The Single Crystal Coefficient of Reflection*

In this section we shall discuss what we shall call the single crystal coefficient of reflection, which has to do with the intensity reflected by a crystal from a beam of x-rays. In speaking of the single crystal coefficient we are attempting to emphasize the distinction between it and the nearest experimental approach to its measurement, the coefficient of reflection as obtained in the double spectrometer. Perhaps the best way to approach the topic is to describe a particular technique devised by Bragg,[17] and by Bragg, James, and Bosanquet[18] for its determination, and since then widely used. In this method, the crystal is mounted in a Bragg single crystal ionization spectrometer. With the crystal backed out of position, the beam from the x-ray tube is allowed to shine into the ionization chamber, and the rate of deflection of the electrometer per second noted. This rate is proportional to the ergs per second entering the ionization chamber and has the dimensions of power. Call it P_0. We then advance the crystal into the beam, and place the ionization chamber at angle $2\theta_0$ with the direct beam, in other words, in a position to receive the diffracted beam. Then, beginning with the crystal making a glancing angle sufficiently far from θ_0, we rotate the crystal with uniform angular velocity through the reflecting range, at the end of the operation noting the total charge which has accumulated on the quadrants of the electrometer, that is, reading the permanent deflection produced. Let this total charge, or permanent deflection, be E, and let the angular velocity with which the crystal was rotated through the reflecting region be ω. Then, if the radiation were

[17] Bragg, W. H., Phil. Trans. Roy. Soc. A **215**, 253 (1915).
[18] Bragg, James, and Bosanquet, Phil. Mag. **41**, 309 (1921); **42**, 1 (1921).

strictly monochromatic and parallel, the coefficient of reflection for the crystal for the wave-length, order, and planes under consideration, would be R_c, where

$$R_c = E\omega/P_o. \qquad (6.56)$$

We shall presently discuss the effect of the divergence and the heterogeneous nature of the actual x-ray beams available on this definition; at present, we shall proceed with the hypothetical case in which the x-rays are strictly monochromatic and parallel and inter-

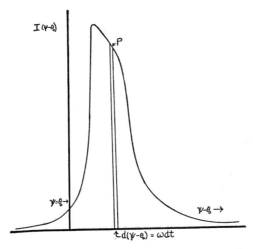

Fig. VI–8. Illustrating the connection between the area under the diffraction pattern and the single crystal coefficient of reflection.

pret this coefficient in terms of the diffraction pattern from the crystal.

Consider an infinitesimal range of glancing angle $d(\psi - \theta_o)$ as shown in Fig. VI–8. Let P be the power in the diffracted beam while the crystal is in a position such that the glancing angle of the radiation upon it lies in the specified range. Then we shall have

$$P = P_o I(\psi - \theta_o)$$

in which the function I is obtained from eq. (6.48). If dt is the time required by the crystal to swing through this angular range $d(\psi - \theta_o)$, the increment of charge received by the electrometer while the crystal is passing through this range will be proportional to dE, where $dE = Pdt$.   But if ω is the angular velocity of rotation of the crystal, we have $\omega = d(\psi - \theta_0)/dt$, so that

$$dE = \frac{1}{\omega} Pd(\psi - \theta_0).$$

E, the total energy entering the ionization chamber during the rotation, will be

$$E = \frac{1}{\omega}\int_{-\infty}^{\infty} Pd(\psi - \theta_0) = \frac{1}{\omega}\int_{-\infty}^{\infty} P_0 I(\psi - \theta_0) d(\psi - \theta_0). \quad (6.57)$$

Comparison of eqs. (6.57) and (6.56) shows us that what we have defined as the coefficient of reflection from an experimental procedure is in terms of the diffraction pattern:

$$R_c = \int_{-\infty}^{\infty} I(\psi - \theta_0) d(\psi - \theta_0). \quad (6.58)$$

This means that the single crystal coefficient of reflection is simply the area under the diffraction pattern curve.

If the diffraction pattern function $I(\psi - \theta_0)$ has the form of eq. (6.48), the integration called for in eq. (6.58) is extremely difficult to carry out analytically, and the only R_c values which have been obtained from this function have been found by plotting the function and then performing graphical integration. Approximate values, good if the absorption is not too high, may be calculated by a formula derived by integration of Darwin's eq. (6.51).   In order to obtain R_c values in which the unit of angle is the radian, we must multiply by $\delta \sec \theta_0 \operatorname{cosec} \theta_0$ since the unit in which l is expressed in eq. (6.51) is not the radian.   Calculating for an unpolarized incident beam from Darwin's equation, we obtain

$$R_c = \tfrac{1}{2}\delta \sec \theta_0 \operatorname{cosec} \theta_0 \times$$

$$\left[\int_{-\infty}^{\infty} \left| \frac{FZ^{-1}}{l \pm \sqrt{l^2 - F^2 Z^{-2}}} \right|^2 dl + \int_{-\infty}^{\infty} \left| \frac{FZ^{-1}\cos 2\theta_0}{l \pm \sqrt{l^2 - F^2 Z^{-2}\cos^2 2\theta_0}} \right|^2 dl \right].$$

It is readily seen that due to the infinite limits of integration, the second integral on the right hand side of the preceding expression will have a value equal to that of the first integral multiplied by

$\cos 2\theta_0$. Using this fact and the values in Table VI–3, we are able to write

$$R_c = \tfrac{1}{2}(1 + \cos 2\theta_0)\delta \sec \theta_0 \csc \theta_0 \times$$

$$\left[\int_{-\infty}^{-FZ^{-1}} \frac{F^2 Z^{-2} dl}{(l - \sqrt{l^2 - F^2 Z^{-2}})^2} + \int_{-FZ^{-1}}^{FZ^{-1}} dl + \int_{FZ^{-1}}^{\infty} \frac{F^2 Z^{-2} dl}{(l + \sqrt{l^2 - F^2 Z^{-2}})^2} \right].$$

The first and third integrals which appear in the preceding expression, and relate to the area under the wings of the diffraction pattern of Darwin, may each be shown[19] to give the result $F/3Z$. We thus attain the following expression for R_c:

$$R_c = \frac{8F\delta(1 + \cos 2\theta_0)}{3Z \sin 2\theta_0}. \tag{6.59}$$

If we use the values $F = 51.6$, $\delta = 1.82 \times 10^{-6}$, $Z = 100$, $\theta_0 = 6° 42'$; applicable to the reflection of Mo $K\alpha_1$ in the first order from the calcite cleavage planes, we obtain $R_c = 2.13 \times 10^{-5}$.

In calculations based on the more general eq. (6.48), taking account of the polarization as in eq. (6.54), we must proceed by calculation of the diffraction patterns for the σ- and π-polarized components, and perform the required integrations graphically. The effect of the absorption is to decrease the coefficient of reflection, and by this method we find the value $R_c = 1.98 \times 10^{-5}$.

Let us now return for a moment to consideration of the actual experimental conditions under which measurement of the coefficient of reflection is made. The incident x-ray beams available for the experimental measurements are of course divergent and heterogeneous with respect to wave-length, rather than parallel and monochromatic as postulated in this section thus far. Let us first examine the effect of divergence, retaining the assumption that the radiation is mono-chromatic. If we make the measurement by rotating a single crystal and collecting the diffracted energy in an ionization chamber-elec-trometer system, as described above, at first glance we appear to be

[19] By a change of variable from l to x through the relation

$$l = \tfrac{1}{2}FZ^{-1}(e^x + e^{-x}),$$

we may write

$$\int_{FZ^{-1}}^{\infty} \frac{dl}{(l + \sqrt{l^2 - F^2Z^{-2}})^2} = \frac{1}{2FZ^{-1}}\left[\int_0^{\infty} e^{-x}dx - \int_0^{\infty} e^{-3x}dx \right] = \frac{Z}{3F}$$

from which the result quoted in the text is clear.

doing something quite different than the ideal experiment described above. For because of the divergent nature of the beam, certain parts of it make glancing angles within the diffraction pattern range over a wide range of positions of the crystal. Thus if the x-ray beam is limited in its horizontal divergence by two slits of equal width w separated by a distance L, then there will be appreciable reflection from the crystal over an angular range of rotation $2\alpha_m$, where $\alpha_m = w/L$, and is in most cases several minutes of arc, in contrast to the reflection of a monochromatic, parallel beam which could only take place in appreciable amount over a rotation range of a few seconds. However, because of the small width of the crystal diffraction pattern compared to the horizontal divergence of the beam, the power in the diffracted beam from the crystal at any given position will simply be the product of the area under the diffraction pattern curve times the power in that part of the incident beam making the correct angle on the crystal. In other words, the variation in the power in the incident beam with horizontal divergence is so slow in comparison to the change in the diffraction pattern with glancing angle that after the crystal has been swept across the beam we have collected in the ionization chamber energy proportional to the product of the area under the diffraction pattern times the power in the entire incident beam. This would not be the case if the slits were so narrow that the horizontal divergence were some few seconds of arc and comparable to the width of the diffraction pattern. We shall return to this point when discussing the rocking curves obtained in the parallel positions of the double spectrometer. Thus we see that even if the x-ray beam is divergent, an experiment as described in this section, with the application of eq. (6.56) will give us R_c, although it will not be possible to discover the actual shape of the diffraction pattern curve, the experiment only giving us the area underneath it.

Furthermore the actual beam from an x-ray tube contains a large range of wave-lengths, including characteristic emission lines of limited wave-length range. The width of an emission line is so small that the variation of R_c with wave-length in this range is negligible. The amount of the integrated reflected intensity due to the general radiation may be corrected for by making a separate run using radiation in the vicinity of the line and subtracting this amount from the amount observed when the line is used. Under these conditions, the only factor preventing an accurate determination of R_c by this method is that the incident beam includes the whole range of wave-lengths emitted by the tube, whereas the crystal selects a small range for reflection into the chamber. This effect may be diminished by the employment of filters in the incident beam to make it as nearly monochromatic as possible.

One way to make the incident beam monochromatic is to reflect it first from a crystal set to select from it the desired wave-length, and then to use the diffracted beam from this crystal as the incident beam on the crystal whose coefficient of reflection is being studied. In this way the instrument was invented which has come to be known as the double x-ray spectrometer. The relation of the results obtained from this instrument to the diffraction pattern curves from a single crystal will be discussed elsewhere.

11. *Experimental Results on the Coefficient of Reflection, Compared*
with the Calculations for a Perfect Single Crystal

In this section we shall compare some of the results obtained experimentally for the coefficient of reflection with the theoretical calculations. We shall only treat here some of the results which have been obtained from reflection from crystal faces, and not use the results of experiments on the transmitted reflection through crystal slabs. Darwin[20] states that after his calculation of R_c from theoretical considerations had been completed, he compared his result with the experiments of Moseley,[21] and although no accurate comparison could be made, it was clear that the experimental value of the intensity of reflection was far greater than that calculated. Moseley's experiments were made with a crystal of potassium ferrocyanide.

An extensive series of measurements on the coefficient of reflection of x-rays by rock salt has been made by Bragg, James, and Bosanquet,[22] and previously a determination of the coefficient for the reflection of Mo $K\alpha$ from the cleavage faces of this crystal had been made by A. H. Compton.[23] In these experiments a first crystal was used to select a wave-length from the heterogeneous x-rays coming from the tube, and the radiation diffracted from this crystal used as the incident radiation upon a second crystal whose coefficient of reflection was being measured (Fig. VI-9). This procedure has

[20] Darwin, Phil. Mag. **43**, 800 (1922).
[21] Moseley, Phil. Mag. **26**, 1024 (1913).
[22] Bragg, James, and Bosanquet, Phil. Mag. **41**, 309 (1921); **42**, 1 (1921).
[23] A. H. Compton, Phys. Rev. **10**, 95 (1917).

been mentioned previously in this chapter. Although as will be shown later rather elaborate corrections are necessary to measurements made in this way, if precise numerical agreement with theory is to be expected, it is not necessary to discuss these in the case of rock salt, where the discrepancy between theory and experiment is large. A. H. Compton found $R = 4.0 \times 10^{-4}$ for NaCl in the first order (100) reflection of Mo $K\alpha$. A calculation of R_c from eq. (6.59), using the value of F given in Table V–6, Chapter V ($N = 2$), and using atomic structure factors from James and Brindley[24] gives the result $E\omega/P_0 = 2.2 \times 10^{-5}$. Bragg, James, and Bosanquet found experimentally $R = 5.5 \times 10^{-4}$ for $\lambda = 0.613$ A for the first order reflection from the cleavage planes of rock salt. At this wave-length

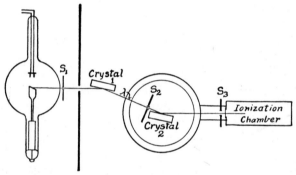

Fig. VI–9. A double crystal spectrometer in the position in which both crystals are parallel. In this position the dispersion of the instrument is zero.

eq. (6.59) leads to a value of 1.9×10^{-5}. It is clear that there is a very large discrepancy here, experiment giving a reflected intensity from 18 to 29 times as large as that theoretically predicted.

Considerable data are also available on the coefficient of reflection from calcite cleavage faces. A. H. Compton[23] found for $\lambda = 0.708$ A, $R = 8.7 \times 10^{-5}$, which may be compared with 2.1×10^{-5} calculated from Darwin's theory in the preceding section. These and other results on calcite crystals which show discrepancy with the theory of a perfect crystal are listed in Table VI–4.

It is seen from this table that these calcite specimens, although giving results much nearer to those calculated on the perfect crystal formula than does rock salt, vary in giving from 2 to 4 times the diffracted

[24] James and Brindley, Phil. Mag. **12**, 81 (1931).

TABLE VI-4

MEASUREMENTS OF THE COEFFICIENTS OF REFLECTION OF THE CLEAVAGE FACE OF
CALCITE IN THE FIRST ORDER WHICH SHOW DISCREPANCY WITH
THE THEORY OF A PERFECT CRYSTAL

λ	R Obs.	R_c Calc. (Eq. 6.59)	Author
0.43 A	4.2×10^{-5}	1.3×10^{-5}	Davis and Stempel
0.58	4.2	1.6	Davis and Stempel
0.68	4.6	2.0	Davis and Stempel
0.71	8.7	2.1	A. H. Compton[23]
1.39	7.7	3.7	Wagner and Kulenkampff
1.54	8.1	4.2	Wagner and Kulenkampff
1.75	8.1	4.8	Wagner and Kulenkampff
1.93	7.9	5.3	Wagner and Kulenkampff

Davis and Stempel, Phys. Rev. **17**, 608 (1921).

Wagner and Kulenkampff, Ann. d. Physik **68**, 369 (1922).

Davis and Purks, Phys. Rev. **34**, 181 (1929) obtained results for R considerably lower than the perfect crystal values. These are not included in this table because on repetition, larger values were found.

intensity predicted. It was therefore concluded that these crystals are not perfect in the sense of being single, complete specimens, but are built up of small blocks, perhaps of the order of 10^{-5} cm. on a side which are roughly, but not accurately, oriented in the direction of the crystal axes. This sort of structure would cause the reflection to spread itself out over a much greater angular width than that calculated for a perfect crystal, and thus increase the area under the diffraction pattern curve, or, in other words, the coefficient of reflection. Thus the extent of the angular range of glancing angle through which some specimens of rock salt reflect a single wave-length has been shown by double spectrometer measurements to be on the order of half a degree,[25] whereas a width of about 3 seconds of arc is indicated in eq. (6.52).

[25] Kirkpatrick and Ross, Phys. Rev. **43**, 596 (1933) have found specimens of rocksalt which give considerably narrower ranges of reflection than this. They found the half width at half maximum of the range to be about 87 seconds of arc, and $R = 18.2 \times 10^{-5}$. M. Renninger, Naturwissenschaften **21**, 334 (1934) has reported finding sodium chloride crystals which in small areas, on the order of 1 mm², give parallel position rocking curves from the cleavage face in the first observable order 7.1 sec. wide at Cu $K\alpha$ (1.54A), the theory predicting about 5 seconds at this wave-length. Coefficients of reflection are also in fair agreement with perfect crystal predictions.

An important purpose in carrying out experiments on the intensity of reflection of x-rays has been the possibility of finding in this way values of the atomic structure factor. The lack of success in the application of the formulae developed for perfect crystals to experimental results lead to the abandonment of this type of approach, and to the use of ideally imperfect crystals, which are powders in which the crystal particles have perfectly random orientation. As described later, these methods have been successful, and it is from them that the atomic structure factors used in this treatment have been taken.

Recently, however, it has been shown that calcite surfaces may be obtained which, if the incident wave-length is not too short, give results in the double spectrometer remarkably close to the perfect crystal calculations, so close, in fact, that the discrepancy is probably not greater than that caused by the lack of consideration of the temperature factor, and our uncertainty as to the exact values of the atomic structure factor.[26, 27] It is significant that polishing increases the coefficient of reflection for a freshly cleaved crystal surface. This presumably is due to the fact that the act of polishing disrupts the regular crystal structure and produces a layer of powdered crystal fragments over the surface. Such an effect may also be produced by scratching or handling the surfaces. The experiments in which agreement with the perfect crystal formula was found were performed with freshly cleaved surfaces, which before cleavage were in contact. The sample to be split was mounted on the carriage of a milling machine, in such a way that the lateral motion of the carriage was accurately parallel to the cleavage direction. A very thin circular saw was then run at slow speed and a groove made across the specimen. By continued sawing in this groove a split soon started and the slight jars due to the impacts of the saw teeth on the crystal spread it until fissure was complete. The two halves of the crystal were then immediately placed in a desiccator and kept until used.

Let us refer to the crystal on which x-rays are first incident as crystal A, the second crystal in the double spectrometer being crystal B. With the cleavage surfaces of A and B parallel, and reflecting in the first order, A is left stationary and B rotated in steps through the region in which appreciable intensity is reflected from it. In the work of Allison and of Parratt, ionization current readings were

[26] S. K. Allison, Phys. Rev. 41, 13; 688 (1932).
[27] L. G. Parratt, Phys. Rev. 41, 561 (1932).

taken for various positions of B in this range, the so-called " rocking curve " plotted, and its area compared with the power in the beam incident on B from A. The ratio of these two quantities does not give R_c, however, which refers to the coefficient of reflection of a single crystal. In the discussion of the theory of the double spectrometer, it will be shown that instead of R_c a quantity R will be observed by this method, where

$$R = \frac{2\delta}{\sin 2\theta_0} \frac{\left[\int_{-\infty}^{\infty} I_\sigma'(l)dl\right]^2 + \left[\int_{-\infty}^{\infty} I_\pi'(l)dl\right]^2}{\int_{-\infty}^{\infty} I_\sigma'(l)dl + \int_{-\infty}^{\infty} I_\pi'(l)dl}. \quad (6.60)$$

In this expression the functions I_σ' and I_π' refer to the diffraction pattern functions from a single crystal for σ- and π-polarization respectively. If the absorption is sufficiently small so that Darwin's diffraction pattern may be used, it will be shown (Sec. 9, Chap. IX) that the preceding expression reduces to

$$R = 2\frac{1 + \cos^2 2\theta_0}{(1 + \cos 2\theta_0)^2} R_c \quad (6.61)$$

in which R_c is given by eq. (6.59).

Table VI-5 shows a comparison of observed and calculated R values for freshly split calcite according to Allison and Parratt.

TABLE VI-5

CALCULATED AND OBSERVED VALUES OF THE DOUBLE CRYSTAL COEFFICIENT OF REFLECTION R FOR CALCITE (100) PLANES IN THE FIRST ORDER

Line	λ	$R_c \times 10^5$ (Calc.)	$R \times 10^5$ (Calc.)	$R \times 10^5$ (Obs.)	
				Cryst. II	Cryst. III
W $K\alpha$	0.21 A	0.626	0.582	2.34	1.17
Mo $K\alpha$	0.71	1.98	2.03	2.31	1.86
Cu $K\alpha$	1.54	3.85	3.82	3.80	3.46
Cr $K\alpha$	2.29	4.67	4.84	4.79	4.68
U M_{III} $O_{IV,V}$.	2.94	4.00	4.49	4.35	
U M_{III} O_I	3.11	6.10	6.80	6.70	
U $M\alpha_1$	3.90	6.78	11.20	10.40	
U M_V N_{III} ...	4.94	13.4	16.4	14.00	

In this Table the calculation of the W $K\alpha$ values is made directly from Darwin's formula, eqs. (6.59), (4.46) and (6.61); all the others are made from the more general eq. (6.48), using values of δ and β from experiments on refractive index and absorption.

The results given in Table VI–5, besides showing that calcite surfaces may be obtained giving no evidence of mosaic structure over a wide wave-length range of reflection, are of considerable interest from the viewpoint of dispersion theory. As shown in Fig. VI–10, they cover the region of the K critical absorption limit of calcium. If the complex refractive index, which includes the absorption, had not been used, the theory would have been unable to handle the region around this limit. It is seen that the theory

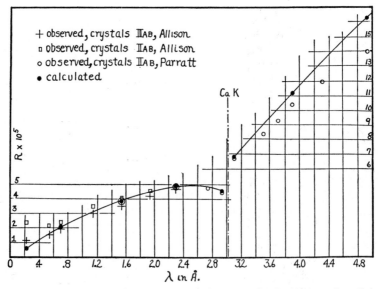

FIG. VI–10. Comparison of theory and experiment on the double crystal coefficient of reflection, R. The solid curve is drawn through the calculated points, which are few in number due to the laborious calculation necessary. The calculations were made in a semi-empirical manner, using eqs. (6.48) and (6.60) and experimental values of δ and β rather than calculated ones from eqs. (4.75) to (4.82).

in its present form adequately predicts the magnitude of the change of R at this point   Other aspects of the rocking curves will be discussed later under the topic of the double x-ray spectrometer.

Brindley [28] has discussed the experiments of Ehrenberg, Ewald, and Mark [29] on the relative values of the intensity of reflection of x-rays from diamond. He has shown that the zero point energy correction and the introduction of the proper structure factors into

[28] G. W. Brindley, Proc. Roy. Soc. Lond. A **140**, 301 (1933).
[29] Ehrenberg, Ewald, and Mark, Z. Krist. **66**, 547 (1928).

Darwin's treatment predict a type of variation of intensity with angle which agrees with perfect crystal formulae.

In conclusion we may state that there is experimental evidence that specimens of calcite, and possibly diamond, may be found which behave in the reflection of x-rays as would a large, single crystal. The great majority of crystals, however, are undoubtedly like rock salt in giving much greater reflected intensities than predicted by the perfect crystal theory.

B. THE DIFFRACTION OF X-RAYS BY AN IMPERFECT CRYSTAL AND THE DETERMINATION OF ATOMIC STRUCTURE FACTORS

12. *The Reflection of X-rays by a Very Small Crystal*

Since the crystals which have been found to agree with the perfect crystal reflection formula are so few in number, the attack on the problem of atomic structure factors from the experimental standpoint has been made almost entirely from the study of the reflection from imperfect crystals. An ideally imperfect crystal would be a perfectly random arrangement of very minute crystalline fragments, that is, a very fine powder made from a non-amorphous substance. The fundamental problem here is the calculation of the intensity of reflection by a particle so small that extinction may be neglected. Such a fragment may be considered to be irradiated throughout by an x-ray beam of uniform intensity. The problem in question has been studied by various writers.[30] The calculations have usually been made for a cubic lattice, using the atom as the diffracting unit. At the present stage of development of the subject it seems advisable to give a more general derivation, applicable to any crystal system, and using the unit cell as the diffracting unit. The derivation given here was suggested by a study of a treatment of the subject by B. E. Warren.[31]

[30] P. Debye, Annalen der Physik **43**, 49 (1914).

M. von Laue, Encyklopädie der mathematischen Wissenschaften, Bd. **5**, 3. Teil, No. 24 (1915). This is a general review of the question of the intensity of crystalline diffraction as far as it had been developed at that time.

C. G. Darwin, Phil. Mag. **27**, 315 (1914). The result we shall obtain here is essentially that given in Eq. 4. Also Phil. Mag. **27**, 675 (1914) and Phil. Mag. **43**, 800 (1922).

A. H. Compton, Phys. Rev. **9**, 29 (1917).

W. L. Bragg, R. W. James, C. H. Bosanquet, Phil. Mag. **42**, 1 (1921).

[31] This was available to the authors in a mimeographed résumé of lectures given by Professor Warren at Massachusetts Institute of Technology. For a simple derivation, see X-Rays and Electrons, p. 121.

Although it is possible to calculate the desired result using the atomic plane as the diffracting unit, as was done in the previous derivation for a perfect crystal, we shall here consider the small crystalline particle as composed of unit cells, each of which is a scattering unit. Figure VI–11 shows the method of locating a unit cell in the crystal. Let the vectors τ_1, τ_2, τ_3 represent the primitive translations along the axes 1, 2, and 3, which may be inclined to each other in any way, but are not coplanar. Let R be a vector from the origin O (conveniently but not necessarily located at a corner of the crystal) to the reference corner of a unit cell in the

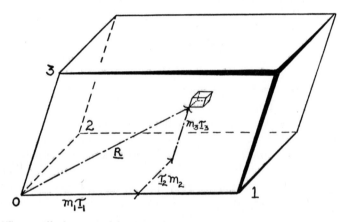

FIG. VI–11.   The location of the unit cell at the terminus of vector R may be specified by giving the values of the vectors $m_1\tau_1$, $m_2\tau_2$, $m_3\tau_3$.

crystal. Then R is related to the primitive translation vectors by the vector equation

$$R = m_1\tau_1 + m_2\tau_2 + m_3\tau_3, \qquad (6.62)$$

where $m_1m_2m_3$ are integers. We wish to combine the disturbances scattered to a distant point from these unit cells. In Fig. VI–12 XOX' represents a plane wave-front advancing from the left. S_o is a unit vector in the direction of the incident radiation. Consider the incident radiation to be of amplitude E_o, so that the wave-motion at point O (Figs. V–11 and VI–12) can be expressed as

$$E_o e^{(2\pi i/\lambda)ct}.$$

The phase and amplitude of the wave-motion at the terminus of R are then contained in the expression

$$E_o e^{(2\pi i/\lambda)(ct - R \cdot S_o)}.$$

Let ρ be the distance from the point O to a remote point P at which the disturbance is observed. Neglecting small quantities, then, we may write for the contribution to the wave-motion at P from the wave scattered by the unit cell in question, the expression

$$\frac{E_o F e^2}{\rho m c^2} e^{(2\pi i/\lambda)[ct - R \cdot S_o - (\rho - R \cdot S)]}$$

or

$$\frac{E_o F e^2}{\rho m c^2} e^{(2\pi i/\lambda)(ct - \rho)} e^{(2\pi i/\lambda) R \cdot (S - S_o)}.$$

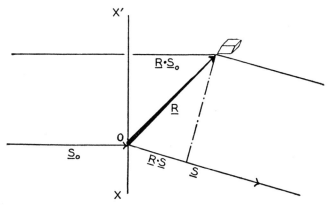

Fig. VI-12. Showing the difference in phase of a ray scattered from the unit cell at the terminus of R and a unit cell at the origin.

In this expression F is the crystal structure factor,[31a] which is the effective number of electrons per unit cell scattering classically at the given angle. The factor e^2/mc^2 comes from the scattering by a free electron. The polarization is assumed here to be of the σ type, that is, the electric vector of the incident x-rays vibrates in a plane perpendicular to that defined by the vectors S and S_o.

[31a] In this chapter, and throughout the book with the exception of Chap. III and Appendix IV, F is used for the crystal structure factor, related to the amplitude scattered by the unit cell, and f for the atomic structure factor. In Chap. III, f is used for an electronic structure factor not discussed elsewhere, and F is used for the atomic structure factor

After substitution of the value of R from eq. (6.62), the wave-motion at P from the entire crystal is

$$E_P = \left[\frac{E_o F e^2}{m\rho c^2} \sum_{m_1} \sum_{m_2} \sum_{m_3} e^{(2\pi i/\lambda)[m_1\mathbf{\tau}_1 + m_2\mathbf{\tau}_2 + m_3\mathbf{\tau}_3]\cdot(\mathbf{S}-\mathbf{S}_o)]} \right] e^{(2\pi i/\lambda)(ct-\rho)}.$$

Let M_1 be the number of primitive translations making up the edge 1 of the crystal particle, and introduce analogous numbers M_2 and M_3. Then the sums in question are to be extended from 0 to $M-1$ along each axis. Let us consider one of these sums:

$$\sum_{m_1=0}^{m_1=M_1-1} e^{(2\pi i m_1/\lambda)\mathbf{\tau}_1\cdot(\mathbf{S}-\mathbf{S}_o)}.$$

It is seen that this sum has the following simple form

$$\sum_{m_1=0}^{m_1=M_1-1} e^{m_1 z} = \frac{e^{M_1 z} - 1}{e^z - 1}$$

so that the expression for E_P becomes

$$\frac{E_P}{E_o} = \frac{Fe^2}{\rho m c^2} e^{(2\pi i/\lambda)(ct-\rho)}$$

$$\left[\frac{(e^{(2\pi i M_1/\lambda)\mathbf{\tau}_1\cdot(\mathbf{S}-\mathbf{S}_o)} - 1)(e^{(2\pi i M_2/\lambda)\mathbf{\tau}_2\cdot(\mathbf{S}-\mathbf{S}_o)} - 1)(e^{(2\pi i M_3/\lambda)\mathbf{\tau}_3\cdot(\mathbf{S}-\mathbf{S}_o)} - 1)}{(e^{(2\pi i/\lambda)\mathbf{\tau}_1\cdot(\mathbf{S}-\mathbf{S}_o)} - 1)(e^{(2\pi i/\lambda)\mathbf{\tau}_2\cdot(\mathbf{S}-\mathbf{S}_o)} - 1)(e^{(2\pi i/\lambda)\mathbf{\tau}_3\cdot(\mathbf{S}-\mathbf{S}_o)} - 1)} \right].$$

The intensity ratio $I_P/I_o = |E_P/E_o|^2$. The process of finding the square of the modulus of each of the three complex factors in the brackets of the preceding expression can be carried out by multiplication of numerator and denominator with the complex conjugate, obtained by replacing i with $-i$, which is the standard method. For example, we should have

$$\left| \frac{e^{iM_1 z} - 1}{e^{iz} - 1} \right|^2 = \frac{(e^{iM_1 z} - 1)(e^{-iM_1 z} - 1)}{(e^{iz} - 1)(e^{-iz} - 1)} = \frac{1 - \cos M_1 z}{1 - \cos z} = \frac{\sin^2 \tfrac{1}{2} M_1 z}{\sin^2 \tfrac{1}{2} z}$$

so that we obtain

$$\frac{I_P}{I_o} = \frac{F^2 e^4}{\rho^2 m^2 c^4} \frac{\sin^2(\pi/\lambda) M_1 \mathbf{\tau}_1 \cdot (\mathbf{S} - \mathbf{S}_o)}{\sin^2(\pi/\lambda)\mathbf{\tau}_1 \cdot (\mathbf{S} - \mathbf{S}_o)}$$

$$\frac{\sin^2(\pi/\lambda) M_2 \mathbf{\tau}_2 \cdot (\mathbf{S} - \mathbf{S}_o)}{\sin^2(\pi/\lambda)\mathbf{\tau}_2 \cdot (\mathbf{S} - \mathbf{S}_o)} \frac{\sin^2(\pi/\lambda) M_3 \mathbf{\tau}_3 \cdot (\mathbf{S} - \mathbf{S}_o)}{\sin^2(\pi/\lambda)\mathbf{\tau}_3 \cdot (\mathbf{S} - \mathbf{S}_o)}. \quad (6.63)$$

It is seen that there are three trigonometric quotients in this expression, of the form

$$\frac{\sin^2 M_1 z}{\sin^2 z}.$$

The behavior of this function is well known because of its frequent
appearance in diffraction problems, notably in the problem of the
diffraction grating.[32] The value of the quotient is relatively small
everywhere except when z is an integral multiple of π, at which its
value rises sharply to M_1^2. A maximum therefore in the intensity
of the diffraction pattern governed by eq. (6.63) means simultaneous
maxima in the three trigonometric quotients in question, or

$$\left. \begin{aligned} \boldsymbol{\tau}_1 \cdot (\boldsymbol{S} - \boldsymbol{S}_o) &= hN\lambda \\ \boldsymbol{\tau}_2 \cdot (\boldsymbol{S} - \boldsymbol{S}_o) &= kN\lambda \\ \boldsymbol{\tau}_3 \cdot (\boldsymbol{S} - \boldsymbol{S}_o) &= lN\lambda \end{aligned} \right\}, \tag{6.64}$$

where h, k, l are integers without a common divisor, and N is an
integer. This is merely a more general statement of the Laue equations which we have previously developed for a simple translatory
cubic lattice in eqs. (5.05), Chap. V.

Equation (6.63) will give us the diffracted intensity in the direction of S from the crystal particle, provided the incident radiation
lies along S_o. But the result thus calculated is not experimentally
observed. The first reason for this is that we have available only
divergent x-ray beams, and thus there are incident upon a given particle x-rays in a range of incident directions ample to cover the complete
range through which diffraction of a single wave-length can take
place. In the second place, the ionization chamber window subtends
a relatively large solid angle at the crystal in the usual arrangement,
and all the diffracted rays in various directions are collected and
measured. Thus the power entering the ionization chamber is the
"integrated" intensity over the various possible incident and emergent directions.

Before setting up the integral called for by these considerations,
we may introduce the concept of crystal planes. The reasoning is
identical with that by which a transition from Laue's equations to
Bragg's equation was made in Sec. 8 of Chap. V. Thus we can select
a plane in the crystal so located that an incident ray upon it along

[32] Cf. e.g. Leigh Page, Introduction to Theoretical Physics, D. Van Nostrand Co.,
New York (1928), p. 532.

S_0 would be reflected according to the laws of geometrical optics along S. It is a consequence of the crystallographic law of integral Miller indices and the Laue equations that when S_0 and S are so chosen as to give a diffraction maximum, the reflection plane defined by them will be an important atomic plane, having a relatively large areal density of atoms.

In Fig. VI–13 such a plane is represented at O. The unit vectors S and S_0 from Fig. VI–12 are also shown, and unit vectors S' and S_0' are introduced, representing slight deviations from the directions of S and S_0. The vector S_0' is supposed to lie in the plane of incidence, because the change in glancing angle produced by a component of S_0' perpendicular to the plane of incidence would be negligible for a

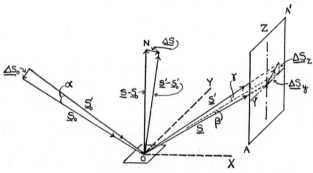

Fig. VI–13. Illustrating the notation used in the description of the rays incident on, and reflected from, a plane in a small crystal at O.

crystalline particle compared to the deviation produced by the component in the plane of incidence. (Cf. eq. (9.45), Chap. IX.) *ON* is normal to the plane of reflection, and the vector $(S - S_0)$ lies along it. The small angles α, β, and γ have the significance indicated. Let θ be the glancing angle of S_0 on the crystal plane. Equation (6.63) would give the intensity at P if the incident waves moved only in the direction of S_0. The unit of area upon plane AA' is $\rho^2 d\beta d\gamma$, and the power passing through any area on this plane is

$$\int\int I_P \rho^2 d\beta d\gamma$$

so that the total power in the diffracted beam from a divergent incident beam is

$$P_\sigma = \int\int\int I_P \rho^2 d\beta d\gamma d\alpha \tag{6.65}$$

where P_σ is the contribution to the power from the radiation polarized so that its electric vector is perpendicular to the plane of incidence. Thus we may write

$$P_\sigma = \frac{I_0 e^4 F^2}{m^2 c^4} \int \int \int \frac{\sin^2 M_1(\pi/\lambda)\boldsymbol{\tau}_1 \cdot (\boldsymbol{S}' - \boldsymbol{S}_o')}{\sin^2 (\pi/\lambda)\boldsymbol{\tau}_1 \cdot (\boldsymbol{S}' - \boldsymbol{S}_o')}$$

$$\frac{\sin^2 M_2(\pi/\lambda)\boldsymbol{\tau}_2 \cdot (\boldsymbol{S}' - \boldsymbol{S}_o')}{\sin^2 (\pi/\lambda)\boldsymbol{\tau}_2 \cdot (\boldsymbol{S}' - \boldsymbol{S}_o')} \frac{\sin^2 M_3(\pi/\lambda)\boldsymbol{\tau}_3 \cdot (\boldsymbol{S}' - \boldsymbol{S}_o')}{\sin^2 (\pi/\lambda)\boldsymbol{\tau}_3 \cdot (\boldsymbol{S}' - \boldsymbol{S}_o')} \, d\beta d\gamma d\alpha. \quad (6.66)$$

In order to evaluate this expression, we must consider the relationship between $\boldsymbol{S}'$, $\boldsymbol{S}_o'$, and $\alpha\beta\gamma$. We know that the directions of $\boldsymbol{S}'$ and $\boldsymbol{S}_o'$ which contribute appreciably to the intensity in the diffraction pattern are very near to those of $\boldsymbol{S}_o$ and $\boldsymbol{S}$ so that we may set

$$(\boldsymbol{S}' - \boldsymbol{S}_o') = (\boldsymbol{S} - \boldsymbol{S}_o) + \Delta\boldsymbol{S} \quad (6.67)$$

and treat $\Delta\boldsymbol{S}$ as a small quantity in magnitude. The geometric interpretation of eq. (6.67) is shown in Fig. VI–13. Considering the first of the trigonometric quotients of eq. (6.66), we obtain

$$\frac{\sin^2 M_1(\pi/\lambda)\boldsymbol{\tau}_1 \cdot (\boldsymbol{S}' - \boldsymbol{S}_o')}{\sin^2 (\pi/\lambda)\boldsymbol{\tau}_1 \cdot (\boldsymbol{S}' - \boldsymbol{S}_o')} = \frac{\sin^2 M_1(\pi/\lambda)\{\boldsymbol{\tau}_1 \cdot (\boldsymbol{S} - \boldsymbol{S}_o) + \boldsymbol{\tau}_1 \cdot \Delta\boldsymbol{S}\}}{\sin^2 (\pi/\lambda)\{\boldsymbol{\tau}_1 \cdot (\boldsymbol{S} - \boldsymbol{S}_o) + \boldsymbol{\tau}_1 \cdot \Delta\boldsymbol{S}\}}$$

$$= \frac{\sin^2 (M_1 N h\pi + M_1(\pi/\lambda)\boldsymbol{\tau}_1 \cdot \Delta\boldsymbol{S})}{\sin^2 (N h\pi + (\pi/\lambda)\boldsymbol{\tau}_1 \cdot \Delta\boldsymbol{S})} = \frac{\sin^2 M_1(\pi/\lambda)\boldsymbol{\tau}_1 \cdot \Delta\boldsymbol{S}}{\sin^2 (\pi/\lambda)\boldsymbol{\tau}_1 \cdot \Delta\boldsymbol{S}}$$

since by the Laue equations $\boldsymbol{\tau}_1 \cdot (\boldsymbol{S} - \boldsymbol{S}_o)$ is an integral number of wave-lengths. Thus eq. (6.66) may be written as

$$P_\sigma = \frac{I_0 e^4 F^2}{m^2 c^4} \int \int \int \frac{\sin^2 M_1(\pi/\lambda)\boldsymbol{\tau}_1 \cdot \Delta\boldsymbol{S}}{\sin^2 (\pi/\lambda)\boldsymbol{\tau}_1 \cdot \Delta\boldsymbol{S}} \frac{\sin^2 M_2(\pi/\lambda)\boldsymbol{\tau}_2 \cdot \Delta\boldsymbol{S}}{\sin^2 (\pi/\lambda)\boldsymbol{\tau}_2 \cdot \Delta\boldsymbol{S}}$$

$$\frac{\sin^2 M_3(\pi/\lambda)\boldsymbol{\tau}_3 \cdot \Delta\boldsymbol{S}}{\sin^2 (\pi/\lambda)\boldsymbol{\tau}_3 \cdot \Delta\boldsymbol{S}} \, d\gamma d\beta d\alpha. \quad (6.68)$$

The treatment of the scalar products $\boldsymbol{\tau} \cdot \Delta\boldsymbol{S}$ is most conveniently carried out by the use of reciprocal vectors which are discussed in Appendix XI. A set of vectors $t_1 \ t_2 \ t_3$ is introduced, which is reciprocal to the set $\boldsymbol{\tau}_1 \ \boldsymbol{\tau}_2 \ \boldsymbol{\tau}_3$, meaning that

$$\boldsymbol{\tau}_1 \cdot t_1 = \boldsymbol{\tau}_2 \cdot t_2 = \boldsymbol{\tau}_3 \cdot t_3 = 1$$

and

$$\boldsymbol{\tau}_1 \cdot t_2 = \boldsymbol{\tau}_1 \cdot t_3 = \boldsymbol{\tau}_2 \cdot t_1 = \boldsymbol{\tau}_2 \cdot t_3 = \boldsymbol{\tau}_3 \cdot t_1 = \boldsymbol{\tau}_3 \cdot t_2 = 0.$$

Any vector such as ΔS, may be expressed in terms of the vectors $t_1\ t_2\ t_3$ in the form

$$\Delta S = \lambda(p_1 t_1 + p_2 t_2 + p_3 t_3),$$

where $p_1 p_2 p_3$ are the appropriate numerical coefficients. It follows from the definitions of the relations between the t's and the τ's that

$$\frac{\pi}{\lambda} M_1 \tau_1 \cdot \Delta S = \pi M_1 \tau_1 \cdot (p_1 t_1 + p_2 t_2 + p_3 t_3) = \pi M_1 p_1,$$

and that similar relations hold for $\tau_2 \cdot \Delta S$ and $\tau_3 \cdot \Delta S$. Thus eq. (6.68) becomes

$$P_\sigma = \frac{I_o e^4 F^2}{m^2 c^4} \int \int \int \frac{\sin^2 M_1 p_1 \pi}{\sin^2 p_1 \pi} \frac{\sin^2 M_2 p_2 \pi}{\sin^2 p_2 \pi} \frac{\sin^2 M_3 p_3 \pi}{\sin^2 p_3 \pi} d\gamma d\beta d\alpha. \quad (6.69)$$

We must now change from integration with respect to $\gamma\beta\alpha$ to integration with respect to $p_1 p_2 p_3$, the values of which depend on the variables $\gamma\beta\alpha$. Returning to eq. (6.67), and referring to Fig. VI–13, we find

$$\Delta S = (S' - S) - (S_o' - S_o)$$

or

$$\Delta S = \Delta S_z + \Delta S_y - \Delta S_o.$$

Let us introduce a set of unit vectors $i\ j\ k$ lying along the rectangular axes having their origin at point O. The Z-axis at O is taken along the normal ON to the plane, and the X-axis lies in the plane and also in the plane of the vectors S_o, S. We have

$$\Delta S_o = - \{|\Delta S_o| \sin \theta\} i - \{|\Delta S_o| \cos \theta\} k,$$

but since the vectors S_o and S_o' are of unit length,

$$\Delta S_o = - (\alpha \sin \theta)i - (\alpha \cos \theta)k,$$

and similarly

$$\Delta S_z = - (\gamma \sin \theta)i - (\gamma \cos \theta)k,$$

$$\Delta S_y = \beta j,$$

so that

$$\Delta S = \{(\alpha - \gamma) \sin \theta\}i + \beta j + \{(\alpha + \gamma) \cos \theta\}k. \quad (6.70)$$

In order to give a geometric interpretation to the next step in the derivation, we may consider the product $d\gamma d\beta d\alpha$ as an element of volume in an orthogonal set of coordinates $\gamma\beta\alpha$. Let us imagine a new set of coordinates $\delta\beta\epsilon$ which is obtained from the old set by a rotation of $45°$ around the β-axis. Then a point whose coordinates in the hypothetical $\gamma\beta\alpha$ set are (γ, β, α) will have the coordinates $(\delta, \beta, \epsilon)$ in the new set, where

$$\delta = \sqrt{\tfrac{1}{2}}(\alpha + \gamma); \quad \epsilon = \sqrt{\tfrac{1}{2}}(\alpha - \gamma); \quad \beta = \beta.$$

The coordinate set $(\delta\beta\epsilon)$ is however still rectangular, and in it the element of volume is $d\delta d\epsilon d\beta$. Thus we are justified in changing eq. (6.70) to

$$\Delta S = (\sqrt{2}\, \epsilon \sin \theta)i + \beta j + (\sqrt{2}\, \delta \cos \theta)k \quad (6.71)$$

and integrating eq. (6.69) with respect to $d\delta d\epsilon d\beta$. The vector ΔS may also be expressed in terms of $p_1 p_2 p_3$ as we have previously postulated, namely

$$\Delta S = \lambda(p_1 t_1 + p_2 t_2 + p_3 t_3). \quad (6.72)$$

The desired connection between $\delta\beta\epsilon$ and $p_1 p_2 p_3$ may be obtained by considering the volume swept out by the terminus of ΔS as increments are given to δ, β, and ϵ, and equating it to the volume swept out when increments are given to $p_1 p_2 p_3$. In the first case, it follows from eq. (6.71) that an increment of volume

$$(\sqrt{2} \sin \theta)d\epsilon d\beta(\sqrt{2} \cos \theta)d\delta = \sin 2\theta \; d\epsilon d\beta d\delta$$

is produced, while in the second case, the volume is

$$\lambda^3 dp_1 dp_2 dp_3 t_1 \cdot t_2 \times t_3.$$

In Appendix XI it is shown that

$$t_1 \cdot t_2 \times t_3 = 1/v,$$

where v is the volume of the unit cell. Equating the two expressions for the element of volume, we obtain

$$d\epsilon d\beta d\delta = \frac{\lambda^3}{v \sin 2\theta} dp_1 dp_2 dp_3,$$

so that the integral for the power in the diffracted beam may be written

$$P_\sigma = \frac{I_o F^2 e^4}{m^2 c^4} \frac{\lambda^3}{v \sin 2\theta} \int\limits_{-\infty}^{\infty}\!\!\int\!\!\int \frac{\sin^2 M_1 \pi p_1}{\sin^2 \pi p_1} \frac{\sin^2 M_2 \pi p_2}{\sin^2 \pi p_2}$$

$$\frac{\sin^2 M_3 \pi p_3}{\sin^2 \pi p_3} dp_1 dp_2 dp_3. \quad (6.74)$$

The integrals are extended from $-\infty$ to ∞ since the quotients in the integrand have appreciable values only for very small values of $p_1p_2p_3$. For the same reason we may set $\sin^2 \pi p_1 = \pi^2 p_1^2$, etc., in the denominators, obtaining

$$P_\sigma = \frac{I_oF^2e^4}{m^2c^4} \frac{\lambda^3}{v\sin 2\theta} \int\!\!\!\int\!\!\!\int_{-\infty}^{\infty} \frac{\sin^2 M_1\pi p_1}{\pi^2 p_1^2} \frac{\sin^2 M_2\pi p_2}{\pi^2 p_2^2}$$

$$\frac{\sin^2 M_3\pi p_3}{\pi^2 p_3^2} \, dp_1 dp_2 dp_3. \quad (6.75)$$

Considering one of the integrals in this expression:

$$\int_{-\infty}^{\infty} \frac{\sin^2 M_1\pi p_1}{\pi^2 p_1^2} \, dp_1 = \frac{2M_1}{\pi} \int_0^{\infty} \frac{\sin^2 z}{z^2} \, dz = M_1,$$

so that integration of eq. (6.75) gives

$$P_\sigma = \frac{I_oF^2e^4\lambda^3}{m^2c^4v \sin 2\theta} M_1M_2M_3. \quad (6.76)$$

If M is the number of unit cells per unit volume,

$$M = 1/v = (M_1M_2M_3)/\delta V,$$

where δV is the volume of the crystalline particle. Substitution in eq. (6.76) gives

$$P_\sigma = \frac{I_oF^2e^4\lambda^3M^2}{m^2c^4 \sin 2\theta} \delta V. \quad (6.77)$$

As indicated by the subscript σ, this expression applies only to radiation polarized so that the electric vector vibrates perpendicular to the plane of incidence. If unpolarized radiation is used, as is usually the case, the expression must be multiplied by $\frac{1}{2}(1 + \cos^2 2\theta)$, giving

$$P/I_o = \frac{1}{2} \frac{1 + \cos^2 2\theta}{\sin 2\theta} \frac{e^4}{m^2c^4} \lambda^3F^2M^2\delta V \equiv Q\delta V. \quad (6.78)$$

In this expression P/I_o is the ratio of the power in the diffracted beam to the power per unit area in the incident beam, M is the number of unit cells per unit volume of the crystal, and F is the crystal structure factor. In Chap. V, Sec. 9, we have shown that for a cubic lattice F has the form

$$F = \sum_i f_i e^{2\pi Ni(hx_i+ky_i+lz_i)} \quad (6.79)$$

where f_j is the atomic scattering factor of the atom j, whose co-ordinates are $x_j y_j z_j$ in the unit cell.[33] This result is, however, independent of lattice type. 2θ in eq. (6.78) is the angle between the incident and diffracted x-ray beam.

13. *The Intensity Diffracted from a Crystalline Powder*

Perhaps the most important assumption made in the treatment of the diffraction from a crystalline particle in the preceding section is that the intensity of the x-rays is constant throughout the small crystal. Thus we have neglected the ordinary absorption, but, what is much more serious, we have also neglected the effect of extinction. In Sec. 9 of this chapter we have shown that for calcite (which incidentally is probably not a good general example, since extinction effects seem especially prominent in this crystal) the effective absorption coefficient, or the primary extinction coefficient, may be of the order of seventy times the ordinary absorption coefficient, and that radiation incident at the Bragg angle may be half extinguished in a depth of 5×10^{-5} cm. Thus for calcite, at least, the particle size for the application of eq. (6.78) would have to be considerably less than 5×10^{-5} cm. The volume of such a minute crystal would be so small that appreciable diffracted intensity could not be observed. We are thus forced to consider using a powder, formed of minute crystals in random orientation.

Let us assume for the present that we have available a powder so finely divided that eq. (6.78) in principle may be applied to it. Such a powder may be considered as an aggregation of very small crystals whose orientation is wholly random. In Fig. VI–14 the incident x-ray beam lies along the direction SOX, and a plane of one of the crystal particles is shown at O. We seek the probability that the particle will be so oriented that the incident ray makes a glancing angle between $\theta + \alpha$ and $\theta + \alpha + d\alpha$ upon it. ON is the normal to the plane, and OA is perpendicular to SOX. The ratio of

[33] For an ideally simple crystal, composed of atoms of the same kind located at the corners of a simple translatory lattice (at 0, 0, 0) the crystal structure factor is the same as the atomic structure factor f, and the number of unit cells per unit volume is the same as the number of atoms per unit volume n_a, so that

$$Q = \frac{1}{2} \frac{1 + \cos^2 2\theta}{\sin 2\theta} \frac{e^4}{m^2 c^4} \lambda^3 f^2 n_a^2.$$

For very simple crystals it is sometimes easier to refer to this formula than to the more general formula.

the area of a band of width $rd\alpha$, part of which is shown at N, to the area of the entire sphere will give the desired probability. This is

$$\frac{2\pi r \cos (\theta + \alpha)rd\alpha}{4\pi r^2} = \frac{1}{2} \cos \theta d\alpha,$$

since α is very small compared to θ. The probability of such an orientation also depends on the number of planes of like spacing in the crystal, as discussed in Sec. 10 of Chap. V. For holohedry

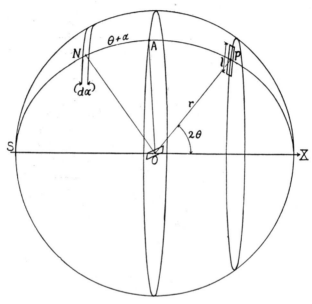

Fig. VI–14. Illustrating the probability that a crystal plane in a powder will be so oriented as to reflect a monochromatic x-ray beam.

of the cubic system this number j is equal to the number of possible permutations of the Miller indices hkl of the plane, taking into account the possibility of negative indices. If all three indices are finite and different, there are forty-eight such permutations possible. The number of permutations possible for some of the planes in a holohedral cubic crystal is given in Table V–7, Chap. V. j values for the various crystal systems have been listed by Wyckoff.[34]

[34] R. W. G. Wyckoff, The Structure of Crystals, Chemical Catalog Co., N. Y. (1931), p. 177.

Thus the probability that some one plane will have this orientation becomes

$$\tfrac{1}{2}j \cos \theta d\alpha.$$

This means that in eq. (6.65) we must consider that the preceding expression is to replace $d\alpha$, so that eq. (6.65) becomes

$$\overline{P}_\sigma = \tfrac{1}{2}j \cos \theta \int \int \int I_P \rho^2 d\beta d\gamma d\alpha$$

where $\overline{P}_\sigma$ is the power of σ-polarized radiation reflected from a random orientation of powdered crystals. Thus the integral is not changed, and eq. (6.78) is multiplied by $\tfrac{1}{2}j \cos \theta$, giving

$$\left. \begin{aligned} \overline{P}/I_0 &= \frac{1}{8} \frac{1 + \cos^2 2\theta}{\sin \theta} \frac{e^4}{m^2 c^4} \lambda^3 j F^2 M^2 \delta V \\ &= \tfrac{1}{2}j \cos \theta \, Q \delta V \end{aligned} \right\} . \qquad (6.80)$$

In this expression we are to interpret δV as the effective volume of the powder rather than the volume of one single crystal particle.

The power P represented by eq. (6.80) is diffracted around a Debye-Scherrer ring, that is, the diffracted beams lie on the surface of a cone of half angle 2θ (Fig. VI–14). If the rays are measured with an ionization chamber at a distance r with a slit of length l which is short compared to $r \sin 2\theta$, and if the width of the slit is great enough to take in the entire diffracted beam, the power entering the chamber is $P_d = \overline{P}l/2\pi r \sin 2\theta$. Also if A is the area of the slit limiting the primary beam, the power of this beam is $P_0 = A I_0$. Thus the ratio of the power of the diffracted beam entering the ionization chamber to that of the primary beam is

$$\left. \begin{aligned} \frac{P_d}{P_0} &= \frac{l}{2\pi A r \sin 2\theta} \tfrac{1}{2} Q j \cos \theta \, \delta V \\ &= Q \frac{j l \delta V}{8\pi r A \sin \theta} \end{aligned} \right\} \qquad (6.81)$$

Let us suppose that the powder is pressed into the shape of a thin rectangular plate, and that the incident and diffracted beams traverse the plate as in Fig. VI–15. If in the study of the various diffracted beams the crystal plate is rotated so that it always bisects the angle $180° - 2\theta$ (Fig. VI–15), the paths of the incident and diffracted beams through the crystal are equal in length. Let h be the thickness of the plate; then the power of the incident beam after having traversed the plate is

$$P = P_o e^{-\mu h \sec \theta} = I_o A e^{-\mu h \sec \theta},$$

where μ is the effective absorption coefficient of the material. The irradiated volume is not the geometrical volume $Ah \sec \theta$, but is less than this due to the interstices between the crystalline particles. If ρ' is the density of the plate and ρ the density of an individual crystal particle, then the volume irradiated is

$$\frac{\rho'}{\rho} Ah \sec \theta.$$

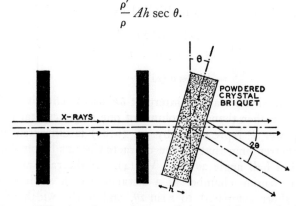

FIG. VI–15. Diffraction of x-rays by transmission through a powdered crystal briquet.

The diffracted beam has been reduced in intensity by a factor $\exp(-\mu h \sec \theta)$, so that eq. (6.81) becomes

$$\frac{P_d}{P_o} = \frac{jlQ}{8\pi r A \sin \theta} e^{-\mu h \sec \theta} Ah \sec \theta, \qquad (6.82)$$

and if we use as a standard of comparison the power P in the transmitted beam rather than that in the slab, we obtain

$$\frac{P_d}{P} = Q \frac{lhj\rho'}{4\pi \rho r \sin 2\theta}. \qquad (6.83)$$

From eq. (6.82) we can discover the optimum thickness of the plate, giving the most powerful diffracted beam. This will occur when

$$e^{-\mu h \sec \theta} h \sec \theta = \text{maximum},$$

which means

$$h_{max} = \frac{1}{\mu \sec \theta}. \tag{6.84}$$

A second experimental procedure used with crystalline powders is to obtain the "reflected" intensity from a plate of the powdered material. This means that the arrangement is as in Fig. VI–16, with the plate placed symmetrically with respect to the incident and emergent beams. Let the vertical depth of a small diffracting volume δV below the surface of the plate be z, then the diffracted rays are reduced in intensity, due to absorption, by the factor

$$e^{-2z\mu \cosec \theta},$$

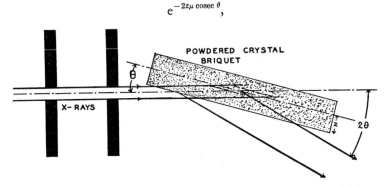

FIG. VI–16. Diffraction of x-rays by reflection from a powdered crystal briquet.

where μ is the effective absorption coefficient. The volume of the crystal particles in the volume δV is

$$\frac{\rho'}{\rho} \delta V$$

and

$$\delta V = A \frac{\rho'}{\rho} \cosec \theta \, dz,$$

where A is the cross-section area of the incident beam. Thus from eq. (6.81)

$$\frac{P_d}{P_o} = \frac{Q j l}{8\pi r A \sin \theta} \int_0^\infty A \frac{\rho'}{\rho} \cosec \theta e^{-2\mu z \cosec \theta} dz$$

$$= \frac{j l}{16\pi r \mu \sin \theta} \cdot Q \frac{\rho'}{\rho}. \tag{6.85}$$

In these expressions, j is the number of equivalent planes in a crystal of the type considered, l is the height of the slit of the ionization chamber, h is the thickness of the crystal plate, r is the distance from the plate to the ionization chamber, ρ' is the density of the plate, ρ is the density of the individual crystals, Q is defined by eq. (6.78), 2θ is the angle between the forward direction of the incident and the diffracted beam, and μ is the effective absorption coefficient of the crystal mass in the plate.

It will be noticed that eq. (6.85) involves the absorption coefficient μ, which is absent in eq. (6.83). If the absorption coefficient is sufficiently small, there is for this reason some advantage in using the transmission method of eq. (6.83).

In powder photograph work in the analysis of crystal structure, as discussed in Sec. 10 of Chap. V, a cylindrical rod of powder is often used. This is satisfactory for the purpose of obtaining the positions of powder lines, but complicated calculations are necessary to correct for absorption in the cylinder. These corrections will not be taken up here; they have been adequately discussed by Greenwood[35] and more completely by Claassen.[36] The necessary corrections have also been reviewed by Blake.[37]

14. *The Intensity Diffracted from a Single, Imperfect Crystal; the Question of Extinction*

We have seen in Sec. 11 of this chapter that the observed values of the coefficient of reflection from rock salt run from 18 to 29 times the value predicted from the theory of a perfect crystal. We have here to consider to what extent rock salt may be treated as an ideally imperfect crystal. Let us suppose for the moment that a rock salt crystal can be treated as a composite, or mosaic, of very small crystal particles, the diffraction from which we have considered in Sec. 12. These particles are oriented at random over a range of angles so narrow that the macroscopic arrangement exhibits many of the characteristics of a single crystal. We will suppose that the phases of the rays from the component little crystals are random, so that we can calculate the power in the diffracted beam by taking the sum of that diffracted from each of the component crystals.

The conventional method of measuring the coefficient of reflection

[35] G. Greenwood, Phil. Mag. **1**, 963 (1927).
[36] A. Claassen, Phil. Mag. **9**, 57 (1930).
[37] F. C. Blake, Rev. Mod. Physics **5**, 169 (1933).

from a single crystal has been described in Sec. 10 of this chapter. It was shown that for a perfect crystal, we should obtain

$$R_c = \frac{E\omega}{P_0} = \text{Area under the single crystal diffraction pattern,}$$

where E is the energy which has entered the ionization chamber window during the time in which the crystal has been rotated past the position of a diffraction maximum with the angular velocity ω, and P_0 is the power entering the ionization chamber window from the direct beam. We note that here the area under the diffraction pattern is involved, which more logically might be called the integrated diffraction. In the derivation of the diffraction by a small crystal in Sec. 12, we did not stop to investigate the shape of the crystal diffraction pattern, but proceeded directly (eq. (6.65)) to calculate the "integrated" diffraction from a divergent incident beam. Thus our result in eq. (6.78) is in this respect analogous to the expression in eq. (6.59) for a perfect crystal.

Thus eq. (6.78) can be written

$$P = \frac{P_0}{A} Q \delta V,$$

and from a discussion exactly similar to that used in the derivation of eq. (6.58) from eq. (6.56) it may be shown that

$$\frac{E\omega}{P_0} = \frac{Q}{A} \delta V, \tag{6.86}$$

where Q is defined in eq. (6.78), and the result applies to a single small crystal.

Let us first consider the case of transmission through a crystal slab. We shall suppose that the slab is cut so that the reflecting planes under consideration are normal to its faces. We may then think of the slab in the position of the briquet of powdered crystals in Fig. VI–15, and the postulated orientation of the reflecting planes with respect to its surface will insure that for a position of Bragg reflection the slab will be symmetrically placed with respect to the incident and diffracted beams. If μ is the effective absorption coefficient of the x-rays in the crystal, since the total path of the ray in the crystal before and after reflection is $h \sec \theta$, all the rays are reduced in intensity by the factor

$$e^{-\mu h \sec \theta}.$$

The volume of the slab irradiated is $Ah \sec \theta$ where A is the cross-section area of the incident x-ray beam. Thus we obtain

$$\frac{E\omega}{P_o} = Qh \sec \theta \ e^{-\mu h \sec \theta} \qquad (6.86a)$$

which has a maximum value at $h = (\cos \theta)/\mu$, at which the thickness of the crystal is sufficient to reduce the power of the transmitted rays to $1/e$ of that of the incident rays. Thus

$$\left(\frac{E\omega}{P_o}\right)_{max.} = \frac{Q}{e\mu}, \qquad (6.87)$$

where e is the base of natural logarithms. If instead of P_o the beam P transmitted by the crystal slab is used, where

$$P = P_o e^{-\mu h \sec \theta},$$

the measure of the diffracted power becomes

$$\frac{E\omega}{P} = Qh \sec \theta. \qquad (6.88)$$

We may now consider the case in which the x-ray beam is reflected from the face of a crystal, the reflecting planes of which are parallel to the face.[38] In this case we may think of the crystal as replacing the briquet of powder in Fig. VI–16. The diffracted intensity from a layer of thickness dz at a vertical depth z beneath the crystal surface and of volume $A \csc \theta \ dz$ will be diminished by absorption through the distance $2z \csc \theta$, so that

$$\frac{E\omega}{P_o} = Q \csc \theta \int_o^\infty e^{-2\mu z \csc \theta} dz = \frac{Q}{2\mu}. \qquad (6.89)$$

On comparing this result with eq. (6.87) we see that the power reflected from a crystal face is greater than the maximum power obtainable in transmission through a crystal slab by a factor of $\frac{1}{2}e = 1.36$.

We must now return to the question of the extinction. Two kinds of extinction are recognized, called primary and secondary extinction. The primary extinction is the effect considered in Sec. 9 of this chapter, and concerns the fact that the individual crystalline

[38] In case the planes are not parallel to the face, as may be the case in a polished face, it can be shown that the average coefficient of reflection observed from two positions of the slab $180°-2\theta$ apart gives the expression derived in the text. (Eq. 6.89)

particles of which a mosaic crystal or a powder is composed may be of such dimensions that it is no longer permissible to consider that the intensity of the x-ray beam traversing them is uniform throughout their volume. In other words the atomic planes on which the x-rays first impinge may reflect so much of the radiation that the lower planes of the particle are much less strongly irradiated than the upper.

The so-called secondary extinction represents the effect of crystal particles or blocks near the outer surface of the large crystal in screening blocks deeper in the crystal from the incident rays. This would lead to an increase in the absorption coefficient over the value which would pertain to an amorphous substance of the same density and chemical constitution, but would not necessarily lead to values of the effective absorption coefficient as high as those due to primary extinction. For even if the primary extinction in each particle were high, the fraction of the number of particles so oriented as to produce diffraction would be small for any one direction in the x-ray beam, and for those not critically oriented only the ordinary absorption coefficient would apply. Hence the secondary extinction would produce an effective absorption coefficient intermediate between the " amorphous " absorption coefficient μ_l and the extinction coefficient μ_e.

The problem of secondary extinction has been considered by Darwin.[39] To a first approximation we may calculate the absorption in a layer of mosaic blocks by adding to the ordinary, or photo-electric absorption, a term representing the energy diffracted upward from this layer by the blocks which are properly oriented for reflection. The entire diffracted beam is made up of multiple reflections from these layers of blocks, but the analysis of Sec. 4 of this chapter is not applicable because the various beams in the crystal are not coherent. To a first approximation the correction to the ordinary absorption coefficient is proportional to the first power of Q, so that the effective μ, which appears in the equations in this section, is to be represented by

$$\mu = \mu_l + gQ, \tag{6.90}$$

where μ_l is the ordinary coefficient and g is a constant of the crystal. It is clear that the difference between μ and μ_l is less for weak than for strong reflections.

[39] C. G. Darwin, Phil. Mag. 43, 800 (1922).

Bragg, James, and Bosanquet[40] have corrected the observed coefficients of reflection from large rock salt crystals for secondary extinction in the following manner. The correction factor is obtained from a study of the intensities diffracted through thin crystal slabs. Replacing $h \sec \theta$ in eq. (6.86) by t, we have, from eq. (6.90)

$$\frac{E\omega}{P_o} = Qte^{-(\mu + gQ)t}.$$

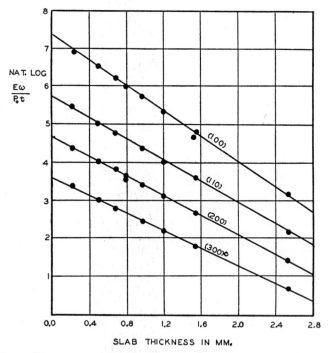

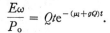

Fig. VI–17. Measurement of secondary extinction according to the method of Bragg, James, and Bosanquet.

In logarithmic form this may be written

$$\log \frac{E\omega}{P_o t} = \log Q - (\mu_l + gQ)t. \qquad (6.91)$$

Thus if $\log (E\omega/P_o t)$ is plotted as a function of t, we should obtain straight lines whose slope is $-(\mu_l + gQ)$ and which intersect the axis $t = 0$ at $\log Q$.

[40] Bragg, James and Bosanquet, Phil. Mag. **41**, 309 and **42**, 1 (1921).

Such a graph is shown in Fig. VI–17, with points representing transmission reflections by crystals varying in thickness from 0.25 mm to 2.5 mm. The curves represent data for the first, second, and third order reflections from the (100) planes and the first order from (110). In many cases it is convenient to designate the order of the reflection by giving the values (nh, nk, nl) instead of (hkl). Thus (200) is interpreted as the observed second order from the (100) planes. As will be seen from Table VI–6, the slope of the (100) graph represents an effective absorption coefficient of 16.30, whereas the normal absorption coefficient μ_l of these rays ($\lambda = 0.613$ A) in rock salt is 10.70. Although the values of g in the fifth column of Table VI–6 cannot be said to be satisfactorily

TABLE VI–6

REFLECTION AND ABSORPTION OF X-RAYS BY ROCK-SALT

(Rh $K\alpha$, $\lambda = 0.613$ A, $\mu_l = 10.70$)

Reflection	Effective Absorption Coefficient	$gQ = \mu - \mu_l$	$10^4 Q/2\mu$ from a Face *	g
100	16.30	5.60	27.3	63
110	13.60	2.90	13.8	77
200	12.66	1.96	5.44	140
300	10.72	0.02	1.33	

* Data in this column from James and Firth, Proc. Roy. Soc. Lond. **A**, **117**, 62 (1922).

constant, the total correction gQ is small in the weaker reflections and it is these on which most confidence is placed.

When an estimate of the secondary extinction has been obtained in this way from transmission experiments, measurements of the coefficient of reflection from crystal faces may be corrected for this effect. Corresponding to eq. (6.89), let

$$\left[\frac{E\omega}{P_0} \right]_0 = \frac{Q}{2\mu_l}, \qquad (6.92)$$

that is, the coefficient of reflection which would result from a crystal in which extinction is absent. The observed coefficient of reflection from a face is according to the theory

$$\frac{E\omega}{P_0} = \frac{Q}{2(\mu_l + gQ)},$$

from which it results that[41]

$$\left[\frac{E\omega}{P_o}\right]_o = \frac{E\omega/P_o}{1 - 2g(E\omega/P_o)} \qquad (6.93)$$

which gives a method of correction. We shall in subsequent discussion omit the special notation $[E\omega/P_o]_o$, and assume that the values of $E\omega/P_o$ are those corrected for secondary extinction.

The problem of primary extinction is much more difficult. On the basis of the analysis given in Sec. 9 of this chapter, the radiation is reduced to half its incident power in traversing 5×10^{-5} cm. of a perfect crystal of calcite at the Bragg angle in the first order from the cleavage planes, and the order of magnitude would be the same for a reflection in the first order from the cleavage planes of rock salt. Thus a particle dimension of 10^{-6} cm. on a side would be necessary to reduce the extinction to a few per cent. This means that in preparing a powder, the grinding would have to be continued until the individual particles were barely visible in a high power microscope. It is probable, however, that in many cases the primary extinction is negligible even for crystals of large size. For on a visible scale we find that rock-salt crystals have their surfaces twisted and bent, and if this is also true on a microscopic scale the phase differences between successive atomic layers must be irregular except for very small thickness of the crystal. Moreover, since we have seen that grinding and polishing makes a crystal face less perfect for an appreciable depth below the surface, it is probable that if a crystal is ground into units of a given size the parts of each unit that are sensibly perfect are much smaller than the units themselves.

There is considerable evidence that primary extinction is actually negligible in rock-salt reflections. In the first place, various crystals of rock salt, appearing to have crystallized in different stages of perfection, give approximately the same values of $E\omega/P_o$ after correction for secondary extinction. The best evidence, however, is the agreement of the values of the coefficients of reflection obtained from work on powdered rock-salt crystals and the values obtained from large single rock-salt crystals by Bragg, James, and Bosanquet. The powdered crystal work relevant to the question of extinction has been done by Bearden[42] and by Havighurst.[43]

[41] W. L. Bragg and J. West, Zeitschrift für Kristallographie **69**, 118 (1928).
[42] J. A. Bearden, Phys. Rev. **27**, 796 (1926).
[43] R. J. Havighurst, Phys. Rev. **28**, 882 (1926).

Havighurst investigated the intensity of reflection of Mo $K\alpha$ x-rays from rock salt powdered to various crystal sizes. A specimen all of whose particles were smaller than 4×10^{-3} cm. in diameter, gave reflected intensities agreeing with those obtained by Bragg, James and Bosanquet from large single rock-salt crystals after correction for secondary extinction. When part of this sample was ground until the particle size ranged from 1×10^{-4} to 2×10^{-3} cm., the same result was observed. Secondary extinction presumably does not exist in powder reflections, because of the relatively small number of crystal particles in any volume that are properly oriented for Bragg reflection of the incident wave-length. The fact that decreasing the particle size had no effect on the coefficient of reflection, and that the observed value agreed with the single crystal value indicates that primary extinction is negligible in both the powder and the large crystal. Havighurst also investigated powdered calcium fluoride and calcite. Three different sizes of CaF_2 particles gave the same coefficients of reflection, but with calcite effects of primary extinction were indicated.

In conclusion we may point out that for certain crystals, such as rock salt, values of $E\omega/P_0$ which can be compared with the formula for the reflection from a very small crystal can be obtained by correction of the observed results for secondary extinction, but probably in general the powdered crystal method gives more reliable results.

15. *Experimental Values of Atomic Structure Factors*

In the preceding section we have shown how an acceptable set of coefficients of reflection may be obtained. From such a set, values of Q may be calculated, depending on the method of measurement of the reflection coefficients, that is, by eqs. (6.85), (6.87), or (6.89). From eq. (6.78) we may then proceed to calculate values of F, the crystal structure factor. Now if the crystal is a simple one, of high symmetry, it may be that F will be a very simple function of the atomic structure factors f_j corresponding to the atoms making up the unit cell. (Eq. (6.79).) The values of F in terms of the f_j's have been tabulated for certain reflections from NaCl in Table V–6, Chap. V. Thus in eq. (6.78) when M refers to the number of cubic unit cells of 5.628×10^{-8} cm. on a side per cubic centimeter, we have for the first order reflection from the (100) planes, $F = 4f_{Na} + 4f_{Cl}$; and first observable order from the (110) planes, $F = 4(f_{Cl} + f_{Na})$; and F has this same value for all observable orders from the planes

(100) and (110), for instance. But for the (111) planes we obtain $F = 4(f_{Cl} - f_{Na})$ in the first observable order. It is sometimes convenient to give the various reflections by specifying the values (Nh, Nk, Nl), where N is the order computed for a simple translatory cubic lattice containing one atom per unit cell, and is given by eq. (6.104). Thus (200) is the first observable order from the (100) planes. In this notation, we may summarize the reflections from NaCl by saying that unless Nh, Nk, Nl are all odd or all even, $F = 0$.

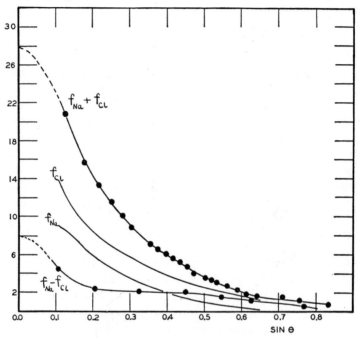

Fig. VI–18. Atomic structure factor curves from diffraction of 0.710 A x-rays by rock salt at room temperatures.

If Nh, Nk, Nl are all even, $F = 4(f_{Cl} + f_{Na})$, if they are all odd, $F = 4(f_{Cl} - f_{Na})$. In this way the values of $(f_{Cl} + f_{Na})$ and $(f_{Cl} - f_{Na})$ listed in Table VI–7 were obtained. The data are taken from experiments by James and Firth [44] and by Havighurst.[45] The experiments were performed at the wave-length of Mo $K\alpha$.

Graphical representation of the data of Table VI–7 is given in Fig. VI–18. From the observed curves of the sum and difference of

[44] James and Firth, Proc. Roy. Soc. Lond. A 117, 62 (1927).
[45] R. J. Havighurst, Phys. Rev. 28, 869 (1926).

TABLE VI–7

SUMS AND DIFFERENCES OF ATOMIC SCATTERING FACTORS OF Na AND Cl FROM MEAS-
UREMENTS ON ROCK SALT AT ROOM TEMPERATURE WITH $\lambda = 0.710$ A

Nh,Nk,Nl All Even				Nh,Nk,Nl All Odd			
		$(f_{Cl}+f_{Na})$				$(f_{Cl}-f_{Na})$	
Reflection	$\sin\theta$	J. & F.	Havighurst	Reflection	$\sin\theta$	J. & F.	Havighurst
200	0.126	20.65	20.80	111	0.109	4.54	4.55
220	0.178	15.62	15.75	311	0.209	2.44	2.40
222	0.218	13.18	13.30	511	} 0.328	2.28	} 2.18
400	0.252	11.60	11.60	333		2.32	
420	0.282	.....	10.20	711	0.450	2.03	
422	0.309	.....	8.95	555	0.546	1.53	
440	0.357	7.46	7.18	933*	0.627	1.12	
600	} 0.378	6.89	} 6.69	777*	0.763	0.56	
442		.....					
620	0.399	.....	6.03				
622	0.418	.....	5.62				
444	0.437	5.28					
640	0.455	.....	4.75				
642	0.472	.....	4.10				
800	0.504	4.04	3.54				
820	} 0.520	.....	3.31				
644							
822	} 0.535	.....	} 3.08				
660		3.34					
840	0.564	.....	2.64				
664	0.590	.....	2.23				
844	0.617	.....	1.75				
1000	0.630	2.22					
1020	0.642	.....	1.54				
880	0.712	1.55					
1200*	0.756	1.12					
1244*	0.836	0.70					

* Measured at liquid air temperatures and extrapolated to room temperature.

the two atomic structure factors it is possible to get the factors indi-
vidually, for

$$f_{Cl} = \tfrac{1}{2}\{(f_{Cl}+f_{Na}) + (f_{Cl}-f_{Na})\}$$

and

$$f_{Na} = \tfrac{1}{2}\{(f_{Cl}+f_{Na}) - (f_{Cl}-f_{Na})\}.$$

The individual curves are also shown in the figure, and are plotted according to the estimates of Havighurst. The very interesting question as to the intersection of these curves with the ordinate $\sin \theta = 0$ is left open, as this involves the decision as to whether the units of the crystals are to be treated as ions or as neutral atoms.

16. Connection between the Radial Distribution of Electricity in an Atom and its Atomic Structure Factor

Atomic structure factor curves, such as those plotted for sodium and chlorine in Fig. VI–18 may be interpreted in such a manner that

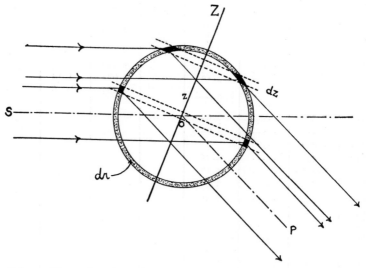

Fig. VI–19.   Illustrating the derivation of the atomic structure factor formula in terms of the radial electron distribution function.

they give us information about the distribution of electricity in the atom. We shall show in the following derivation how the falling off of the observed atomic structure factor curve with the angle is related to the distribution of electricity in the atom.

In Fig. VI–19, let SO be a ray in the direction of the incident x-ray beam, and let the center of the atom be located at O. OP is a ray in the direction of the scattered beam, and ϕ is the scattering angle. In order to compute the composition of the wave in the direction OP, it is convenient to slice up the atom into parallel layers. Draw the bisector of the angle SOP and call this the z axis. Then a slice of the atom of thickness dz around point O will act as a plane of reflection for the ray SOP. As shown in Fig. V–21, Chap. V, the phase difference between rays coming from any point on a plane of reflection is zero. Hence the path difference between the radiation

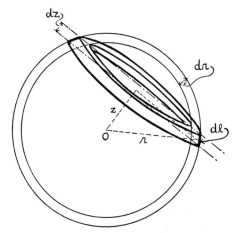

FIG. VI–20. The number of electrons in a slice of the spherical shell between two parallel planes separated by distance dz is proportional to the ratio of the volume of the ring to the volume of the spherical shell.

scattered by the material in the slice through the origin and a slice at height z, both slices being of infinitesimal thickness, is

$$2z \sin \tfrac{1}{2}\phi.$$

Consider the scattering from the material inclosed between the spheres of radius r and $r + dr$. Let the fraction of the total number of electrons in the atom contained between the radii r and $r + dr$ be

$$U(r)dr,$$

so that the actual number in this spherical shell is

$$ZU(r)dr,$$

where Z is the atomic number. The amplitude scattered from each slice is proportional to the number of electrons lying in each slice, located in the ring-shaped volume bounded by the two spheres and the planes which define the slices. Assuming spherical symmetry of the electron cloud, the number of electrons in the slice of the spherical shell is proportional to the ratio of the volume of the ring to the volume of the entire spherical shell (Fig. VI–20). Thus the number is

$$\frac{2\pi\sqrt{r^2 - z^2}\,dl\,dr}{4\pi r^2 dr} ZU(r)dr,$$

where

$$dl = \frac{r\,dz}{\sqrt{r^2 - z^2}},$$

so that the number in the slice from the spherical shell of thickness dr becomes

$$\left[\frac{1}{2r} ZU(r)dz\right]dr. \tag{6.94}$$

Let the expression for the incident plane wave motion, measured at O, be

$$e^{ikct},$$

then the expression for the scattered wave from the slice through the origin, at distance ρ, is

$$\left[\left\{\frac{1}{2r} ZU(r)dz \frac{e^2}{mc^2}\right\} dr\right]e^{ik(ct - \rho)},$$

since the scattered amplitude from each electron is e^2/mc^2.

We assume that the incident radiation is polarized so that its electric vector is perpendicular to the plane of Fig. VI–19. The analogous expression for the wave scattered from a slice at height z will be

$$\left[\left\{\frac{1}{2r} ZU(r) \frac{e^2}{mc^2} dz\right\}dr\right]e^{ik(ct - \rho - 2z \sin \frac{1}{2}\phi)},$$

and if dE is the contribution to the diffracted wave-motion from the spherical shell of thickness dr, we obtain

$$dE = \left[\left\{\frac{1}{2r} ZU(r) \frac{e^2}{mc^2}\right\}dr\right]e^{ik(ct-\rho)}\int_{-r}^{r} e^{-2ikz \sin \frac{1}{2}\phi}\,dz. \tag{6.95}$$

If we assume spherical symmetry, the integral in the preceding expression is

$$2\int_{0}^{r} \cos (2kz \sin \tfrac{1}{2}\phi)dz = \frac{\sin (2kr \sin \tfrac{1}{2}\phi)}{k \sin \tfrac{1}{2}\phi}.$$

The entire scattered wave from the atom may be obtained by summation of a set of spherical shells, thus

$$E = \left[\frac{Ze^2}{mc^2} \int_0^\infty U(r) \frac{\sin\left(2kr \sin \frac{1}{2}\phi\right)}{2kr \sin \frac{1}{2}\phi} dr \right] e^{ik(ct - \rho)}.$$

The atomic structure factor f is defined as the ratio of the amplitude scattered by the atom at angle ϕ to that scattered at the same angle by an electron according to the equation of J. J. Thomson. Under conditions similar to those of the above expression, the analogous equation for a single electron would be

$$E_0 = \frac{e^2}{mc^2} e^{ik(ct - \rho)}.$$

Comparison of the last two formulae shows that

$$f = Z \int_0^\infty U(r) \frac{\sin\left\{ (4\pi r/\lambda) \sin \frac{1}{2}\phi \right\}}{(4\pi r/\lambda) \sin \frac{1}{2}\phi} dr. \qquad (6.96)$$

It is often convenient to express the atomic structure factor in terms of the variable z, which represents the perpendicular distance from some plane through the atomic center. In the case of crystalline diffraction of x-rays this plane would be parallel to the crystallographic planes under investigation. Let $Zp(z)dz$ be the number of electrons per atom in a layer of thickness dz at distance z from a plane through the center of the atom parallel to the reflecting planes. Then from eq. (6.94)

$$Zp(z)dz = \left[Z \int_0^\infty \frac{1}{2r} U(r)dr \right] dz$$

or

$$p(z) = \int_0^\infty \frac{1}{2r} U(r)dr. \qquad (6.97)$$

This has the effect of changing the order of integration; in the present case the final integration will be with respect to z rather than r as formerly. Equation (6.95) becomes

$$E = \left[\frac{Ze^2}{mc^2} \int_{-r}^r p(z) e^{-2ikz \sin \frac{1}{2}\phi} dz \right] e^{ik(ct - \rho)}.$$

In case the atom is in a crystal lattice, the limits $-r$ and r of the integration are understood to include that portion of the space above and below the plane which is considered to be filled by the atom in question. Thus in terms of z,

$$f = Z \int_{-r}^{r} p(z) \cos \{(4\pi z/\lambda) \sin \theta\} \, dz, \qquad (6.98)$$

where θ, the glancing angle in a crystal plane, is identified with $\phi/2$.

We are now prepared to undertake the interesting and important problem of finding what arrangement of electrons will account for the experimental f curves, such as are given in Fig. VI–18 for Na and Cl. Previous to the introduction of the method of Fourier analysis, discussed in a subsequent section, the attempts in this direction consisted in testing some postulated atomic structure against the experimental f curve. Bragg, James, and Bosanquet tested various models consisting of electrons arranged on concentric spherical shells. If these shells are assumed to be of negligible thickness, the integral of eq. (6.96) may be replaced by a sum. Under these conditions $ZU(r)$ takes on a series of values z_q, where z_q is the number of electrons of the type q in the atom ($q = K, L, M$, etc.). Thus on this model we obtain [45a]

$$f = \sum_q z_q \frac{\sin \{(4\pi r_q/\lambda) \sin \tfrac{1}{2}\phi\}}{(4\pi r_q/\lambda) \sin \tfrac{1}{2}\phi}.$$

Bragg, James and Bosanquet[46] found that the observed f-factors, after correction for thermal agitation in a manner to be described later, were best represented as regards their dependence on angle by the following distribution, which assumes the atoms to be singly ionized:

11Na	7 electrons on a shell of radius	0.29 A.
	3 " " " " "	0.76 A.
17Cl	10 electrons on a shell of radius	0.25 A.
	5 " " " " "	0.86 A.
	3 " " " " "	1.46 A.

A more satisfactory method is to choose a set of r's and use the experimental data to calculate the number z of electrons located at this distance. A smooth curve drawn through the resultant points will give the electron density in the atom as a continuous function.

[45a] A. H. Compton, Phys. Rev. **9**, 49 (1917), eq. 18.
[46] Bragg, James, and Bosanquet, Phil. Mag. **44**, 433 (1922).

The results are shown in Figs. VI–21 and VI–22 for sodium and chlorine. It is interesting to note that these early results showed quite definitely that we cannot assume a ring of 8 electrons, corresponding to the L shell, all at uniform distance from the nucleus, as

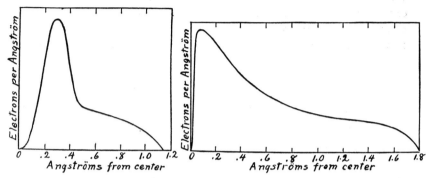

Fig. VI–21. The electron distribution in the sodium atom in NaCl as calculated in 1922 by Bragg, James, and Bosanquet.

Fig. VI–22. The electron distribution in the chlorine atom as calculated in 1922 by Bragg, James, and Bosanquet.

would be indicated by a literal interpretation of the earliest form of the Bohr theory, and obtain agreement with experiment.

17. *The Effect of Thermal Agitation on the Intensity of Reflection of X-rays from Crystals*

At all finite temperatures on the absolute scale, and probably at absolute zero also, the atoms in a crystal are in thermal agitation, and this movement of the diffracting centers from their equilibrium positions has the effect of lowering the intensity of the diffracted x-ray beam. The discussion in this section will deal only with the effect of temperature on the diffracted maxima, that is, the Laue spots. There is also an effect on the x-rays diffusely scattered from a crystal. The theory of the temperature effect was first investigated by Debye[47] and later by Darwin[48] and by Waller.[49] Discussions

[47] P. Debye, Verh. d. Deutsch. Phys. Ges. **15**, 678; 738; 857 (1913); Annalen der Physik **43**, 49 (1914).

[48] C. G. Darwin, Phil. Mag. **27**, 315 (1914).

[49] I. Waller, Zeitschr. f. Physik **17**, 398 (1923); Annalen der Physik **79**, 261 (1926); **83**, 154 (1927); Zeitschr. f. Physik **51**, 213 (1928); Diss. Uppsala (1925).

by Faxen,[50] v. Laue,[51] and Brillouin[52] have also appeared. In his early papers, Debye considered that each atom in the crystal vibrates independently, and that the Boltzmann statistics governs the probability that an atom has any given energy. It is clear that the assumption of independent vibration cannot be correct, since each atom is bound to its neighbors by forces, and the displacement of any one of them will create a wave of displacement which will traverse the crystal. A method of treating thermal motions in a crystal in this way was advanced by Born and Karman.[53] Debye therefore recalculated his result, and obtained an approximate formula applicable to the effect in a crystal containing identical atoms at the lattice corners of a simple translatory cubic lattice. The result was given by Debye in connection with the calculation of the intensity of diffraction from a very small crystal, as in Sec. 12 of this chapter, and was expressed as an exponential factor which decreases the intensity of a diffraction maximum as the temperature rises. We will, however, give the result here as an exponential factor with which the atomic structure factor is to be multiplied. We have

$$f_T = f_o \, e^{-M},$$

where

$$M = \frac{3h^2}{m_a k \Theta} \left(\frac{\phi(x)}{x} + \frac{1}{4} \right) \frac{\sin^2 \theta}{\lambda^2}. \qquad (6.99)$$

In these expressions f_T is the atomic structure factor at absolute temperature T, and f_o is the atomic structure factor when the atom is at rest. h is Planck's constant, m_a is the mass of the atom, k is Boltzmann's constant, $x = \Theta/T$, where Θ is the characteristic temperature of the crystal, and $\phi(x)$ is a function of x which is given by

$$\phi(x) = \frac{1}{x} \int_o^x \frac{\xi d\xi}{e^\xi - 1}$$

Values of $\phi(x)$ are given in Table VI–8, taken from Debye's paper.

[50] H. Faxén, Annalen der Physik 54, 615 (1917); Zeitschr. f. Physik 17, 266 (1923).

[51] M. v. Laue, Annalen der Physik 81, 877 (1926).

[52] L. Brillouin, Annales de Physique 17, 88 (1922).

[53] Born and Karman, Physikal. Zeitschr. 13, 297 (1912); 14, 15; 65 (1913). To give an adequate derivation of the equations for the temperature effect, it is necessary to go rather deeply into the theory of the crystalline state, and for that reason such derivations are not given here. A good discussion may be found in an article by P. P. Ewald, Handbuch der Physik, Vol. 24, p. 270 (1933).

The additive term $\frac{1}{4}$ in eq. (6.99) is due to the assumption that zero point energy exists, that is, that the atoms are vibrating with a half quantum of energy at absolute zero. If the calculation is made

TABLE VI-8

VALUES OF THE FUNCTION $\phi(x)$

x	$\phi(x)$	x	$\phi(x)$	x	$\phi(x)$	x	$\phi(x)$
0.0	1	1.2	0.740	3	0.483	9	0.183
0.2	0.951	1.4	0.704	4	0.388	10	0.164
0.4	0.904	1.6	0.669	5	0.321	12	0.137
0.6	0.860	1.8	0.637	6	0.271	14	0.114
0.8	0.818	2.0	0.607	7	0.234	16	0.103
1.0	0.778	2.5	0.540	8	0.205	20	0.0822

without the zero-point energy assumption, the same result is obtained, except that the additive term $\frac{1}{4}$ does not appear, the factor $(\phi(x)/x + \frac{1}{4})$ being replaced by $\phi(x)/x$ alone.

The characteristic temperature is defined[53a] in terms of the quantum theory of specific heats. C_v, the heat capacity of one atomic weight of a substance may be expressed as

$$C_v = 3R\left[\frac{e^{h\nu/kT}}{(e^{h\nu/kT} - 1)^2}\left(\frac{h\nu}{kT}\right)^2\right],$$

where R is the gas constant in calories per degree centigrade, k is as before Boltzmann's constant, h is Planck's constant, T is the absolute temperature, and ν the characteristic frequency of vibration of the atoms. Let Θ be the value of T at which $h\nu = kT$, then the preceding expression gives

$$C_v = 3R[0.921] = 5.49,$$

so that the characteristic temperature of a substance may be defined as the temperature at which its atomic heat capacity first reaches the value 5.49. Values of the characteristic temperatures of some substances are given in Table VI-9.

[53a] Cf. Richtmyer, Introduction to Modern Physics, 1st Ed. McGraw-Hill (1928), p. 259.

TABLE VI-9

CHARACTERISTIC TEMPERATURES OF VARIOUS SUBSTANCES

Substance	Θ, Deg. K	Substance	Θ, Deg. K
Pb...............	88	KCl..............	230
Tl...............	96	Zn...............	235
Hg..............	97	NaCl.............	281
I................	106	Cu..............	315
Cd..............	168	Al..............	398
Na..............	172	Fe.............	453
KBr.............	177	CaF$_2$............	474
Ag..............	215	FeS$_2$.............	645
Ca..............	226	Diamond.........	1860

The treatment of Debye has been reconsidered by Waller,[49] with the result that the temperature factor of Debye appears to be too small. Where M appears in Debye's result, Waller finds that $2M$ should occur. Thus according to Waller

$$f_T = f_0 e^{-M_w},$$

where

$$M_w = \frac{6h^2}{m_a k\Theta}\left(\frac{\phi(x)}{x} + \frac{1}{4}\right)\frac{\sin^2\theta}{\lambda^2}. \tag{6.100}$$

After early qualitative experiments had shown the existence of the predicted temperature effect, quantitative experimental studies were carried out by James,[54] James and Firth,[55] Waller and James,[56] James and Brindley,[57] and James, Brindley and Wood.[58] Measurements have been taken on NaCl, KCl and Al crystals, with some observations on CaF$_2$. The intensity of reflection from rock salt has been studied from 290° K to 900° K and from the temperature of liquid air, about 86° K, to room temperature. In the case of rock salt, the interpretation of the measurements is complicated by the fact that the lattice is composed of two different kinds of atoms, whereas the theory in the form in which it has been quoted here

---

[54] R. W. James, Phil. Mag. **49**, 585 (1925).
[55] James and Firth, Proc. Roy. Soc. Lond. A **117**, 62 (1927).
[56] Waller and James, Proc. Roy. Soc. Lond. A **117**, 214 (1927).
[57] James and Brindley, Proc. Roy. Soc. Lond. A **121**, 155 (1928).
[58] James, Brindley, and Wood, Proc. Roy. Soc. Lond. A **125**, 401 (1929).

applies to lattices containing only one atomic species. Thus the amplitudes of the thermal vibrations of the different atoms are not the same. Here Waller[56] has shown that each atomic species has its own temperature factor, i.e., in NaCl,

$$(f_{Cl})_T = (f_{Cl})_0 \, e^{-M_{Cl}}$$

and

$$(f_{Na})_T = (f_{Na})_0 \, e^{-M_{Na}}.$$

The crystal structure factor F is then built up at any temperature from the atomic f_T's as shown in Table V–6, Chapter V.

In the case of reflection from KCl crystals, the masses of the two atoms concerned are so nearly equal that the existence of two different atomic species in the temperature effect can be ignored. We will discuss experiments carried out by James and Brindley[57] on sylvine and the extent to which they agree with the theoretical predictions. Observations of the intensities of several reflections from the crystal at the temperature of liquid air, room temperature, and temperatures between room temperature and 900° C were carried out. The results are shown in Table VI–10. The wave-length used was 0.71A.

The reflections in the first column of the table are designated by the values (Nh, Nk, Nl), where N is the order calculated from a simple translatory cubic lattice containing one atom per unit cell. Since KCl has the sodium chloride structure with a unit cell of 3.13 A edge, the (400) reflection is the second observable order from the cleavage (100) planes. R_c in the third and fourth columns is the value of $E\omega/P_0$ resulting from experiment as described in Sec. 10 of this chapter. The corrections which are applied to obtain the fourth column from the third are for secondary extinction and for the effect of temperature in shifting the location of the maximum of the diffraction pattern.[59]

The average sample of KCl may be treated as an imperfect crystal, and hence the coefficient of reflection is given by eqs. (6.89) and (6.78), that is,

$$R_c = \frac{E\omega}{P_0} = \frac{Q}{2\mu} = \frac{1}{2\mu} \frac{1 + \cos^2 2\theta}{2 \sin 2\theta} \frac{e^4}{m^2 c^4} M^2 \lambda^3 F^2.$$

[59] This correction arises from the fact that due to the shift of glancing angle with temperature (eq. (9.28), Chap. IX) the value of $(\sin \theta)/\lambda$ changes and for convenient comparison of experiment with theory the observed R_c values must be reduced to the same value of $(\sin \theta)/\lambda$.

TABLE VI-10

THE TEMPERATURE EFFECT IN THE DIFFRACTION OF X-RAYS FROM POTASSIUM
CHLORIDE, AFTER JAMES AND BRINDLEY

Reflection		T Deg. K	$(R_c)_T/(R_c)_{290}$		$\left(\dfrac{\lambda}{\sin \theta}\right)^2 \log_{10} \dfrac{(R_c)_T}{(R_c)_{290}}$
			Observed	Corrected	
(400)	$\sin \theta = 0.227$	86	1.22	1.24	0.918
		290	1.00	1.00	0.000
		455	0.81	0.79	−1.006
		543	0.74	0.72	−1.403
		663	0.60	0.58	−2.326
		807	0.45	0.43	−3.602
		936	0.36	0.336	−4.656
(600)	$\sin \theta = 0.341$	86	1.607	1.624	0.9216
		412	0.73	0.73	−0.5982
		588	0.44	0.44	−1.560
		652	0.35	0.35	−1.995
(800)	$\sin \theta = 0.454$	86	2.46	2.46	0.9600
		336	0.78	0.78	−0.2650
		430	0.48	0.48	−0.7830
		471	0.38	0.38	−1.032
		587	0.21	0.21	−1.665

If we equate the scattering powers of K and Cl, the crystal structure factor F is finite only when the sum $(Nh + Nk + Nl)$ is even, and here it takes the value $8f$, where f is the atomic structure factor of a nucleus with 18 external electrons (argon, approximately). There are four molecules of KCl, or 8 such diffracting centers per unit cell, so that $8M$ is the number of atoms per unit volume. Thus for KCl we may write

$$\frac{E\omega}{P_o} = \frac{1}{2\mu} \frac{1 + \cos^2 2\theta}{2 \sin 2\theta} \frac{e^4}{m^2 c^4} \lambda^3 n_a{}^2 f^2, \qquad (6.101)$$

where n_a is twice the number of KCl molecules per cc. When the temperature effect is under consideration, we must replace f in the preceding expression by $f_o e^{-M}$, where M is given by eq. (6.99) or (6.100), according to Debye or Waller respectively. Considering that the temperature effect on $(\sin \theta)/\lambda$ has been corrected for, we may write eqs. (6.101) and (6.99) for two different temperatures, denoted by subscripts 1 and 2, obtaining

$$\left(\frac{\lambda}{\sin\theta}\right)^2 \ln\frac{(R_c)_2}{(R_c)_1} = \frac{12h^2}{m_a k\Theta}\left\{\frac{\phi(x_1)}{x_1} - \frac{\phi(x_2)}{x_2}\right\}, \qquad (6.102)$$

in which the larger value of the temperature coefficient due to Waller has been used. Letting $\Theta = 230°$ K, and setting $m_a = 6.149 \times 10^{-23}$ gm. as the average of the atomic masses of K and Cl, we can calculate the theoretical variation of the left-hand member of the preceding expression with temperature, using values of $\phi(x)$ from Table VI-8.

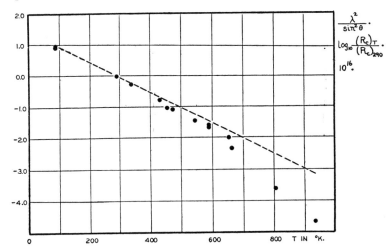

Fig. VI-23. The dotted line represents the predicted behavior of the function specified as ordinate with the temperature, according to Waller. The experimental values are by James and Waller, taken from observations on KCl.

The result is shown in Fig. VI-23, in which the dotted line shows the variation computed from the right-hand member of eq. (6.102) and the experimental values from column 5 of Table VI-10 are shown as circles.

It is seen that theory and experiment are in agreement between 86° K and 400° K, but that the decrease of intensity with increasing temperature is more rapid above 400° K than can be accounted for theoretically. If the original M of Debye from eq. (6.99) had been used, the rate of variation would be less rapid than that of the dotted curve of Fig. VI-23; hence the experiments favor Waller's correction to Debye's result.

James and Brindley found that in an entirely empirical manner the decline in intensity with increasing temperature in KCl at temperatures above 400° K can be represented by multiplying the observed results by

$$e^{-A} \quad \text{where} \quad A = 1.330 \times 10^{-5} \, T^2 \, (\sin^2 \theta)/\lambda^2.$$

A should be compared with $2M$ since it refers to the intensity and M refers to the amplitude factor. In rock salt at high temperatures an analogous empirical factor for intensity is

$$e^{-A} \quad \text{where} \quad A = 1.162 \times 10^{-5} \, T^2 \, (\sin^2 \theta)/\lambda^2.$$

In these two preceding expressions λ is to be used in angstrom units rather than in cm.

The above test of the theory does not give any indication of the presence or absence of zero-point energy, since in setting up eq. (6.102) from (6.100) the essential feature contributed by this concept, the additive term $\frac{1}{4}$, disappears. In order to obtain evidence on this interesting question, the functions $U(r)$ which occur in eqs. (6.96) must be computed from some atomic model, and the atomic scattering factor computed as a function of angle, assuming the atom to be at rest. From this result the atomic structure factor at the temperature of liquid air can be computed using the factor e^{-M}; one set of computed values being calculated on the assumption of zero-point energy and another set without this assumption. From experimental measurements of the absolute values of R_c at this temperature, it may be possible to show better agreement with one or the other of the computed sets and thus obtain evidence as to the presence or absence of zero-point energy.

In the case of KCl, James and Brindley computed the $U(r)$ functions for K^+ and Cl^- by the method of Hartree,[60] using the Schrödinger wave equation to give the probable charge density at any distance from the nucleus. The only observable spectra in KCl represent the sum of the scattered amplitudes from K and Cl so that the f curves computed from the theoretical charge density were added and thus the computed F values at 86° K were calculated. It was found that the experimental F values obtained at liquid air temperatures agreed better with those computed on the assumption of a half quantum of vibrational energy at zero absolute, thus giving evidence for the existence of zero-point energy.

[60] Hartree, Camb. Phil. Soc. Proc. **24**, 89; 111 (1928).

A similar test was carried out on aluminium by James, Brindley, and Wood,[58] who also obtained evidence for zero-point energy.

In the paper of Waller and James, it is stated that the temperature factor may be written

$$e^{-8\pi^2 \overline{\mu_x^2} (\sin^2 \theta)/\lambda^2},$$

where $\overline{\mu_x^2}$ is the mean square displacement of an atom above or below the average position in the atomic plane under consideration. $\overline{\mu_x^2}$ thus depends on the temperature, and can be expressed in a power series in T, the coefficients of which are related to the elastic coefficients of the crystal. In this way temperature data may be used to give information as to the nature of the forces holding an atom in the lattice.

The temperature effect and the question of zero-point energy have recently been investigated by J. J. Shonka.[61] He used powdered sodium fluoride crystals, and measured the integrated reflection by a photographic method. The incident radiation was the Mo $K\alpha$ line. The test of the theoretical expressions for the exponent M was carried out with the use of eq. (6.102). It is seen that λ and θ do not enter the right-hand member of this expression, and hence the left-hand member, which can be experimentally measured, should be independent of λ and $\sin \theta$, at the two temperatures indicated by the subscripts 1 and 2. Measurements were made at liquid air temperature and at room temperature, with the results shown in Table VI–11. The constant values of the fourth column in this table indicate that the form of M is correct.

TABLE VI–11

THE TEMPERATURE EFFECT IN NaF, ACCORDING TO J. J. SHONKA

Reflection	$(\sin \theta)/\lambda$	$(R_c)_{86}/(R_c)_{290}$	$\left(\dfrac{\lambda}{\sin \theta}\right)^2 \log \dfrac{(R_c)_{86}}{(R_c)_{290}}$
420	0.484	1.249	0.947
422	0.531	1.349	1.059
440	0.612	1.434	0.957
600	0.650	1.531	0.993
620	0.684	1.566	0.956
622	0.718	1.635	0.949
			Average, 0.976

[61] J. J. Shonka, Phys. Rev. **43**, 947 (1933).

Taking the average value of the fourth column, and thus setting

$$\frac{12h^2}{m_a k\Theta}\left\{\frac{\phi(x_1)}{x_1} - \frac{\phi(x_2)}{x_2}\right\} = 0.976$$

one obtains $\Theta = 442°$ K, and Shonka shows that this is an acceptable value of the characteristic temperature of the crystal.

Shonka obtained evidence on the existence of zero-point energy from considerations differing from those of James, Brindley, and Wood. In his calculations he treated NaF as a crystal built of atoms whose mass is the average of the atomic masses of Na and F, or close to that of neon. The atomic structure factor of gaseous neon has been determined by Wollan,[62] and since the atoms in the gas scatter independently, the result should not be influenced by zero-point energy. Using Havighurst's data[63] on NaF at room temperature, and the measured critical temperature, Shonka calculated the atomic structure factor of $\frac{1}{2}(Na + F)$ at $0°$ K as a function of scattering angle, and compared the result with Wollan's curves for Ne. The calculation on sodium fluoride was made with and without the zero-point energy assumption, and the comparison indicated that zero-point energy is present. NaF is a good crystal for the purpose, since its critical temperature is relatively high, and the mass of its atoms is small.

18. *The Application of Fourier Analysis to Electron Density Distributions in Crystals*

The structure of a crystal is an ideal example of a solid with periodic variations in its electron density, and it is not strange that shortly after the x-ray studies of crystal structure began, W. H. Bragg suggested the use of Fourier's series in crystal analysis problems.[64] It is surprising, however, that quantitative use of this method was not made until 1925, and it is an interesting incident in the development of physics that attention was called to the application of these series in an attempt to treat the diffraction of x-rays assuming only the corpuscular theory of light. Duane[65] had succeeded in deriving Bragg's equation from the photon theory of light by assuming quantized momentum transfers to the crystal

[62] E. O. Wollan, Phys. Rev. **37**, 862 (1931).
[63] R. J. Havighurst, Phys. Rev. **28**, 869 (1926).
[64] W. H. Bragg, Phil. Trans. Roy. Soc. **215**, 253 (1915).
[65] W. Duane, Proc. Nat. Acad. Sci. **9**, 159 (1923).

by the impinging x-ray photons. In an attempt to discover the extent to which this result could be generalized, Epstein and Ehrenfest[66] used Fourier's series to represent the distribution of diffracting material in the crystal. Following this idea, Duane[67] put the method in usable form, and Fourier analyses were made by Havighurst[68] and by A. H. Compton,[69] who invented several new forms of the series.

In eq. (5.34), Chap. V, we developed an expression for the crystal structure factor F as a kind of vector sum of the atomic structure factors f_j of the various atoms in the unit cell. This was

$$F_{hkl} = \sum_j f_j e^{2\pi Ni(hx_j + ky_j + lz_j)}. \tag{6.103}$$

In this expression $x_j y_j z_j$ are the coordinates of an atom j in the unit cell, expressed in the conventional manner as fractions of the cell edges. N is the order computed from a simple translatory lattice corresponding to the classification of the crystal under investigation (i.e. cubic, orthorhombic, triclinic, etc.) and having one atom per unit cell. For a cubic crystal, N may be found from a combination of eqs. (5.22) and (5.23), namely

$$N = \frac{2a_0 \sin \theta}{\lambda \sqrt{h^2 + k^2 + l^2}}, \tag{6.104}$$

which is a special case of the formula for an orthorhombic crystal whose unit cell has edges of length τ_1, τ_2, τ_3, which is

$$N = \frac{2\tau_1 \tau_2 \tau_3 \sin \theta}{\lambda \sqrt{h^2 \tau_2^2 \tau_3^2 + k^2 \tau_1^2 \tau_3^2 + l^2 \tau_1^2 \tau_2^2}}. \tag{6.105}$$

We now wish to reconsider eq. (6.103), trying to express it in as general a form as possible, without assuming localized atoms in the unit cell. All we will assume is that throughout the cell there exists some scalar point function $\rho(x, y, z)$ such that $\rho(x, y, z)dV$ gives the fraction of the entire diffracting material of the unit cell inside the small volume dV located in the immediate vicinity of the

[66] Epstein and Ehrenfest, Proc. Nat. Acad. Sci. 10, 133 (1924).

[67] W. Duane, Proc. Nat. Acad. Sci. 11, 489 (1925).

[68] R. J. Havighurst, Proc. Nat. Acad. Sci. 11, 502 (1925) and subsequent papers mentioned in the text.

[69] A. H. Compton, X-rays and Electrons, Van Nostrand (1926), p. 151 et seq.

point whose coordinates are (x, y, z). Thus the actual number of diffracting units (electrons) in volume dV at (x, y, z) in the unit cell is

$$Z\rho(x, y, z)dV,$$

where Z is the total number of electrons in the unit cell.

In the general case we use a set of axes such that the positive direction of x is the positive direction of τ_1, and y and z are similarly related to τ_2 and τ_3. The volume of the unit cell is

$$V = \tau_1 \cdot \tau_2 \times \tau_3.$$

Consider an infinitesimal volume dV in the form of a parallelopiped with sides parallel to those of the unit cell. The edges of this parallelopiped may be represented by

$$dx\tau_1, \; dy\tau_2, \; dz\tau_3,$$

remembering the conventional definitions of the fractions dx, dy, and dz. The volume of this infinitesimal parallelopiped is

$$dV = dx\tau_1 \cdot (dy\tau_2 \times dz\tau_3) = \tau_1 \cdot \tau_2 \times \tau_3 dx dy dz = V dx dy dz,$$

so that the number of electrons in this volume dV may be written

$$VZ\rho(x, y, z)dx dy dz,$$

so that by analogy with eq. (6.103) we may write

$$F_{hkl} = VZ \int_0^1 \int_0^1 \int_0^1 \rho(x, y, z) e^{2\pi N i (hx + ky + lz)} dx dy dz, \quad (6.106)$$

in which F_{hkl} is in general complex. For convenience we will introduce the symbols $H = Nh$, $K = Nk$, $L = Nl$. The trigonometric form of the preceding expression then is

$$F_{HKL} = VZ \int_0^1 \int_0^1 \int_0^1 \rho(x, y, z)$$

$$[\cos 2\pi(Hx + Ky + Lz) + i \sin 2\pi(Hx + Ky + Lz)] dx dy dz. \quad (6.107)$$

We shall now assume that $Z\rho(x, y, z)$ is developable into a three-dimensional Fourier series, namely

$$Z\rho(x, y, z) = \sum_0^\infty \sum_{-\infty}^\infty \sum_{-\infty}^\infty A_{pqr} \cos 2\pi(px + qy + rz)$$

$$+ \sum_0^\infty \sum_{-\infty}^\infty \sum_{-\infty}^\infty B_{pqr} \sin 2\pi(px + qy + rz). \quad (6.108)$$

In this series p, q, and r are any integers, positive or negative or zero. In order to illustrate in more detail the type of series which is postulated, we will write out some of the terms in the triple sum involving the cosines. Neglecting the sine terms we would have

$Z_\rho(x, y, z)$

$$= A_{000} + A_{001} \cos 2\pi z + A_{002} \cos 2\pi 2z + A_{003} \cos 2\pi 3z \cdots$$

$$+ A_{100} \cos 2\pi x + A_{101} \cos 2\pi(x+z) + A_{102} \cos 2\pi(x+2z) \cdots$$

$$+ A_{10\bar{1}} \cos 2\pi(x - z) + A_{10\bar{2}} \cos 2\pi(x - 2z) \cdots$$

. . . . . .

One of the sums in eq. (6.108) is extended only from o to ∞ because of the relations

$$A_{\bar{p}\bar{q}\bar{r}} \cos 2\pi(-px - qy - rz) = A_{\bar{p}\bar{q}\bar{r}} \cos 2\pi(px + qy + rz)$$

and

$$B_{\bar{p}\bar{q}\bar{r}} \sin 2\pi(-px - qy - rz) = -B_{\bar{p}\bar{q}\bar{r}} \sin 2\pi(px + qy + rz),$$

which mean that the total coefficient of any term such as $\cos 2\pi(px + qy + rz)$ is $(A_{pqr} + A_{\bar{p}\bar{q}\bar{r}})$, and the total coefficient of any term $\sin 2\pi(px + qy + rz)$ is $(B_{pqr} - B_{\bar{p}\bar{q}\bar{r}})$. Thus the term built on the integer triple pqr will not have the same trigonometric part as one built on $\bar{p}\bar{q}\bar{r}$, so that the q and r sums may be extended over the entire range, but term pqr will combine with term $\bar{p}q\bar{r}$, thus necessitating only a half range variation in p.

Now if by experiment we can determine the coefficients A_{pqr} and B_{pqr} for a given crystal, we have a complete analysis of the crystal as respects the distribution of its diffracting power. This is a rather involved method of stating the problem of crystal analysis. Let us see how far we can hope to go toward its solution. We will substitute eq. (6.108) in eq. (6.107), obtaining

$$F_{HKL} = V \int_0^1 \int_0^1 \int_0^1 \Sigma \Sigma \Sigma_{p\ q\ r} A_{pqr} \cos 2\pi(px + qy + rz)$$
$$\cos 2\pi(Hx + Ky + Lz)dxdydz \quad (6.109)$$

$$+ V \int_0^1 \int_0^1 \int_0^1 \Sigma \Sigma \Sigma_{p\ q\ r} B_{pqr} \sin 2\pi(px + qy + rz)$$
$$\cos 2\pi(Hx + Ky + Lz)dxdydz \quad (6.110)$$

$$+ Vi \int_0^1 \int_0^1 \int_0^1 \Sigma \Sigma \Sigma_{p\ q\ r} A_{pqr} \cos 2\pi(px + qy + rz)$$

$$\sin 2\pi(Hx + Ky + Lz)dxdydz \quad (6.111)$$

$$+ Vi \int_0^1 \int_0^1 \int_0^1 \Sigma \Sigma \Sigma_{p\ q\ r} B_{pqr} \sin 2\pi(px + qy + rz)$$

$$\sin 2\pi(Hx + Ky + Lz)dxdydz. \quad (6.112)$$

An investigation of these four integrals will disclose the possibility of considerable simplification. It can be shown[70] that every term

[70] The proof can be carried out in the following direct but laborious manner. The general term of the triple sum in eq. (6.109) is

$$\int_0^1 \int_0^1 \int_0^1 A_{pqr} \cos 2\pi(px + qy + rz) \cos 2\pi(Hx + Ky + Lz)dxdydz$$

or

$$A_{pqr} \int_0^1 \int_0^1 \int_0^1 \cos[2\pi px + 2\pi(qy + rz)] \cos[2\pi Hx + 2\pi(Ky + Lz)]dxdydz.$$

The integrand of this function may then be expanded from the formula for the cosine of the sum of two angles. It is then found that the expanded integrand may be written

$$\cos 2\pi px \cos 2\pi Hx \cos 2\pi(qy + rz) \cos 2\pi(Ky + Lz) \quad (1)$$

$$- \cos 2\pi px \sin 2\pi Hx \cos 2\pi(qy + rz) \sin 2\pi(Ky + Lz) \quad (2)$$

$$- \cos 2\pi Hx \sin 2\pi px \sin 2\pi(qy + rz) \cos 2\pi(Ky + Lz) \quad (3)$$

$$\sin 2\pi Hx \sin 2\pi px \sin 2\pi(qy + rz) \sin 2\pi(Ky + Lz). \quad (4)$$

The integral can then be broken up into four parts, the part corresponding to eq. (1) above being

$$\int_0^1 \int_0^1 \cos 2\pi(qy + rz) \cos 2\pi(Ky + Lz)dydz \int_0^1 \cos 2\pi px \cos 2\pi Hxdx.$$

The integral with respect to x in this expression may be written, using the well-known trigonometric formula

$$\cos \alpha + \cos \beta = 2 \cos \tfrac{1}{2}(\alpha + \beta) \cos \tfrac{1}{2}(\alpha - \beta),$$

in the form

$$\int_0^1 \cos 2\pi px \cos 2\pi Hxdx = \tfrac{1}{2}\int_0^1 \cos 2\pi x(p + H)dx + \tfrac{1}{2}\int_0^1 \cos 2\pi x(p - H)dx. \quad (5)$$

It is seen that if $p \neq H$, both integrals in the right-hand member of (5) vanish. If $p = H$, the first of these integrals is zero, the second, $\tfrac{1}{2}$. Consideration of expressions (2) and (3) reveals that the integrals will be zero for any values of the parameters. Integration of (4) with respect to x will give $\tfrac{1}{2}$. By a further expansion in the same manner of the remaining double integrals the result quoted in the text may be attained.

in eq. (6.109) is zero except that one for which $p = H$, $q = K$ and $r = L$, and that the result of the indicated operations in this equation is simply $\frac{1}{2}A_{pqr}$. By a similar examination it is found that integrals (6.110) and (6.111) are zero for any values of p, q, and r. Eq. (6.112) gives the value $\frac{1}{2}B_{pqr}$ provided that $p = H$, $q = K$, $r = L$; otherwise it is zero. Thus we obtain

$$F_{HKL} = \tfrac{1}{2}V(A_{HKL} + iB_{HKL}) \qquad (6.113)$$

so that if we denote real and imaginary parts of F by F' and F'' respectively, we have

$$A_{HKL} = \frac{2}{V}F'_{HKL} \qquad (6.114)$$

$$B_{HKL} = \frac{2}{V}F''_{HKL}. \qquad (6.115)$$

We can see from eq. (6.108) that $B_{ooo} = o$, but the interpretation of A_{ooo} requires a little consideration. We note that

$$Z = Z\int_V \rho(x,y,z)dV = Z\left[\int_V \rho(x,y,z)e^{2\pi i(Hx + Ky + Lz)}dV\right]_{H = K = L = o},$$

so that, remembering that $B_{ooo} = o$,

$$\left[\int_V \Sigma\,\Sigma\,\Sigma\, A_{pqr} \cos 2\pi(px + qy + rz)\right.$$

$$\left.\cos 2\pi(Hx + Ky + Lz)dV\right]_{p=q=r=H=K=L=o} = Z,$$

and the above at once simplifies to

$$A_{ooo}\int_V dV = Z \quad \text{or} \quad A_{ooo} = Z/V.$$

Thus the Fourier series for $Z\rho(x, y, z)$ may be written

$$Z\rho(x, y, z) = \frac{Z}{V} + \frac{2}{V}\sum_o^\infty \sum_{-\infty}^\infty \sum_{-\infty}^\infty F'_{HKL} \cos 2\pi(Hx + Ky + Lz)$$

$$+ \frac{2}{V}\sum_o^\infty \sum_{-\infty}^\infty \sum_{-\infty}^\infty F''_{HKL} \sin 2\pi(Hx + Ky + Lz) \qquad (6.116)$$

in which we are to remember that in expanding the sum involving the cosines we are to omit the term for $H = K = L = o$, since we have explicitly written it in the formula as Z/V. Another method[71] for writing eq. (6.116) is as follows:

$$Z\rho(x, y, z) = V^{-1}\left[\sum_{-\infty}^{\infty} \sum_{-\infty}^{\infty} \sum_{-\infty}^{\infty} F'_{HKL} \cos 2\pi(Hx + Ky + Lz) \right.$$

$$\left. + \sum_{-\infty}^{\infty} \sum_{-\infty}^{\infty} \sum_{-\infty}^{\infty} F''_{HKL} \sin 2\pi(Hx + Ky + Lz) \right] \quad (6.117)$$

in which the value of the cosine triple sum for $H = K = L = 0$ is to be taken as Z.

From eq. (6.117) it is clear that a solution of the problem of the distribution of electrons in the unit cell of a crystal will depend on measurements of F'_{HKL} and F''_{HKL}. Our determinations of the intensity of reflection of x-rays from crystals will not, however, give us the required information, for in the experiment we measure the quantity F^2 which occurs in Q of eq. (6.80). We must now remember that the F's themselves are in general complex and that our measurements give only

$$F^2 = (F')^2 + (F'')^2.$$

Thus eq. (6.117) allows us to state in a rather elegant manner the impossibility of a unique determination of a crystal structure from a set of intensity of reflection data and nothing else. Our intensity data do not give us the phases of the waves arriving at our measuring instrument, that is, we are unable from an intensity measurement

[71] The justification for writing the series in this form comes from consideration of the relation between terms characterized by HKL and by $\overline{HKL}$. In the case of the cosine terms,

$$F'_{\overline{HKL}} \cos 2\pi(-Hx - Ky - Lz) = F'_{\overline{HKL}} \cos 2\pi(Hx + Ky + Lz)$$

and from eq. (6.106) we see that $F'_{\overline{HKL}} = F'_{HKL}$ so that

$$F'_{\overline{HKL}} \cos 2\pi(-Hx - Ky - Lz) + F'_{HKL} \cos 2\pi(Hx + Ky + Lz)$$
$$= 2F'_{HKL} \cos 2\pi(Hx + Ky + Lz).$$

In the case of the sine terms, we have

$$F''_{\overline{HKL}} \sin 2\pi(-Hx - Ky - Lz) = -F''_{\overline{HKL}} \sin 2\pi(Hx + Ky + Lz)$$

but again, referring to the imaginary part of eq. (6.106),

$$F''_{\overline{HKL}} = -F''_{HKL},$$

so that we obtain

$$F''_{\overline{HKL}} \sin 2\pi(-Hx - Ky - Lz) + F''_{HKL} \sin 2\pi(Hx + Ky + Lz)$$
$$= 2F''_{HKL} \sin 2\pi(Hx + Ky + Lz)$$

to decide whether or not F is complex, and furthermore we cannot give the real and imaginary parts, if they both exist, their proper signs. In order to solve crystal structure problems we have to appeal to our knowledge of the symmetry characteristics of the crystal, its chemical composition and macroscopic density, etc.

Many crystals are characterized by a center of symmetry, and if such a symmetry element is located at the origin of coordinates, a considerable simplification of eq. (6.117) is possible. For in such a case, for constant HKL, there are two points, characterized by xyz and $\bar{x}\bar{y}\bar{z}$ at which the function $\rho(x, y, z)$ is identical. Referring to eq. (6.107), this means that the imaginary part of F_{HKL} will vanish, all the coefficients F''_{HKL} are zero, and $F'_{HKL} = F_{HKL}$. Hence eq. (6.117) becomes

$$Z\rho(x, y, z) = V^{-1} \sum_{-\infty}^{\infty} \sum_{-\infty}^{\infty} \sum_{-\infty}^{\infty} F_{HKL} \cos 2\pi(Hx + Ky + Lz). \quad (6.118)$$

Sodium chloride is an example of a very simple structure and has been extensively investigated. It has a center of symmetry and hence eq. (6.118) is applicable. If we call on our knowledge of the structure of the crystal, gained from other sources, we may specialize eq. (6.118) even more. If we expand the expression for the crystal structure factor from eq. (6.103), using the coordinates of eq. (5.24), Chap. V, we find

$$F_{HKL} = f_{Na}[1 + \cos \pi(H+K) + \cos \pi(K+L) + \cos \pi(H+L)]$$
$$+ f_{Cl}[\cos \pi(H+K+L) + \cos \pi H + \cos \pi K + \cos \pi L]. \quad (6.119)$$

By examination of this expression it can be at once demonstrated that

$$F_{HKL} = F_{\bar{H}KL} = F_{H\bar{K}L} = F_{HK\bar{L}}. \quad (6.120)$$

Taking account of this result we may examine a typical term of the sum in eq. (6.118). In writing out the sum we will have, when varying L, two terms,

$$F_{HKL} \cos 2\pi(Hx + Ky + Lz) \quad \text{and} \quad F_{HK\bar{L}} \cos 2\pi(Hx + Ky - Lz).$$

Expanding, we have

$$F_{HKL} \cos 2\pi(Hx + Ky + Lz)$$
$$= F_{HKL}[\cos 2\pi(Hx + Ky) \cos 2\pi Lz - \sin 2\pi(Hx + Ky) \sin 2\pi Lz]$$

and

$$F_{HK\bar{L}} \cos 2\pi(Hx + Ky - Lz)$$

$$= F_{HKL}[\cos 2\pi(Hx + Ky) \cos 2\pi Lz - \sin 2\pi(Hx + Ky) \sin 2\pi Lz].$$

Addition of the two preceding equations gives us the result

$$F_{HK\bar{L}} \cos 2\pi(Hx + Ky + Lz) + F_{HK\bar{L}} \cos 2\pi(Hx + Ky - Lz)$$

$$= 2F_{HKL} \cos 2\pi(Hx + Ky) \cos 2\pi Lz.$$

Thus eq. (6.118) may be written

$$VZ\rho(x, y, z) = Z + 2 \sum_{0}^{\infty} \sum_{-\infty}^{\infty} \sum_{-\infty}^{\infty} F_{HKL} \cos 2\pi(Hx + Ky + Lz)$$

$$= Z + 4 \sum_{0}^{\infty} \sum_{-\infty}^{\infty} \sum_{0}^{\infty} F_{HKL} \cos 2\pi(Hx + Ky) \cos 2\pi Lz,$$

and using one more expansion, with the relation $F_{HKL} = F_{H\bar{K}L}$, we obtain

$$Z\rho(x, y, z) = \frac{8}{V} \sum_{0}^{\infty} \sum_{0}^{\infty} \sum_{0}^{\infty} F_{HKL} \cos 2\pi Hx \cos 2\pi Ky \cos 2\pi Lz, \quad (6.121)$$

in which it is understood that the term having $H = K = L = 0$ has the value ZV^{-1}. This equation is applicable to crystals of the rock-salt structure. It may be mentioned again that the x, y, z used in these formulae represent fractions of the elementary cube edges.

Although it is certain that all of the F's in NaCl are real, it is not so certain that all of them are positive. If the origin of coordinates in NaCl is located at the center of a chlorine atom at a corner of one of the unit cells it is reasonable to suppose that we have at this point the maximum value of $Z\rho(x, y, z)$ and thus that the coefficients of all the terms are positive. We shall see later that the effect of making some of the F's negative at random in NaCl has been tested out, and leads to curves giving a negative value of $Z\rho(x, y, z)$ at certain places in the unit cell, so that it seems demonstrated that the F's in this simple crystal are all to be taken positive if Cl is placed at the origin.

From eq. (6.121) with a large amount of data on coefficients of reflection it would be possible to construct a three-dimensional plot of the function $Z\rho(x, y, z)$ for rock salt, but the labor involved is so great that this has not been carried out. The variation of $Z\rho(x, y, z)$ along certain lines through the crystal has, however, been studied by Havighurst.[72] Suppose we wish to study the function $Z\rho(x, y, z)$ along the x-axis, i.e., at points $(x, 0, 0)$. Then our series becomes

$$Z\rho(x, 0, 0) = \frac{8}{V} \sum_0^\infty \sum_0^\infty \sum_0^\infty F_{HKL} \cos 2\pi Hx. \qquad (6.122)$$

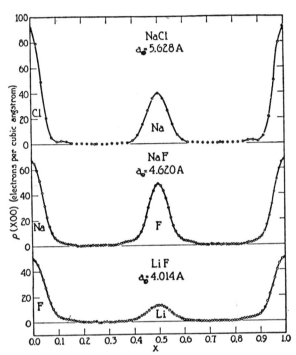

Fig. VI-24. The electron density as a function of distance along the edge of the unit cell in NaCl, NaF, and LiF, according to Havighurst.

Curves showing $Z\rho(x, 0, 0)$ for NaCl, NaF, and LiF obtained by Havighurst are shown in Fig. VI-24. In these curves we see the electron density per cubic angstrom along the edge of a unit cell with the origin taken at the center of the heaviest atom. The curves contain the thermal agitation at room temperature, since the temperature correction has not been made. On a more expanded scale of ordinates it would be evident that the electron density falls to zero within experimental error only for a very narrow region

[72] R. J. Havighurst, Phys. Rev. **29**, 1 (1927).

between the atoms, thus indicating that they extend well out into the unit cell and are actually in contact.

Another method of obtaining electron distributions in crystals by Fourier analysis, involving considerably less labor in computation, has been pointed out by W. L. Bragg.[73] In this case a projection of the electron density upon one of the faces of the unit cell is studied. Such a projection may be achieved by finding the coefficients of reflection from the planes lying in one of the principal zones, that is, planes having common intersections along the edges of the unit cell. Let us consider the set of planes having a common intersection along the direction of the vector τ_1 which is the edge of the unit cell along the X axis. Since these planes are parallel to this axis, they never intersect it, and they all have the Miller index $h = 0$, being characterized by the indices $(0, k, l)$. If we use the F's derived from the coefficients of reflection of the planes in a Fourier expansion which is a special case of eq. (6.118), we obtain

$$Z\sigma(y, z) = A^{-1} \sum_{-\infty}^{\infty} \sum_{-\infty}^{\infty} F'_{0KL} \cos 2\pi(Ky + Lz), \quad (6.123)$$

where A is the area of the face of the unit cell whose edges are τ_2 and τ_3. For any given point $(0, y, z)$ this series represents the electron density per unit area, where the entire unit cell is considered as projected upon this face. It may be mentioned that the condition that the unit cell have a center of symmetry at the origin is more restrictive than necessary for eq. (6.123). This equation may be used in cases where the unit cell does not have such a center, provided only that the projection upon the plane in question has such a center. The constant term of eq. (6.123), that is, the value of $Z\sigma(y, z)$ when $K = L = 0$, is Z/A.

The derivation of eq. (6.123) is probably best accomplished by retracing, in two dimensions, the steps taken in the derivation of eq. (6.116). Thus we may assume that the areal density function with which eq. (6.123) is concerned may be expressed as

$$Z\sigma(y, z) = \sum_{0}^{\infty} \sum_{-\infty}^{\infty} \alpha_{qr} \cos 2\pi(qy+rz) + \sum_{0}^{\infty} \sum_{-\infty}^{\infty} \beta_{qr} \sin 2\pi(qy+rz) \quad (6.124)$$

and consider the expression for the crystal structure factor for planes $(0, K, L)$, which is

$$F_{0KL} = AZ \int_0^1 \int_0^1 \sigma(y, z) e^{2\pi i(Hx+Ky+Lz)} dy dz. \quad (6.125)$$

[73] W. L. Bragg, Proc. Roy. Soc. Lond. A, **123**, 537 (1929).

The justification for writing the expression for F_{OKL} in this form is shown in Fig. VI–25. In this figure, some of the planes (oKL) are indicated as $ABFG$, $ACDB$, etc. The function $Z\sigma(y, z)$ gives the areal density of scattering material on the face bounded by τ_2 and τ_3. When the planes indicated are acting as reflecting planes, according to Fig. V–21, Chap. V, the phase of the scattered wave is independent of the x coordinate along these planes, so that we can consider all the scattering material concentrated at one value of x, namely, $x = 0$. By a combination of eqs. (6.125) and (6.124),

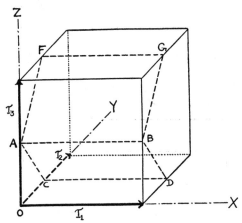

FIG. VI–25. Showing planes of the type (oKL) which are parallel to the X-axis. The function (o, y, z) gives the electron density projected on the face bounded by τ_2 and τ_3.

eq. (6.123) may be deduced exactly as eq. (6.118) was obtained from eqs. (6.106) and (6.108).

These two dimensional Fourier series plots have been studied in many crystals by W. L. Bragg and his collaborators. Figure VI–26 shows such a projection in the case of crystalline sodium chlorate, $NaClO_3$, worked out by Zachariasen.[74] $NaClO_3$ is built on a cubic lattice with $a_0 = 6.570 \pm 0.006$ A, and the unit cell contains four molecules. The crystal does not contain a center of symmetry, but there is such a center in the projection on a cube face. The upper chart in the figure shows a contour map of the projection, the lines being drawn through points of equal $Z\sigma(y, z)$. The contour interval is 100. The lower chart in the figure shows the atomic

[74] W. H. Zachariasen, Zeitschr. f. Kristallographie 71, 517 (1929).

positions projected on the cube face and serves to interpret the upper chart. The contours around the chlorine positions lie close together, and indicate the small volume occupied by a pentavalent

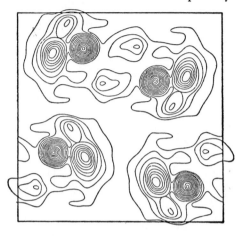

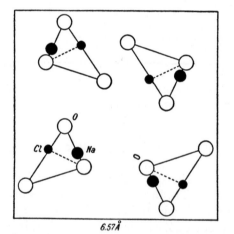

6.57Å

Fɪɢ. VI–26.   The electron density in a unit cell of sodium chlorate, projected on a face of the unit cube.   (After Zachariasen.)

chlorine atom.   Zachariasen estimates from this figure 12.0 electrons per chlorine atom, which indicates that the chlorine is in ionic form.

The most extensive two-dimensional study has been carried out on diopside, a monoclinic crystal which gives on analysis Ca, Mg, Si, and O in the proportions indicated by $CaMg(SiO_3)_2$.   The lengths of side of the unit cell are $\tau_1 = 9.71$ A, $\tau_2 = 8.89$ A, $\tau_3 = 5.24$ A; the monoclinic angle is $74° 10'$ and the total number of electrons in

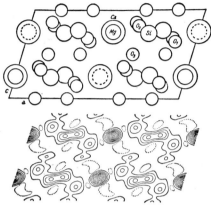

FIG. VI-27. Projection of the diopside unit cell on face (010). (After W. L. Bragg.)

the unit cell is $Z = 432$. An extensive study of the coefficients of reflection has been made by Warren and Bragg.[75] The approximate positions of the atoms in the unit cell are first found by trial, using

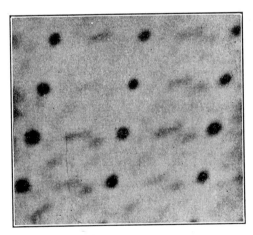

FIG. VI-28. A "microphotograph" of diopside taken parallel to the τ_3 or c axis, according to W. L. Bragg.

the expression for the crystal structure factor and checking against observed intensities. From these approximate results, the signs of

[75] B. Warren and W. L. Bragg, Zeitschr. F. Krist. **69**, 467 (1928).

the coefficients in the Fourier series may be determined. They are positive or negative, according to whether the diffracted wave has a phase the same as, or opposite to, that of a wave scattered by an electron at the origin. Figures VI–27 and VI–28 show the projection upon the (o1o) face of the unit cell. Ca and Mg lie directly over each other on this projection.[76]

Figure VI–28 shows an artificially prepared x-ray " micro-photograph " of diopside, the " photograph " being taken without per-

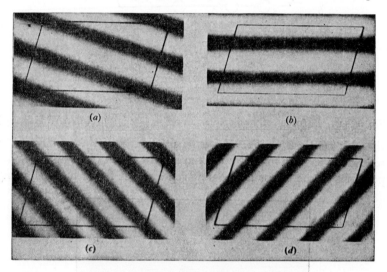

(a)   (b)

(c)   (d)

Fig. VI–29. A pictorial representation of single terms in a double Fourier series. (After W. L. Bragg.)

(a) F_{102}, phase negative. (b) F_{302}, phase negative. (c) F_{002}, phase positive.
(d) F_{301}, phase positive.

spective along the τ_2 axis, so that the projection of Fig. VI–27 is obtained. The method of preparation of this picture is as follows. An individual term $F'_{0KL} \cos 2\pi(Ky + Lz)$ of the sum in eq. (6.123) may be thought of as representing a sinusoidal variation of the quantity $Z\sigma(y, z)$ on the y, z plane. The loci of points of the same phase will be straight lines determined by the expression

$$Ky + Lz = \text{integer}.$$

If F' is negative a minimum instead of a maximum lies at the origin. A set of such stripes is shown in Fig. VI–29, which refers to planes of the type (HoL). The double sum in question represents a super-

[76] From W. L. Bragg, Zeitschr. F. Krist. **70**, 475 (1929).

position of a great number of such simple fringes, the proper amplitude being assigned to each.

Bragg has devised an ingenious method of accomplishing this. A lantern slide is prepared with sinusoidal alternations of light and dark portions across it. These are projected on a distant sheet of photo-sensitized paper on which a parallelogram representing the base of the unit cell under consideration has been drawn. The distance of the projector from the screen can be varied, and the lantern slide turned about a horizontal axis normal to its plane until orientation and spacing of the projected fringes are those desired. In this way Fig. VI–29 was prepared. Superposition of a large number of such fringes can be accomplished by exposing each orientation for a time proportional to the magnitude of the corresponding F_{OKL}. The resultant pattern of Fig. VI–28 is a pictorial presentation of the graphical result of Fig. VI–27.[77]

A third method of using the Fourier series in the study of the electron density in crystals was devised by A. H. Compton.[78] This method is to study the projection of the electron density upon some line through the crystal. This line is taken normal to some important set of planes, and thus the projection gives the amount of diffracting material in a layer of the unit cell of thickness dz parallel to the planes in question and at height z above one of them. It is thus closely related to the function appearing in eq. (6.98). Let us modify this equation to suit our present needs. We will restrict the generality of the following derivation by assuming that the crystal is built on orthogonal axes. We are now using the symbol z to represent the fraction of the length τ_3 of the unit cell in the z direction, not to represent an actual length in centimeters as it does in eq. (6.98). Referring for a moment to the z of eq. (6.98) as z', our present $z = z'/\tau_3$. Furthermore we wish to adapt the equation to a unit cell rather than a plane of identical atoms. Proceeding in a more general manner than that in which eq. (6.98) was obtained (spherical symmetry was assumed in passing from eq. (6.95) to the next expression) we obtain as a generalization of eq. (6.98)

$$F = Z\tau_3 \int_0^1 p(z)e^{i\,(4\pi/\lambda)\tau_3\,z\,\sin\theta}dz \qquad (6.126)$$

---

[77] This pictorial presentation has an elegant analogy in Abbe's theory of the resolving power of the microscope. See Porter, Phil. Mag. **2**, 154 (1906); W. L. Bragg, The Crystalline State, Macmillan (1934), p. 229 et seq.

[78] A. H. Compton, X-rays and Electrons, Van Nostrand (1926), p. 151.

where Z is the number of electrons in the unit cell, and τ_3 is the length of side of the unit cell in the z direction. Then let us assume that

$$Zp(z) = \sum_{r=0}^{r=\infty} A_r \cos 2\pi rz + \sum_{r=0}^{r=\infty} B_r \sin 2\pi rz. \qquad (6.127)$$

Remembering our assumption of orthogonal axes we have

$$N\lambda = 2\tau_3 \sin \theta,$$

so that eq. (6.126) becomes

$$F = Z\tau_3 \int_0^1 p(z) \cos 2\pi Nz dz + iZ\tau_3 \int_0^1 p(z) \sin 2\pi Nz dz. \qquad (6.128)$$

Substituting eq. (6.128) in eq. (6.127), and following steps entirely analogous to those immediately subsequent to eqs. (6.109) to (6.112), we find that the only finite values are contributed by $r = N$, and

$$A_r = A_N = 2F'_N/\tau_3$$

$$B_r = B_N = 2F''_N/\tau_3$$

where F'_N is the real part of the crystal structure factor for reflection of order N from the planes in question, and F''_N is the corresponding imaginary part of F. Thus the series becomes

$$Zp(z) = A_0 + \frac{2}{\tau_3}\sum_1^\infty F'_N \cos 2\pi Nz + \frac{2}{\tau_3}\sum_0^\infty F''_N \sin 2\pi Nz. \qquad (6.129)$$

The evaluation of A_0 may be accomplished by steps entirely analogous to those preceding eq. (6.116). The result is

$$A_0 = Z/\tau_3. \qquad (6.130)$$

Equation (6.129) shows that the coefficients of reflection from the various orders of a single plane may be used to give the electron distribution in layers parallel to that plane. In many simple crystals the presence of sine terms is unnecessary. Equation (6.129) may then be written, keeping in mind the application to a cubic lattice with $\tau_1 = \tau_2 = \tau_3 = a_0$,

$$Zp(z) = Z/a_0 + (2/a_0)\sum_1^\infty F_N \cos 2\pi Nz. \qquad (6.131)$$

Equation (6.131) is applicable to rock-salt, for instance, because of its high symmetry, but in a cubic crystal like zinc blende the presence of sine terms would be necessary for certain planes, and the more general eq. (6.129) would have to be used.

An especially interesting application of this series is to the electron distribution in sheets parallel to the (111) planes of NaCl, for in moving through the crystal in a direction perpendicular to these planes we encounter alternately planes of Na and Cl atoms. Although eq. (6.131) has been devised to represent the layer structure in planes parallel to one face of the unit cell, it is easily adapted to the (111) planes by replacing a_0 by $a_0/\sqrt{3}$ and for F_N taking the series F_{111}, F_{222}, F_{333}, etc. Probably the most complete work on these planes has been done by James and Firth,[79] with the results shown

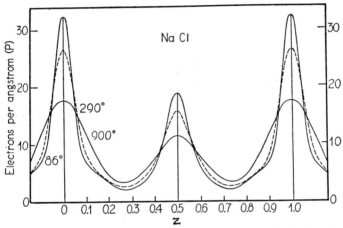

Fig. VI–30. The electron density in layers parallel to the (111) plane in NaCl as a function of temperature. (After James and Firth.)

in Fig. VI–30. The curves are calculated for three different temperatures. The high peaks are the chlorine atoms, and a sodium peak lies between them. The slight change in slope near the base of the chlorine peaks is probably real, and represents an outer electron shell. The thermal motion of the atoms is clearly shown in the lowering and broadening of the peaks as the temperature rises. This takes place in such a way that the area beneath them remains constant. The curve at 86° K is based on 10 F-values, and this curtailment of the series represents a limitation of the accuracy with which the curves represent the actual electron layer distribution in the crystal.

[79] James and Firth, Proc. Roy. Soc. Lond. A **117**, 62 (1927).

In treating the (100) planes of NaCl we would expect peaks of electron density of equal height separated by 2.814 A, and representing Na + Cl. We can study the problem more advantageously by not following so literally the crystal structure problem. We may assume a set of chlorine planes, say, 7.10 A apart. The reason for assuming this large spacing, which does not exist in rock salt, is that with such a spacing the atoms will not overlap. The reason for the

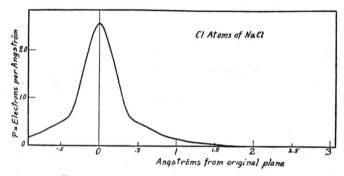

Fig. VI–31. The electron population in layers bounded by parallel planes at various distances from the center of the chlorine atom. Calculated from the atomic structure factor curve of chlorine in rock salt assuming a spacing of 7.10 A. (After A. H. Compton.)

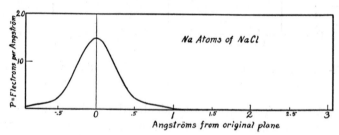

Fig. VI–32. An analysis of the sodium atom in rock salt carried out in a similar manner to that portrayed for chlorine in Fig. VI–31. (After A. H. Compton.)

choice of the particular figure 7.10 A is that with this numerical value sin θ for the first observable order, $(Nh\ Nk\ Nl) = (200)$, is 0.05 when molybdenum $K\alpha$ radiation is used, and hence the F's for chlorine can be conveniently read off the curve of Fig. VI–18. An analysis of the chlorine in NaCl in this manner, carried out by A. H. Compton, is shown in Fig. VI–31. In order to obtain this figure it was necessary to extrapolate the structure factor curve of chlorine at 0.710 A out to a value of sin θ corresponding to the 16th order, and the available data (Bragg, James, and Bosanquet) stopped at the 10th order. The area under the curve is not affected greatly by the manner in which this extrapolation is carried out,

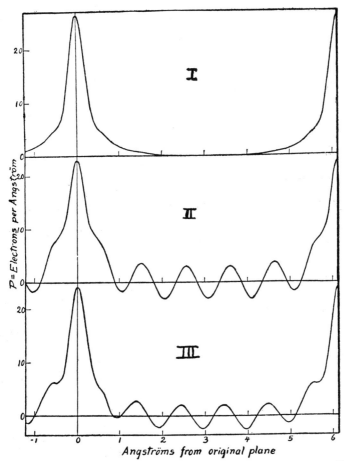

FIG. VI-33. Showing the effect of arbitrary changes of sign and phase in the Fourier series terms giving the layer analysis of the chlorine atom. (After A. H. Compton.)

but the shape of the curve may be appreciably affected thereby. Different methods of extrapolation to zero introduce different "humps" in the $U(r)$ curve at the outer distances, and probably account for the differences between the analyses of Havighurst (Figs.

VI–35, 36) and those of Compton. Figure VI–32 shows a similar analysis by Compton of sodium in NaCl.

Compton also investigated the effect of introducing negative F values into the series, since without using symmetry properties it is impossible to decide whether the individual F's are negative or positive. In Fig. VI–33 are plotted in three different ways the values of $Zp(z)$ for chlorine using the data of Table VI–18. Curve I is that given in Fig. VI–31, as calculated from eq. (6.131). In curve II the coefficient of the 6th term has been taken to be negative, the other terms having their former values. In curve III the 6th term has been taken as $(2/a_0)F_6 \cos (2\pi 6z + \frac{1}{2}\pi)$, showing the effect of introducing an arbitrary phase angle. The fact that curves II and III indicate negative densities in some places, whereas curve I does not, confirms the correctness of the assumptions that all the Fourier coefficients are positive and that the assumed phases are correct if Cl is taken at the origin.

19. A Fourier Analysis of the Atomic Structure Factor Curves

The procedure by which the chlorine curve of Fig. VI–31 was obtained suggests the possibility of a Fourier analysis of the atomic structure factor curves. Before we take this up we may mention an obvious consequence of the "layer" distribution curves of Figs. VI–31 and VI–32. If these functions $Zp(z)$ are known, the function $U(r)$ of eq. (6.96) may be obtained from

$$U(r)dr = p(r)4\pi r^2 dr, \qquad (6.132)$$

the derivation of which is clear from Fig. VI–34.

A second method of obtaining $U(r)$ has been devised by A. H. Compton,[80] which makes use of the atomic structure factor curves, as in Fig. VI–18, directly. From eq. (6.96) we have

$$f[(\sin \theta)/\lambda] = Z \int_0^\infty U(r) \frac{\sin [(4\pi r/\lambda) \sin \theta]}{(4\pi r/\lambda) \sin \theta} \, dr, \quad (6.133)$$

---

[80] A. H. Compton, X-rays and Electrons, Van Nostrand (1926), p. 163. The treatment given in the present text can be greatly simplified by the introduction of Fourier's integral theorem. The result, eq. (6.135), would then appear as an integral instead of the series, of the form

$$ZU(r) = (2r/\pi) \int_0^\infty kf(k) \sin kr \, dk$$

where k is $(4\pi \sin \theta)/\lambda$.

in which we have written $f\{(\sin\theta)/\lambda\}$ for the atomic structure factor to emphasize that it depends on $(\sin\theta)/\lambda$ only, at a given temperature, assuming always that the wave-length is far from the critical absorption limits of the atom. Thus for a given set of crystal planes, f is really dependent on the order alone, being the same for the first order, for instance, of any wave-length. We can introduce the order into the expression by setting

$$(\sin\theta)/\lambda = N/2D$$

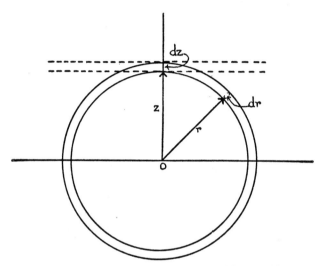

Fig. VI-34.   The connection between $p(z)$ and $U(r)$.

as suggested by Bragg's law.   Thus we obtain

$$f\left(\frac{N}{2D}\right) = Z\int_0^\infty U(r)\,\frac{\sin\,(2\pi Nr/D)}{2\pi Nr/D}\,dr.$$

In this equation Z is the total number of electrons per atom. D will be a length and will depend on what value of N we choose to correspond to a given $(\sin\theta)/\lambda$. Let us suppose that the integer N is chosen so that D is large enough so that $U(r)$ is not appreciably different from zero outside the distance $\frac{1}{2}D$. If this condition is fulfilled, we may put a finite limit on the integral and write

$$f\left(\frac{N}{2D}\right) = Z\int_0^{\frac{1}{2}D} U(r)\,\frac{\sin\,(2\pi Nr/D)}{2\pi Nr/D}\,dr. \qquad (6.134)$$

We may now assume that our function $U(r)$ may be represented by a Fourier series as follows:

$$ZU(r) = r \sum_{0}^{\infty} A_m \sin (2\pi mr/D).$$

In setting up this expression we have deliberately supposed that the factor r exists before the summation sign for the purpose of cancelling the r in the denominator of the integrand of eq. (6.134), in order that we may determine the coefficients A_m by the usual method. Substitution of the postulated series for $U(r)$ in eq. (6.134) gives

$$f\left(\frac{N}{2D}\right) = \int_{0}^{\frac{1}{2}D} \left[\sum_{0}^{\infty} A_m \sin (2\pi mr/D)\right] \frac{\sin (2\pi Nr/D)}{2\pi N/D} \, dr$$

$$= \sum_{0}^{\infty} \int_{0}^{\frac{1}{2}D} \frac{A_m D}{2\pi N} \sin (2\pi mr/D) \sin (2\pi Nr/D) \, dr.$$

Using a well-known trigonometric transformation for the product of two sines, we obtain

$$\int_{0}^{\frac{1}{2}D} \sin (2\pi mr/D) \sin (2\pi Nr/D) \, dr$$

$$= -\tfrac{1}{2} \int_{0}^{\frac{1}{2}D} \cos \{2\pi(m+N)r/D\} dr + \tfrac{1}{2} \int_{0}^{\frac{1}{2}D} \cos \{2\pi(m-N)r/D\} dr.$$

The first of the integrals on the right-hand side of this equation vanishes for all integral values of m and N, and the second vanishes for all values except those at which $m = N$. Here we obtain

$$\tfrac{1}{2} \int_{0}^{\frac{1}{2}D} dr = \tfrac{1}{4}D,$$

so that the coefficients $A_m = A_N$ of the series are determined by

$$A_m = A_N = \frac{8\pi N}{D^2} f(N/2D)$$

and our series is

$$ZU(r) = \frac{8\pi r}{D^2} \sum_{0}^{\infty} Nf(N/2D) \sin (2\pi Nr/D). \qquad (6.135)$$

From this equation the form of the $U(r)$ curve may be deduced from the atomic structure factor curves, examples of which are shown in Fig. VI–18, which represents data taken from x-rays of wave-length 0.710 A. If as in the preceding section we take $N = 1$ at a value of $\sin \theta = 0.05$, the value of D is given by $N\lambda/2 \sin \theta$ which is 7.10 A. This D is large enough so that the $U(r)$ curve has fallen to zero within the distance 3.55 A.

The total number of electrons per atom will be given by

$$Z \int_0^{\frac{1}{2}D} U(r)dr = \sum_0^{\infty} \frac{8\pi Nf(N/2D)}{D^2} \int_0^{\frac{1}{2}D} r \sin (2\pi Nr/D) \, dr$$

$$= 2\left[\sum_0^{\infty} f(N/2D) - (-1)^N \sum_0^{\infty} f(N/2D) \right]. \qquad (6.136)$$

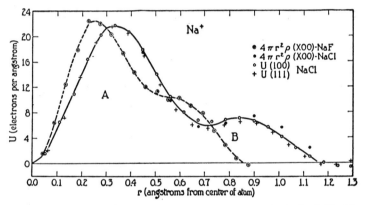

Fig. VI–35. An analysis of the sodium atom electron distribution by R. J. Havighurst.

Havighurst[81] has studied his structure factor data by the use of eq. (6.132) and by eq. (6.135) and finds in general good agreement in the $U(r)$ curves calculated by the two methods. His results on the sodium atom are shown in Fig. VI–35. The points marked $\odot$ were obtained by eq. (6.132) from a $p(z)$ curve for the (100) planes of NaF. All other points are for Na in NaCl. The points marked $\bullet$ were obtained from eq. (6.132) applied to (100) reflection from NaCl. Points $\bigcirc$ and $+$ were obtained from eq. (6.135) applied to various orders of reflection in the (100) and (111) planes of NaCl, respectively. The curve for Na in NaF is markedly different from that for Na in NaCl, and seems to indicate a greater compression of the atom in the fluoride. The total area under the Na in NaCl

[81] R. J. Havighurst, Phys. Rev. 29, 1 (1927).

curve is 10.4 electrons; under hump A the area is about 8, and under B, about 2 electrons. The total area may be affected by the method of extrapolation to zero.

Fig. VI–36 shows a $U(r)$ curve for chlorine in NaCl obtained by

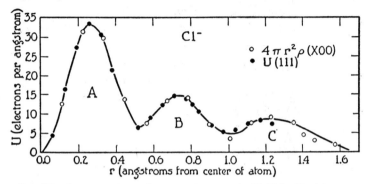

FIG. VI–36.   An analysis of the chlorine atom in NaCl by Havighurst.

Havighurst, and Fig. VI–37 a curve of calcium in CaF_2. In the chlorine curve the total area is 17.85 electrons, that under A being 10, under B, 5, and under C, 3. In the calcium curve the total area is 18 electrons, hump A having 10; B, 6; and C, 2. This indicates

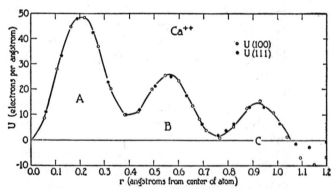

FIG. VI–37.   Calcium in CaF_2 according to Havighurst.

rather strongly the presence of doubly ionized calcium, since the neutral atom would have 20 electrons. The shapes of the curves in Havighurst's work are affected by thermal agitation, as the structure factors used are at room temperature, but the area under the curves should be independent of temperature.

Other studies of $U(r)$ curves by this method have been carried out by Compton[82] and by Bearden.[83] Compton calculated his results from the old data of Bragg, James and Bosanquet on atomic structure factor curves. Bearden took new experimental data on NaCl and Al crystals, and performed the analysis. The $U(r)$ curves obtained by Compton and Bearden differ somewhat from each other and from those of Havighurst, and cast some doubt upon the reality of the outermost parts of the curves. The number of humps obtained in the outer region of the curve depends considerably on the method of extrapolation of the atomic structure factor curve to small values of sin θ, and undoubtedly much of the difference lies in this method of extrapolation. It would seem, however, that Havighurst's curves are as good approximations to the $U(r)$ function as can be experimentally obtained from crystals at present. The reality of the "humps" is given support by the analysis of the scattering from the rare gases, discussed in Chapter III, in which the outer hump clearly appears.

20. *Attempts to Influence the Intensity of Reflection from Crystals by the Application of Electric and Magnetic Fields*

The problem of finding the cause of the enormous magnetic permeability of iron compared to other substances has long been of great interest. It is not surprising that shortly after the discovery of the diffraction of x-rays by crystals the effect of a magnetic field on the intensity of reflection by iron crystals was carried out.[84, 85] De Broglie used a crystal of magnetite, but found no difference between the magnetized and unmagnetized sample, and negative results were independently obtained by K. T. Compton and E. A. Trousdale.

An experiment to detect a possible change in the intensity of reflection of x-rays by a magnetite crystal due to magnetization was carried out by A. H. Compton and O. Rognley.[86] A balance method employing two Bragg ionization spectrometers was used, which was capable of detecting a change in intensity of 1 per cent, even in the

[82] A. H. Compton, X-rays and Electrons, Van Nostrand (1926), Figs. 81 and 82, p. 166.

[83] J. A. Bearden, Phys. Rev. **29**, 20 (1927).

[84] M. de Broglie, Le Radium **10**, 186 (1913).

[85] K. T. Compton and E. A. Trousdale, Phys. Rev. **5**, 315 (1915).

[86] A. H. Compton and O. Rognley, Phys. Rev. **16**, 464 (1920).

fourth order.   The magnetite was magnetized to about one-third of saturation, perpendicular to the reflecting surface in one experiment, and parallel to the surface in another.   No effect due to the magnetization was observed.

These experiments were extended by J. C. Stearns,[87] who improved the sensitivity of the apparatus and investigated both magnetite and silicon steel.   The method was capable of detecting a change of 0.1 per cent in the stronger reflections, but the results were also negative.   Stearns made a rough calculation of the change that might be expected if the magnetization were accomplished by the rotation of the planes of electron orbits in the atoms of iron.   If the orientation is such that the plane of the orbit lies in the plane of reflection from the crystal, the contribution of the electron in the orbit to the atomic structure factor is one, since it scatters in phase from every point in the orbit.   Likewise if the orientation is such that the plane of the orbit is perpendicular to the plane of reflection, the contribution to the atomic structure factor is calculable.   If one assigns one Bohr magneton as the orbital magnetic moment, one can calculate the number of orbits oriented in a sample of magnetic material the extent of whose magnetization is known.   In this way Stearns showed that in the fourth order from magnetite an effect 35 times the undetected experimental value should result, and in the second order 9 times the observed effect in silicon steel would be expected.   It thus seems proven that the orientation of electronic orbits cannot account for the magnetization of iron or ferromagnetic substances.   It therefore appears that the magnetic property must reside in some other mechanism, and the most probable one at present would seem to be the electron spin.

Various authors have attempted to influence the intensity of reflection from crystals, or of scattering from solids in general, by subjecting them to an electric field.[88]   The first experiments of Bennett and those of Hengstenberg were attempts to influence the intensity of reflection from rock salt by the application of an electric field parallel to one of the cubic axes of the crystal.   If the planes (100) are populated by sodium and chlorine ions, positively and

[87] J. C. Stearns, Phys. Rev. **35**, 1 (1930).
[88] J. Hengstenberg, Zeitschr. f. Physik **58**, 345 (1929).
R. D. Bennett, Phys. Rev. **36**, 65 (1930).
M. Ewing, Phys. Rev. **36**, 378 (1930), Abstract.
R. D. Bennett, J. Frankl. Inst. **211**, 481 (1931).

negatively charged, the field should stagger these charged units, pulling one type above, and one below the plane. Bennett was not able to detect any change in the intensity of reflection due to such a process, but Hengstenberg claims to have found a small effect of the order of 1/10 per cent. This experimental result has been criticized by Bennett, who believes that such an effect, if it exists, is not detectable.

Another type of experiment, initiated by Ewing, and carried on by Bennett, consists in the x-ray investigation of the haloes scattered from paraffin or waxes which have solidified under an electric field. Ewing showed that a mixture of waxes, solidified under such circumstances, has anisotropic scattering power for x-rays, and Bennett found a similar effect in paraffin. These experiments indicate that x-ray methods may prove a useful tool in the investigation of molecular motions in dielectrics.

CHAPTER VII

Phenomena Associated with the Ejection of Photo-electrons by X-rays

1. *The Ionization of Gases by X-rays*

When an x-ray beam passes through a limited volume of gas, part or all of the energy in the form of x-rays may be transformed into energy of other types. Thus we have as a first step, part of the x-ray energy going into kinetic energy of ejected photo-electrons or recoil electrons, and part into potential energy of the excited atoms remaining. The moving electrons in the gas dissipate their energy in the formation of ions. The excited atomic states are in general short-lived, and radiation is emitted which may be absorbed in the parent atom or in adjacent atoms, with the ejection of electrons and subsequent loss of their energy in the formation of ions. If the dimensions of the absorbing volume of gas are adequate, the x-rays scattered classically from the primary beam are eventually absorbed; the energy appearing as the energy of electrons in motion, and this being used in ionization.

Thus, eventually, all the x-ray energy is used in the production of gaseous ions, but it is important to note that there is the same intermediate step in all cases, namely, the x-ray energy is transformed into the kinetic energy of moving electrons, and these β-rays then ionize the gas. It is important to realize that the number of ions formed by direct action of the x-rays on the gas is minute compared to the number formed by the β-rays produced. Consider the passage of radiation of wave-length 0.71 A through argon gas. Most of the absorption acts will consist of the ejection of an argon K electron. The energy of the incident quantum will be 1.74×10^4 electron volts. The energy necessary to eject an argon K electron is 3.19×10^3 electron volts. Hence a photo-electron of 1.42×10^4 volts is produced. We shall see that the average energy expended by such an electron in producing a pair of ions in argon is about 29 volts. Hence this photo-electron produces some 490 ion pairs.

In addition, more ions are formed by Auger electrons ejected from the same primarily ionized atom. Thus in this case the ratio of the number of ions produced by the primary action of the x-rays to the total number produced is much less than $1/500$.

Due to this fact that the actual production of ions in a gas irradiated with x-rays is due to the action of β-rays, it should be possible, by measurement of the saturation ionization current in a gas, to find the average energy expended by a β-particle in the production of a pair of ions. This quantity, when measured in electron volts, is given the symbol ϵ. This same quantity should be measurable by allowing β-rays to pass into a gas and noting the amount of ionization produced. Both methods have been used, but in this discussion we shall limit ourselves to those experiments in which x-rays have been the primary agent. Besides finding the numerical value of ϵ, an interesting question arises as to whether ϵ is a function of the wave-length of the x-rays, that is, of the initial energy of the electrons liberated in the gas.

The work on this subject up to 1917 has been reviewed by Glocker,[1] and indicated that ϵ is a function of wave-length. Holthusen[2] pointed out that ionization by x-rays is intimately connected with that produced by β-rays, and using experiments by Lenard[3] attempted to construct a table from which absolute energies of x-ray beams could be read off, knowing the ionization currents produced by them. These β-ray results apparently showed that ϵ is a function of wave-length.

Other investigations which indicated that the average energy expended in the production of a pair of ions is a function of the wave-length of the x-rays were carried out by Boos,[4] Grebe and Kriegesmann,[5] and Kriegesmann.[6]

In 1926 Kulenkampff[7] made a very careful investigation of this subject, with results qualitatively different from those of the earlier investigators. In order to measure the value of ϵ, the power in the x-ray beam incident on the gas must be known. The usual method has been to degrade the x-ray energy into heat in a properly designed

[1] Glocker, Physikalische Zeitschrift **18**, 302 (1917).
[2] Holthusen, Fortschr. a. d. Geb. der Röntgen. **26**, 211 (1919).
[3] P. Lenard, Quantitatives über Kathodenstrahlen, Heidelberg. Akad. (1918).
[4] Boos, Zeitschr. f. Physik **10**, 1 (1922).
[5] Grebe and Kriegesmann, Zeitschr. f. Physik **28**, 91 (1924).
[6] Kriegesmann, Zeitschr. f. Physik **32**, 542 (1925).
[7] H. Kulenkampff, Ann. d. Physik **79**, 97 (1926).

calorimeter, and by measuring the rise in temperature of an amount of material of known heat capacity, determine the incident energy. Difficulties with this method are its lack of sensitivity and the necessary correction for scattered and fluorescence x-rays and β-rays from the calorimetric material. Kulenkampff found that with the most sensitive galvanometer available to him, a flux of energy of 2×10^{-7} cal. sec.$^{-1}$cm.$^{-2}$ was necessary for sufficient accuracy, and he was unable to obtain this amount in a beam monochromatized by crystal reflection. It was therefore necessary to use filtered beams of primary x-rays. An iron-bismuth thermopile was used, the " hot " junctions being made on small sheets of silver foil 0.01 cm. in thickness. The x-ray beam was absorbed in the silver, the entire absorbing area being about 1.5 cm.^{2} The wave-lengths used were not short enough to excite the K radiation of silver. The thermopile was calibrated by blackening the silver and allowing radiation from a standard lamp to fall on it. With a galvanometer sensitivity of 6×10^{-10} amp. per scale division (mm), one scale division was equivalent to a flux of energy of $(7.8 \pm 0.2) \times 10^{-9}$ cal. sec.$^{-1}$ over the entire absorbing area.

An ionization chamber was constructed in such a manner that the necessary corrections (discussed in a later section of this chapter) for loss of energy in the form of x-rays could be applied with some certainty. The thermopile could be moved in and out of the beam entering the chamber. The energy distribution in the filtered radiation was spectrometrically determined, and an effective wave-length calculated. The result of Kulenkampff's work is that the energy expended in the production of a pair of ions in air is 35 ± 5 electron volts, and is independent of the wave-length from 0.56 to 2.0 A.[8]

At about the same time, Kircher and Schmitz[9] published the

[8] In a later paper, Kulenkampff (Ann. der Physik **80**, 261 (1926)) shows that his result may be reconciled with the results of Lenard on the total ionization produced by a β-particle of known velocity. Lenard had measured the number of ions produced along a small part of the path, and obtained the total number by integration along the path. In this integration he assigned a very important role to total absorption of the electrons; Kulenkampff points out that the known efficiency of production of x-rays shows that such a process is extremely rare and can play no important part in the stoppage of a beam of electrons in a gas. Assuming that diffusion is the more important process, and that the β-rays have a definite range, Kulenkampff recalculates Lenard's results which originally showed that there is a variation of ϵ with initial velocity, and shows that such a variation does not exist.

[9] Kircher and Schmitz, Zeitschr. f. Physik **36**, 484 (1926).

results of measurements of ϵ in air.   The energy of the beam causing the ionization was measured by allowing the x-rays to be absorbed in an air-tight, heat-insulated vessel.   This vessel was connected to an exactly similar vessel by a capillary tube in which a drop of liquid was placed.   When the x-rays were being absorbed, the rise of temperature in the absorbing vessel increased the pressure of the air, causing the drop to move.   By passing an electric current through a resistance in the second vessel heat could be liberated at such a rate that the motion of the liquid drop in the capillary ceased.   In this way the equivalent of the energy of the x-ray beam could be measured. Bolometric measurements in the two vessels were also made.   Filtered primary x-rays were used.   The experiments indicated that the average energy required to produce a pair of ions in air is 21 volts, and is independent of the wave-length from 0.05 to 1.5 A.   Thus there is a large and unexplained discrepancy between the numerical values of ϵ due to Kulenkampff and to Kircher and Schmitz, but the constancy of ϵ was indicated in both researches.   Other determinations of ϵ for air have made it almost certain that the Kircher and Schmitz value is too low.

Since these early results, many investigations have been reported. After Rump[10] had corrected his first results by a re-calibration of his ionization chamber, he found a value of ϵ of 33 volts.   This was independent of wave-length, and this last property has been confirmed by many other investigators.   Berthold and Glocker[11] have pointed out that the early experiments of Bouwers[12] on the power in x-ray beams indicate that ϵ does not change when the incident wave-length varies from 0.15 to 0.7 A.   The results of Aurén[13] likewise showed no variation of ϵ with wave-length.

Steenbeck[14] has attacked the problem with an entirely different method of measuring the power in an x-ray beam.   This consists in counting by means of a Geiger counter the actual number of absorption acts in a known thickness of gas.   The x-ray beam passed between the plates of a parallel plate condenser and the counter was placed behind an aperture in one of the plates, so that the ions produced opposite this opening were drawn in and counted.   If the

[10] Rump, Zeitschr. f. Physik **43**, 254 (1927); ibid. **44**, 396 (1927).

[11] Berthold and Glocker, Zeitschr. f. Physik **31**, 259 (1925).

[12] Bouwers, Diss. Utrecht (1924).

[13] Aurén, T., Vetenskapsakad. Nobelinst. Medd. **6**, No. 13, 1 (1927).

[14] M. Steenbeck, Ann. der Physik **87**, 811 (1928).

length of path in which the ions formed are counted is l, η the number of counts per second, μ the absorption coefficient in the gas, and ν the frequency, then

$$P = \frac{\eta h \nu}{1 - e^{-\mu l}}$$

where P is the power in the beam. The method is of course subject to statistical fluctuations, and the fraction of the ions entering the counter which are actually counted must be known. After surmounting these difficulties, Steenbeck found that $\epsilon = 28 \pm 6$ electron volts for air, at the wave-lengths 2.29 A (Cr $K\alpha$) and 1.54 A (Cu $K\alpha$).

Crowther and Bond,[15] using two small calorimeters filled with transformer oil and a balance method, found ϵ for air to be 42.5 ± 0.4 electron volts, and independent of incident wave-length. Gaertner[16] has made measurements of ϵ for various gases, using a thermo-couple to measure the energy in the x-ray beam. These results are summarized in Table VII–1, part A.

Relative measurements of the ionization produced by complete absorption of a given amount of x-rays in various gases can be made with considerably greater accuracy than can any one absolute determination[17] of ϵ. It is necessary only to use a constant source of x-rays, and measure the relative ionization currents produced in the two gases, making corrections, if necessary, for the energy escaping from the volume from which the ionization current is drawn. This volume can usually be made so large that only losses due to energy escaping in the form of x-rays need be considered, the β-rays produced coming to the end of their ionizing range in the gas volume. A large number of gases have been investigated in this way by Crowther and Orton.[18] They define T as the number of ions produced in a given gas by the complete absorption of a certain amount of x-ray energy of a given wave-length, relative to the number of ions produced in air by complete absorption of the same x-ray energy. Thus

$$T = \epsilon_{air} / \epsilon_{gas}.$$

[15] Crowther and Bond, Phil. Mag. 6, 401 (1929).

[16] Gaertner, Ann. der Physik 2, 94 (1929); 3, 325 (1929); 10, 825 (1931); 11, 648 (1931).

[17] H. Küstner, Ann. der Phys. 5, 10, 616 (1931) estimates that absolute values of ϵ accurate to more than 1.5 per cent would be extraordinarily difficult to obtain, whereas relative values of the total ionization may be accurate to a few tenths of a per cent.

[18] Crowther and Orton, Phil. Mag. 10, 329 (1930); and Phil. Mag. 13, 505 (1932)

Their results for T are given in Table VII–1, part B. They also point out that those gases having low ionization potentials give relatively large numbers of ions.

Gaertner[19] has also made relative measurements, for which high accuracy is claimed. These are included in Table VII–1B. It is interesting to note that Gaertner obtained for argon $T = 1.232$, whereas Crowther and Orton obtained 1.32, and Wilhelmy[20], 1.309. The experiments of Wilhelmy are of interest because the x-radiation used was much softer than in the other researches. The total radiation from an x-ray tube operating at various voltages from 2.0 to 2.7 kv. was passed into neon, air, and argon, and the relative ionizations measured. For such soft radiation no corrections are necessary for escaping energy. The argon experiments were made over a voltage range from 2.0 to 4.0 kv. Wilhelmy observed a slight variation of T with wave-length for these soft x-rays, T increasing in neon from 1.20 at 2.7 and 2.5 kv. to 1.26 at 2.0 kv. A similar trend was observed in argon. This makes it seem probable that it is the ϵ for air which is changing. It may be that for these slow electrons, the energy losses in resonance impacts become appreciable and hence the average value of ϵ, which has to do with ionization, increases as the energy decreases. This appears to agree with results of Thomson[21] on ionization by slow electrons.

2. The Fluorescence Yield

Let us suppose that a substance, which for simplicity we will assume contains only one kind of atom, is irradiated with a beam of x-rays which ejects K photo-electrons from n_K atoms per second. In the steady state, n_K atoms per second are returning to the unionized or normal configuration. Of these n_K atoms, a number n_1 will emit

[19] O. Gaertner, Ann. der Physik 16, 613 (1933).

[20] E. Wilhelmy, Zeitschr. f. Physik 83, 341 (1933).

[21] Determinations of ϵ by allowing β-rays of known energy to pass through a gas and noting the ionization produced have not been treated in this text. It is quite likely that absolute values of ϵ more reliable than those obtained by x-ray methods are given by such measurements. A few references are:

C. T. R. Wilson, Proc. Roy. Soc. Lond. A 104, 1; 192 (1923).

P. Lenard, Quantitatives über Kathodenstrahlen, Heidelberg (1925).

Lehmann and Osgood, Proc. Roy. Soc. Lond. A 115, 608 (1927).

A. Eisl, Ann. der Physik 3, 277 (1929).

Thomson, Proc. Edinburgh 51, 27 (1930–31).

TABLE VII-1

QUANTITATIVE RESULTS ON IONIZATION OF GASES BY X-RAYS

A. Experimental determinations of the average energy used in producing a pair of ions.

Author	Gas	Wave-length (Angstroms)	ϵ Electron-volts
Kulenkampff (1926)............	Air	$0.56 \to 2.0$	35 ± 5
Kircher and Schmitz (1926)......	Air	$0.5 \to 1.5$	21
Rump (1929).................	Air	$\sim 100 \to 150$ kv.	40
Steenbeck (1928)..............	Air	2.29; 1.54	28.6
Crowther and Bond (1929)......	Air	0.225	42.5 ± 0.4
	Air	1.38	36.4
	N_2	1.38	40.8
	O_2	1.38	34.4
	A	1.38	39.6
	A	0.71	29.3
Gaertner (1929).............	Cl_2	1.38	23.6
	Br_2	1.38	27.9
	I_2	1.38	28.8
	CH_3Cl	1.38	26.0
	CH_3Br	1.38	28.7
	CH_3I	1.38	29.8
	Ne	1.38	43.2 ± 3
Gaertner (1931).............	A	1.38	28.8 ± 1
	Kr	1.38	32.4 ± 3
	Xe	1.38	47.5

B. Measurements of total ionization relative to air.

Author	Gas	Wave-length (Angstroms)	$\epsilon_{air}/\epsilon_{gas} = T$
	N_2	1.54	0.99_3
	O_2	1.54	1.10_3
	O_2	1.93	1.10_1
	CO_2	1.54	1.03_5
	CO_2	1.93	1.04_2
	H_2S	1.54	1.41
	A	1.54	1.32
	C_5H_{12}	1.54	1.45
Crowther and Orton (1932)....	C_5H_{12}	1.93	1.41
	C_6H_{14}	1.54	1.50
	C_6H_{14}	1.93	1.50
	C_2H_5Cl	1.54	1.31
	$CHCl_3$	1.54	1.28_5
	CCl_4	1.54	1.33
	$Zn(CH_3)_2$	1.54	1.37
	$(C_2H_5)_2O$	1.93	1.40
	C_2H_5Br	1.54	1.31
	CH_3I	1.54	1.36
	A	1.38	1.232
O. Gaertner (1933)..........	N_2	1.38	0.902
	O_2	1.38	1.077
E. Wilhelmy (1933)..........	Ne	~ 2.5 kv.	1.193
	A	~ 3.0 kv.	1.309

the line $K\alpha_1$ as a step in the process, n_2 will emit $K\alpha_2$, etc. Let us define as the fluorescence yield for the K level, w_K, the ratio

$$w_K = \frac{n_1 + n_2 + n_3 + \ldots \ldots}{n_K} = \frac{\Sigma n_f}{n_K}. \qquad (7.01)$$

At first thought it would seem that the fraction w_K must necessarily be equal to unity, since in order to replace the vacancy in the K shell an electron must drop in from the L, M, N, . . . shell with the concomitant emission of a quantum of K series radiation. The earliest experiments on the yield of fluorescence radiation, however, indicated that w_K is distinctly less than one. Barkla and Sadler[22] found that in the excitation of fluorescence radiation in radiators of 24 Cr, 26 Fe and 27 Co, w_K appeared to be on the order of 0.3 if the incident wavelength was not too far removed from the fluorescence wave-lengths.

Kossel[23] became interested in this problem, and remarked that the fractional value of w_K might be due to a radiationless transfer of energy to an electron, the transfer taking place within the parent atom.[24] This amounts to a radiationless transfer of the type discussed by Klein and Rosseland,[25] which may occur when in a gas an excited atom transfers its energy to another atom on impact without the necessity of postulating radiation as an intermediate step. Such internal conversions are known to occur in radioactive processes since β-rays appear whose kinetic energies are given by the energy of a nuclear γ-ray minus the binding energy of the K or L shell.[26]

Such an effect in the x-ray region would tend to decrease the yield of fluorescence radiation and increase the yield of β-rays from the ionized material. The increase in the number of β-rays emitted has been noted by Barkla and Dallas,[27] and the interpretation in terms of an internal radiationless transfer put forward.

The existence of such a phenomenon in the x-ray region was first clearly shown in the Wilson cloud track photographs obtained

[22] Sadler, Phil. Mag. **18**, 107 (1909); Barkla, Phil. Trans. **217**, 315 (1917).

[23] Kossel, Zeitschr. f. Physik **19**, 333 (1923).

[24] Kossel recalculated the results of Sadler, assuming that the observed ionization currents for the incident and fluorescence beams should be corrected for the fact that the energy expended by a photo-electron in producing a pair of ions varies with its energy. Since such an effect apparently does not exist in the x-ray region we shall not take up Kossel's corrections.

[25] Rosseland, Zeitschr. f. Physik **14**, 173 (1923).

[26] L. Meitner, Zeitschr. f. Physik **17**, 54 (1923).

[27] Barkla and Dallas, Phil. Mag. **47**, 1 (1924).

by Auger.[28]   Indication of simultaneous ejection of two electrons from the same atom had previously been obtained by Wilson,[29] but the importance of this result was not stressed. Auger took expansion photographs with an atmosphere of argon in the chamber, and with x-rays passing through whose frequencies were much higher than necessary to eject argon K-electrons. The tracks of photo-electrons ejected from the K levels of argon atoms were plainly visible, and in a large proportion of these tracks, Auger noted that a second, ball-like track occurred at the origin of the photo-electron track. Concluding that these very short tracks were low-speed electrons, Auger diluted the argon with hydrogen to make these secondary tracks longer. For convenience we shall speak of the short tracks as caused by Auger electrons, in order to distinguish them from the photo-electrons. In a mixture of 95 parts H_2 and 5 parts A, the Auger electron tracks were sufficiently extended in length so that the following properties were noted:

(1) The photo-electron and the accompanying Auger electron arise at the same point.

(2) The length of the Auger electron track is independent of the wave-length of the incident x-rays, whereas the length of the photo-electron track increases as the wave-length decreases.

(3) The direction of ejection of the Auger electron track is independent of that of the photo-electron.

(4) Not all photo-electron tracks show an Auger track at their source.

In experiments with different gases it was found that the length of the Auger tracks increases as the atomic number increases. With krypton gas and 30-kv. x-rays, the Auger tracks and the photo-electron tracks were approximately the same length.

The absorption coefficient of the argon for x-rays of wave-lengths corresponding to its own K series is so low that the possibility that the K radiation might be emitted from the atom which had a K electron removed, and eject a photo-electron from an adjacent atom, causing a track which is seen as that of the Auger electron, is definitely excluded.

These observed facts are consistent with the following explanation.

[28] P. Auger, Compt. rend. **180**, 65 (1925); Journal de Physique **6**, 205 (1925); Compt. rend. **182**, 773; 1215 (1926).

[29] C. T. R. Wilson, Proc. Roy. Soc. **104**, 192 (1923).

When a K photo-electron is ejected from an argon atom, the vacancy in the K shell may be filled by one of the L electrons, but it is not necessary that one quantum of argon K radiation actually leave the atom. Instead, the quantum of K radiation may be absorbed or converted by the L shell, for instance, into the energy necessary for the ejection of an L electron plus the kinetic energy of the β-ray produced. Thus if $\frac{1}{2}mv^2$ is the kinetic energy of the Auger electron in this case (neglecting relativity corrections),

$$\frac{1}{2}mv^2 = h\nu_\alpha - (E_{L^{II}} - E_L) \qquad (7.02)$$

where $E_{L^{II}}$ is the energy of an atom with two L electrons missing, and the energy difference in parentheses is the work required to remove the second L electron. But

$$h\nu_\alpha = E_K - E_L. \qquad (7.03)$$

Hence eq. (7.02) becomes

$$\frac{1}{2}mv^2 = E_K - E_{L^{II}} \doteq E_K - 2E_L \qquad (7.04)$$

if we make the approximate assumption that the energy required to remove the second L electron is the same as required to remove the first. It is also possible that the quantum having the wavelength of the $K\alpha$ line may eject an electron from the M levels, leaving the L undisturbed. In this case the kinetic energy of the Auger electron would be

$$\frac{1}{2}mv^2 = h\nu_\alpha - (E_{LM} - E_L) = E_K - E_{LM}. \qquad (7.05)$$

If we follow the process of eq. (7.04) a step further it may be that the two vacancies produced in the L shell will be filled by the transfer of two M electrons, and that the quanta thus liberated be absorbed in the M shell, producing two more Auger electrons from the same atom. These may be called secondary Auger electrons. Their energies will be less than that of the primary Auger electron. Auger observed such secondary electrons from 35 Br and higher atomic number gases. In these heavier gases, point or sphere tracks were also occasionally observed, and attributed to the tertiary Auger electrons ejected from the N shells by radiation resulting from the filling of vacancies in the M shells.

An estimate of the fluorescence yield, defined in eq. (7.01), can be made by observing the abundance of Auger electrons in a large number of K ionizations revealed by the photo-electron tracks in the Wilson cloud chamber. If such a photo-electron track is observed, and has no associated track with it whose length corresponds to the ejection by a K-series line quantum of an electron from an outer shell in the atom, this atom must have emitted a quantum of radiation corresponding to a K-series line, and hence is counted as one of the n_f's in the numerator of eq. (7.01). In 223 instances in 36 Kr in which the incident radiation ejected a K electron, Auger found that 109 were accompanied by an electron arising from an internal conversion of one of the K lines, hence

$$36 \text{ Kr} \quad w_K = \frac{223 - 109}{223} = 0.51.$$

In the heavier elements Auger was also able to estimate the L-level fluorescence yield. His results are given in Table VII–2.

TABLE VII–2

AUGER'S RESULTS ON THE FLUORESCENCE YIELD

Element	w_K	w_L
18 A	0.07	
36 Kr	0.51	0.1
54 Xe	0.71	0.25

The method of Auger, although elegant in its directness and simplicity of interpretation, is obviously limited to the study of the fluorescence yield of substances which may be put into the expansion chamber in gaseous form. A method capable of wider application is to measure the power in the x-ray beams incident on, and fluorescent from, a secondary radiator. In order to secure homogeneity of wave-length in the incident beam, some observers have used the secondary radiation from a metal plate which is exposed to primary x-rays. A typical experimental arrangement is shown in Fig. VII–1, taken from a paper by A. H. Compton.[30] In this figure, the radiator whose fluorescence yield is to be measured is R_2. The primary radiation on R_2 comes from the secondary radiator R_1, which is caused to fluoresce by the incidence of primary x-rays from the x-ray tube drawn below it. If the atomic weight of the radiator

[30] A. H. Compton, Phil. Mag. 8, 961 (1929).

R_1 is sufficiently high, the secondary radiation from it will consist almost entirely of its own characteristic x-ray lines, the scattered radiation being relatively very weak. In actual experimental cases the voltage on the x-ray tube is made sufficiently high to excite the K-series radiation in R_1, and these lines are then used. With R_2 removed, the ionization current produced in chamber I_1 at position A is read, then, with R_2 in place, the ionization current from the fluorescence radiation is read in position B. In the experiments of Compton, the chamber I_2 was used to measure the fraction of the radiation absorbed in I_1, which was equipped with thin windows at front and rear. We shall derive an expression for the calculation of

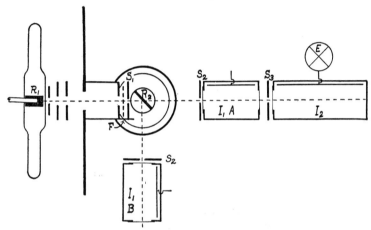

Fig. VII–1. An experimental arrangement used by A. H. Compton for the study of fluorescence yields.

the fluorescence yield from such an experiment. We shall assume that the observed ionization current readings have been properly corrected in a manner to give the power in the incident and in the fluorescence beam entering the chamber. The necessary corrections are discussed in the next section. We shall also assume that absorption corrections have been made so that the power incident on R_2, measured at the surface of R_2, and the power leaving R_2 destined to enter the ionization chamber window, and measured at R_2, are known.

Let us begin with a more general definition of the fluorescence yield than appears in eq. (7.01), writing

$$w_q = \frac{n_1 + n_2 + \ldots n_f \ldots}{n_q} = \frac{\Sigma n_f}{n_q}, \qquad (7.06)$$

where q may be $K, L, M, \ldots$, and n_f refers to an atom emitting a line whose initial state is the q-state.

We will also take account of the fact that the radiation incident on R_2 from R_1 will consist of a number of spectrum lines of wave-lengths

$$\lambda_1, \lambda_2 \ldots \ldots \ldots \lambda_i \ldots \ldots$$

Let the relative intensities of these lines be proportional to the numbers

$$I_1, I_2, I_3 \ldots I_i \ldots$$

Let P be the total power in ergs per second, measured at R_2, in the beam from R_1 incident on R_2, and let P_i be the part of P of wave-length λ_i. Then

$$P_i = P x_i$$

where

$$x_i = \frac{I_i}{\Sigma I_i}.$$

The power absorbed from P_i photoelectrically in a layer of radiator R_2 of thickness dl at depth l below the surface is

$$dP_i = P x_i \tau_i \operatorname{cosec} \theta_i \, e^{-\mu_i l \operatorname{cosec} \theta_i} \, dl. \tag{7.07}$$

In this expression μ_i is the linear absorption coefficient of the wave-length λ_i in the material of the radiator R_2, and τ_i is the corresponding true absorption coefficient. θ_i is the glancing angle of the beam from R_1, which is supposed not widely divergent, upon R_2, which is in the form of a flat plate.

Let r be the ratio of the values of τ on the short and long wave-length sides of the q-limit of radiator R_2. This may be called the absorption jump ratio. Then the fraction[31] of the absorbed power dP_i used in the ejection of q-photo-electrons is

$$P x_i \tau_i \frac{r-1}{r} \, e^{-\mu_i l \operatorname{cosec} \theta_i} dl \operatorname{cosec} \theta_i,$$

and since this power is absorbed in quanta of energy $h\nu_i$, the number

---

[31] If the exponent of λ in the expression for τ is not the same on both sides of the limit, then the fraction in question will be a function of the wave-length; we will at present neglect this refinement.

of atoms ionized in the q level per second by the incident wave-length λ_i is

$$dn_i = \frac{Px_i\tau_i(r-1)\cosec\theta_i}{rh\nu_i} e^{-\mu_i l \cosec\theta_i} dl.$$

Of these dn_i atoms ionized per second, a fraction $w_q dn_i$ will, in their return to the normal state, radiate an x-ray line of which q is the initial state. Let the lines which may be radiated have the wave-lengths

$$\lambda_1, \lambda_2, \ldots \ldots \lambda_f \ldots \ldots$$

and let their intensities be proportional to the numbers

$$I_1, I_2, \ldots . I_f \ldots .$$

Then the number per second of the $w_q dn_i$ atoms radiating the line of wave-length λ_f is

$$(dn_f)_i = w_q dn_i z_f$$

where

$$z_f = \frac{(1/\nu_f)I_f}{\Sigma(1/\nu_f)I_f} \sim \frac{\text{Number of quanta of frequency } \nu_f}{\text{Total number of quanta radiated}}.$$

Let the ionization chamber be so placed that the fluorescence radiation which enters it left the radiator R_2 at a glancing angle θ_f. The validity of this simplification is limited by the solid angle Ω which the ionization chamber window subtends at the radiator, which must not be too great. Then the power in the line of wave-length λ_f in the fluorescence beam, excited by the wave-length λ_i in the incident beam, measured at the surface of the radiator, and destined to enter the ionization chamber window, is

$$(dP_f')_i = \frac{\Omega}{4\pi} h\nu_f(dn_f)_i e^{-\mu_f l \cosec\theta_f}$$

or

$$(dP_f')_i = \frac{P\Omega x_i\nu_f(r-1)\tau_i w_q z_f \cosec\theta_i}{4\pi r\nu_i} \int_0^\infty e^{-l(\mu_i \cosec\theta_i + \mu_f \cosec\theta_f)} dl.$$

$$(7.08)$$

It is convenient to place R_2 so that θ_i and θ_f are equal; an important position of this type being one in which $\theta_1 = \theta_f = 45°$. If we limit our treatment to such positions, eq. (7.08) is integrable, and becomes

$$(P_f')_i = w_q \frac{P\Omega(r-1)\tau_i \nu_f x_i z_f}{4\pi r \nu_i(\mu_i + \mu_f)}.$$

The power P' in the fluorescence beam destined to enter the ionization chamber will be a double sum of the form

$$P' = w_q \frac{P\Omega}{4\pi} \frac{r-1}{r} \sum_i \sum_f \frac{\tau_i}{\mu_i + \mu_f} \frac{\nu_f}{\nu_i} x_i z_f. \tag{7.09}$$

Thus w_q may be calculated from measurements of the incident power P and the secondary power P', if the dimensions of the apparatus, and the absorption coefficients, frequencies, and relative intensities of the lines in the incident and fluorescence beam are known.

The early experiments of Barkla and Sadler[22] were of this type, and Bothe[32] has indicated that they give data approximately in agreement with that of Auger. Harms[33] used as an incident beam on R_2 primary x-rays from a molybdenum target. The x-rays were passed through a zirconium oxide filter, and it was assumed that this filtered beam was monochromatic, of the wave-length of 42Mo $K\alpha$. In such a case only a single sum in eq. (7.09) is necessary, and $x_i = 1$. Harms used as secondary radiators plates of 26 Fe, 29 Cu, 30 Zn, 34 Se, and 38 Sr (this last in the form of the sulfate), and measured w_K. In computing the power in the incident and fluorescence beams from his ionization current readings, Harms followed a method advocated by Kossel,[23] in which the average energy expended by a high-speed β-ray in producing a pair of ions in a gas depends upon its energy. Since such a dependence is known not to occur, Compton[30] has corrected the results of Harms. Harms extrapolated his measurements of the fluorescence yields to molybdenum, and this extrapolated value is independent of any assumptions about the constancy of the average energy used in producing a pair of ions, since here the incident and fluorescence wave-lengths would be the same. Harms' results, as corrected by Compton, are given in Table VII–3, column 4.

Balderston[34] has made measurements of the fluorescence yield from radiators of 26 Fe, 28 Ni, 29 Cu, 30 Zn, 42 Mo and 47 Ag. His primary radiation was monochromatized by reflection from a crystal

[32] W. Bothe, Physikal. Zeitschr. **26**, 410; 473 (1925).
[33] M. I. Harms, Ann. d. Physik **82**, 87 (1920).
[34] M. Balderston, Phys. Rev. **27**, 696 (1926).

in a Bragg spectrometer. The general conclusions of his work agree well with those of other experimenters, in that he found that w_K is distinctly less than unity, is independent of incident wave-length, and increases with increasing atomic number. His numerical values, however, especially for the elements of higher atomic number, do not agree well with those of other observers. Compton[30] has pointed out that serious errors were introduced into his work by the assumption that the ionization produced by different wave-lengths in air is proportional to their absorption in air, whereas for the shorter wave-lengths a large part of the absorption in air is due to scattering, and does not result in ionization. Corrections to Balderston's results are also discussed in a paper due to Smekal,[35] in which general aspects of internal conversion of x-rays are also treated. Balderston's results, uncorrected, are given in column 3, Table VII–3.

Martin[36] has measured w_K for 26 Fe, 28 Ni, 29 Cu, and 30 Zn, using the elements in the form of metal plates and a filtered beam of primary x-ray as incident radiation. This incident radiation was assumed to be monochromatic, and by means of various filters wave-lengths from 0.6 A to the K limits of the respective radiators were selected. The ionization chamber in which the fluorescence radiation was measured was semi-cylindrical in shape, with the radiator on the axis, and the solid angle subtended was so large that equations essentially different from eq. (7.08) were used in the estimation of w_K. The results are given in column 5 of Table VII–3.

A. H. Compton,[30] using the arrangement shown in Fig. VII–1, has measured the values of w_K for 42 Mo, 34 Se, and 28 Ni. From phenomena observed in the ionization chamber, which was filled with methyl bromide, it was estimated that w_K for 35 Br is 0.565, using considerations to be discussed in the next section. The incident radiation was varied in wave-length by using different radiators R_1 for the same radiator R_2.

Locher[37] has examined the fluorescence yields from the K levels of oxygen, neon, and argon by the original method of Auger. One thousand nine hundred and fifty stereoscopic pictures were taken of cloud tracks formed in a Wilson chamber through which filtered primary x-rays of wave-length 0.709 A were passing. In the light gases, O_2 and Ne, the identification of the tracks of the Auger elec-

[35] Smekal, Annalen der Physik 81, 391 (1926).
[36] L. H. Martin, Proc. Roy. Soc. Lond. A 115, 420 (1927).
[37] G. L. Locher, Phys. Rev. 40, 484 (1932).

trons was made difficult by their shortness, due to the small energy. In the measurements on oxygen, the chamber was filled with hydrogen, and the oxygen atoms were supplied by the water-vapor molecules. In the case of neon it was difficult to distinguish between

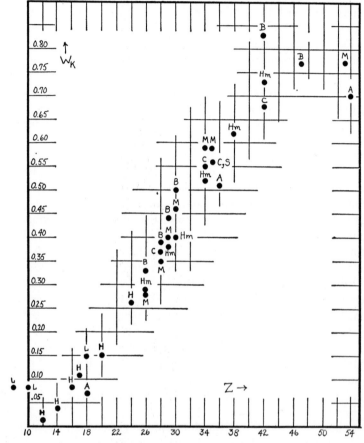

FIG. VII–2. Values of the fluorescence yield from the K level according to various observers. A, Auger; B, Balderston; C, A. H. Compton; H, Haas; Hm, Harms; L, Locher; M, Martin; S, Stockmeyer.

tracks due to oxygen in the water vapor, and due to neon itself, because of the proximity of the two atomic numbers. In argon, tracks due to the internal conversion of L and M series lines were noted. The results are given in Table VII–3.

The data on w_K has also been extended toward the region of lower atomic numbers by the work of Haas.[38]   In these experiments the incident radiation was made monochromatic by reflection of primary x-rays from a crystal in a vacuum spectrometer. The fluorescence radiation was measured in a wedge-shaped ionization chamber. In the calculation of the fluorescence yield, the contribution of the $K\beta$ lines to the fluorescence beam was neglected, but this produces less error for the light elements in question than for heavier elements, due to relatively low intensity of the $K\beta$ relative to the $K\alpha$ lines for the lower atomic numbers. Haas measured w_K for 12 Mg, 14 Si, 16 S, 17 Cl, 20 Ca, and 24 Cr. He found no evidence of a variation of w_K with the incident wave-length.

A summary of the results on the fluorescence yield in the K level

TABLE VII–3

FLUORESCENCE YIELDS IN THE K SERIES

Element	Auger	Balderston	Harms	Martin	Compton	Stockmeyer	Locher	Haas
8 O	......	......	......	......	......	......	0.082	
10 Ne	......	......	......	......	......	......	0.083	
12 Mg	......	......	......	......	......	......	......	0.013
14 Si	......	......	......	......	......	......	......	0.038
16 S	......	......	......	......	......	......	......	0.083
17 Cl	......	......	......	......	......	......	......	0.108
18 A	0.07	......	......	......	......	......	0.149	
20 Ca	......	......	......	......	......	......	......	0.150
24 Cr	......	......	......	......	......	......	......	0.263
26 Fe	......	0.33	0.28	0.29	......	......		
28 Ni	......	0.39	......	0.35	0.37	......		
29 Cu	......	0.44	0.38	0.40	......	......		
30 Zn	......	0.50	0.40	0.46	......	......		
34 Se	......	......	0.52	0.59	0.55	......		
35 Br	......	......	......	0.59	0.56	0.56		
36 Kr	0.51							
38 Sr	......	......	0.62					
42 Mo	......	0.83	0.73	......	0.68			
47 Ag	......	0.75						
53 I	......	......	......	0.75				
54 Xe	0.70							

[38] M. Haas, Ann. der Physik (5), **16**, 473 (1933).

is given in Table VII–3. The values of w_K for 53 I and 35 Br were obtained from observations of the change in the ionization current in the chamber as the frequency passed the K limit of the gas, as described in the next section.

Very little work has been done on the fluorescence yields from other levels than the K level. As we have seen, Auger estimated the value of w_L for 36 Kr as 0.1 and for 54 Xe as 0.25. Since there are actually three L sub-levels, which were not resolved in Auger's tracks, these values represent some average of the w values of the individual levels.

Stephenson[39] has measured the value of the fluorescence yield for the L_{III} level of uranium by a method similar to that used by Compton for K levels (Fig. VII–1). The radiator R_1 was a plate of 42 Mo so that the incident radiation on R_2, the uranium, consisted of the K lines of Mo. These lie in the wave-length range between $K\beta_2$, 0.62 A, and $K\alpha_2$, 0.71 A. The L_{III} absorption limit of uranium lies at 0.7208 A; the L_{II} limit at 0.5913 A. Hence the molybdenum characteristic K lines can eject electrons from the L levels of uranium in such a way as to leave the atom in the L_{III}, but not in the L_{II}, state. In other words, the fluorescence lines which can be emitted in the L group have L_{III} as their initial state, and are $L\alpha_1$, $L\alpha_2$, $L\beta_2$, $L\beta_5$, $L\beta_6$, $L\beta_7$, Ll. The radioactivity of the uranium was a disturbing factor in the experiments, but it was found that by inserting a paraffin screen between R_2 and the ionization chamber, the ionization from the uranium β-rays could be stopped without large absorption of the L fluorescence radiation. Extending the f-sum of eq. (7.09) over the L lines mentioned above, and the i-sum over the molybdenum K-series lines, Stephenson found

$$92 \; U \quad w_{L_{III}} = 0.67.$$

The method of attack on the problem of theoretical calculation of the fluorescence yield has been outlined by Wentzel.[40] The possibility of processes entirely analogous to the Auger effect in the region of optical spectra exists. Such processes are sometimes referred to as "auto-ionization." For instance, in the calcium arc spectrum term table, energy levels are known which are positive with respect to a zero of energy represented by the configuration $1s^2 \, 2s^2 2p^6 \, 3s^2 3p^6 \, 4s$ in which one valence electron has been removed

[39] R. J. Stephenson, Phys. Rev. 43, 527 (1933).
[40] G. Wentzel, Zeitschr. f. Physik 43, 524 (1927).

The electronic configurations underlying such terms of positive energy are ones in which both valence electrons are displaced from their $4s$ orbit. The possibility exists that if one of the displaced electrons returns to the $4s$ orbit, the energy released may remove the other electron from the atom, accomplishing ionization without radiation. From the point of view of wave-mechanics, this merely represents one of the many possible transitions of the excited atom, this particular kind involving as a final state configurations in the continuous region. If a simple enough model is assumed, the matrix elements corresponding to such a transition may be calculated from the Schrödinger equation, and the probability of such a transition computed. Wentzel's discussion deals with a two-electron atom of high nuclear charge. The treatment has not as yet been extended to actual x-ray levels because of the mathematical complexities involved. The treatment is somewhat analogous to the perturbation method of calculating the photo-electric emission, discussed in Sec. 10 of this chapter, except that in this case the perturbation is the action of the second electron on the first, rather than the action of an external electric field.

Without a rigorous calculation in the x-ray region, Wentzel is able to show that the reciprocal of the life time of the K state with respect to an Auger transition in which an L electron is emitted is of the order of 10^{15} seconds. From eq. (4.17), Chap. IV, we see that the reciprocal of the effective life of an excited K state with respect to radiation of x-rays is proportional to $\nu_0{}^2$, which by Moseley's law is proportional to $(Z - 1)^4$. Also in Table IV–1 it is shown that this effective lifetime for radiation of 0.50 A is 2.3×10^{-16} sec., which means that for radiation of 1.0 A the reciprocal of the life time is about 10^{15}. Thus for K series radiation of about 1.0 A we should find about equal probability of the emission of an Auger electron or of a quantum, that is, the fluorescence yield should be 0.5, in rough agreement with experiment.

If we call p_f the probability of emission of a quantum of fluorescence radiation, and p_e the probability of ejection of an Auger electron from the L shell, then we have

$$p_f \sim (Z - 1)^4$$

and

$$p_e \sim k$$

according to Wentzel. Haas[38] has pointed out that the fluorescence yield of the K level, since it depends primarily on the possibility of ejection from the L shell, may be expressed as

$$w_K = \frac{p_f}{p_e + p_f} = \frac{(Z - 1)^4}{k + (Z - 1)^4}.$$

This expression, with its adjustable constant k, agrees fairly well with experimental data up to atomic number 30; at higher atomic numbers the experimental increase in w_K appears not to be so rapid as predicted by the equation.

3. *Use of the Ionization Chamber in Measuring the Relative Intensities of X-ray Beams of Different Wave-lengths*

We have seen in Sec. 1 of this chapter that when x-rays are absorbed in a gas, the energy used in producing a pair of ions is a constant, ϵ, independent of wave-length. The simplicity of this relationship indicates that the ionization chamber is the most convenient instrument for measuring the power in an x-ray beam, and that if properly used, the relative ionization currents observed will give the true relative powers in two beams of different wavelength, for instance, P and P' of eq. (7.09). Another possible application is the measurement of the relative intensity of x-ray spectrum lines.

Most of the absolute determinations of the energy required to produce a pair of ions have been made in air, and thus the direct proofs of the constancy of ϵ have been made on light gases. It is not always convenient to use such a light gas as air in ionization chambers due to the small fraction of the beam absorbed in a chamber of convenient length. Furthermore, in the heavier gases often used, it is not always convenient to build the chamber large enough so that all fluorescence and scattered radiation produced by the primary beam are absorbed before reaching the walls. In this section we shall discuss a method of correcting for the escape of energy in the form of x-rays from the chamber.

We shall assume that the potential drop across the gas in the chamber is everywhere sufficiently high so that recombination of the ions need not be considered. Webster and Yeatman[41] have investigated the voltage drop necessary to insure reliable measurements of two beams of different intensity in an ionization chamber of common design. The chamber was of brass, 30 cm. long and 7 cm

[41] Webster and Yeatman, Journ. Opt. Soc. Am. and R. S. I. **17**, 254 (1928).

inside diameter, in cylindrical form. The electrodes were flat plates, one 6.5 cm. wide and mounted parallel to the long axis of the chamber. The other was 3.8 cm. wide, mounted in a plane parallel to the first, with a distance of 3.6 cm. between them. They found that reliable ratios of two beams differing in intensity by a factor of 10 or more could be obtained when the voltage drop between these electrodes was in the range from 45 to 225 volts. These beams were obtained by reflection from a crystal, and hence were of low intensity as compared to primary x-rays. They interpret their results as showing that what recombination takes place in the chamber is of an initial or columnar type, and not a volume recombination. By initial recombination is meant recombination of an ion and the identical electron which was removed from it. Columnar recombination means that the recombination occurs along the same photo-electron track. If the recombination is of these first two types only, a change in the intensity of the x-rays of the same wave-length should change the photo-electrons in number only, and should not affect the amount of recombination which takes place along one photo-electron track. In other words, in this case the powers in two beams of the same wave-length can be accurately compared even if a certain amount of recombination occurs. With volume recombination, the recombination of two ions from different photo-electron tracks takes place. The effect is proportional to the square of the number of ion pairs per cm.^{3}, and hence dependent on the power of the entering beam. The experiments of Webster and Yeatman cannot be relied upon as a guide for the necessary saturation voltages for the intense beams obtained directly from an x-ray tube. They indicate, however, that in x-ray spectrometry reliable results may be obtained with ionization chambers operated at quite low voltages.

In our derivation of the corrections to be applied to ionization current readings we shall not attempt to give a general derivation, applicable to all shapes and designs of chambers, all wave-lengths, and all gases. Instead we shall make simplifying assumptions which greatly limit the complexity of the problem, yet apply to common experimental practice in x-ray spectrometry.

The most limiting of these assumptions is that the incoherent scattering, accompanied by change of wave-length, plays no appreciable rôle in the ionization chamber. This implies either that the absorbing gases have high enough atomic numbers, or that the incident wave-length is not too short. For gases commonly used in chambers, such as CH_3Br, CH_3I, A, Kr it seems that with the possible exception of argon, the condition is fulfilled for wave-lengths greater than about 0.6 A.

We shall further assume that the ionization chamber is large enough so that practically all the photo-electrons liberated within it come to the end of their ionizing range in the gas without striking the walls. Very rough calculations are sufficient to establish the proper dimensions. For such purposes we may represent the length of path x of a photo-electron as

$$x = V^2/b,$$

where V is the energy of the photo-electron in kilovolt-electrons, and b is proportional to the density of the gas. For air at atmospheric pressure b is 4.4×10^2, and in one atmosphere of argon b is 6.1×10^2. Hence, if the entire energy of a quantum of wave-length 0.61 A is transformed into the kinetic energy of a photo-electron in one atmosphere of argon, the path length is 0.7 cm.

Again, we shall assume that the only fluorescence radiation which reaches the walls of the ionization chamber is the K radiation (if excited) of the gas. The L, M, and higher radiations will be assumed to be totally absorbed and converted into photo-electron energy before reaching the walls.

If the path of the primary radiation through the chamber is not sufficiently long so that it practically is completely absorbed in the gas, the beam must leave the chamber through a thin window, or precautions must be taken so that photo-electrons are not ejected back into the gas volume from solid material irradiated by the direct beam. The effect of photo-electrons ejected back into the chamber from fluorescence or scattered radiation reaching the walls will be neglected. The chief justification of this is the agreement with experiment to be reported below.

The problem may then be analyzed as follows: Let P be the power in the incident beam, measured just inside the window through which the radiation enters the chamber. Let λ be the wave-length and ν the frequency of this incident beam. Let the length of path of the incident beam in the chamber be l. We are here considering a beam canalized by two slits in such a way that its divergence in the chamber is not so great that the interpretation of l is indefinite. Then the power absorbed from the primary beam will be

$$P(1 - e^{-\mu l}) \equiv PF.$$

We shall suppose that the frequency is sufficiently great to eject photo-electrons from the K levels of some of the gas atoms. Let r be the K absorption jump ratio of the gas; then the number of K photo-electrons ejected per second will be

$$\frac{PF(r-1)}{rh\nu},$$

and the number of such atoms per second which in their return to the normal state emit some line of the K series is

$$w_K \frac{PF(r-1)}{rh\nu}.$$

Let the various wave-lengths of the K series of the gas be

$$\lambda_1, \lambda_2, \dots \dots \lambda_f \dots \dots$$

and let the relative intensities of these lines be proportional to the numbers

$$I_1, I_2, \dots \dots I_f \dots$$

Then the number of atoms which in one second emit the K series line of wave-length λ_f will be

$$w_K \frac{PF(r-1)}{rh\nu} z_f,$$

where

$$z_f = \frac{(1/\nu_f)I_f}{\Sigma(1/\nu_f)I_f},$$

and the power radiated in the entire fluorescence K series of the gas will be

$$w_K \frac{PF(r-1)}{rh\nu} \sum_f h\nu_f z_f.$$

We are interested in the amount of this fluorescence which reaches the walls of the chamber in the form of x-rays. The computation will in general be complicated, involving an integration over the possible paths to the wall from an element dl in the path of the primary beam. Such an integration has been made by Stockmeyer[42] for a certain ionization chamber used by him. In general we can if we wish represent the result by a factor $e^{-\tau/d}$ for each fluorescence

[42] W. Stockmeyer, Ann. der Physik (5), **12**, 71 (1932).

wave-length, where d is the effective path length, which we shall roughly assume the same for each wave-length. τ_f is the true absorption coefficient of the gas for its K line of wave-length λ_f. Thus the power escaping to the walls in the form of x-rays from fluorescence radiation is

$$w_K \frac{PF(r-1)}{vr} \sum_f v_f z_f e^{-\tau_f d}.$$

In addition to fluorescence radiation, radiation may be scattered from the incident beam. If σ is the scattering coefficient, the power escaping to the walls may be written

$$PF \frac{\sigma}{\mu} e^{-\tau d},$$

where τ is the true absorption coefficient of the gas for the incident wave-length, and μ is the corresponding total linear absorption coefficient. In summary we may write the power converted into photo-electron kinetic energy and thus used in producing ions in the chamber as

$$P_{\text{abs}} = PFR,$$

where

$$F = 1 - e^{-\mu l}$$

and

$$R = 1 - \frac{w_K}{v} \frac{r-1}{r} \sum_f v_f z_f e^{-\tau_f d} - \frac{\sigma}{\mu} e^{-\tau d}.$$

The number of pairs of ions produced is then obtained by dividing this P_{abs} by the energy required to produce one pair of ions, so that the ionic saturation current, in electrostatic units, is

$$J = \frac{e P_{\text{abs}}}{\epsilon \times 1.59 \times 10^{-12}}$$

where e is the charge on the electron in e.s.u. and ϵ is the energy in electron volts required for the production of one pair of ions.

Let us imagine an ionization chamber long enough to absorb practically all the primary beam, so that $F = 1$ for all wave-lengths, and consider a case in which scattering is negligible. Furthermore, suppose that the diameter of the volume from which the ionization current is drawn is so small that the K fluorescence radiation of the gas escapes without contributing any ions; that is, $e^{-\tau_f d} = 1$. Let us take two wave-lengths in the general radiation entering such a chamber, lying just on opposite sides of the K absorption discontinuity of the gas in the chamber. Then the discontinuity in the ionization current observed at the K limit, with the above limiting assumptions, will be

$$\frac{J_{K+L}}{J_L} = 1 - \frac{w_K}{v} \frac{r-1}{r} \sum_f v_f z_f,$$

where J_{K+L} is the ionization current on the high frequency side of the limit, etc.

The equations developed here have been tested experimentally by Allison and Andrew,[43] who were interested in showing that they indicated the proper corrections to be applied to measurements of the relative intensities of x-ray spectrum lines. The experiment consisted in comparing the ionization currents produced by the lines α_1, β_1 and γ_1 in the L-spectrum of an element in various gases. With constant conditions outside the ionization chamber, the values of P for the lines α_1 and β_1, for instance, will have the ratio P_α/P_β, and if J_α/J_β is the observed ionization current ratio,

$$\frac{P_\alpha}{P_\beta} = \frac{J_\alpha}{J_\beta} \frac{F_\beta}{F_\alpha} \frac{R_\beta}{R_\alpha}, \qquad (7.10)$$

or in a more convenient notation

$$P_{\alpha\beta} = J_{\alpha\beta} F_{\beta\alpha} R_{\beta\alpha}.$$

This means that with various gases, if the observed ionization current ratios $J_{\alpha\beta}$ are corrected by the factors $F_{\beta\alpha}$ and $R_{\beta\alpha}$, values of $P_{\alpha\beta}$ independent of the gas used should result.

Allison and Andrew used a cylindrical ionization chamber 28.1 cm. long and 7.2 cm. in diameter (Fig. VII–3), with a collecting electrode parallel to the axis of the cylinder, but offset from it sufficiently so that the primary beam, which entered and left through thin windows at the ends, did not strike it. In their calculations they made the rough assumption that d, the effective absorption distance for the fluorescence radiation, was equal to the radius of the cylindrical chamber. A second section of the ionization chamber was used to measure the fraction of the primary beam absorbed in the gas of the main section. Measurements were made on the relative ionization currents obtained from the lines $L\alpha_1$, $L\beta_1$, and $L\gamma_1$ of tungsten in the

[43] S. K. Allison and V. J. Andrew, Phys. Rev. 38, 441 (1931).

gases CH_3I, CH_3Br, A, SO_2, and air.   The wave-lengths of these lines are: 1.473, 1.279, and 1.095 A respectively.   Application of eq. (7.10) showed in each case that uniform values of $P_{\alpha\gamma}$ and $P_{\alpha\beta}$ could be calculated from the observed ratios $J_{\alpha\beta}$ and $J_{\alpha\gamma}$, which varied, in the case of $J_{\alpha\gamma}$ from 6.97 in CH_3I at 20.49 cm. pressure to 16.34 in air at 74.30 cm. pressure.   In these tungsten trials, however, the most interesting factor, the R factor, did not play a significant role, since in all the cases no fluorescence radiation was excited which reached the walls.   The R ratios were therefore unity in all cases except for air, where a slight effect due to scattering was noted.

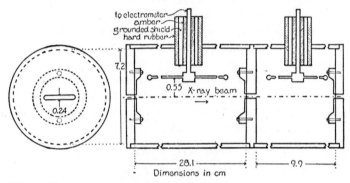

Fig. VII-3.   The two-compartment ionization chamber used by Allison and Andrew in testing the ionization chamber method of measuring relative intensities of x-ray lines.   The x-ray beam passed through the chamber from left to right; the second compartment was used for measuring the fraction of the primary beam absorbed in the first compartment.

J. H. Williams,[44] using the same gases and the same chamber, carried out a similar experiment which extended the wave-length range investigated up to 2.29 A.   He used in one set of experiments x-rays from a target which was approximately a 50 : 50 mixture of 28 Ni and 26 Fe, and measured the observed ionization current ratios due to the iron and nickel $K\alpha$ lines.   Another set of measurements was made with a target which was a mixture of 24 Cr and 26 Fe, and again the $K\alpha$ lines were compared.   In all trials it was found that the observed ionization current ratios, when corrected as in eq. (7.10), gave a set of constant P values.

The more interesting part of the experimental work of Allison and Andrew dealt with the $L\alpha_1$, $L\beta_1$, and $L\gamma_1$ lines of uranium,

[44] J. H. Williams, Phys. Rev. 44, 146 (1933).

whose wave-lengths are given in Table VII-4. With these shorter wave-lengths it was possible to excite the K radiation of some of the gases used in the chamber, and in the case of krypton, the K limit of the gas lies between the uranium $L\alpha_1$ and $L\beta_1$ lines. The results are shown in Table VII-4. It is seen that in krypton the measured

TABLE VII-4

IONIZATION CURRENTS DUE TO THE ABSORPTION OF THE L LINES OF URANIUM IN VARIOUS GASES

A. Comparison of $UL\alpha_1$ (0.909 A), and $UL\beta_1$ (0.7185 A)

Gas	λ_K	Pressure	$J_{\alpha\beta}$ (Obs.)	$F_{\beta\alpha}$ (Obs.)	$R_{\beta\alpha}$ (Calc.)	$P_{\alpha\beta}$ (Calc.)
	A	cm.				
CH₃I	0.373	20.07	3.19	0.820	1.00	2.61
Argon.......	3.866	74.74	4.05	0.631	0.99	2.53
Krypton....	0.864	10.10	1.65	2.55	0.62	2.62
CH₃Br......	0.919	14.26	2.89	0.801	1.15	2.66

B. Comparison of $UL\alpha_1$ (0.909 A), and $UL\gamma_1$ (0.614 A)

Gas	λ_K	Pressure	$J_{\alpha\gamma}$ (Obs.)	$F_{\gamma\alpha}$ (Obs.)	$R_{\gamma\alpha}$ (Calc.)	$P_{\alpha\gamma}$ (Calc.)
	A	cm.				
CH₃I.......	0.373	20.07	12.8	0.668	1.00	8.56
Argon.......	3.866	74.74	18.6	0.463	0.98	8.43
Krypton....	0.864	10.10	6.22	2.04	0.675	8.56
CH₃Br......	0.919	14.26	10.7	0.634	1.22	8.27

$J_{\alpha\beta}$ ratio was 1.65, whereas the observed ionization current ratio for the same lines in CH₃I was 3.19. If the F correction alone is made, the lack of agreement persists; the product $J_{\alpha\beta}F_{\beta\alpha}$ being for krypton 4.22 and for CH₃I, 2.61. It is most gratifying in this case to find that the calculated $R_{\beta\alpha}$ ratios are just the correct factors to make the $P_{\alpha\beta}$ ratios agree in the two gases. In the ionization of CH₃Br by $UL\alpha_1$, the incident wave-length is so near the bromine K limit that practically all the ionization in the gas is due to the Auger electrons rather than to the photo-electrons, which is the more usual case.

In a trial in a pressure of CH₃Br of 74 cm. results on $P_{\alpha\beta}$ and $P_{\alpha\gamma}$

discordant with those of Table VII–4 were obtained. This is inter-preted as due to the failure of the assumption that d is the radius of the chamber in this case. Calculation showed that at this pres-sure 50 per cent of $UL\alpha_1$ was absorbed in the first 1.9 cm. of path, so that the effective absorption distance of the fluorescence radiation was certainly less than the radius of the chamber in this case. If the existence of such an effect is suspected, it can be detected by measuring the variation of the ionization current ratio with pressure of the gas.

The results of Allison and Andrew offer indirect evidence that ϵ is independent of wave-length for the gases studied. If ϵ depends on wave-length in exactly the same manner in all the gases tried, such a variation would not have been detected. But a variation of ϵ with wave-length of exactly the same nature in such different gases is hardly to be expected, and by far the most probable conclusion is that ϵ is independent of wave-length.

In the work of Compton on the fluorescence yield mentioned in the preceding section, equations similar to those developed above were used to obtain the correct power ratio of the incident and fluorescence beams. The results offer another indirect proof of the constance of ϵ, for if such a dependence existed, a variation of w_K with the incident wave-length would have appeared. Such a varia-tion of the fluorescence yield would be difficult to reconcile with our ideas of the nature of the underlying atomic process.

Martin[45] developed equations for the relation between the ob-served ionization current and the power in the beam similar to those derived here, and using them, calculated w_K for 34 Se, 35 Br, and 53 I from older work by Barkla and Beatty on the ionization jumps at the K limit of gases containing these atoms.

By a similar analysis of the action of an ionization chamber, Stockmeyer[46] showed that the value of w_K for 35 Br is 0.56.

4. *Magnetic Spectra of Electrons Emitted by Substances Irradiated with X-rays*

Quantitative experiments on the velocity and kinetic energy of electrons produced by the action of x-rays on matter have been made by bending the electrons in a magnetic field and determining the radius of curvature. Experiments of this type were attempted by

[45] L. H. Martin, Proc. Roy. Soc. Lond. A **115**, 420 (1927).
[46] Stockmeyer, Annalen der Physik **12**, 71 (1932).

Robinson and Rawlinson[47] in 1914. Figure VII–4 shows the type
of apparatus used by them. The trajectories of the electrons emitted
from the radiator R lie in an evacuated vessel. The magnetic field
is perpendicular to the plane of the figure. X-rays are admitted
through the window S, and fall on R. The ejected electrons which
pass through the broad slit F are registered by their impressions on a
photographic plate at PP'. If the slit F is not too wide, a focussing,
or concentration of beams of electrons of uniform velocity takes
place at the surface of the plate. Thus if the irradiated area is not
too great, the impression on the photographic plate due to electrons
of uniform velocity will be a narrow line. The radii of curvature of
the electrons will be half the distances RP, RP', etc. A slight

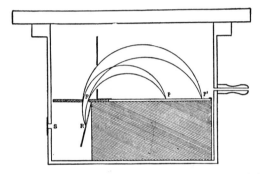

Fig. VII–4. Arrangement for observing the magnetic spectrum of electrons ejected
from a solid plate by x-rays.

modification of the design, suitable to higher precision work, is
shown in Fig. VII–5 of the next section.

Because of the high velocities of the electrons ejected by x-rays
it is necessary to use formulae for their energies and momenta which
are derived from the special relativity theory. We have, analogous
to the elementary equation

$$\frac{mv^2}{r} = \frac{Hev}{c}$$

the more accurate expression,

$$Hr = \frac{m_0c^2}{e}\frac{\beta}{\sqrt{1-\beta^2}}, \qquad (7.11)$$

[47] Robinson and Rawlinson, Phil. Mag. 28, 277 (1914).

and instead of

$$E_{kin} = \tfrac{1}{2}mv^2,$$

the expression

$$E_{kin} = m_0 c^2 \left\{ \frac{1}{\sqrt{1 - \beta^2}} - 1 \right\}. \qquad (7.12)$$

In these expressions, e, the charge on the electron, is measured in electrostatic units, β is the ratio of the velocity of the electron to the velocity of light, and m_0 is the mass of the electron at rest. From these equations, the energy of the ejected electrons can be calculated from observed values of the magnetic field H, in gauss, and the radius of curvature, r, in cm.

M. de Broglie[48] was the first to show that a class of ejected electrons exists for which the photo-electric equation

$$E_{kin} = h\nu - h\nu_q \qquad (7.13)$$

accurately holds. These are the photo-electrons ejected from the q-level of the secondary radiator by the incident radiation of frequency ν. de Broglie used incident radiation from a tungsten target x-ray tube, operated with sufficient voltage to excite the tungsten K lines. The photo-electrons ejected from various substances by these characteristic wave-lengths appeared prominently on the plates so that ν in the preceding equation could be given the frequency value corresponding to one of the tungsten K series lines. de Broglie used secondary radiators of 30 Zn, 38 Sr, 42 Mo, 45 Rh, 47 Ag, 50 Sn, 51 Sb, 53 I, 56 Ba, and 70 Yb. In some cases the radiators were compounds of the elements in question.

In his experiments on silver, de Broglie could detect the photo-electrons ejected from the silver K levels by the $K\alpha_1$, $K\alpha_2$, and $K\beta_1$ lines of tungsten. Other lines in the magnetic spectrum were observed whose energies roughly correspond to

$$h\nu(\text{Ag } K\alpha) - h\nu(\text{Ag } L)$$

and

$$h\nu(\text{Ag } K\alpha) - h\nu(\text{Ag } M).$$

These were undoubtedly Auger electrons; the accuracy was not sufficient to detect the difference between the approximate formulae given above and those of eq. (7.04). The probability that these lines are due to the absorption of silver fluorescence radiation in other

[48] M. de Broglie, Journ. de Physique 6, 2, 265 (1921).

than the parent atoms is remote, as discussed in a later communication by de Broglie and Thibaud.[49]

Most of the recent work on the energies of electrons ejected by x-rays has been done by Robinson and his associates. In 1923 the results of an extensive investigation of photo-electrons ejected by primary x-rays of the wave-length of Cu $K\alpha$ (1.537 A) from various radiators were reported.[50] Secondary radiators of 29 Cu, 38 Sr, 42 Mo, 47 Ag, 50 Sn, 53 I, 56 Ba, 74 W, 79 Au, 82 Pb, and 83 Bi were used. Thus in all cases the photo-electrons were ejected from L or more loosely bound levels in the atom. An example selected from the numerous data reported is given in Table VII–5. In the

TABLE VII–5

EJECTION OF PHOTO-ELECTRONS FROM A COPPER PLATE BY Cu $K\alpha$ INCIDENT RADIATION

ν/R of the Incident Radiation = 592.8

Intensity	Hr Obs.	ν/R Calc.	592.8- ν/R	Interpretation	X-ray Values (Siegbahn, 1931) ν/R
6	280.6	510.8	82.0	Cu $K\alpha$–Cu L_I	Cu L_I=81.0
4–5	284.0	523.1	69.7	Cu $K\alpha$–Cu $L_{II}L_{III}$	L_{II}=70.3, L_{III}=68.9
4	300.8	586.3	6.5	Cu $K\alpha$–Cu M	M_I, 8.9; $M_{II}M_{III}$, 5.7; $M_{IV}M_V$, 0.4.

third column of the table are given values of ν/R corresponding to the kinetic energies of the observed photo-electrons, calculated from

$$\nu/R = E_{kin}/Rhc.$$

The values in the fourth column should, by the equation for the photo-electric effect, give the ν/R value of the level from which the photo-electron was ejected. This is to be compared with the energy level values determined through x-ray spectroscopy which are given in the last column.

A very interesting phenomenon relating to the relative absorption of x-rays by the sub-groups of the L, M, etc. levels was discovered in Robinson's work. If the frequency of the primary radiation is very nearly that of the L levels of the secondary radiator, it is found

[49] M. de Broglie and J. Thibaud, Journ. de Physique 6, 2, 265 (1921).
[50] H. Robinson, Proc. Roy. Soc. Lond. A 104, 455 (1923).

that the line in the magnetic spectrum due to electrons ejected from the L_{III} level is considerably more intense than that from L_I. This is to be expected, because in absorption measurements of x-rays it is found that the discontinuity in the absorption coefficient at L_{III} is much the greatest of any of the L jumps. But when the incident frequency is far above that of the L critical absorption discontinuities, most of the absorption occurs in L_I, rather than in the remaining L levels. In the case given in Table VII–5, where the incident ν/R is 593 and the ν/R of the L levels between 69 and 81, it was found that the line of $Hr = 280.6$ was the most intense of the two observed L lines. A comparison of the ν/R obtained in the table for the M levels by magnetic spectroscopy with the x-ray values indicates that here, also, most of the absorption is being done by the more tightly bound of the M electrons, whereas Pauli's exclusion principle indicates a greater electron population in the 3_2 than in the 3_1 or 3_0 levels.

Wentzel[51] has given a wave-mechanical discussion of this effect in qualitative form, which is essentially a calculation of the probability of photo-electric emission from an irradiated atom. This type of calculation will be more fully discussed in Sec. 10 of this chapter. He finds that roughly a relation

$$\frac{N_{III} + N_{II}}{N_I} = \text{const.} \frac{\lambda}{\lambda_L} \tag{7.13a}$$

should hold, where N_{III} is the number of photo-electrons ejected per second from the L_{III} level by the incident radiation of wave-length λ, etc. λ_L is the average critical absorption wave-length of the L levels. Comparison with the experiment indicates that the constant has approximately the numerical value 10.

As a consequence of this effect a type of variation of relative intensities in the fluorescence spectrum can be expected. For instance in the L series, lines having the initial state L_I should be the most intense lines in the fluorescence spectrum if the exciting frequency is very much greater than the L critical absorption frequencies. In primary x-rays the most intense lines involving L_I are weak compared to the stronger lines involving L_{II} or L_{III}. Such an effect in the fluorescence spectrum has been found by various observers.[52]

[51] G. Wentzel, Zeitschr. f. Physik **40**, 574 (1927).
[52] Skinner, Proc. Camb. Phil. Soc. **379**, 22 (1923).
Hevesey and Alexander, Nature **129**, 315 (1932).

An analogous effect has been found by Coster and van Zuylen[53] in the excitation of primary x-rays by cathode rays. Thin films were used as targets, so that to a good approximation it may be considered that the x-rays were excited by cathode rays of uniform velocity. Using a tungsten film, they found that in increasing the voltage from 15 to 40 kv., the line $L\beta_1$ ($L_{II}-M_{IV}$) becomes about 10 per cent more intense, compared to $L\beta_2$ ($L_{III}-N_{IV}$) while the line $L\beta_3$ (L_I-M_{III}) becomes 30 per cent more intense with respect to $L\beta_2$. This seems to show that when the energy of the impinging electron is large compared to the binding energy of the L levels (in tungsten, about 11 kv.), a larger part of the ionization occurs in the more tightly bound L sub-levels.

In more recent work by Robinson and Cassie[54] the primary radiation was from a molybdenum target and the secondary radiators were 29 Cu, 33 As, 35 Br, 40 Zr, 42 Mo, 47 Ag, 56 Ba, 58 Ce, 74 W, 79 Au, 83 Bi, 90 Th, and 92 U. Special attention was paid to lines in the magnetic spectrum due to Auger electrons. The accuracy of the experiments was sufficient to show clearly that in the ejection of Auger electrons the final state is an atom with two inner electrons missing, and that the final energy level concerned is not one of those which appear in the ordinary x-ray diagram. The results obtained with a copper radiator are shown in Table VII–6. In the column headed " Interpretation " the ejected electrons ascribed to internal conversions in the copper atom are listed with an A. The ν/R values of the ejected electrons in these internal conversions are seen to be uniformly less than those listed in Table VII–5 which are due to the absorption of the Cu K lines in an unionized atom. As we expect, the work of removal is increased in the case of the internal conversion, because the atom is left with two inner vacancies instead of one.

The energy levels which are computed for these lines are primed in the tables, indicating that they occur in doubly ionized atoms, and are uniformly higher than the unprimed levels of Table VII–5. This primed notation is perhaps insufficiently precise, for one would not expect the L_I' of the first row to be the same as the L_I' of the fourth. In the first row, since we are dealing with the internal conversion of Cu $K\alpha_1$, the level is probably $L_I L_{III}$ in the notation of Chap. VIII. In the fourth row, representing the internal conversion

[53] Coster and van Zuylen, Nature **129**, 943 (1932).
[54] Robinson and Cassie, Proc. Roy. Soc. Lond. A **113**, 282 (1926).

TABLE VII–6

ELECTRONS EJECTED FROM A COPPER PLATE BY INCIDENT X-RAYS OF THE WAVE-
LENGTHS OF THE Mo K SERIES

ν/R of the Incident Radiation: $K\alpha_2$, 1280.1; $K\alpha_1$, 1287.8; $K\beta_1$, 1444.7; $K\beta_2$, 1471.5

Intensity	Hr	ν/R Calc.	Interpretation	ν_q/R	X-ray Values of ν_q/R
2–3	279.5	506.9	A : Cu $K\alpha_1$–L_I'	$L_I'=85.9$	
6	283.0	519.3	A : Cu $K\alpha_1$–$(L_{II}L_{III})'$	$(L_{II}L_{III})'=73.5$	
1	286.5	532.3	?		
2–3*	297.2	572.4	A : Cu $K\beta_1$–L_I'	$L'=83.5$	
3–4†	300.9	589.6	A : $\begin{cases} \text{Cu } K\beta_1\text{–}(L_{II}L_{III})' \\ \text{Cu } K\alpha_1\text{–}M' \end{cases}$	$\begin{cases} (L_{II}L_{III})'=69.3 \\ M'=6.2 \end{cases}$	
3–4	309.2	619.4	Mo $K\alpha_2$–Cu K	$K=660.7$	661.6
6	311.2	627.2	Mo $K\alpha_1$–Cu K	$K=660.6$	661.6
4	348.4	784.7	Mo $K\beta_1$–Cu K	$K=660.0$	661.6
1	354.6	812.6	Mo $K\beta_2$–Cu K	$K=658.9$	661.6
5–6	433.8	1209.5	Mo $K\alpha_1$–Cu L_I	$L_I=78.3$	81.0
1	435.9	1221.0	Mo $K\alpha_1$–Cu $L_{II}L_{III}$	$L_{II}L_{III}=66.8$	70.3, 68.9
3	446.9	1282.4	Mo $K\alpha_1$–Cu M	$M=5.4$	8.9→0.4
2–3	461.5	1366.1	Mo $K\beta_1$–Cu L_I	$L_I=78.6$	81.0

* Tail of a band, barely resolved, inaccurate.
† Head of a band.

of Cu $K\beta_1$, we presumably have $L_I M_{III}$. It is obvious that these levels should be important in the study of the so-called non-diagram x-ray lines but as yet no extensive correlation has been made.

5. A Precision Measurement of the Velocity of Ejected Photo-electrons

An accurate determination of the velocity of ejected photo-electrons has been made by Kretschmar[55] with the purpose of establishing new quantitative relations between the fundamental constants e, e/m, and h. The incident x–rays were produced in a metal x–ray tube equipped with a molybdenum target and operated at 75 to 85 milliamperes and 30,000 volts. The lines due to photo-electrons ejected by the $K\alpha$ lines of molybdenum from inner levels of various substances were easily observable in the magnetic spectrum, and the resolving power was sufficient to separate lines due to Mo $K\alpha_1$ and to Mo $K\alpha_2$. The substances from which photo-

[55] G. G. Kretschmar, Phys. Rev. **43**, 417 (1933).

electrons were ejected were in the form of very thin films, evaporated or sputtered on cellophane. Films of 79 Au, 47 Ag, 29 Cu, and 78 Pt were used, and although the exact thickness was not measured, the films were thin enough to be translucent. Thin films were used in order to produce sharp lines in the magnetic spectrum: if thick films are used, photo-electrons liberated beneath the surface are slowed down before emerging from the secondary radiator, and the magnetic spectrum lines are bands, sharp on the high velocity edge only. The camera is shown in Fig. VII–5.

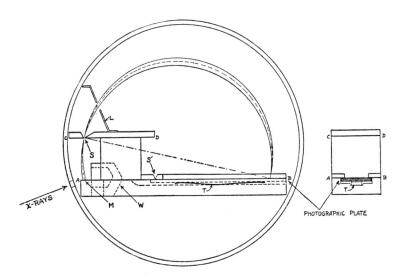

Fig. VII–5. A magnetic spectrograph used by Kretschmar in a precise determination of energies of ejected electrons. A fiducial mark is made on the plate by light shining through slit S'. The vertical and horizontal distances between S and S' are measured, and the distance from S' to the line.

The magnetic field was produced in a carefully constructed solenoid 100 cm. long and 22 cm. in diameter. The magnetic field of this larger solenoid was calibrated by inserting into it a smaller, " standard " solenoid whose dimensions were very accurately known. A flip coil was put into the center of the standard solenoid, and the current determined which, when passing through the standard solenoid, produced a magnetic field which neutralized the field from the large solenoid. The quantity directly measured in the experiments was Hr, the product of the magnetic field strength in gauss by the radius of curvature of the ejected photo-electrons from an x-ray level q in a known substance.

Let λ be the wave-length of the primary x-rays; in this case, of Mo $K\alpha_1$, and let λ_q be the wave-length of the q critical absorption limit of the secondary radiator. Then by Einstein's equation, we have

$$m_0 c^2 \left(\frac{1}{\sqrt{1 - \beta^2}} - 1 \right) = hc \left(\frac{1}{\lambda} - \frac{1}{\lambda_q} \right). \tag{7.14}$$

In this expression we have used the relativity theory form of the kinetic energy. m_0 is the rest mass of the electron; c, the velocity of light, and β is the ratio of the velocity of the ejected photo-electron to the velocity of light.

The photo-electrons which make the impressions on the photographic plate have travelled at right angles to the lines of force of the magnetic field, and hence in circles. The magnitude of the linear momentum of the electron at any instant is equal to Her/c, where r is the radius of the circle, and c enters because e is expressed in electrostatic units. Thus

$$\frac{m_0}{\sqrt{1 - \beta^2}} \beta c = \frac{Her}{c}. \tag{7.15}$$

By the elimination of β between these two equations, one may obtain

$$\left(\frac{e}{m_0} \right) \left(\frac{e}{h} \right) = \frac{2c^3 (\lambda^{-1} - \lambda_q^{-1})}{H^2 r^2 - c^2 (h/e)^2 (\lambda^{-1} - \lambda_q^{-1})^2}. \tag{7.16}$$

If we wish to use the results of the experiment as a precision determination of a relation between e, e/m, and h, we must scrutinize the right-hand member of the above equation carefully, to see that it does not contain quantities which cannot be measured independently of these fundamentals. The second term in the denominator of eq. (7.16) is in the nature of a correction term to $H^2 r^2$, and is comparatively small. If values of h, e, and λ approximately correct are used, the accuracy is sufficient. In the numerator, however, x-ray wave-lengths appear. Let us suppose these wave-lengths have been determined by observing the corresponding Bragg angles of reflection from calcite. In such a case the λ values involve the value of e, and we must explicitly express this in eq. (7.16). From eq. (9.39), Chap. IX, we have

$$\lambda = \frac{1}{n} \sqrt[3]{\frac{4M}{Q\rho\Phi(\beta)}} \, e^{\frac{1}{3}} \left(1 - \frac{\delta}{\sin^2 \theta} \right) \sin \theta, \qquad (7.17)$$

where

n = order of reflection,
M = molecular weight of calcite,
Q = Faraday constant,
ρ = density of calcite,
$\Phi(\beta)$ = geometric factor related to volume of cleavage unit,
δ = unit decrement of the refractive index.

In applying this equation to the λ_q values in the numerator of eq. (7.16) we will omit the factor in parentheses, involving the unit decrement of the refractive index. This is permissible since the entire term λ_q^{-1} which is subtracted from λ^{-1} is in all cases considerably smaller than λ^{-1}, and the index of refraction correction to λ_q will produce an entirely negligible effect on the entire expression. We thus find that the combination of fundamental constants measured in Kretschmar's experiment, using data on the Bragg angle of reflection of x-rays from crystals, is

$$\frac{e}{m_0} \cdot \frac{e^{\frac{1}{3}}}{h} = \frac{2c^3 \left[\dfrac{Q\rho\Phi(\beta)}{4M} \right]^{\frac{1}{3}} \left\{ \dfrac{n}{[1 - (\delta/\sin^2 \theta)] \sin \theta} - \dfrac{n_q}{\sin \theta_q} \right\}}{H^2 r^2 - c^2(h/e)^2 \{ \lambda^{-1} - \lambda_q^{-1} \}^2}. \qquad (7.17)$$

The results of the measurements are shown in Table VII–7. The values of $\sin \theta_q$ have been calculated from the tabulated values of λ_q by dividing them by twice the conventional grating space of calcite, or 3.02904×10^{-8} cm. The conventions concerning x-ray wave-lengths are discussed in Chapter IX.

In the farthest right-hand column of the table are given the best values as selected by Kretschmar. A weighted average was obtained by weighting the values in C–11 and C–12 by a factor of two, and the value in C–13 by 3. The product $he^{-\frac{1}{3}}$ may be obtained from measurements of the smallest angle of reflection corresponding to the general radiation from an x-ray tube operating at known voltage, as shown in Sec. 7 of Chap. IX, and the value thus obtained for this product is independent of any assumptions as to the value of e, h, or e/m. Using these results in connection with Kretschmar's, a value

TABLE VII-7

Precision Measurements of Photo-electron Velocities. Eq. (7.17)

$c = 2.99796 \times 10^{10}$ cm./sec.

$Q = 2.89270 \times 10^{14}$ esu/gm. mol

$\rho = 2.71024$ gm./cm^3

$\theta = 6° 42' 35.5''$

* $\delta = 1.82 \times 10^{-6}$

* $\lambda = 0.707830 \times 10^{-8}$ cm.

$\Phi(\beta) = 1.09594$

$M = 100.078$ gm./mol.

* $h = 6.622 \times 10^{-27}$ ergs sec.

* $e = 4.803 \times 10^{-10}$ esu

$n = n_q = 1$

Plate	Source	* λ_q	Source of λ_q	$\sin \theta_q$	Hr	$\dfrac{e}{m_0} \cdot \dfrac{e^{2/3}}{h} \times 10^{31}$	Selected Values
C-3	79 Au M_I	3.603	Johnson	0.5947	402.201	2.9964	
	79 Au M_{III}	4.508	Lindberg	0.7441	412.043	2.9972	2.9972
	79 Au M_{IV}	5.330	Lindberg	0.8798	418.439	2.9909	
	79 Au M_V	5.529	Lindberg	0.9127	419.741	2.9890	
C-7	47 Ag L_I	3.2474	v. D. & L.	0.53605	396.960	2.9928	
	47 Ag L_{III}	3.6908	v. D. & L.	0.60924	403.537	2.9943	2.9943
C-11	29 Cu K	1.3777	Siegbahn	0.22742	311.891	2.9995	2.9995
C-12	78 Pt M_I	3.742	Johnson	0.6177	404.317	2.9924	
	78 Pt M_{II}	4.085	Johnson	0.6743	408.125	2.9953	
	78 Pt M_{III}	4.676	Lindberg	0.7719	413.588	2.9951	2.9951
	78 Pt M_{IV}	5.544	Lindberg	0.9151	419.565	2.9927	
	78 Pt M_V	5.746	Lindberg	0.9485	421.176	2.9852	
C-13	78 Pt M_I	3.742	Johnson	0.6177	404.165	2.9947	
	78 Pt M_{II}	4.085	Johnson	0.6743	407.868	2.9991	
	78 Pt M_{III}	4.676	Lindberg	0.7719	413.318	2.9991	2.9991

* Quantities marked with this asterisk need not be known accurately since variations in them produce only small changes in the right-hand member of eq. (7.17).

Wave-length references:

Johnson, Phys. Rev. **34**, 1106 (1929).

Lindberg, Zeitschr. f. Phys. **54**, 632 (1929).

van Dyke and Lindsay, Phys. Rev. **30**, 562 (1927).

Siegbahn, Spektroskopie der Röntg. (1931), p. 265, average of last five values.

of e/m_0 from x-ray measurements may be found. The weighted average of Kretschmar's results gives

$$\left(\frac{e}{m_0}\right)\left(\frac{e^{2/3}}{h}\right) = (2.9976 \pm 0.0044) \times 10^{31}.$$

In this value e is expressed in electrostatic units. Using the values of $he^{-\frac{4}{3}}$ given in Table IX–14, Chapter 9; and changing e in e/m_0 to electromagnetic units, using the value of c at the head of the previous table, we obtain

if

$$e/m_0 = (1.7569 \pm 0.0035) \times 10^7 \; emu/gm$$

$$he^{-\frac{4}{3}} = (1.7571 \pm 0.0009) \times 10^{-14}, \tag{a}$$

or

if

$$e/m_0 = (1.7604 \pm 0.0035) \times 10^7 \; emu/gm$$

$$he^{-\frac{4}{3}} = (1.7606 \pm 0.0009) \times 10^{-14}. \tag{b}$$

The $he^{-\frac{4}{3}}$ value marked (a) in the above is the value deduced from Feder's[56] experiments; that marked (b) comes from the work of Duane, Palmer, and Chi-Sun Yeh.[57]

6. *Absorption Coefficients and Their Measurement*

When a monochromatic x-ray beam of power P traverses normally a very thin sheet of material of thickness dx, the power in the emergent beam has been decreased by an amount dP, so that the following relationship holds:

$$\frac{dP}{P} = -\mu dx. \tag{7.18}$$

μ depends on the wave-length of the incident beam and on the absorber. It is seen to have the dimensions of a reciprocal length, and hence is often referred to as the linear absorption coefficient. In Chapter IV, this coefficient is written μ_l, to distinguish it from the refractive index, but we can here use the symbol without the subscript and avoid ambiguity.

We may, however, prefer to think in terms of the fraction of the beam removed by each atom which it traverses. Let us imagine that the material traversed consists of one kind of atom only. We would then write

$$\frac{dP}{P} = -\mu_a dn, \tag{7.19}$$

[56] H. Feder, Ann. der Physik 5, 1, 497 (1929).
[57] Duane, Palmer and Chi-Sun Yeh, Proc. Nat. Acad. Sci. 7, 237 (1921).

where dn is the number of atoms in the path of the beam as it passes through the absorber, and μ_a is the atomic absorption coefficient. If we consider a beam of 1 cm.^{2} cross-section we see that

$$dn = \frac{N\rho dx}{A}, \qquad (7.20)$$

where ρ is the density of the material, A the atomic weight, and N the Avogadro number; the quotient A/N representing the mass of an atom in the material. By a comparison of the preceding equations, it is seen that

$$\mu_a = \mu \frac{A}{\rho N}. \qquad (7.21)$$

The mass absorption coefficient, μ_m, refers to the power diverted per gram of material traversed by the beam. In this sense, we write

$$\frac{dP}{P} = -\mu_m dm, \qquad (7.22)$$

where dm is the number of grams in the path of the beam. But

$$dm = \rho dx$$

and therefore

$$\mu_m = \mu/\rho = \mu_a(N/A). \qquad (7.23)$$

The mass absorption coefficient is the most commonly used of the various coefficients. Its superiority over the linear absorption coefficient lies in the fact that in contrast to the latter, it is independent of the physical state of the absorbing medium. This is shown by eq. (7.23), which indicates that the mass absorption coefficient is simply N/A times the atomic coefficient. Thus the mass absorption coefficient of mercury for a given wave-length is the same (at least to the degree of approximation considered here) for gaseous, liquid, and solid mercury.

In a compound, whose formula may be

$$X_x Y_y Z_z \ldots$$

it is typical of the behavior of x-rays that a molecular absorption coefficient μ_{mol} may be used which is defined by additive relations involving the atomic absorption coefficients of the constituents of the compound. Thus

$$\mu_{mol} = \frac{A}{\rho N}\mu = x(\mu_a)_X + y(\mu_a)_Y + z(\mu_a)_Z \ldots \qquad (7.24)$$

where $(\mu_a)_X$ is the atomic absorption coefficient of the atom X for the wave-length in question. Thus

$$\mu_{CaCO_3} = \mu_{Ca} + \mu_C + 3\mu_O.$$

If P_0 is the power incident upon an absorber, and P is the transmitted power, integration of the above differential expressions gives

$$P = P_0 e^{-\mu x} = P_0 e^{-\mu_m \rho x} = P_0 e^{-\mu_a(\rho N/A)x} \qquad (7.25)$$

where x is the thickness of the absorber in cm.

It is well to remember that these simple absorption equations do not apply if the beam of x-rays is a highly divergent one, nor if the beam is too broad. In the first case, the different rays in the beam will traverse different thicknesses of the absorber. Condon[58a] and Millikan and Cameron[58b] have pointed out that if radiation is incident from all directions upon the plane surface of an absorber of infinite lateral extent, the intensity at a depth x below this surface due to the primary radiation is

$$I = I_0 \int_0^{\pi/2} e^{-\mu x \sec \theta} \sin \theta d\theta.$$

Putting $z = \sec \theta$ this takes the form

$$I = I_0 G(\mu x), \qquad (7.25a)$$

where

$$G(\mu x) = \int_1^\infty z^{-2} e^{-\mu x z} dz. \qquad (7.25b)$$

The function $G(\mu x)$, known as the " Gold integral," has been tabulated by Gold[58c] for various values of μx. This expression is useful;

[58a] E. U. Condon, Proc. Nat. Acad. Sci. U.S.A. 12, 323 (1926).
[58b] R. A. Millikan and G. H. Cameron, Phys. Rev. 28, 860 (1926).
[58c] E. Gold, Proc. Roy. Soc. A 82, 62 (1908).

for example, in calculating the absorption of cosmic radiation traversing the atmosphere.

If the beam is broad, considerable portions of the scattered and
fluorescence x-rays from the absorber will remain within the direct
beam and add to its power. This indicates an error that may arise
in experimental measurements of the absorption coefficient using
an ionization chamber. If the absorber subtends a sufficiently large
angle at the ionization chamber window, fluorescence and scattered
radiation from it may enter the chamber and the amount of absorption may be underestimated.

This effect is clearly shown in Figs. VII–6 and VII–7, representing

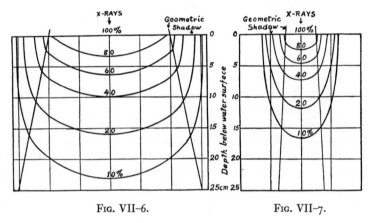

FIG. VII–6.   FIG. VII–7.

FIG. VII–6 and FIG. VII–7. Intensity of x-rays at various depths below a water
surface on which broad beams of hard x-rays are incident. (After Bachem.)

data obtained by Bachem.[59] In this case the secondary radiation
is entirely of the scattered type. Figure VII–6 shows the intensity
of the x-rays at various positions in a deep water bath when the water
is irradiated from above by hard x-rays (200 kv., 1 mm copper filter)
passing through an opening 20 cm. in diameter. The curves of
Fig. VII–7 are exactly similar except that the diameter of the incident
beam is 5 cm. It will be seen that because of the presence of a greater
amount of scattered rays, the intensity falls off with depth less
rapidly when the broader beam is used. This is also accompanied

[59] A. Bachem, Principles of X-ray and Radium Dosage, Chicago (1923), p. 152
et seq.

by a greater intensity outside the geometrical shadow. Bachem finds that under the conditions of Fig. VII–6, at the surface of the water 33 per cent of the x-rays are secondary rays coming back from the water, while at a depth of 20 cm. 85 per cent of the x-rays are secondary, only 15 per cent coming directly from the primary beam.

It has become customary to consider two main types of absorption processes. The first is the photo-electric, or true absorption, in which the energy of an entire quantum of the incident radiation is transformed into the kinetic energy of an ejected electron plus the potential energy of an excited atom. Under the second, or scattering process, both scattering with and without change of wave-length is grouped. If we let τ refer to the photo-electric absorption and σ to the scattering, the total linear absorption coefficient may be written

$$\mu = \tau + \sigma. \qquad (7.26)$$

In order to obtain precise measurements of the absorption coefficients it is necessary to use homogeneous x-rays. For if more than one wave-length is present, the longer waves will be strongly absorbed by the first portions of the screen traversed, making the fraction of the energy removed per unit path decrease with increasing length of path. From eq. (7.25) we obtain

$$\mu = \frac{1}{x} \ln \frac{P_0}{P}, \qquad (7.27)$$

but the equations on which this is based depend on the assumption that μ is independent of x, hence the necessity of homogeneity.

We may, however, speak of the " effective " absorption coefficient of a heterogeneous beam, meaning usually the value calculated by eq. (7.27) for some particular value of x. This effective value approaches a maximum limit for small values of x, the limiting value depending on the distribution of wave-lengths in the incident beam.

The homogeneity necessary to make accurate measurements may be obtained in various ways. Some experiments have been made using filtered primary x-rays. This is the least satisfactory of the various methods, and great care must be exercised in interpreting the results, since a single filter seldom gives a sufficiently narrow range of wave-lengths. This does not apply to a selective filtration method devised by Ross, which will be discussed in a later section. In his early experiments, Barkla[60] secured nearly homogeneous radiation by exciting the fluorescence radiation of various elements. This method has been described in this chapter in the section on the fluorescence yield. This marked a great advance in the attempts to obtain monochromatic x-ray beams.

With the advent of crystal spectrometry it became a comparatively simple matter to secure nearly homogeneous x-rays. The apparatus used by Bragg and Pierce[61] and in many of the later

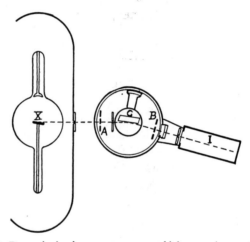

Fig. VII–8. A Bragg ionization spectrometer which may be used in absorption measurements. The absorber may be placed at A or at B.

absorption measurements is shown diagrammatically in Fig. VII–8. From the crystal C a ray is reflected to the ionization chamber I. Early experiments by Moseley and Darwin[62] and more recent ones by Woo[63] have shown that it makes no difference whether the absorption screen is placed at A in the path of the direct beam or at B in the path of the reflected beam.

It will be seen that this arrangement satisfies the geometrical conditions for measuring the total absorption, for the ray reflected

[60] C. G. Barkla, Phil. Mag. 22, 396 (1911).
[61] W. H. Bragg and S. E. Pierce, Phil. Mag. 26, 211 (1913).
[62] H. G. J. Moseley and C. G. Darwin, Phil. Mag. 26, 211 (1913).
[63] Y. H. Woo, Proc. Nat. Acad. Sci. U.S.A. 10, 145 (1924).

from the crystal is necessarily narrow, and the aperture of the ionization chamber is ordinarily small. Of course if the absorption screen were placed against the window of the ionization chamber, an appreciable amount of scattered radiation might enter, but this will not occur if the screen is placed near the crystal.

If λ_θ is the wave-length of the first order ray reflected at the angle θ, rays may also be reflected whose wave-lengths are $\lambda_\theta/2$, $\lambda_\theta/3$, etc. These higher orders can be eliminated by taking the precaution of operating the x-ray tube at a potential too low to excite the wave-length $\lambda_\theta/2$. This condition is satisfied if $V_{max.} = 2hc/e\lambda_\theta$, where $V_{max.}$ is the maximum potential applied to the tube. There is thus a sufficient margin of potential to make possible the excitation of the desired radiation with a considerable intensity, even when it consists merely of a portion selected from the general radiation.

The shape and purity of the absorbing screen are also of great importance when precise absorption measurements are to be made. In view of the rapid increase in absorption coefficient with atomic number, even a very small impurity of a heavy element may greatly increase the absorption of a screen composed mainly of a light element such as carbon or aluminium. In the case of the heavy elements, especially for the longer wave-lengths, the absorbing screen must be so thin that it is difficult to obtain uniform thickness. The effect of non-uniformity is to give an apparent absorption coefficient smaller than the true value. A common practice has been to weigh a portion of the absorbing sheet of known area, and thus calculate an effective thickness. In order to insure that this thickness actually acts in the absorption, the screen is kept in motion during a measurement so that the portion of the absorber being used is large.

Either photographic or ionization methods can be used in measuring the diminution in the power of the beam due to passage through the absorber. The photographic methods are successful here largely because the problem is the relatively simple one of measuring the relative power in two beams of the same wave-length.

Considerable work has been done on the absorption coefficients of gases, and here the experimental arrangement may be considerably modified from that of Fig. VII–8. An advantage of the measurements in gases is that there is usually no difficulty in estimating the thickness of the absorbing layer. A balance method originally described by Crowther[64] and later used by Crowther and Orton[65] is shown in Fig. VII–9. We have here three chambers in succession through which the x-ray beam passes. The central chamber is fitted with collecting electrodes, but it is not necessary to use them for an experiment whose sole object is the determination of the absorption coefficient. Chambers I and III always contained air; the pressure in chamber III was that of the atmosphere. Chambers I and II were air tight, their windows being covered with cellophane diaphragms. As shown in the figure, the high potential electrodes in chambers I and III were so charged that the insulated electrodes in these two chambers collected ions of opposite sign.

A determination is begun with chamber II evacuated. With x-rays passing through, the pressure of the air in chamber I is adjusted

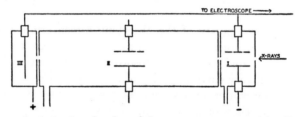

Fig. VII–9. An ionization chamber of three compartments used by Crowther and Orton in measurements on absorption and ionization in gases.

until zero current flows to the electroscope from the insulated electrodes of chambers I and III. Let p_1 be the pressure of the air in chamber I when the electroscope shows zero deflection, and thus equal numbers of positive and negative ions are being collected in chambers I and III. In this condition the chambers are said to be balanced.

Chamber II is then filled to a known pressure with the gas whose absorption coefficient it is desired to measure. The balance is now destroyed, since, due to the absorption, fewer ions are being produced and collected in chamber III. The electroscope acquires a negative charge. The pressure in chamber I is now changed until again a balance is attained, say, at pressure p_1'.

To a first approximation, since the fraction of the x-ray beam absorbed in chamber I is small, the ionization in I will be proportional

[64] J. A. Crowther, Phil. Mag. 14, 653 (1907).
[65] Crowther and Orton, Phil. Mag. 10, 329 (1930).

to the pressure. Since at balance the ionization in chamber I is a measure of that in III, we may write

$$p_1'/p_1 = e^{-\mu d},$$

where μ is the linear absorption coefficient of the gas in chamber II, and d is the path-length in chamber II.

This method is advantageous in that its result is independent of fluctuations in the intensity of the x-ray beam, and also of changes in the sensitivity of the electroscope. In actual experiments, the temperature in the compartments must be noted, and also one must take account of the slight lack of proportionality which must always exist between ionization and pressure in chamber I. A correction for this involves a knowledge of the absorption coefficient for air, which can be found by using air in the central chamber. The value thus found by the simple equation can be used to correct results in other gases.

Dershem and Schein[66] measured the absorption coefficients of gases for the wave-length of the carbon $K\alpha$ line. A vacuum spectrometer containing a ruled grating was used. The gas to be measured was admitted to the spectrometer and the distance from the defining entrance slit for x-rays to the photographic plate was used as the length of path in the absorption formula. Uber[67] measured the absorption coefficients of gaseous mercury in the region of its L series by superheating mercury vapor in the contact with a reservoir of liquid mercury of known temperature. From the known vapor pressure of mercury the pressure of the gas used could be computed.

Stephenson[68] in measuring the absorption coefficient of uranium, has introduced the method of using a solution of the material. Two absorption cells are prepared of the same thickness, and the window thicknesses are adjusted by trial until the same absorption is observed in both cells when empty, and in both when filled with water. Then measurements are taken with one cell containing a known uranium nitrate solution, the other containing water. With slight corrections for the absorption by the nitrate group the absorption coefficient of the uranium can be computed. This method is successful for

[66] Dershem and Schein, Phys. Rev. **37**, 1238 (1931).

[67] F. M. Uber, Phys. Rev. **38**, 217 (1931).

[68] R. J. Stephenson, Phys. Rev. **43**, 527 (1933).

very heavy elements, where the absorption by the dissolved material is much greater than that due to the water.

The data which have been accumulated on absorption coefficients have now become so extensive that no attempt is made here to publish all known absorption coefficient values.   Table VII–8, parts A, B, and C, contains the results which have been obtained on the absorption of x-rays in gases.   This information is useful in experiments with ionization spectrometers as it stands, and a resolution of the results into atomic absorption coefficients is therefore not given.   In connection with these results, Williams[69] has given useful information on the linear absorption coefficients of mica and cellophane, two substances which with aluminium are widely used as diaphragms over ionization chamber windows.   Williams found that for mica, between 0.4 and 2.3 angstroms, the linear absorption coefficient may be expressed by

$$\mu_{mica} = 36.56 \, \lambda^{2.76},$$

where λ is expressed in angstroms.   It should be remembered that the composition of mica may be variable.   From 0.6 to 2.3 angstroms a similar formula for cellophane is

$$\mu_{cellophane} = 3.52 \, \lambda^{2.66}.$$

Considerable information on the absorption of radiation of wavelength of the order of 100 angstroms in gases and in foils has been obtained by Holweck.[70]   It has not been included in the tables given in this book.

In Appendix IX is given a table of mass absorption coefficients of the elements, compiled from various sources by S. J. M. Allen, and most kindly sent to us for publication in this book.

Appendix X gives values of the mass absorption coefficient of various substances for the $K\alpha_1$ line of tungsten, 0.2086 A.   These were obtained by T. M. Hahn, using a double x-ray spectrometer set for the line in question, so that the radiation used was extremely homogeneous as to wave-length range.   These probably constitute the most accurate data on absorption at this wave-length at present available.

[69] J. H. Williams, Phys. Rev. **44**, 146 (1933).

[70] F. Holweck, De la Lumière aux Rayons-X, Presses Universitaires de France, Paris (1927).

TABLE VII–8

Mass Absorption Coefficients of Gases and Vapors According to Various Observers

Part A. Wave-length Region from 0.496 to 1.274 Angstroms

Gas	Molecular Weight	0.496	0.560	0.6136	0.631	0.709	0.7185	0.885	0.9087	1.081	1.095	1.274
Ne	20.18	0.84 C	1.20 C	....	1.69 C	2.50 C	....	....		....		
Air	28.98	C	C	....	C	C	....	....			3.4 AA	
A	39.94	5.06 C	6.89 C	....	9.80 C	12.98 C	....	....				30.35 St
SO₂	64.06	1.92	2.67 St	....	3.60	5.55 St	....	11.47 St		18.89 St		
SO₂	64.06	C	2.50 C	....	C	5.53 C	....					
Cl₂	70.91	4.14	5.76	........AA	8.18 C	11.52 C	........AA	....	24 AA		....	
Kr	82.9	....	....	59 AA	....	....	79 AA	....	24 AA			
Kr	82.9			59 AA			79 AA		115 AA			
CH₃Br	94.94	....	........St	40 AA	....	56.6 St	62 AA	105.3 St	....	25.6 St	....	38.66 St
C₂H₅Br	108.96	See table of collected formulae — 29.25 St		See table of formulae.		See table of formulae				
CH₃I	141.95										
Hg	200.61										

See end of table for references.

TABLE VII-8—*Continued*

Part B. Wave-length Region from 1.279 to 3.8637 Angstroms

Gas	Molecular Weight	1.279	1.389	1.473	1.537	1.935	2.081	2.287	3.378	3.592	3.716	3.8637
								λ				
Ne	20.18	......	16.0 C	......	23.3 C	......	......	74.7 W	235 W	279 W		
Ne	20.18	......	......	......	......	......	......	75.5 C				
C$_2$H$_4$	28.03	......	......	......	C–O¹ 4.32 C–O²	......	......	......				
N$_2$	28.02	5.6 AA	......	8.3 AA	7.33 S	......	......	......				
Air	28.98	......	......	......	9.54 St	18.9 St	......	29.3 S	79.5 W	96.3 W		
Air	28.98				C–O² 9.50	18.8 C–O²		31.8 W	101.9 W	122 W		
Air	28.98				9.44 G							
Air	28.98				9.64 G	C–O² 22.20		36.4 W	116.8 W	141 W		
O$_2$	32.00				11.5 C–O²	22.20		35.5 S				
O$_2$	32.00				11.1 S							
O$_2$	32.00				11.6 C–O²							
H$_2$S	34.08				82.7 C		282 W	354 W	1025 W	1210 W	1320 S	1465 S
A	39.94	......	85.7 C	......	114 G	......	......	339.4 C				
A	39.94	......	......	......	119.6 G	......	......					

Substance	Mol. wt.							
A	39.94	……	C–O 2 112.5 S	C–O 2 18.27 St	……	344 S		W
A	39.94	……	112 C–O 2 9.15 St	……	……			
CO₂	44.00	……	……	99.4	……	161 W	452 W	545 W
SO₂	64.06	38.5 C	51.1 C	……	……	162.6 C		
SO₂	64.06	……	51.8 C–O 2	C–O 2 107.5	……			
C₂H₅Cl	64.496	……	60 C	……	……			
Cl₂	70.914	76.9 C	102.7 C–O 2	C–O 2 7.36	……	315.0 C	41.5 W	49.9 W
C₅H₁₂	72.094	……	3.58	C–O 2 10.48	……			
(C₂H₅)₂O	74.078	See table of formulae.	C–O 2 3.62	C–O 2 7.04	……			
C₆H₁₄ / CH₃Br	86.109 / 94.939	……	30.3 C–O 2 / 66.6 St	St	……			
Zn(CH₃)₂	95.43	51.7 St	……	125	……			
C₂H₅Br	108.96	……	68.3	……	……			
C₂H₅Br	108.96	……	92.4 C–O 2	……	……			
CHCl₃	119.38	……	259.8	……	……			
CH₃I	141.95	……	……	……	……			
CCl₄ / Hg	153.83 / 200.61	See tabulated formulae.	……	……	……		741 W	896 W

See end of table for references.

TABLE VII-8—Continued

Part C. Wave-length Region from 3.8677 to 68 Angstroms

λ

Gas	Molecular Weight	3.8677	3.927	3.946	4.146	4.359	5.166	5.394	6.973	8.323	9.868	43.5	68
H_2	2.02											1000 M	2980 M
He	4.00												
CH_4	16.03		356 W		416 W	478 W	763 W	865 W	1727 W	2750 W	4310 W	3600 M	4430 M
Ne	20.18											1540 DS; 13,100 M	
C_2H_2	26.02											1920 M	5460 M
C_2H_4	28.03											1930 M	5520 M
N_2	28.02		120.7 W		144.3 W	166 W	273 W	312 W	645 W	1109 W	1796 W	3790 DS; 3850 K	10,900 M
N_2	28.02											3800 M	
N_2	28.02												12,380 M
CO	28.00				163.4 W	192 W	314 W	356 W	740 W	1200 W	1964 W	4300 K	
CO	28.00				168 S				747 S			4450 M	
Air	28.98		139.4 W		222 W	258 W	413 W	476 W	976 W	1585 W	2540 W	5100 DS; 5350 K	14,600 M
Air	28.98				221 S				971 S			4650 M	
Air	28.98												
C_2H_6	30.05		188.8 W										
O_2	32.00											1940 DS; 5765 M	5580 M
O_2	32.00											5650 K	16,250 M
O_2	32.00											6000 DS	
A	39.94	147 S	152.7 W		174.3 W	202 W	324 W	360 W	748 W	1157 W	1865 W	45,700	
A	39.94			151 S	171 S				762 S				

Gas											Observer
C₃H₈	44.06									2360 M	6730 M
CO₂	44.00									4740 K	13,590 M
CO₂	44.00									4900 DS	
CO₂	44.00									4780 DS	
SO₂	64.06	664 W	786 W	910 W	317	363	738 W	1189 W	1905 W		
C₅H₁₂	72.094	64.7 W	76.8	88.8	145.2	167.5	352	593	964		
Kr	82.9									31,800 DS	
Xe	130.2									6740 DS	
CCl₄	153.83	1164 W	1368 W	1666 W	269	302	595	941	1538 W		

Part D. Formulae for the Computation of Mass Absorption Coefficients
In These Formulae λ is to be Expressed in Angstroms

Gas	Formula	Range of Validity	Observer	Gas	Formula	Range of Validity	Observer
Air......	$\mu_m = 2.64\lambda^{2.79}$	$1.5 < \lambda < 2.0$	Stockmeyer	CH₃I.....	$\mu_m = 65.46\lambda^{2.62}$	$0.4 < \lambda < 0.9$	Williams
Argon....	$\mu = 33.4\lambda^{2.8} + 0.67\lambda^{0.94}$	$0.35 < \lambda < 2.0$	Yu	Hg.......	$\mu_m = 286\lambda^{2.56}$	$0.7 < \lambda < 0.834$	Uber
SO₂......	$\mu_m = 14.81\lambda^{2.93}$	$0.5 < \lambda < 2.0$	Stockmeyer	Hg.......	$\mu_m = 242\lambda^{2.56}$	$0.834 < \lambda < 0.871$	Uber
CH₃Br....	$\mu_m = 19.2\lambda^{2.79}$	$1.1 < \lambda < 2.3$	Williams	Hg.......	$\mu_m = 175\lambda^{2.59}$	$0.871 < \lambda < 1.008$	Uber
C₂H₅Br..	$\mu_m = 20.52\lambda^{2.76}$	$0.918 < \lambda < 2.0$	Stockmeyer	Hg.......	$\mu_m = 71.8\lambda^{2.66}$	$1.008 < \lambda < 1.4$	Uber
C₂H₅Br..	$\mu_m = 147.2\lambda^{2.76}$	$0.5 < \lambda < 0.918$	Stockmeyer				

REFERENCES TO TABLE VII-8

AA = Allison and Andrew, Phys. Rev. **38**, 441 (1931). Absorption coefficients obtained from this paper are only listed above in regions in which other data are not available.

C = Colvert, Phys. Rev. **36**, 1619 (1930).

C-O I = Crowther and Orton, Phil. Mag. **10**, 329 (1930). The measurements reported in this paper were largely repeated and reported in C-O 2. In such cases only the values in C-O 2 are listed.

C-O 2 = Crowther and Orton, Phil. Mag. **13**, 505 (1932).

DS = Dershem and Schein, Phys. Rev. **37**, 1238 (1931).

G = Gaertner, Ann. d. Phys. **2**, 94; **3**, 325 (1920).

K = Kurtz, Annalen der Physik **85**, 529 (1928). Kurtz used direct radiation from a carbon target filtered through celluloid.

M = Messner, Zeitschr. f. Physik **85**, 727 (1933).

S = Spencer, Phys. Rev. **38**, 1932 (1931).

St = Stockmeyer, Annalen der Physik 5, **12**, 71 (1932).

Wm = J. H. Williams, Phys. Rev. **44**, 146 (1933).

U = F. M. Uber, Annalen der Physik 5, **38**, 217 (1931).

Y = S. A. Yu, Sci. Rep. Tsing Hua Univ. I, 155 (1932).

7. Critical Absorption Wave-lengths

Fig. VII–10 shows the results on the mass absorption coefficient of argon in the region from 0.496 to 9.868 angstroms. A striking feature of the results is the apparently discontinuous jump in the absorption coefficient at 3.866 angstroms. This is the K critical absorption wave-length of argon. Radiation of greater wave-length cannot eject the K electrons of argon photo-electrically; therefore the gas is relatively transparent. The fundamental significance of

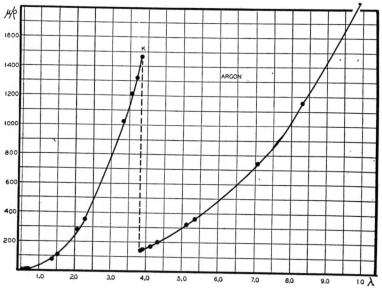

FIG. VII–10.   The mass absorption coefficient of argon as a function of wave-length.

these critical absorption wave-lengths in the interpretation of x-ray spectra is discussed in the opening sections of Chapter VIII.

Fig. VII–11 shows the absorption coefficients of bismuth in the region of its L discontinuities. Three absorption jumps occur in this region. There are five critical absorption wave-lengths in the M region. These have been experimentally detected, but few actual measurements of absorption coefficients within the M group exist. E. Jönsson[71] has measured the absorption coefficient of platinum at two wave-lengths between the M_I and the M_V limits.

[71] E. Jönsson, Thesis, Uppsala (1928).

Considerable work has been done on the magnitude of the so-called absorption jumps. The absorption jump r is defined as the ratio of the two absorption coefficients at the critical absorption wave-length. In making this definition we are considering for the moment that the absorption jump is discontinuous at one wave-length. With high resolving power instruments such as the double spectrometer, a finite width and a continuous range of values of the coefficient through the limiting region may be found.[72] It has become customary to take

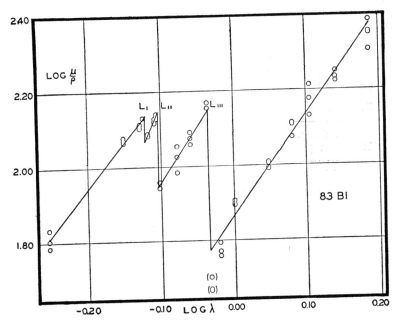

Fig. VII–11. A logarithmic plot of the mass absorption coefficient of bismuth in the region of its L discontinuities. (After Carr.)

the ratio r in such a sense that the values are greater than unity. Table VII–9 shows values of r_K, the absorption jump ratio of the K limit. It is seen that the jump ratio diminishes as the atomic number increases.

In the L group, there are three absorption jump ratios, which we shall call $r(I, II)$, $r(II, III)$ and $r(III, M)$. These are best defined

[72] See for instance Ross, Phys. Rev. 44, 977 (1933). W. H. Zinn, ibid. 46, 659 (1934).

TABLE VII-9
Data Concerning the K Absorption Jump

Element	Jönsson	Spencer	Martin and Lang	Allen	Walter	Woernle
13 Al	12.6					
16 S	....	....	....	....	....	11.0
17 Cl	....	....	....	....	....	10.4
18 A	....	9.96	... .	....	....	10.0
		Richtmyer and Warburton				Stoner and Martin
26 Fe	....	....	8.8	9.2	9.4	
28 Ni	8.3	....	8.0	8.2	9.1	
29 Cu	8.2	....	8.3	8.5	9.0	
30 Zn	....	....	7.7	7.5	8.9	
	Stockmeyer					
35 Br	7.3					
	Richtmyer					
38 Sr	....	....	....	7.4		
42 Mo	8.7	7.5				
46 Pd	....	....	6.6	....	7.6	6.8
47 Ag	7.3	7.8	6.7	7.3	7.6	6.7
50 Sn	....	6.6	....	8.9		
53 I	....	....	....	5.5		
56 Ba	....	....	....	5.2		
73 Ta	....	....	....	4.2		
74 W	....	5.65				
78 Pt	....	....	....	6.0		
79 Au	....	5.65				
82 Pb	....	5.40				
92 U	....	....	....	2.9		

References:

S. J. M. Allen, Phys. Rev. **28**, 907 (1926); **27**, 266 (1926); **24**, 1 (1924). In some cases the values of Allen have been calculated by other observers from his data. Some of the values given are the most recent estimates of Allen as shown in the table in the appendix.

Jönsson, Diss. Uppsala (1928).
Martin and Lang, Proc. Roy. Soc. Lond. A **137**, 199 (1931).
Richtmyer, Phys. Rev. **18**, 13 (1921); **27**, 1 (1926).
Richtmyer and Warburton, Phys. Rev. **23**, 291 (1924).
Spencer, Phys. Rev. **38**, 1932 (1931).
Stoner and Martin, Proc. Roy. Soc. Lond. A **107**, 312 (1925).

TABLE VII–10

DATA CONCERNING THE ABSORPTION JUMPS IN THE L-REGION

$r(\text{I, II}) \sim$ absorption coefficient ratio at L_I limit.
$r(\text{II, III}) \sim$ absorption coefficient ratio at L_II limit.
$r(\text{III}, M) \sim$ absorption coefficient ratio at L_III limit.
$r(\text{I}, M) = \{r(\text{I, II})\} \{r(\text{II, III})\} \{r(\text{III}, M)\}$
$r(\text{II}, M) = \{r(\text{II, III})\} \{r(\text{III}, M)\}$

Element	$r(\text{I, II})$	$r(\text{II, III})$	$r(\text{III}, M)$	$r(\text{I}, M)$	$r(\text{II}, M)$	Author
47 Ag	1.25	1.47	3.17	5.83	4.66	Kellström
47 Ag	1.23	1.47	3.50	6.34	5.15	Wolf
47 Ag	1.14	1.16	3.98	5.25	4.68	Jönsson
56 Ba	1.12	1.33	3.06	4.64	4.01	Küstner
57 La	....	....	....	4.25	....	Küstner
58 Ce	1.13	1.39	2.84	4.53	3.92	Küstner
74 W	1.15	1.36	2.48	3.99	3.45	Küstner
74 W	....	....	....	5.5	....	Allen
78 Pt	1.4	1.8	2.8	7.1	3.9	de Broglie
78 Pt	1.247	1.371	2.477	4.23	3.41	Backhurst
78 Pt	1.13	1.58	2.68	4.79	4.23	Wolf
78 Pt	....	....	....	5.3	....	Allen
79 Au	1.2	1.4	2.5	4.2	3.5	Dauvillier
79 Au	1.26	1.36	2.52	4.25	3.37	Backhurst
79 Au	1.16	1.36	2.47	3.78	3.28	Küstner
79 Au	1.10	1.62	2.70	4.81	2.90	Wolf
79 Au	1.164	1.393	2.480	4.02	3.46	Uber-Patten
80 Hg	1.18	1.39	2.45	4.02	3.40	Uber
81 Tl	1.15	1.33	2.36	3.64	3.15	Küstner
82 Pb	1.12	1.40	2.38	3.70	3.21	Küstner
82 Pb	....	....	....	5.6	....	Allen
90 Th	1.12	1.35	2.27	3.68	3.19	Küstner
92 U	1.11	1.31	2.17	3.52	3.05	Küstner
92 U	....	....	....	4.	....	Stoner-Martin
92 U	....	....	2.27	....	....	Stephenson

References:

S. J. M. Allen, Phys. Rev. 28, 907 (1926).   Kellström, Zeitschr. f. Physik 44, 269 (1928).
Backhurst, Phil. Mag. 7, 353 (1929).   Küstner, Physikal. Zeitschr. 33, 46 (1932).
de Broglie, Compt. rend. 171, 1137 (1920). Uber and Patten, Phys. Rev. 42, 229 (1932).
Dauvillier, Compt. rend. 178, 719 (1924). Uber, Phys. Rev. 38, 217 (1931).
Jönsson, Dissertation, Uppsala (1928).   Stephenson, Phys. Rev. 43, 527 (1933).
Stoner and Martin, Proc. Roy. Soc. Lond. A 107, 312 (1925).
Wolf, Annalen der Physik (5), 16, 973 (1933).

C. G. Patten, Phys. Rev. 45, 662 (1934) finds for $r(\text{I, II})$, $r(\text{II, III})$ and $r(\text{III}, M)$ in 81 Tl, 82 Pb, and 83 Bi the values 1.15, 1.36, 2.38; 1.16, 1.39, 2.42; 1.16, 1.38, 2.38.

L. H. Carr, Phys. Rev. 46, 92 (1934) finds for $r(\text{I, II})$, $r(\text{II, III})$, and $r(\text{III}, M)$ in 83 Bi the values 1.16, 1.57, and 2.39 respectively.

by reference to Fig. VII–12, in which log (μ/ρ) is plotted against log λ for a reason which will appear presently.   The jump $r(\text{I, II})$ is the ratio of the mass absorption coefficient at point A to its value at B. Similarly $r(\text{II, III})$ concerns points C and D, and $r(\text{III}, M)$ points E and F.

In addition to these ratios, two other ratios are introduced in Table VII–10.   These are called $r(\text{II}, M)$ and $r(\text{I}, M)$, and refer to the jumps C, H and A, G respectively, where GF is an extrapolation

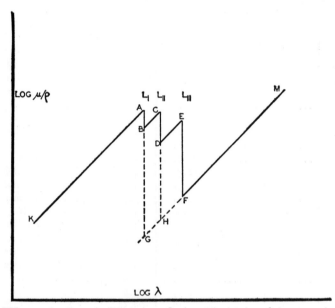

FIG. VII–12.   A schematic illustration of a logarithmic plot of the mass absorption coefficient in the L region.

of the long wave-length branch of the curve.   The calculation of these two ratios from the three former ones is made in a somewhat arbitrary fashion.   To anticipate the discussion in the next section, we may state that logarithmic plots of absorption coefficients such as we have in Fig. VII–12 reveal approximately a linear relation between log (μ/ρ) and log λ.   This means that the relation is

$$\mu/\rho = C\lambda^n.$$

The constant C will take on different values along the various branches of the curve.   Let $C(L_{\text{I}})$ be the value along the branch KA,

$C(L_{II})$ along BC; $C(L_{III})$ along DE and $C(M)$ along FM. Then we shall have

$$r(I, II) = \left\{ \frac{C(L_I)\lambda^n}{C(L_{II})\lambda^{n'}} \right\}_{\lambda = \lambda(L_I)},$$

and similar relations for $r(II, III)$ and $r(III, M)$. If we make the assumption that the curves on the logarithmic plot are parallel, that is, that the value of n is independent of the branch of the curve, then we may write

$$r(I, II) = \frac{C(L_I)}{C(L_{II})},$$

and similar expressions for $r(II, III)$ and $r(III, M)$. Keeping in mind the assumption about the constancy of n, we may also write

$$r(II, M) = \frac{C(L_{II})}{C(M)}, \quad \text{and} \quad r(I, M) = \frac{C(L_I)}{C(M)}.$$

From the preceding relations it becomes clear that

$$r(I, M) = \{r(I, II)\} \{r(II, III)\} \{r(III, M)\} \qquad (7.28)$$

and

$$r(II, M) = \{r(II, III)\} \{r(III, M)\}. \qquad (7.29)$$

If we define $r(I, M)$ and $r(II, M)$ in this way, their significance is not necessarily the same as that of the other r-values, which are experimentally determined ratios at the critical wave-lengths. The definition involves an extrapolation and the assumption that the exponent of λ is the same for all the branches of the curve. This assumption is probably not strictly true, but the procedure above will at any rate give approximate values of $r(I, M)$ and $r(II, M)$.

This approximate procedure is useful because values of the absorption jump ratio may be measured without measuring the absolute values of the mass absorption coefficient, that is, a material of unknown thickness may be used. From eq. (7.27) it results that

$$r = \frac{\mu_1}{\mu_2} = \frac{\log (P_o/P_1)}{\log (P_o/P_2)} \qquad (7.30)$$

where P_1 is the power in the transmitted beam when the measurement is taken just at the short wave-length edge of the limit, and P_2 the corresponding value at the long wave-length edge. From

$$\mu = \frac{1}{x} \log \frac{P_o}{P} = C\lambda^n$$

it results that

$$\log \log(P_0/P) = \text{const.} + n \log \lambda. \qquad (7.31)$$

Thus from data taken in the transmission of an absorber of unknown thickness, if $\log \log (P_0/P)$ is plotted against $\log \lambda$, approximately straight lines will result, which, if extrapolated to the critical absorption wave-lengths, will yield values of $\log (P_0/P)$, which may then be used to find r values from eq. (7.30). Values of $r(I, M)$ and $r(II, M)$ may then be found by eqs. (7.28) and (7.29).

The phenomenon of critical absorption has been utilized in the construction of filters to produce more or less homogeneous beams of x-rays. The most commonly used procedure is to filter the beam from a molybdenum target x-ray tube with a screen containing zirconium. The K critical absorption limit of zirconium (0.68738 A) lies between the $K\beta_3$ and $K\alpha_1$ lines of molybdenum (0.631543 and 0.707831 A). Hence the $K\beta$ lines will be strongly suppressed in the emergent spectrum, and in the wave-length region of the Mo K group, practically nothing but the Mo $K\alpha$ doublet will get through. The disadvantage of this single filter method is that when the x-ray tube is run at sufficiently high potential to give strong molybdenum lines, a considerable amount of general radiation near the short wave-length limit penetrates the filter. This is shown by the total curve of Fig. III–11, Chap. III, which represents the transmitted spectrum through the zirconium filter. The $K\alpha$ lines of other elements can also be selected out by using appropriate filters.

A great improvement over the single filter is the double or balanced filter method of Ross.[73] Two filters are used, composed of adjacent elements in the periodic system. By adjusting the thickness of the two filters, the transmitted spectrum is made to coincide at all wave-lengths except those in the region between the two K limits. This is illustrated in Fig. VII–13, which shows a balanced filter of 48 Cd and 47 Ag foils. When a balance has been attained, one filter is inserted in the beam, and the effect of the filtered beam noted in scattering, ionization, or whatever experiments are being carried out. The readings are then repeated with the first filter withdrawn and only the second in the beam. The difference between the two effects can only be attributed to the narrow range of wave-lengths between the two absorption limits. In the case of the Ag–Cd filter of Fig. VII–13 this wave-length range is about 0.022 A wide and the mean

[73] P. A. Ross, J.O.S.A. and R.S.I., U.S.A. **16**, 433 (1928).

wave-length of the radiation 0.474 A. A great gain in intensity over monochromatization by crystal diffraction can be achieved by this method.

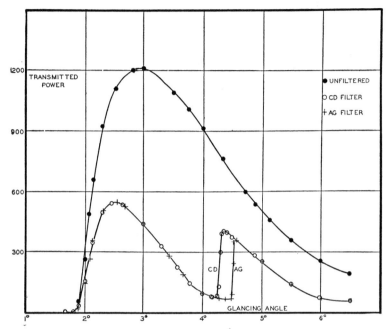

Fig. VII–13. Monochromatization by the method of balanced filters. (After Ross.)

8. Empirical Absorption Formulae[74]

Empirical absorption formulae result from the attempt to represent the mass absorption coefficient μ_m, or the atomic absorption coefficient μ_a as a function of the wave-length and the atomic number of the absorber. In 1914 Siegbahn[75] showed that the values of μ_m for a given element available at that time could be expressed by the formula

$$\mu_m = C'\lambda^n \qquad (7.32)$$

where C' is a constant for a given substance, which may have sudden jumps in value at critical absorption limits, but remains fixed over

[74] A comprehensive discussion of this topic may be found in Handbuch der Physik, Bd. 24, 1 "Allgemeine Physik der Röntgenstrahlen" by F. Kirchner; Leipzig (1930). Some aspects of the treatment given here were suggested by this work.

[75] M. Siegbahn, Physikalische Zeitschrift 15, 753 (1914).

wave-length ranges which do not include such a limit. Siegbahn found that n took on values from 2.55 to 2.71 for various solid elements, and from 2.66 to 2.94 for various gases.

In the same year, independently, Bragg and Pierce[76] developed a similar expression for atomic absorption coefficients measured by them. In 1912 Owen[77] had investigated the absorption of fluorescence x-rays in various gases. He used as secondary radiators substances ranging from 26 Fe to 42 Mo, finding that if the absorption in a given gas was under consideration, the mass absorption coefficient varied inversely as the fifth power of the atomic weight of the secondary radiator. After the work of Moseley in 1913, and the discovery of the Moseley law, it was pointed out by Darwin that Owen's result could be interpreted as showing that for a given absorber

$$\mu_m = C'\lambda^{5/2}. \tag{7.33}$$

Bragg and Pierce were able to investigate how the constant C' depends on the atomic number of the absorber, and showed that their results on absorbers ranging from 13 Al to 79 Au could be represented by

$$\mu_a = CZ^4\lambda^{5/2}, \tag{7.34}$$

the value of C changing at critical absorption wave-lengths.

W. H. Bragg[78] in 1915 pointed out that data on absorption obtained by him indicated that the exponent of λ is nearer 3 than 5/2. In 1916, Hull and Rice[79] used the λ^3 law and expressed the mass absorption coefficients of aluminium and copper as follows:

$$13 \text{ Al} \quad \mu_m = 14.9\lambda^3 + 0.12$$
$$29 \text{ Cu} \quad \mu_m = 150\lambda^3 + 0.12$$

Here we have introduced a second term in the right hand member of the absorption formula. Although Hull and Rice assumed this additive term to be a constant, we may write as a general form of the empirical absorption equation

$$\mu_a = CZ^m\lambda^n + \sigma_a(Z, \lambda) \tag{7.35}$$

indicating that the additive term $\sigma_a(Z, \lambda)$ is present, which may vary with Z and λ. The form of eq. (7.35) was suggested by eq.

[76] W. H. Bragg and S. E. Pierce, Phil. Mag. **28**, 626 (1914).
[77] E. A. Owen, Proc. Roy. Soc. Lond. **A 86**, 426 (1912).
[78] W. H. Bragg, Phil. Mag. **29**, 407 (1915).
[79] A. W. Hull and M. Rice, Phys. Rev. **8**, 326 (1916).

(7.26), and the first term in the right-hand member is identified with the photo-electric or true absorption, leaving the second as exemplifying the absorption due to both modified and unmodified scattering.

For the absorption of x-rays of wave-lengths ranging above 0.5 A in elements heavier than about 26 Fe, the scattering contribution to the atomic absorption is so small relative to the photo-electric absorption that the second term in the formula is usually neglected. It is important, however, in the absorption of harder radiation, and in the absorption by light elements. A first approximation to an interpretation of $\sigma_a(Z, \lambda)$ is given by the most elementary form of the classical theory of scattering. This assumes that the wave-length of the x-rays is small compared to inter-electronic distances, so that the electrons scatter independently and the scattered intensities may be summed. The classical scattering per electron is, as we have seen in Chap. III,

$$\sigma_0 = \frac{8\pi e^4}{3m^2 c^4}$$

and independent of wave-length. Therefore according to this simplest approach, we would write

$$\sigma_a(Z \lambda) = Z\sigma_0. \tag{7.36}$$

This apparent independence of σ_a with wave-length cannot be real, because we know that in the other limiting case, where the x-ray wave-length is large compared to the inter-electronic distances, the amplitudes rather than the intensities of the scattered waves will add, and we will have

$$\sigma_a(Z, \lambda) \sim Z^2.$$

As the wave-length of the x-rays decreases below the stage at which eq. (7.36) describes the atomic scattering coefficient, the modified scattering becomes more and more prevalent, and this reduces the scattering coefficient per electron below the classical value σ_0. It is seen, therefore, that the form of the term $\sigma_a(Z\lambda)$ in eq. (7.35) is a complex matter from the theoretical standpoint. Experimentally it is difficult to obtain good values of the term from ordinary absorption measurements, because it is usually small in comparison to the photo-electric term. Recent measurements of scattering in gases have made possible estimates of the form of the term. Attention is directed to the absorption formula for argon developed by Yu and shown in Table VII–8D, in which such considerations underlie the scattering term.   In general, it may be said that $\sigma_a(Z, \lambda)$ increases more slowly, both with λ and with Z, than does the photo-electric term.

To turn to a discussion of the photo-electric term in eq. (7.35), a considerable amount of work has been done in the attempt to find the best value of n for a given absorbing material.   In a large number of absorption coefficient measurements carried out by Richtmyer[80] and his associates, the data are judged by them to be best fitted by an exponent of 3.   Wingardh[81] found that for the range of wave-lengths between 0.156 and 0.709 A the absorption in a given substance varied with the cube of the wave-length. S. J. M. Allen[82] as a result of many absorption measurements came to the conclusion that the best value of the exponent was near 2.92, although in certain wave-length regions values as low as 2.6 were found.   The conclusion was reached that no simple law is adequate to express the absorption over a wide range of wave-lengths and materials.

In later work, Richtmyer[83] carried out accurate absorption measurements on 50 Sn from 0.19 to 0.42 A, and found that within the experimental error, there is no departure from the λ^3 law.   The data obtained definitely disagreed with a $\lambda^{2.9}$ law.   The λ^3 law was shown to represent the data up to wave-lengths as close to the K critical absorption limit as could be measured with the single crystal spectrometer used.   A disturbing feature in the experimental attempts to find the best exponent of λ is always the fact that experiment determines the sum of the true absorption and the scattering, and independent data on the scattering are difficult to obtain.   Such considerations must be taken into account in experiments which attempt to detect the possibility of small deviations from the λ^3 law.

The question of the exponent of Z in eq. (7.35) has probably not been so extensively investigated.   Since the original proposal of the fourth power by Bragg and Pierce, Wingardh has advocated a much lower power, $m = 2.95$, over the range of Z from 13 Al to

[80] F. K. Richtmyer and K. Grant, Phys. Rev. **15**, 547 (1920).

F. K. Richtmyer, Phys. Rev. **17**, 264 (1921); **18**, 13 (1921).

F. K. Richtmyer and E. W. Warburton, Phys. Rev. **21**, 721; **22**, 539 (1923).

[81] K. A. Wingardh, Diss. Lund (1923), Zeitschr. f. Physik **8**, 363 (1922); **20**, 315 (1923).

[82] S. J. M. Allen, Phys. Rev. **24**, 1 (1924); **27**, 266 (1926); **28**, 907 (1926).

[83] F. K. Richtmyer, Phys. Rev. **30**, 755 (1927).

50 Sn. Dershem and Schein[84] investigated the absorption of carbon $K\alpha$ (43.5 A) in various gases, and concluded that for elements in which

$$\lambda_K < 43.5 < \lambda_L$$

$$\mu_a = 1.65 \times 10^{-23} Z^{4.4}.$$

In a summary of the data available on x-ray absorption, and an attempt to find formulae which would best represent the results, Walter[85] gave the equations

$$\left. \begin{array}{ll} \lambda < \lambda_K & \tau_a = 2.64 \times 10^{-26} Z^{3.94} \lambda^3 \\ \lambda_K < \lambda < \lambda_L & \tau_a = 8.52 \times 10^{-28} Z^{4.30} \lambda^3 \end{array} \right\}. \qquad (7.37)$$

In these formulae τ_a is the atomic true absorption coefficient, supposedly represented by the first right-hand term of eq. (7.35) The wave-lengths are to be expressed in angstrom units.

The magnitudes of the critical absorption jumps have been empirically correlated with the energies of the adjacent levels of the absorbing atom. E. Jönsson[86] finds that the magnitude of the K absorption jump is well represented by

$$r(K) = \frac{\lambda_{LI}}{\lambda_K} = \frac{E_K}{E_{LI}}, \qquad (7.38)$$

where E_K and E_{LI} are the energies of the K and L_I states respectively. Columns 2 and 3 of Table VII–11 show to what extent the formula agrees with the observations. Jönsson furthermore suggested that a similar equation might be found to hold for $r(I, M)$, namely,

$$r(I, M) = E_{LI}/E_{MI}. \qquad (7.39)$$

This relation was indicated to be correct by the experiments of Backhurst.[87] In addition to this relation concerning the L series, Backhurst found evidence for the following:

$$r(II, M) = 2^{-1/4} E_{LII}/E_{MI}, \qquad (7.40)$$

$$r(III, M) = 2^{-1/2} E_{LIII}/E_{MI}. \qquad (7.41)$$

[84] Dershem and Schein, Phys. Rev. **37**, 1238 (1931).
[85] B. Walter, Fortschritte a. d. Geb. der Röntgen. **35**, 929; 1308 (1927).
[86] E. Jönsson, Thesis, Uppsala (1928).
[87] I. Backhurst, Phil. Mag. **7**, 353 (1919).

TABLE VII–11

TEST OF THE EMPIRICAL RELATIONS OF EQS. (7.38), (7.39), (7.41)

Experimental r Values Are Averages of Those Given in Tables VII–9 and VII–10

Element	E_K/E_{LI}	$r(K)$ Obs.	E_{LI}/E_{MI}	$r(I, M)$ Obs.	$\dfrac{0.707E_{LIII}}{E_{MI}}$	$r(III, M)$ Obs.
26 Fe	8.38	8.8	9.06	....	5.35	
28 Ni	8.22	8.3	9.12	....	5.44	
29 Cu	8.17	8.3	9.10	....	5.47	
30 Zn	8.05	7.9	8.76	....	5.28	
35 Br	....	7.3	....	....	4.21	
38 Sr	7.26	7.4	6.22	....	3.86	
42 Mo	6.95	8.1	5.63	....	3.50	
46 Pd	6.73	6.7	5.33	....	3.31	
47 Ag	6.72	7.0	5.16	5.81	3.22	3.55
50 Sn	6.53	7.8	5.12	....	3.18	
53 I	6.38	5.5	4.83	....	3.00	
56 Ba	6.24	5.2	4.63	4.64	2.85	3.06
57 La	6.19	....	4.56	4.25	2.82	
58 Ce	6.18	....	4.55	4.53	2.81	2.84
73 Ta	5.74	4.2	4.31	....	2.57	
74 W	5.74	5.65	4.28	4.74	2.54	2.48
78 Pt	5.65	6.0	4.04	5.35	2.37	2.65
79 Au	5.63	5.65	4.32	4.21	2.54	2.53
80 Hg	5.60	....	....	4.02	....	2.45
81 Tl	5.59	....	4.14	3.64	2.41	2.36
82 Pb	5.56	5.40	4.11	4.6	2.39	2.38
90 Th	5.36	....	3.96	3.68	2.22	2.27
92 U	5.32	2.9	3.92	3.8	2.18	2.22

In a recent paper Backhurst[88] reviews the evidence for these empirical expressions and concludes that only the one concerning $r(III, M)$ is at present well established. Equation (7.40) does not represent the data of Küstner as well as it does those of other observers. The data on $r(II, M)$ appear to agree better with the expression

$$r(II, M) = 0.96E_{LII}/E_{MI}$$

than with eq. (7.40). The evidence for eqs. (7.38), (7.39), and (7.41) is indicated in Table VII–11.

In a study of the absorption of x-rays of wave-lengths from

[88] I. Backhurst, Phil. Mag. 16, 310 (1933).

0.7 to 12 A in 13 Al, 28 Ni, 29 Cu, 47 Ag, and 78 Pt, E. Jönsson introduced a new method of classification of absorption data. The first empirical rule discovered by him has been referred to as eqs. (7.38) and (7.39). Jönsson's relations presumably apply to the true absorption, and only to the observed total absorption if the contribution from scattering is negligible. We may interpret eqs. (7.38) and (7.39) in the following manner. Consider values of

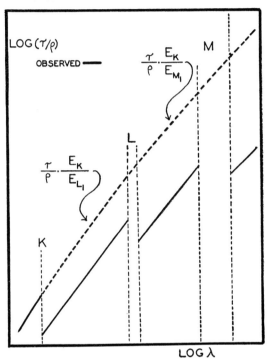

Fig. VII–14. Calculation of a "reduced" absorption curve with no critical absorption jumps, according to E. Jönsson. The figure is qualitative only.

τ/ρ between the K and $L_{\rm I}$ limits of a given substance. If these values are multiplied by the ratio $E_K/E_{L_{\rm I}}$ and plotted together with the observed values at wave-lengths shorter than the K limit, a smooth curve will result, showing no trace of the K absorption discontinuity. Observed values of τ/ρ for wave-lengths between the L and the M limits will, when multiplied by the factor $E_K/E_{M_{\rm I}}$. also lie on this curve. A schematic illustration of this result is shown in Fig. VII–14.

The method of tabulation adopted by Jönsson deals with the absorption curves constructed by the method outlined above, that

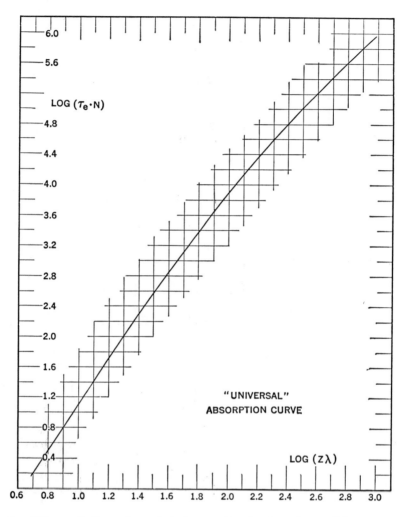

Fɪɢ. VII–15. E. Jönsson's method of expressing the absorption coefficient results over a wide range of wave-lengths and elements.

is, with the curves corresponding to the dotted curve in Fig. VII–14 for different elements. Jönsson introduces a new true absorption coefficient, which we may call the electronic true absorption coefficient τ_e, where

$$\tau_e = \tau_a/Z = \frac{\tau}{\rho}\frac{A}{NZ},\qquad(7.42)$$

A being the atomic weight and N Avogadro's number. The relation used by Jönsson may then be stated as follows: τ_e is a function of $Z\lambda$ only. That is, no matter what the absorber, equal values of $Z\lambda$ give the same value of τ_e. In Jönsson's thesis roughly 600 measured absorption coefficients are tabulated and used to construct a graph showing the relation between τ_e and $Z\lambda$. This is shown in Fig. VII-15. Only values of $Z\lambda$ greater than 8 are used, due to the large correction for scattering at lower values. Most of the data used by Jönsson gives values of $\tau_e N$ falling within ± 5 per cent of the values through which the smooth curve in Fig. VII-15 passes. Occasionally deviations as large as ± 15 per cent occur.

This curve serves as a rough method of rapidly determining the mass absorption coefficient for any substance at any wave-length. We will illustrate by calculating τ/ρ for 50 Sn at 1.0 A. The value of $Z\lambda$ is 50 (λ must always be expressed in angstroms). From the graph of Fig. VII-15, we find $\tau_e N = 1320$. The wave-length in question lies between the K and the L critical wave-lengths of tin, therefore to reduce to the observed values (that is from the dotted to the solid curve in Fig. VII-14), we must multiply by E_{L_1}/E_K which is 0.153 (see Table VII-11). From eq. (7.42) we may now obtain $\tau/\rho = 85$. A calculation of τ_a from Walter's eq. (7.37) gives 17.0×10^{-21}, from which $\tau/\rho = 86$. The average of the measured values, listed by S. J. M. Allen, and tabulated in Appendix IX, is 86. This example, although chosen at random, gives better agreement between the three sources than would in general be found.

Criticisms and comments on Jönsson's result have been advanced by several authors. Woernle,[89] who investigated the absorption of gases containing relatively light elements (below 18 A) in the wavelength range between 2 and 10 angstroms, reports systematic deviations in his results from Jönsson's method of representation, and calls attention to the fact that most of Jönsson's measurements were made on the absorption of elements of relatively high atomic number. It is in this range that the rule appears to hold best. In their investigation of the absorption of carbon $K\alpha$ by various gases, Dershem and

[89] B. Woernle, Annalen der Physik 5, 475 (1930).

Schein[90] found that Jönsson's rule gave results of an order of magnitude agreeing with experiment.

If we interpret the logarithmic plot of Fig. VII–15 as meaning that

$$\tau_a/Z \sim (Z\lambda)^p,$$

where p may be a function of Z and of λ, then at any given value of Z and λ we would have

$$\tau_a \sim Z^{p+1}\lambda^p.$$

If we set $p = 3$, we obtain an approach to Walter's eq. (7.37). The fact that the graph of Fig. VII–15 is not a straight line means that p varies; it decreases as $Z\lambda$ increases. When $Z\lambda$ is about 770, p has decreased to about 2.3.

9. Dispersion and Absorption; the Concept of Oscillator Strength

It is usual to consider the true absorption of a given wave-length in a medium as the sum of the absorptions by all the electron groups whose critical wave-lengths are longer than the incident wave-length. Thus in the absorption of radiation of 1 A wave-length in copper, we may consider the absorption due to the K, L, M, etc., electron groups, since the K critical absorption wave-length of copper is 1.377 A. At wave-lengths close to the short wave-length side of the q-limit, it is possible to say with some certainty what fraction of the absorption is due to the q, and what to the remaining electrons in the atom. If r_q is the absorption jump ratio, then

$$\frac{r_q - 1}{r_q}$$

is the fraction of the total number of ejected photo-electrons which come from the q-shell. If the exponent of λ in the expression for τ_a on the short wave-length side of the limit is different from its value on the long wave-length side, then the above fraction will be a function of wave-length. If, however, we take Walter's eq. (7.37) as representing with sufficient accuracy the experimental data, we have the λ^3 law on both sides of the K limit, at least. We can then write, for wave-lengths less than that of the K limit

$$\tau_a = \tau_K + \tau_L + \tau_M \ldots \ldots = 2.64 \times 10^{-26} Z^{3.94}\lambda^3 \qquad (7.43)$$

[90] Dershem and Schein, Phys. Rev. **37**, 1238 (1931). See also A. Sandström, Phys. Rev. **46**, 825 (1934).

where
$$\tau_K = (2.64 \times 10^{-26}Z^{3.94} - 8.52 \times 10^{-28}Z^{4.30})\lambda^3 \qquad (7.44)$$
and
$$\tau_L + \tau_M + \ldots = (8.52 \times 10^{-28})Z^{4.30}\lambda^3. \qquad (7.45)$$
Also
$$\frac{r_K - 1}{r_K} = \frac{\tau_K}{\tau_a},$$

which for 50 Sn takes the numerical value

$$\frac{r_K - 1}{r_K} = \frac{11.3 \times 10^{-20}}{13.0 \times 10^{-20}} = 0.87.$$

For a given element, we may write

$$\tau_a = C''\lambda^3,$$

where

$$C'' = c''_K + c''_L + c''_M + \ldots\ldots\ldots \qquad (7.46)$$

Again, using the example of 50 Sn with Walter's formulae, we have

$$C'' = 13.05 \times 10^{-20}$$

$$c''_K = 11.33 \times 10^{-20}$$

$$c''_L + c''_M + \ldots = 1.72 \times 10^{-20}.$$

In case we are dealing with the sub-levels of the L series, and attempting to compute how much of the absorption at a given wavelength shorter than that of the L_I limit is due to the L_I, $(L_{II} + L_{III})$, levels respectively, we encounter what is at present a more difficult problem. The work of Robinson and his collaborators, discussed in Sec. 4 of this chapter, has shown that at wave-lengths sufficiently far from the L region, most of the L photo-electrons are ejected from the L_I shell; whereas for wave-lengths near the L region, ejection of the more loosely bound L electrons is more probable, leaving the atom in the state L_{II} or L_{III}. This point has been discussed by Wolf,[91] who has used a theoretical paper of Stobbe[92] as a guide.

It may be estimated from Stobbe's result that as the wave-length decreases the absorption giving rise to the $L_{II}L_{III}$ states falls off somewhat faster than is indicated by the λ^3 law, but the difference is quite small. The λ^3 law is, however, not even approximately ful-

[91] M. Wolf, Annalen der Physik 16, 973 (1933).
[92] M. Stobbe, Annalen der Physik 7, 661 (1930).

filled for the L_I absorption, the absorption decreasing much more slowly than λ^3. At a wave-length corresponding to a frequency about five times that of the L limits, the absorption in L_I begins to be greater than in $L_{II}L_{III}$.

We may, however, apply the λ^3 law in the wave-length region near the L limits, and Wolf's absorption measurements were made here. Writing

$$\tau/\rho = C'\lambda^3 = (c'_{L_I} + c'_{L_{II}} + c'_{L_{III}} + c'_M + \ldots)\lambda^3,$$

Wolf found the values in the following table.

TABLE VII-12

VALUES OF c' ACCORDING TO WOLF

Element	c'_{L_I}	$c'_{L_{II}}$	$c'_{L_{III}}$	$c'_{M+\cdot\cdot}$	C'
47 Ag	9.0	12.2	18.56	7.44	47.2
78 Pt	36.2	99.3	106.6	63.5	305.6
79 Au	30.0	110.0	110.3	65.1	315.4

In Chapter IV we developed a semi-empirical theory of the absorption of x-rays in connection with a theory of the refractive index. The theory is partly empirical in that it takes the λ^3 law from experimental results. In the revised form of Lorentz's theory the absorption corresponding to the q electrons is supposed to be due to a set of virtual oscillators having frequencies extending from ν_q to ∞ ; and we developed the distribution function for these oscillators. The total number of oscillators assigned to a given level of the atom is sometimes called the oscillator strength of that level. We shall discuss here the method of obtaining this oscillator strength of a given level from experimental results on absorption.

In eq. (4.63), Chap. IV, we have deduced the expression

$$z_q = \frac{mc}{2\pi^2 e^2} \int_{\omega_q}^{\infty} \mu_a{}^q d\omega.$$

z_q was introduced as the electron population of the q-level, but at present we shall not be so definite about the interpretation of z_q, and merely consider that the right-hand member of the preceding equation gives the oscillator strength associated with the q-electrons. $\mu_a{}^q$ is the contribution to the atomic absorption coefficient from electrons of the type q, and $\omega_q/2\pi$ is the frequency of the q critical absorption limit. If we introduce into this expression the frequency, ν, and the mass absorption coefficient for true absorption, $\tau_m{}^q$, we obtain

$$z_q = \frac{A}{N}\frac{mc}{\pi e^2}\int_{\nu_q}^{\infty} \tau_m{}^q d\nu. \qquad (7.47)$$

The process of finding the oscillator strength assigned to a certain level may then be carried out by graphical integration of the curve of $\tau_m{}^q$ as a function of frequency. If we assume that the function is sufficiently well expressed by an empirical law such as

$$\tau_m{}^q = c_q'\lambda^3$$

we may write

$$z_q = \frac{A}{N}\frac{mc}{\pi e^2}\int_{\lambda_q}^{0} c_q'\lambda^3\left(-\frac{c}{\lambda^2}\right)d\lambda = \frac{A}{N}\frac{mc^2}{2\pi e^2} c_q'\lambda_q{}^2. \qquad (7.48)$$

If λ_q is expressed in angstrom units in the preceding equation, the right-hand member must be multiplied by 10^8. Table VII-13 shows some values of z_K which have been calculated by application of this equation to the K level.

TABLE VII-13

EXPERIMENTALLY MEASURED OSCILLATOR STRENGTHS OF THE K LEVEL

Element	c'_K Richtmyer*	c'_K Walter†	K Oscillator Strength (Richtmyer)	K Oscillator Strength (Walter)
13 Al	....	13.3	....	2.11
29 Cu	....	130	....	1.46
42 Mo	325	363	1.12	1.25
47 Ag	475	501	1.13	1.19
50 Sn	485	578	0.97	1.15
79 Au	1835	2361	0.79	1.02

* F. K. Richtmyer, Phys. Rev. **27**, 1 (1926).
† Walter, loc. cit.; eqs. (7.37).

A set of oscillator strength values found in this way is given by J. A. Wheeler and J. A. Bearden, Phys. Rev. **46**, 755 (1934).

The calculations whose results are reported in this table could undoubtedly be more accurately performed by graphical integration of an experimentally observed absorption curve. The result is, how-ever, seen clearly to indicate that values of z_K less than 2, the electron population of the K level, are obtained. It has been indicated in Chap. IV that a similar result is obtained when the number of equiv-alent virtual oscillators is computed from measurements of the unit decrement of the refractive index. Before discussing the interpreta-tion of this result, we will report in Table VII–14 the values obtained by Wolf for the oscillator strengths of the L levels.

TABLE VII–14

Oscillator Strengths of the L Levels According to Wolf. c' Values from ₁Table VII–13.

Element	L_I	L_{II}	L_{III}	L_{total}
47 Ag	(1.3)	1.49	2.52	5.2
78 Pt	(1.3)	1.64	2.18	5.2
79 Au	(1.3)	1.69	2.20	5.2

In view of the fact that the λ^3 law certainly does not hold for absorption from the L_I level, eq. (7.48) cannot be applied, and it is necessary to return to the original form, eq. (7.47). Wolf evaluated the number of oscillators equivalent to the L_I electrons as follows. The equivalent oscillators for L_{II} and L_{III} were first computed, and then the number for L_I assumed to be one third of the sum of L_{II} and L_{III}. This procedure was suggested by the theoretical work of Stobbe, previously mentioned. According to the Pauli principle, the number of electrons in L_I is 2, in $L_{II, III}$ is 6, a total of 8, which is considerably greater than the observed oscillator strength 5.2. Thus we have a behavior similar to that of the K level.

In interpreting the fact that the values of z_q are found to be less than the electron populations of the q-level, according to the Pauli principle, we must consider more carefully the quantum theoretical analogue of what on the classical dispersion theory is the number of electronic oscillators per cubic centimeter. This question has been discussed by Ladenburg.[93] In the absorption of radiation by a set of classical electronic oscillators, each electron shares to some extent in the process, and the absorption is in this way simply proportional to the number of electrons per cubic centimeter. In the quantum

[93] R. Ladenburg, Zeitschr. f. Physik **4**, 451 (1921).

theory, the situation is not at first so clear. We have the atomic systems in the absorbing material in a quantized state, which, for example, may correspond to the normal state of the atom. There is then a certain probability that absorption will be accomplished by an induced transfer to a quantized state of higher energy. The quantum theoretical interpretation of the number of oscillators per cm.^{3} must be found by consideration of systems in temperature equilibrium with black body radiation. Here classical oscillators and quantized atoms can be compared, since it is well known that the energy density of the radiation in a hohlraum is independent of the nature of the oscillators in its walls. Considering the classical oscillators first, let n_q be the number of electrons of characteristic frequency ν_q per cm.^{3} Let $\bar{E}$ be the average energy of these oscillators, and τ_q the time in which the energy of a classical electronic oscillator is reduced to $1/e$ of its initial value by radiation damping. In eq. (4.17), Chap. IV, we find an expression for the time interval in which the amplitude of a classical harmonic electronic oscillator is reduced to $1/e$ of its initial value. Since energy is proportional to (amplitude)^2, the time required for a given decrease in energy is half that for the equivalent decrease in amplitude, and we obtain

$$\tau_q = \frac{3mc^3}{8\pi^2 e^2 \nu_q^2}.$$

The energy radiated by these oscillators per second will be

$$\left(\frac{dE}{dt}\right)_{cl.} = \frac{\bar{E}}{\tau_q}n_q.$$

Planck[94] has shown that in a hohlraum, the average energy $\bar{E}$ is related to the radiation density ρ_q by:

$$\bar{E} = \frac{3c^3}{8\pi\nu_q^2}\rho_q,$$

thus leading to the result

$$\left(\frac{dE}{dt}\right)_{cl} = \frac{\pi e^2}{m}n_q\rho_q. \tag{7.49}$$

[94] See for instance the discussion in M. Born, Vorlesungen über Atommechanik, J. Springer, Berlin (1924), pp. 2–7. This book contains also a discussion of Einstein's derivation of Planck's distribution law which is relevant to the discussion here.

At temperature equilibrium the preceding expression must also represent the energy absorbed per second by the oscillators.

We now turn to the quantum theoretical viewpoint. Let N_i be the number of atoms per cubic centimeter in the initial quantized state i, from which a transition to a state f can be made, resulting in the absorption of radiation of frequency ν_{if}. The energy absorbed per second will be represented by

$$\left(\frac{dE}{dt}\right)_Q = h\nu_{if}N_ib_{if}\rho_{if},$$

where ρ_{if} is the density of radiation of frequency ν_{if}, and b_{if} is a transition probability, a concept fundamental to the quantum theory in its early form. The emission of the frequency ν_{if} is accomplished by a transition from the excited state f to the state i. Let N_f be the number of atoms per cm.[3] in the excited state f; Einstein showed that the energy radiated, which at equilibrium must be equal to that absorbed, is

$$h\nu_{if}N_f(a_{fi} + b_{fi}\rho_{if}).$$

a_{fi} is the probability of a spontaneous transition from state f to state i, and b_{fi} is the probability of such a transition induced by the presence of the radiation.[95]   Einstein showed that since the states i and f are in thermal equilibrium and thus their relative populations governed by the Boltzmann factor, and since in the limit of long wavelengths the Rayleigh-Jeans radiation law must be fulfilled, it must result that

$$b_{fi} = a_{fi}\frac{c^3}{8\pi h\nu_{if}^3}, \tag{7.49a}$$

and hence

$$\left(\frac{dE}{dt}\right)_Q = N_ia_{fi}\frac{c^3}{8\pi\nu_{if}^2}\rho_{if}.$$

Setting the classical and quantum theoretical expressions for the rate of radiation equal, we identify ν_{if} with ν_q and ρ_{if} with ρ_q, obtaining

$$n_q = N_ia_{fi}\frac{mc^3}{8\pi^2e^2\nu_{if}^2},$$

---

[95] For discussion and amplification of this point see Ruark and Urey, Atoms, Molecules, and Quanta, McGraw-Hill (1930), pp. 60–63.

which may be written

$$n_q = \tfrac{1}{3} N_i a_{fi} \tau_{if} \equiv N_i f_{if}. \tag{7.50}$$

In the preceding discussion it has been assumed that the system is entirely non-degenerate, so that statistical weights[96] g of the states i and f do not enter; for a partially degenerate system the above expression becomes

$$n_q = \frac{1}{3} N_i \frac{g_f}{g_i} a_{fi} \tau_{if} \equiv N_i f_{if}. \tag{7.51}$$

We have thus deduced an expression giving the quantum theoretical analogue of the classical number of electronic oscillators per cubic centimeter. The relation will hold outside the hohlraum, since aside from N_i, which is simply the number of atoms in the initial state, it contains no factors dependent on the temperature. f_{if} is called the oscillator strength of the atom for the absorption transition from state i to state f.

By comparison of this result with eq. (8.45), Chap. VIII, we may deduce an expression for the f's in terms of the components of the electric moment of the radiating atom. In applying eq. (8.45) we will generalize it to some extent. In it P represents the amplitude of the motion, so that eP represents the amplitude of the electric moment. Since this may be a complex number, if there is a phase shift between incident and scattered radiation, we represent its components by $|X|$, $|Y|$, and $|Z|$, meaning the product of the electric moment by its complex conjugate in each case. The equation may then be written, if applied to one oscillator,

$$\frac{dw}{dt} = - \frac{(2\pi \nu_{if})^4}{3c^3} (|X|^2 + |Y|^2 + |Z|^2)$$

where the amplitude components refer to the transition from f to i. If we equate this to its quantum theoretical analogue,

$$- a_{fi} h \nu_{if},$$

and introduce f_{if} from eq. (7.50), we obtain

$$f_{if} = \frac{2\pi^2 m}{3he^2} \nu_{if} (|X|^2 + |Y|^2 + |Z|^2). \tag{7.52}$$

We may interpret this result by the following statement: the reaction

[96] See Chap. VIII, Sec. 10.

of an atomic system in an initial state i to incident radiation of frequency ν, as respects scattering and absorption, is the same as that of f_{ij} classical electronic oscillators.

Kramers[97] has added a very important generalization to the above discussion. If the initial state i of the atomic system is such that both absorptive and emissive quantum jumps may be made from it, we must introduce the idea of negative oscillator strengths associated with emission, and positive oscillator strengths associated with absorption. The introduction of these negative strengths corresponding to emission is not so startling when one considers that the transition probability b_{fi} introduced into the previous discussion is really a kind of negative absorption. As an example of Kramers' treatment, consider the classical expression for the unit decrement of the refractive index. This is given by eq. (4.45), Chap. IV, as

$$\delta = \frac{e^2}{2\pi m} \sum_q \frac{n_q}{\nu^2 - \nu_q{}^2}. \qquad (7.53)$$

Kramers would replace this expression by

$$\delta = \frac{e^2}{2\pi m} \left(\sum_f \frac{N_i f_{ij}}{\nu^2 - \nu_{ij}{}^2} - \sum_i \frac{N_i f_{fi}}{\nu^2 - \nu_{fi}{}^2} \right), \qquad (7.54)$$

where the first term has reference to possible absorptive, the second to possible emissive transitions. If the transitions involve the continuous region of absorption or emission; that is, if we are dealing with the photo-electric effect or its inverse, we replace eq. (7.52) by

$$\frac{df_{ij}}{dE} = \frac{2\pi^2 m}{3he^2} \nu_{ij} \frac{d}{dE} (|X|^2 + |Y|^2 + |Z|^2), \qquad (7.55)$$

where df_{ij} is the oscillator strength assigned to the energy interval dE about the frequency ν_{ij}.

Kuhn[98] and Thomas[99] independently suggested a summation or permanence rule for the f values. Consider the application of eq. (7.54) to the hydrogen atom in its normal state, when the incident wave-length is shorter than the limit of the Lyman series.

[97] H. A. Kramers, Nature 113, 673; 114, 310 (1924).

H. A. Kramers and W. Heisenberg, Zeitschr. f. Physik 31, 681 (1925).

[98] W. Kuhn, Zeitschr. f. Physik 33, 408 (1925).

[99] W. Thomas, Naturw. 13, 627 (1925); F. Reiche and W. Thomas, Zeitschr. f. Phys. 34, 510 (1925).

The numbers $N_i f_{ij}$ would then refer to oscillators associated with the absorption of the various lines of the Lyman series and the continuous absorption. Since no emission is possible with the normal state of hydrogen as the initial state, no negative oscillator strengths occur. According to Thomas and to Kuhn

$$\Sigma f_{ij} = 1,$$

corresponding to the one electron in hydrogen. Guided by the fact that eq. (7.53), with the actual total electron populations of the atoms used in the n_q's gives good results in the x-ray region, the preceding expression has been generalized to

$$\Sigma f_{ij} = Z, \qquad (7.56)$$

where Z is the total electron population of the atom, and the sum is to be extended over the K, L, . . . electrons.

The above results, summarized in eqs. (7.52), (7.55), and (7.56), have been shown to be compatible with wave-mechanical treatments, and have been taken over into wave-mechanics.[100] Sugiura[101] has calculated the oscillator strengths corresponding to the normal state of hydrogen, since the components of the polarization may be obtained from the characteristic functions of the appropriate wave equation. The results are given in Table VII–15.

We now come to the interpretation of the oscillator strength sums in atoms of more than one electron. This has been discussed by Kronig and Kramers.[102] In the application to K electrons, for instance, the new feature is essentially that certain transitions in absorption (namely, those to $L_{II}L_{III}$, $M_{II}M_{III}$, etc.) which are permitted by the selection principles, are excluded by the Pauli principle. That is, the L shell is already full. In this case the oscillator strengths in absorption do not appear, and diminish the total oscillator strength for the K level below the value of the electron population, which is 2. Thus the oscillator strength for a K electron is more nearly that for continuous absorption in the hydrogen Lyman series, which as is seen from Table VII–15 is 0.44, considerably less than unity. This neglects the interactions of the two electrons;

[100] Born, Heisenberg, and Jordan, Zeitschr. f. Physik **35**, 557 (1926).

O. Klein, Zeitschr. f. Physik **41**, 407 (1927).

P. A. M. Dirac, Proc. Roy. Soc. Lond. A **114**, 710 (1927).

[101] Y. Sugiura, Journal de Physique **8**, 113 (1928).

[102] R. de L. Kronig and H. A. Kramers, Zeitschr. f. Physik **48**, 174 (1928).

TABLE VII–15

Oscillator Strengths in the Lyman Series According to Sugiura

n	Source	f_{1n}
2	Lyman α	0.4162
3	Lyman β	0.0791
4	....	0.0290
5	....	0.0139
6	....	0.0078
7	....	0.0048
8	....	0.0032
9	....	0.0022
$\sum_{10}^{\infty} f_{1n}$	10th Lyman line to limit of series	0.0079
$\sum_{2}^{\infty} f_{1n}$	Lyman α to limit	0.5641
$\int_{0}^{\infty} df$	Continuous spectrum	0.437
$\sum f_{1f}$	Line+continuous.	1.001

their screening, relativity, etc. Thus if the binding energy of the K electrons greatly exceeds their interaction energy and the other correction effects, the total oscillator strength for the K level should be about 0.88.

Let us consider now what happens in the absorption from the L shell. As before, certain absorptive transitions to the M and other more loosely bound shells are blocked off, but a new effect enters, namely, that some emissive processes to the K shell, permitted by the selection principles, are also blocked off. This last effect subtracts some negative virtual oscillators and hence increases the total number allotted to the L shell. The result is as if the oscillator deficiency of the K shell were in part transferred to the L shell. The fraction is that indicated by the intensity of the $K\alpha$ lines relative to the sum of the intensities of the entire K series. None of the K oscillator deficiency can be transferred to L_I because the selection rules themselves permit no such transition. Thus for the 6 electrons of total quantum number 2 and quantum azimuthal number 1 ($2p^6$) we should have

$$6 = \Sigma f \text{ (absorption to } M, N, \text{ etc.)} + \Sigma f(\text{continuous})$$
$$+ \Sigma f \text{ (emission to } K),$$

and only the Σf (continuous) is observed in absorption measurements.

Wolf[103] has applied these considerations to his measurement of the absorption coefficients in the L region. He assumes that the oscillator defect for the K level is 0.5, a value which has more support from measurements of the refractive index[104] than from absorption data (see Table VII–13). Taking the data of Williams[105] on the K series relative intensities for 30 Zn, it is found that the intensity in the $K\alpha$ lines is 0.878 of the total. This means that 0.4 of the total defect of 0.5 is transferred to the $2p^6$ electrons. Wolf assumes that the amount transferred in 47 Ag is 0.4, and in 78 Pt and 79 Au, 0.37. Using the values of Σf(continuous) which are observed, and recorded in Table VII–14, the value of Σf(absorption to $M, N \ldots$) may be computed, giving for the $2p^6$ electrons of 47 Ag, 2.39, and for 78 Pt and 79 Au, 2.55. These line absorption oscillators are then divided between L_{II} and L_{III} in proportion to the sums of the L series lines having these two levels as initial states. In the case of L_I, since no oscillator strength is transferred from the K levels, we should have

$$2 = \Sigma f(\text{continuous}) + \Sigma f(\text{line absorption}).$$

If we compute the Σf(line absorption) from the intensities of the lines having the initial state L_I relative to those having the initial state $L_{II}L_{III}$, we obtain a value of 0.2, which, together with the value

TABLE VII–16

Oscillator Strengths of L_I, L_{II}, and L_{III} According to Wolf

	L_I		L_{II}		L_{III}		$L_{II}L_{III}$	
	Cont.	Line	Cont.	Line	Cont.	Line	Cont.	Line
47 Ag	(1.3)	(0.2)	1.49	0.68	2.52	1.71	4.01	2.39
	2.00		2.17		4.23		6.40	
78 Pt, 79 Au	(1.3)	(0.2)	1.67	0.55	2.19	1.96	3.86	2.51
	2.00		2.22		4.15		6.37	

[103] M. Wolf, Annalen der Physik **10**, 973 (1933).
[104] A. Larsson, Diss. Uppsala (1928); J. A. Prins, Zeitschr. f. Physik **47**, 479 (1928).
[105] J. H. Williams, Phys. Rev. **44**, 146 (1933); Table VIII–17.

of 1.3 of Table VII–14 for the continuous absorption, falls short of the expected value 2. The reason for this discrepancy is not yet clear. The oscillator strengths assigned by Wolf are shown in Table VII–16.

H. Hönl[106] has made a theoretical calculation of the oscillator strengths of the K and L electrons. The method is a modification of that used by Sugiura for the hydrogen atom. The wave-equation for an x-ray level must take account of screening by other electrons and, if possible, of relativity and spin effects. Hönl shows that by legitimate approximations, Sugiura's result for the continuous absorption of the hydrogen atom from the normal state may be written

$$\int_1^\infty df = \frac{2^7}{9} e^{-4} \int_1^\infty \left(\frac{4}{p^3} - \frac{1}{p^4}\right) dp = \frac{2^7 \cdot 5}{27} e^{-4} = 0.434, \qquad (7.57)$$

where

$$p = 1 + E/(h\nu_0) = \nu_i/\nu_0.$$

E is the energy of the system atom-plus-electron after the photo-electric ejection; this is positive, and numerically equal to the kinetic energy of the ejected electron. $h\nu_0$ is the ionization energy from the normal state, and $h\nu_i$ is a quantum of energy of the absorbed radiation. Values of p are $\geqq 1$.

When screening is taken into consideration, it is shown that an analogous equation may be used for the K electrons. It is necessary to replace p in eq. (7.57) by

$$p_K = 1 - \Delta_K,$$

where

$$\Delta_K = \frac{(Z - s)^2 - h\nu_K/Rhc}{(Z - s)^2}, \qquad (7.58)$$

in which ν_K is the frequency of the K critical absorption limit and R is the Rydberg number in cm^{-1}. s is the appropriate screening constant for the K level. To a first approximation, the effect of relativity may be included by replacing the right-hand member of eq. (7.58) by

$$\frac{(Z - s)^2 + \frac{1}{4}\alpha^2(Z - s)^4 \ldots - h\nu_K/Rhc}{(Z - s)^2},$$

[106] H. Hönl, Zeitschr. f. Physik **84** 1 (1933).

where α is the fine structure constant. It may then be shown that

$$[\Sigma f(\text{cont.})]_K = 2 \int_{\nu_K}^{\infty} \left(\frac{df}{d\nu_j}\right)_K d\nu_j = \frac{2^8 e^{-4}}{9} \left(\frac{2}{(1 - \Delta_K)^2} - \frac{1}{3(1 - \Delta_K)^3}\right).$$

The results of computation from this formula are shown in column 2 of Table VII–17. In an analogous manner the oscillator strengths assigned to the L levels have been calculated, and are shown in columns 3, 4, and 5 of the same table.

TABLE VII–17

OSCILLATOR STRENGTHS OF K AND L ELECTRONS THEORETICALLY CALCULATED BY HÖNL

Element	$f(\text{cont})_K$	$f(\text{cont})_{L_I}$	$f(\text{cont})_{L_{II}+L_{III}}$	$f(\text{cont})_L$
14 Si	1.53			
20 Ca	1.41			
24 Cr	1.34			
26 Fe	1.33			
30 Zn	1.31			
40 Zr	....	1.53	5.14	6.67
42 Mo	1.24			
46 Pd	....	1.50	4.70	6.20
60 Nd	1.17	1.42	3.93	5.35
74 W	1.15	1.35	3.55	4.90
92 U	1.12	1.28	3.22	4.50

10. *Theories of the True Absorption of X-rays*

We shall first discuss briefly the theories of true absorption which appeared previous to the invention of the wave-mechanics. In 1919 A. H. Compton[107] showed that a theory giving the correct order of magnitude of the absorption could be built from J. J. Thomson's theory of x-ray pulses. When such a pulse passes over an electron, it results that a finite displacement from its equilibrium position has occurred, assuming that the time for the pulse to pass is small compared to the natural period of the electron. The work involved in this displacement against the restoring force is computed, and this is

---

[107] A. H. Compton, Phys. Rev. **14**, 249 (1919). The theory is also discussed in X-rays and Electrons, Van Nostrand (1926), pp. 195–198.

the absorbed energy.   The thickness of the pulse is identified with a half wave-length of the incident radiation.   It is found that the absorption is proportional to the fourth power of the atomic number and to the cube of the wave-length, and is of the observed order of magnitude.   The inadequacy of the pulse theory on which Compton's treatment is based unfortunately invalidates to a large extent this theory of absorption.

In terms of the quantum theory it is clear that the problem of photo-electric emission is closely allied to the problems of the capture of electrons by atoms ionized in x-ray levels.   Since this capture would result in radiation, the problem also involves the emission of the continuous spectrum.   At temperatures high enough to produce thermal equilibrium between atoms and x-rays a considerable fraction of atoms ionized in x-ray levels, or having large numbers of electrons removed from inner shells would result.   The capture of electrons by such ionized atoms would result in the emission of a line and a continuous spectrum.   The reverse of the process leading to the continuous emission spectrum is the photo-electric process in which we are interested here.   Theories of x-ray absorption by L. de Broglie[108] and by Kramers[109] have appeared, based on this idea, using the correspondence principle in calculating the intensities of emission.   All attempts to calculate intensities of emission on the older form of the quantum theory come, however, to a characteristic difficulty.   If the motions in the initial and final states are expanded in a Fourier series, the intensity emitted is determined by some sort of average of the amplitude coefficients of the appropriate terms in the expansions for the two states.   But the correspondence principle does not indicate what sort of average is the correct one, and hence the procedure to be followed is not sharply defined.

Kramers investigated on purely classical, non-relativistic theory, the radiation from an electron whose path is deflected in the neighborhood of an atomic nucleus.   A continuous distribution of energy in the emitted spectrum between $\nu = 0$ and $\nu = \infty$ is predicted. This is shown as the dotted curve of Fig. VII–16.   On the quantum theory, we should expect a spectrum like that under the solid lines in the figure.   The continuous spectrum, of frequencies less than ν_0, corresponds to the radiation produced when the incident electron radiates various fractions of its energy in transitions between hyper-

[108] L. de Broglie, Journ. de Phys. et le Rad. 3, 33 (1922).
[109] H. A. Kramers, Phil. Mag. 46, 836 (1923).

bolic orbits. The continuous spectrum would be produced as a statistical result of such losses from a large number of electrons of uniform initial speed. The limiting frequency ν_0 corresponds to a loss of the entire kinetic energy of the electron. The lines at higher frequencies than ν_0 represent transitions in which the incident electron is bound in quantized states characterized by the total quantum numbers 1, 2, . . ., etc.

In the region of lower frequencies than ν_0, where both classical and quantum theories predict a continuous spectrum, Kramers assumed that the frequency in the classical spectrum which by the correspondence principle must be correlated with the quantum fre-

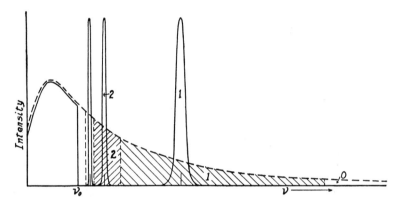

Fig. VII–16. Kramers' method of correlation of classical and quantum theoretical absorption curves.

quency is just equal to the quantum frequency. This amounts to the assumption that the energy distribution for frequencies less than ν_0 for the case in which electrons collide with a neutral atom is approximately the same as that calculated on the classical theory for an electron deflected by a bare nucleus.

In the region of the line spectrum, the assumption is made that " a certain frequency interval in the radiation emitted on the classical theory corresponds with a process by which the electron is bound in a certain stationary state." Since the energy of binding of an electron in a quantum orbit of total quantum number n is

$$E_n = -\frac{2\pi^2 m e^4}{h^2}\frac{Z^2}{n^2},$$

Kramers assumed that the frequency interval in the classical spectrum which corresponds to the line is given by

$$| \Delta \nu | = \frac{2\pi^2 m e^4}{h^3} \left(\frac{1}{(n - \frac{1}{2})^2} - \frac{1}{(n + \frac{1}{2})^2} \right) \sim \frac{4\pi^2 m e^4 Z^2}{n^3 h^3}.$$

The areas under the classical (dotted) curve are these frequency intervals, and are shaded in the figure for $n = 1$ and $n = 2$. These areas are then proportional to the probabilities that a collision between an electron and a bare nucleus will result in the binding of the electron in the orbit in question.

In this way a set of probabilities of emission can be calculated, and the corresponding probabilities of absorption computed by Einstein's relation between emission and absorption probabilities. For a given nucleus, the emission probabilities will depend on the kinetic energy of the colliding electron, and, conversely, the absorption probabilities will depend on the frequency of the incident radiation. In this way Kramers found, for the atomic absorption coefficient of the K electrons,

$$\tau_K = 0.0104 Z^4 \lambda^3$$

where λ is expressed in centimeters. In Sec. 8 of this chapter we have indicated that the experimental result for τ_K for 50 Sn is close to

$$\tau_K = 11.33 \times 10^{-20} \lambda^3 \quad (50 \text{ Sn})$$
$$= 1.81 \times 10^{-26} Z^4 \lambda^3$$

in which λ is expressed in angstroms. If λ is expressed in centimeters to agree with Kramers' constant, the experimental constant becomes 0.0181, about 1.8 times that calculated.

Since the advent of the wave mechanics, considerable work has been done on theoretical calculations of x-ray absorption coefficients.[110] One line of attack is to use the methods of the perturbation

[110] G. Wentzel, Zeitschr. f. Physik **38**, 518 (1926).

R. Oppenheimer, Zeitschr. f. Physik **41**, 268 (1927), cf. Gaunt, ibid., **59**, 508 (1930).

Y. Nishina and I. I. Rabi, Verh. d. Deutsch. Phys. Ges. **9**, 6 (1928).

Y. Sugiura, Phys. Rev. **34**, 858 (1929).

Sommerfeld and Schur, Ann. d. Phys. **4**, 409 (1930).

Schur, Ann. d. Phys. **4**, 433 (1930).

J. A. Gaunt, Proc. Roy. Soc. Lond. A **126**, 654 (1930).

M. Stobbe, Ann. d. Phys. **7**, 661 (1930).'

J. Fischer, Annalen der Physik **8**, 821 (1931).

Roess and Kennard, Phys. Rev. **38**, 1263 (1931).

theory as applied in wave mechanics.[111] The electric field of the incident wave is considered as a perturbing factor in the wave-equation. If the perturbation is sufficient, a continuous set of characteristic functions may appear, corresponding to what in the older form of the quantum theory were hyperbolic orbits of positive energy. The characteristic functions corresponding to these orbits differ from those of negative energy in that they do not fall off so rapidly as the radius increases. Over a sphere of infinite radius, the continuous functions have a finite surface integral, whereas those representing discrete states vanish. Thus in the photo-electric effect the continuous characteristic functions can be interpreted as representing a divergent flow of electricity outwards from the atom, corresponding to the ejection of photo-electrons. The integration previously mentioned will give an estimate of the amount of charge escaping per second and hence of the atomic absorption coefficient.

Another method of attack is to compute the intensities of emission lines from a state of positive to one of negative energy. This involves the calculation of the matrix elements in the continuous-discrete polarization matrix from the characteristic functions obtained by solution of Schrödinger's equation, using the appropriate values of the energy. This process may be rigorously carried out for the hydrogen atom. The emission probabilities so obtained are then connected with absorption probabilities by Einstein's relation, eq. (7.49a). The work of Stobbe will be discussed here. His calculations were based on the assumption of hydrogen-like matrices and characteristic functions. Thus his results apply strictly only to very highly ionized atoms. The effects of radiation pressure and retarded potentials were neglected, also, relativity and spin corrections were not included. The absence of the spin term means that only the total absorption of L_{II} and L_{III} could be calculated.

The following result is obtained for the contribution to the atomic absorption coefficient from the K electrons, τ_K.

$$\tau_K \sim 2\tau_1 = \frac{2^8\pi e^2}{3mc}\frac{\nu_1^{3}}{\nu^4}\frac{e^{-4\sqrt{\nu_1/(\nu-\nu_1)}\,\tan^{-1}\sqrt{(\nu-\nu_1)/\nu_1}}}{1-e^{-2\pi\sqrt{\nu_1/(\nu-\nu_1)}}}. \qquad (7.59)$$

In this expression $h\nu_1$ is the energy of binding of an electron in a

---

[111] See, for instance, Sommerfeld, Atombau und Spektrallinien, Wellenmechanischer Ergänzungsband (1929), p. 208 et seq.

quantized state of total quantum number 1 by the otherwise bare nucleus, and

$$\nu_n = \frac{RcZ^2}{n^2},$$ (7.60)

where R is the Rydberg number in reciprocal centimeters. ν is the frequency of the incident radiation. A more exact interpretation of eq. (7.59) is that the quantity expressed is twice the contribution to the atomic absorption coefficient from a single electron in an orbit of total quantum number unity. This may differ from τ_K due to the screening of one K electron by the other, and to the screening by external electrons in the atom, just as ν_1 may differ from the observed ν_K. In the region in which $\nu \sim \nu_1$, we obtain, after introduction of Z from eq. (7.60),

$$\tau_K \sim 2\tau_1 = \frac{2^8 \pi e^2 R^3 e^{-4}}{3mc^2} Z^6 \lambda^4 = 1820 Z^6 \lambda^4.$$ (7.61)

In the other direction, as $\nu \gg \nu_1$, the last factor in eq. (7.59) approaches

$$\frac{1}{2\pi} \sqrt{\frac{\nu}{\nu_1}}$$

so that the absorption asymptotically approaches the value

$$\tau_K \sim 2\tau_1 = \frac{2^7 e^2 R^{5/2}}{3mc^2} Z^5 \lambda^{7/2} = 478 Z^5 \lambda^{7/2}.$$ (7.62)

Thus the calculations do not predict that for a given element the absorption in the K level will uniformly follow a λ^3 law.

In the L_I and $L_{II}L_{III}$ shells, the results are as follows:

$$\tau_{L_I} \sim 2\tau_2^0 = \frac{2^{11} \pi e^2 \nu_2^3}{3mcv^4} \left(1 + 3\frac{\nu_2}{\nu}\right) \frac{e^{-8\sqrt{\nu_2/(\nu-\nu_2)} \tan^{-1}\sqrt{(\nu-\nu_2)/\nu_2}}}{1 - e^{-4\pi\sqrt{\nu_2/(\nu-\nu_2)}}}.$$ (7.63)

Here τ_2^0 is the contribution to the atomic absorption coefficient from a single electron bound to a bare nucleus in an orbit with $n = 2$, $l = 0$. Also

$$\tau_{L_{II}} + \tau_{L_{III}} \sim 6\tau_2^1 = \frac{2^{12} \pi e^2 \nu_2^4}{3mcv^5} \left(3 + 8\frac{\nu_2}{\nu}\right) \frac{e^{-8\sqrt{\nu_2/(\nu-\nu_2)} \tan^{-1}\sqrt{(\nu-\nu_2)/\nu_2}}}{1 - e^{-4\pi\sqrt{\nu_2/(\nu-\nu_2)}}}.$$ (7.64)

In the region $\nu \sim \nu_2$, that is, near the L absorption limits, the above formulae reduce to

$$2\tau_2{}^0 = \frac{2^5\pi e^2 R^3 e^{-8}}{3mc^2} Z^6 \lambda^4 \left(1 + 3\frac{\lambda}{\lambda_2}\right) = 4.17 Z^6 \lambda^4 \left(1 + 3\frac{\lambda}{\lambda_2}\right) \quad (7.65)$$

$$6\tau_2{}^1 = \frac{2^4\pi e^2 R^4 e^{-8}}{3mc^2} Z^8 \lambda^5 \left(3 + 8\frac{\lambda}{\lambda_2}\right) = 2.29 \times 10^5 Z^8 \lambda^5 \left(3 + 8\frac{\lambda}{\lambda_2}\right). \quad (7.66)$$

In the region where $\nu \gg \nu_2$, that is, far to the short wave-length side of the L limits, the values asymptotically approach

$$2\tau_2{}^0 = \frac{2^4 e^2 R^{5/2}}{3mc^2} Z^5 \lambda^{7/2} = 5.98 Z^5 \lambda^{7/2} \quad (7.67)$$

$$2\tau_2{}^1 = \frac{2^3 e R^{7/2}}{mc^2} Z^7 \lambda^{9/2} = 9.84 \times 10^5 Z^7 \lambda^{9/2}. \quad (7.68)$$

At frequencies near ν_2, which is an average L frequency, the relative absorption in the L_{I} and in the $L_{\mathrm{II}} L_{\mathrm{III}}$ shells can be obtained by dividing eq. (7.63) by eq. (7.64), and setting $\nu = \nu_2$, giving the result

$$\nu \sim \nu_2 \qquad \frac{\tau_{L\mathrm{I}}}{\tau_{L\mathrm{II}} + \tau_{L\mathrm{III}}} = \frac{2}{11}.$$

Thus there is approximately 6 times the absorption in $L_{\mathrm{II}} L_{\mathrm{III}}$ as in L_{I} near the L limits. At frequencies far greater than those of the L levels, the same operation gives

$$\nu \gg \nu_2 \qquad \frac{\tau_{L\mathrm{I}}}{\tau_{L\mathrm{II}} + \tau_{L\mathrm{III}}} = \frac{1}{6}\frac{\nu}{\nu_2}.$$

so that practically all the absorption is in L_{I}. This is in the form of the more qualitative result obtained by Wentzel.[112] The experimental evidence for this behaviour has come from the magnetic spectra of ejected electrons obtained by Robinson and his associates and discussed in Sec. 4 of this chapter.

In the numerical computation of absorption coefficients, Stobbe has taken account of the inner screening by using instead of Z in the formulae the values $(Z - 0.3)$ in the K level, and $(Z - 2 \times 0.85 - 7 \times 0.35)$ or $(Z - 4.15)$ for the L level. These screening constants

[112] G. Wentzel, Zeitschr. f. Physik 40, 574 (1927); reported in eq. (7.13a), this chapter.

for inner screening have been recommended by J. C. Slater.[113]   In attempting to take account of the effect of outer electrons in a neutral atom, it is at first thought possible to introduce the screening constant which results from the equation

$$\nu_q = \frac{(Z - s_q)^2 Rc}{n_q^2},$$

where ν_q is the critical absorption frequency of the q-limit, and n_q is the total quantum number of the shell in question.   Such a procedure is incorrect, however, because $h\nu_q$ represents the energy required to remove an electron from the q-shell, through all the outlying shells. This removal energy is diminished by the screening of external electron shells, but if we assume that these have an equal distribution of energy on a spherical surface, they do not affect the field in the volume inside them.   Thus the characteristic functions for the inner electrons depend on a field considerably more intense than that calculated from the removal energy.   The correct procedure would be to consider the charge density of the K electrons in the configuration space at a radius equal to that of the L shell and consider the perturbing action on this part of the K charge.   The important contributions to the matrix elements would, however, always come from the relatively large charge density in the region of the K orbit, where the attraction of the nucleus far outweighs the influence of the outer shells.

The numerical results of Stobbe's equations are compared with experimental data in Figs. VII-17 and VII-18.   The experimental points are taken partly from a paper by S. J. M. Allen[114] and partly from the tables in the appendix of this book, which were also compiled by him.

The equations of Stobbe may be used to predict the amount of the K absorption jump in the heavy elements.   One obtains

$$r_K = 1 + 8\,\frac{Z_K}{Z_L}\,e^{-4}\,\frac{(1 - e^{-(4\pi/x_2)})\,e^{(8/x_2)\,\tan^{-1}x_2}}{1 + \frac{9}{4}(Z_K/Z_L)^2 + (Z_K/Z_L)^4}$$

where

$$x_2 = \sqrt{4\left(\frac{Z_K}{Z_L}\right)^4 - 1}.$$

[113] J. C. Slater, Phys. Rev. **36**, 57 (1930).
[114] S. J. M. Allen, Phys. Rev. **27**, 266 (1926).

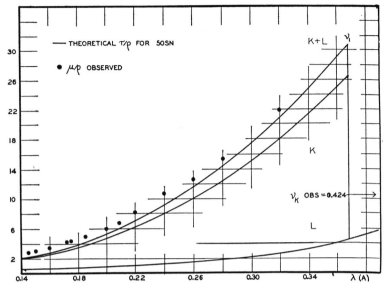

FIG. VII–17. Comparison of Stobbe's theoretical absorption calculations for the K shell with experiment. The limit ν_1 is calculated without reference to external screening and hence does not agree with the observed ν_K.

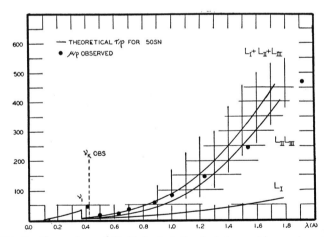

FIG. VII–18. Comparison of Stobbe's L shell calculations with experiment. Note the increasing relative absorption in the L_1 shell as the wave-length decreases.

Z_K is the effective nuclear charge for K electrons, or $(Z - 0.30)$; Z_L is $(Z - 4.15)$. The equation gives values of r_K ranging from 5.39 to 5.38 from $Z = 78$ to $Z = 92$, in good agreement with experiment.

11. *The Direction of Ejection of Photo-electrons by X-rays*[115]

When electrons are ejected from atoms by the recoil process which results in scattering with change in wave-length, the photon theory of light predicts that the electrons should possess a component of velocity in the forward direction, from the application of the principle of conservation of linear momentum to the photon-electron impact. Wilson chamber photographs clearly show this to be the case. We are now to consider whether the photo-electrons, ejected by a process which converts all the energy of the incident quantum into kinetic and potential energy, also exhibit evidence of the photon's momentum.

It has long been known that when hard radiation falls on a thin foil normally to its surface, more electrons are ejected from the side of the foil from which the radiation emerges than from the side on which it is incident.[116] In the early experiments, particularly those on γ-rays, the effect was confused by the lack of distinction between recoil electrons and photo-electrons; the former, of course, exhibiting the more pronounced asymmetry. The existence of such an asymmetry has been confirmed by many investigators, using the method of solid foils.[117] Cooksey investigated the electron emission from an 0.8×10^{-5} cm. thick gold foil and a 1.8×10^{-5} cm. silver foil with incident wave-lengths varying from 0.5 to 2 A. He found that the ratio of the number of photo-electrons on the emergent side to that on the incident side varied from 1.15 to 1.27. Beatty and Philpot both found evidence of a variation of the asymmetry with

[115] An adequate treatment of this subject up to 1930 has been given by Kirchner, "Allgemeine Physik der Röntgenstrahlen," Akademische Verlagsgesellschaft, Leipzig, 1930.

[116] An early paper describing this effect with x-rays is that of R. T. Beatty, Proc. Phil. So. Camb. **15**, 492 (1910). The effect was first discovered with γ-rays.

[117] C. D. Cooksey, Phil. Mag. **24**, 37 (1912).
A. J. Philpot, Proc. Phys. Soc. Lond. **26**, 131 (1914).
W. H. Bragg and H. L. Porter, Proc. Roy. Soc. Lond. A **85**, 355 (1911).
W. Seitz, Phys. Zeitschr. **25**, 546 (1924); **26**, 610 (1925).
L. Simons, Phil. Mag. **10**, 387 (1930).
H. Schenck, Ann. d. Phys. **17**, 146 (1933).

wave-length, in the sense that the emergent-incident ratio increases
for a given element as the wave-length of the exciting radiation decreases. Bragg and Porter found that for a given incident wave-
length the asymmetry decreases as the atomic number of the radiator
increases.

E. C. Watson and his associates[118] have greatly refined the technique of measuring the direction of photo-electric emission from thin
foils by a magnetic analysis of the ejected electrons. The apparatus

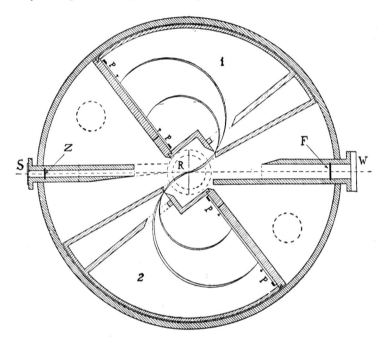

Fig. VII–19. Watson's apparatus for observing by the method of magnetic deviation
the probability of ejection of photo-elecrons at various angles.

used is shown in Fig. VII–19. It consists essentially of two magnetic
spectrographs, shown as the quadrants 1 and 2. The lines of force of
the magnetic field are perpendicular to the plane of the figure. The
radiator R from which the photo-electrons are ejected can be turned

[118] E. C. Watson, Phys. Rev. **30**, 479 (1927).

E. C. Watson and J. A. van den Akker, Proc. Roy. Soc. Lond. A **126**, 138
(1929). Later (Phys. Rev. **37**, 1631 (1931)), van den Akker and Watson attempted to
increase the sensitivity by substituting a tube counter for the photographic plate.

about an axis perpendicular to the figure. The x-ray beam enters through the slit S, covered with mica, and leaves through W. The quadrant-shaped spectrographs are attached to a plate which can be rotated about an axis perpendicular to the figure at its center, thus enabling photo-electrons ejected near any predetermined angle to be registered. The magnetic analysis enables the electrons ejected from the various levels to be distinguished, and thus the angle distribution curves of electrons from the K, L_I, L_{II}, etc., shells can be compared. The first experiments with ordinary gold foil, thick enough to be opaque to visible light, showed no appreciable difference in the number of electrons in various directions when incident radiation from a molybdenum target x-ray tube operated at 30,000 volts was used. The asymmetry appeared, however, when the electrons were ejected from thin, translucent films of sputtered gold, and its absence in the thicker films was ascribed to diffusion of electrons in the film.

It was found that the asymmetry with angle measured from the forward direction of the x-ray beam was greater in electrons ejected from the K and L_I shells than from electrons from $L_{II}L_{III}$. Appreciable numbers of the latter type were ejected in the forward and backward directions, where the K and L_I photo-electrons were too infrequent to be detected. Another result is that the angle at which the probability of photo-electric ejection is a maximum is smaller in the case of $L_{II}L_{III}$ photo-electrons than for K and L_I. This means that the average forward momentum of the $L_{II}L_{III}$ electrons is greater than that of the K and L_I photo-electrons. Similar results were obtained from M photo-electrons; the M_I photo-electrons behaving as respects longitudinal asymmetry like L_I and K; $M_{II}M_{III}$ like $L_{II}L_{III}$. As a result of taking magnetic spectra at various angles of the electrons ejected from a film of nickel chloride formed by exposing a nickel film to chlorine gas, it was shown that the more tightly bound nickel K photo-electrons have a maximum probability of ejection at a larger angle from the forward direction of the incident beam than did the more loosely bound K electrons of chlorine.

The problem has been studied to a considerable extent with the use of the Wilson cloud chamber and of the Geiger point counter.[119]

[119] W. Bothe, Zeitschr. f. Physik **26**, 59 (1924).

P. Auger, Compt. Rend. **178**, 929; 1535 (1924); Journal de Physique et le Radium, **6**, 205 (1925); **8**, 85; 110 (1927); Compt. Rend. **180**, 1939 (1925); **186**, 758 (1928); **188**, 477 (1929).

Auger and Meyer, Compt. Rend. **192**, 672 (1931).

If the Wilson chamber photographs are taken with stereoscopic cameras, complete information about the direction of ejection of each photo-electron may be obtained. The information desired is illustrated in Fig. VII–20. The beam of x-rays lies along the *x*-axis, and is proceeding in its positive direction. The vector p lies in the direction of ejection of a photo-electron. θ is the longitudinal angle, which is the angle between the direction of ejection and the

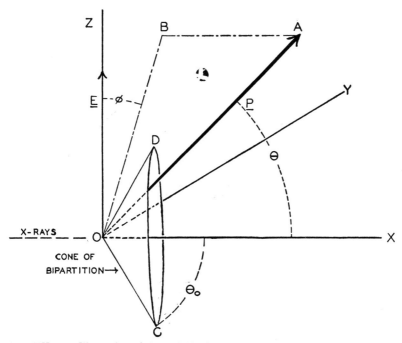

Fɪɢ. VII–20. Illustration of the variables involved in the discussion of the direction of ejection of photo-electrons.

E. J. Williams, Nature **121**, 134 (1928).

E. J. Williams, J. M. Nuttall and H. S. Barlow, Proc. Roy. Soc. Lond. A **121**, 611 (1928).

D. H. Loughridge, Phys. Rev. **26**, 697 (1925).

C. T. R. Wilson, Proc. Roy. Soc. Lond. A **104**, 1 (1923).

F. W. Bubb, Phys. Rev. **23**, 137 (1924).

F. Kirchner, Ann. d. Phys. **83**, 521 (1927).

C. J. Pietenpol, Phys. Rev. **32**, 564 (1928).

C. D. Anderson, Phys. Rev. **35**, 1139 (1930).

P. Kirkpatrick, Phys. Rev. **38**, 1938 (1931).

positive direction of the beam. ϕ is the azimuthal or lateral angle. No fundamental significance can be attached to ϕ unless the incident x-ray beam is plane polarized. Let us assume that the direction of the electric vector lies along OZ. Then ϕ is the angle between the projection of the photo-electron track on a plane normal to the direction of advance of the x-ray beam and the direction of the electric vector.

Another concept of importance in describing the results is illustrated by the cone OCD, of half-angle θ_0. This is the so-called cone of bipartition, such that as many photo-electron tracks lie inside it as outside it.

We may first discuss some results obtained with unpolarized

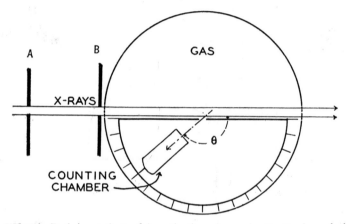

FIG. VII–21. Bothe's method of investigating the angle distribution of ejected photo-electrons.

x-rays. In 1924 Bothe studied the problem with the point counter. A schematic arrangement of the apparatus is shown in Fig. VII–21. The x-ray beam, whose divergence is limited by the slits A and B, passes through the gas-filled drum, and some of the photo-electrons produced in a volume near M and making angle θ with the beam can enter the Geiger counter. Correction must of course be made for the effective volume at various angles, etc. The path in the gas must be short enough so that serious deviations of the direction of the photo-electrons do not occur. Bothe experimented on photo-electrons from air, CH_3I, C_2H_5Br, and $CHCl_3$. With an effective voltage of 60 kv. he found values of θ_0, the half-angle of the cone of bipartition, of 79.9° for CH_3I, 76.5° for C_2H_5Br, and 73.7° for $CHCl_3$, showing the decrease in this angle as the binding energy decreases. Other results indicated a decrease in θ for a given source of photo-electrons as the hardness of the x-rays increased. Auger has pointed out that this method does not always distinguish between primary photo-electrons and electrons arising from internal conversions of fluorescence lines. These Auger electrons are symmetrically

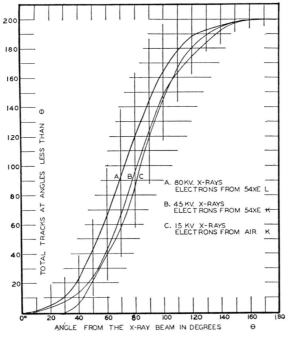

FIG. VII-22. Results obtained by Auger on the directions of ejection of photo-electrons by x-rays.

distributed, hence the observed asymmetry is superimposed upon a symmetrical background.

Auger has investigated the problem with a Wilson chamber and two cameras, mounted at right angles. From the two photographs obtained of every photo-electron track it is possible to deduce the angles θ and ϕ of Fig. VII-20. Auger presented his results in the form of the curves of Fig. VII-22, which shows three of the six curves obtained by him. Each curve represents readings on 200 photo-electron tracks. A point on the curve represents the total number of photo-electrons among the 200 for which θ was less than the corresponding abscissa. Thus in the curve showing the distribution of the L photo-electrons from xenon with an effective incident voltage of 90 kv., 93 of the 200 tracks observed occurred at angles less than 70°. The angle θ_0 can be read off at once from these curves, being the abscissa of the ordinate 100 in each case. Auger obtained the values of θ_0 shown in Table VII–18.

TABLE VII–18

ANGLES OF BIPARTITION θ_0 FOR PHOTO-ELECTRONS, FROM OBSERVATIONS BY AUGER AND BY ANDERSON

Conditions	Source of Photo-electrons	θ_0	Observer
15 kv x-rays	Oxygen or nitrogen	84°	Auger
20 kv x-rays	Oxygen or nitrogen	83°	Auger
80 kv x-rays	Argon, K shell	75°	Auger
80 kv x-rays	Xenon, L shell	73°	Auger
22 kv x-rays	Krypton, K shell	85°	Auger
45 kv x-rays	Xenon, K shell	82°	Auger
0.71 A	Air	76°	Anderson
0.56 A	Air	73°	Anderson
0.59 A	C_2H_5Br, K of Br	79°	Anderson
0.71 A	CH_3I, L of I	80°	Anderson
0.49 A	CH_3I, L of I	76°	Anderson

Note: A more extensive table of this type is given by Kirchner, Allgemeine Physik der Röntgenstrahlen, Akademische Verlagsgesellschaft, Leipzig (1930).

Anderson has also worked on this problem, using x-rays which were probably more nearly monochromatic than those used in the previously mentioned experiments. Radiation of 0.708 A wavelength was obtained by reflection from a crystal of x-rays from a molybdenum target tube. Other wave-lengths were obtained from secondary radiators in the manner previously described in the section on the measurement of fluorescence yields. Anderson obtained the bipartition angles shown in the lower part of Table VII–18. He was able to confirm previous results indicating a more isotropic space distribution from L than from K electrons. The distribution of the electrons from the L levels becomes less isotropic with increasing frequency of the incident x-rays. This is partially due to the fact that relatively more photo-electrons come from the L_I level as the frequency increases and these, as shown by Watson and van den Akker, are more asymmetric than the $L_{II}L_{III}$ photo-electrons. He found, furthermore, that although asymmetry of the K photo-electrons for a given wave-length increased as the atomic number decreases, that K electrons of the same initial velocity have the same average forward momentun.

We will now consider some experiments performed with polarized x-rays. There is the added possibility here of an asymmetry with respect to the angle ϕ of Fig. VII–20. The problem was first investigated by Bubb in 1923. He reported a strong concentration of ejected photo-electrons near the direction of the electric vector of the incident x-rays, which were polarized by being scattered from a paraffin block. More recently, investigations on this subject have been carried out by Kirchner, by Pietenpol, and by Kirkpatrick. As will be seen in the next section, it was predicted from theoretical grounds that if p is a vector in the direction of the path of the ejected photo-electron, and E a vector representing the direction of the electric field intensity in the incident radiation,

$$n_p \sim \cos^2 (E, p), \qquad\qquad (7.69)$$

where n_p is the probability of a photo-electron being ejected along p. The aim of most of the experimenters since Bubb has been to test this prediction. Kirchner investigated the distribution around the electric vector in photo-electrons ejected from CO_2, N_2, and argon by x-rays from 0.3 to 0.8 A in wave-length. After some reconsideration of his results, he came to the conclusion that the predicted law adequately expressed the experimental results. He called special attention to subjective errors in choosing electron tracks from the photographs. These may occur because the investigator tends to look for good tracks, suitable for measurement, in the direction in which the majority lie, that is, in the direction of the electric vector. Thus unless special precautions are taken, a greater concentration in this direction than actually occurs may result. Kirchner found that this lateral, or azimuthal distribution was independent of the wave-length of the incident radiation, and also independent of the binding energy of the photo-electron.

Pietenpol used a point counter mounted with its opening and axis in a plane normal to the direction of propagation of a polarized x-ray beam through air.   The entire gas-filled chamber and counter could be rotated about the direction of the beam, thus measuring the azimuthal distribution.   The experiment showed agreement with the cos² law.

Kirkpatrick has obtained results on 2008 condensation tracks of electrons ejected from argon atoms by partially polarized x-rays having the average wave-length 0.53 A.   The continuous radiation from a tungsten target tube was used.   The tube was operated at about 30 kv.   A portion of the radiation near the short wave-length limit was monochromatized by diffraction from a crystal.   It is known that this portion of the general radiation is highly polarized. The camera which took the track photographs was mounted on the

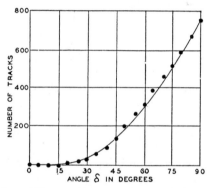

FIG. VII–23.   Kirkpatrick's test of the cos² (E, p) law.   The solid curve is based upon the theory, the solid circles are experimental points.

opposite side of the chamber from the source, such that the extended direction of the x-ray beam would pass along the axis of the lens.   Thus the projection of the tracks in a plane normal to the x-ray beam was obtained.[120]   A portion of the tracks was discarded as due to photo-electrons ejected by the unpolarized x-rays.   In this procedure Kirkpatrick was guided by the use of the cos² law.   The remaining tracks showed a lateral distribution closely following the law, as shown in Fig. VII–23.   The abscissae of this figure are the angles δ, measured from the minimum of photo-electric ejection which lies normal to the electric vector, in a plane transverse to the direction of the beam.   The circles show the number of photo-electron tracks due to completely polarized x-rays making angles of less than δ with the minimum direction.   Thus the point at δ = 60° means that slightly over 300 of 752 tracks occurred at angles between 90° and 30° of the electric vector.   Since the angles δ of Fig. VII–23 are the complements of the angles (E, p), the dis-

[120] It may be seen from eq. (7.72) that this projection should have a cos² φ distribution of probability of ejection, since this is true for all the electrons ejected at a certain value of θ.

tribution should be as $\sin^2 \delta$. The solid curve of Fig. VII–23 is a plot of the expression

$$n_\delta = k(\delta - \sin \delta \cos \delta)$$

where n_δ is the ordinate of the curve. The right-hand member of this expression is proportional to

$$\int_0^{\pi/2} \sin^2 \delta \, d\delta.$$

Kirkpatrick concludes that the theoretical and experimental curves agree within experimental error.

12. Theoretical Treatment of Space Distribution of Photo-electrons

An attempt to explain the longitudinal asymmetry of photo-electron emission from the view-point of the classical electro-magnetic theory would naturally call upon the phenomenon of radiation pressure. The effect of the electric field in the advancing electro-magnetic wave is to displace the electron in a direction normal to the direction of propagation of the disturbance. As this displacement goes on, the magnetic field of the radiation gives the electron's motion a component in the direction of propagation. If the electron's motion were entirely undamped, the total displacement after a complete cycle would be zero. It is due to the radiation damping that a forward resultant momentum occurs.[121] Although the classical theory gives this effect, qualitatively in the right direction, any attempt at quantitative calculation encounters the same difficulty as that met by purely classical theories of the momentum acquired by recoil electrons in scattering with change of wave-length. This is that the rate at which the momentum is acquired is enormously greater than can be accounted for on the classical theory.

The next attempt to develop a theory follows a suggestion made by O. W. Richardson[122] and subsequently developed in various ways by other investigators. According to this idea we suppose that the primary effect is to eject the photo-electron in a direction parallel to the electric vector, and the deviation from this direction is caused by the electron assuming the momentum of the incident photon, which is $h\nu/c$. This of course neglects the momentum im-

[121] See A. H. Compton, X-rays and Electrons, Van Nostrand (1926), footnote, page 241.

[122] O. W. Richardson, Phil. Mag. 46, 721 (1912).

parted to the ionized atom left after the ejection of the photo-electron. According to Fig. VII–24 we have

$$\cos \theta_0 = \frac{h\nu}{mcV} \qquad (7.70)$$

where V is the speed of the photo-electron.   If we neglect the energy expended by the incident quantum in the removal of the electron from the atom, we may write, non-relativistically,

$$h\nu = \tfrac{1}{2}mV^2$$

so that eq. (7.70) can be put in the form

$$\cos \theta_0 = \sqrt{\frac{h}{2mc\lambda}} = \frac{1}{2}\frac{V}{c} = \frac{1}{2}\beta. \qquad (7.71)$$

This expression shows that as λ decreases, θ_0 decreases.   If we sup-

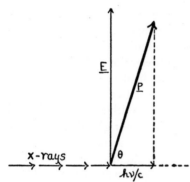

FIG. VII–24. Vector addition of the momentum of the ejected photo-electron and of the incident photon.

pose that the angle in question is to be correlated with the bi-partition angle of the experi-mental observations, the effect is in the correct direction to agree with observations.

It is experimentally ob-served, however, that there is a real spread in the directions of the ejection of photo-elec-trons, and there is no evidence that the emission is confined to one angle θ_0 with the direct beam of x-rays. This becomes specially noticeable in the studies of photo-electrons from polarized x-rays, where a definite distribution about the direction of the electric vector is observed.   E. C. Wat-son[123] proposed the explanation that the effect was due to nuclear scattering, which occurred after the ejection.   The importance of such an effect for photo-electron tracks photographed in a cloud chamber has been investigated by Kirchner,[124] and the conclusion

[123] E. C. Watson, Phys. Rev. **30**, 479 (1927).
[124] F. Kirchner, Ann. der Physik **84**, 899 (1927).

reached that there is no appreciable distortion of initial photo-electron directions in gases at ordinary pressures. F. W. Bubb[125] attempted to account for this distribution in direction by considering the momentum of the electron in the atom before ejection, due to its motion in a Bohr orbit. This point of view, however, predicts a different type of distribution in light and in heavy atoms, which is not experimentally observed. A similar attempt has been made by Bothe.[126]

Assuming that a distribution of photo-electrons of some sort takes place about the electric vector of a polarized wave, Auger and Perrin[127] proceeded by quite general considerations to determine how this distribution must vary with the angle (E, p). In the first place, they assumed that a beam of x-rays composed of two incoherent components polarized at right angles would exhibit the same properties as an ordinary beam of unpolarized x-rays. This means that for such a beam, the photo-electron distribution must have complete rotational symmetry about the direction of the x-ray beam. They further postulated that for each plane polarized component, the distribution must have rotational symmetry about the electric vector. They then found that the only distribution (except that of spherical symmetry about E) compatible with these two postulates is the $\cos^2 (E, p)$ distribution of eq. (7.69). Figure VII–25 shows the type of distribution predicted by them for long wave-lengths, where the forward momentum imparted to the electron is negligible. The length of the radius vector is proportional to the probability that an electron will be ejected in the given direction. The three-dimensional figure would be obtained by rotation about the axis of E.

For harder radiation, as shown in Fig. VII–26, the axes of the pear-shaped surfaces are tilted forward by the momentum $h\nu/c$, imparted by the impinging photon. To a first approximation the directions of the axes are given by the angle θ_0 of the cone of bipartition.

The theory of the effect has been approached from the point of

[125] F. W. Bubb, Phil. Mag. **49**, 824 (1925).

[126] W. Bothe, Zeitschr. f. Physik **26**, 74 (1924).

[127] Auger and Perrin, Journal de Physique, **8**, 93 (1927). In addition to the result quoted in the text, these authors show that a more general distribution, of the type $a + b \cos^2 (E, p)$ is possible, in which a represents a spherically symmetrical component. They considered this part to be negligible in ejection of K electrons. It is theoretically predicted in the ejection of $L_{II}L_{III}$ electrons, as is indicated later.

view of the wave-mechanics with considerable success.[128]   Here the problem becomes part of the larger problem of the emission of photo-electrons, from which the true absorption coefficient, the oscillator strengths, etc., are calculated.   The space distribution problem has

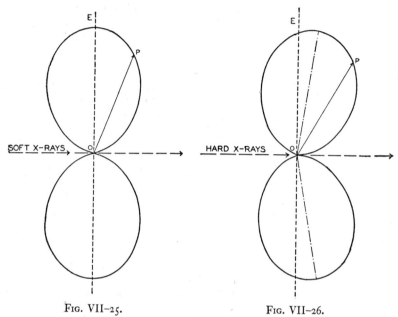

FIG. VII–25.   FIG. VII–26.

FIG. VII–25.   The $\cos^2(E, p)$ law for soft x-rays where the photon momentum can be disregarded.   The length of the radius vector OP is proportional to the probability of ejection at the angle EOP with the electric vector E.   There is rotational symmetry about OE.

FIG. VII–26.   When the momentum of the incident photon is considered, the surfaces of Fig. VII–25 are tilted forward.

[128] G. Wentzel, Zeitschr. f. Physik 41, 828 (1927).
   A. Sommerfeld, Wellenmechanischer Ergänzungsband (1929).   The treatment of the longitudinal asymmetry given here is modified in
   Sommerfeld and Schur, Annalen der Physik 4, 409 (1930).
   J. Fischer, Annalen der Physik 8, 821 (1931).
   Schur, Annalen der Physik 4, 433 (1930).
   T. Muto, Sci. Pap. Inst. Phys. Chem. Res. Tokio, 15, 111 (1931).
   S. E. Szczeniowski, Phys. Rev. 35, 347 (1930).   This treatment has been criti-cized because of the use of sums instead of integrals in the continuous characteristic functions.
   F. Sauter, Annalen der Physik 11, 454 (1931).

been attacked mainly by the methods of perturbation theory. The method of procedure and the type of result which comes from the perturbed wave-equation has been discussed in the section on theories of the true absorption. The continuous set of characteristic functions which appear are found to contain a factor which predicts less than spherical symmetry. The perturbing electric field of the advancing light may be represented as

$$E = A \cos 2\pi(\nu t - x/\lambda)$$
$$= \tfrac{1}{2}A(e^{-2\pi i\nu t}e^{2\pi i(x/\lambda)} + e^{2\pi i\nu t}e^{-2\pi i(x/\lambda)}).$$

The expansion of the exponential which does not involve the time is

$$e^{\pm 2\pi i(x/\lambda)} = 1 \pm 2\pi i \frac{x}{\lambda} \pm \left(2\pi i \frac{x}{\lambda}\right)^2 \ldots$$

and if the wave-length is long compared to atomic dimensions, which is true for ultra-violet light, we may set

$$e^{\pm 2\pi i(x/\lambda)} = 1 \qquad \lambda \gg x.$$

With this simplification, we may also neglect the momentum imparted in the ejection of the electron, and to confirm this, no longitudinally asymmetric term appears in the result.

We obtain, according to Wentzel,

$$n(\theta, \phi) \sim \sin^2 \theta \cos^2 \phi, \qquad (7.72)$$

where the angles refer to Fig. VII–20. With a little consideration it is seen that this expression is identical with that of Auger and Perrin, namely,

$$n(E, p) \sim \cos^2 (E, p).$$

We have already shown that this is confirmed by experiments with polarized x-rays.

If the wave-length of the incident radiation is so short that it cannot be considered infinite with respect to atomic dimensions, we cannot neglect x/λ, and to a first approximation we must set

$$e^{\pm 2\pi i(x/\lambda)} = 1 \pm 2\pi i \frac{x}{\lambda}.$$

Under this condition a new form of asymmetry appears in the characteristic functions and the probability for ejection of K electrons in a given direction is given by

$$n(\theta, \phi) \sim \frac{\sin^2 \theta \cos^2 \phi}{(1 - \beta \cos \theta)^4} \sim (1 + 4\beta \cos \theta) \sin^2 \theta \cos^2 \phi, \quad (7.73)$$

where β is the ratio of the velocity of the photo-electron to the velocity of light. Here the velocity is to be calculated non-relativistically. The effect of this added term is to weight more heavily those probabilities at small θ's, amounting to a shift of the most probable direction toward the direction of propagation of the x-rays. This is

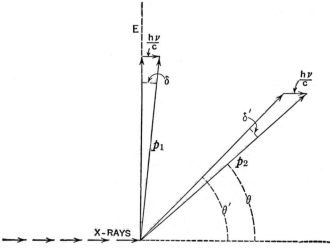

Fig. VII–27. Illustration of the calculation of the average forward momentum imparted to the photo-electrons on the basis of the photon theory. (After Sommerfeld and Schur.)

what is interpreted on the photon theory as the effect of the photon's momentum.

Let us return for a moment to the photon theory of the effect, considering non-polarized light so that the $\cos^2 \phi$ may be dropped in eq. (7.73). Let p_1, Fig. VII–27, be the vector representing the momentum of a photo-electron whose deviation from the direction of E is due to the momentum $h\nu/c$ imparted by an incident photon. Since $p_1 = mV$, and the angle $(E, p) = \delta$ is small, we may write

$$\delta = \frac{h\nu}{mcV}.$$

If the binding energy to be overcome in the ejection of the photo-electron is W_0, we have the Einstein equation

$$h\nu = \tfrac{1}{2}mV^2 + W_0,$$

so that

$$\delta = \tfrac{1}{2}\beta \left(1 + \frac{W_0}{\tfrac{1}{2}mV^2}\right). \tag{7.74}$$

In the case of p_2, the deviation produced by the photon's momentum is

$$\delta' = \delta \sin \theta.$$

The number of photo-electrons, which, disregarding the effect of the photon momentum, would be emitted in a ring-shaped region between θ' and $\theta' + d\theta'$, would be

$$dn \sim \pi \sin^2 \theta' \sin \theta' \, d\theta', \tag{7.75}$$

the $\sin^2$ term corresponding to the $\cos^2$ law of eq. (7.69). This infinitesimal number of photo-electrons would be deviated forward into the angular range characterized by θ and $d\theta$, where

$$\theta' = \theta + \delta' = \theta + \delta \sin \theta$$

and

$$d\theta' = (1 + \delta \cos \theta)d\theta.$$

Also

$$\sin \theta' = \sin (\theta + \delta \sin \theta) = \sin \theta \, (1 + \delta \cos \theta),$$

remembering that δ is small. Substitution in eq. (7.75) gives

$$dn \sim \sin^3 \theta \, (1 + \delta \cos \theta)^4 \, d\theta$$
$$\sim \sin^2 \theta \, (1 + 4\delta \cos \theta) \sin \theta \, d\theta.$$

Substitution of the value for δ from eq. (7.74) leads to

$$dn \sim \pi \sin^2 \theta \left\{1 + 2\beta \left(1 + \frac{W_0}{\tfrac{1}{2}mV^2}\right) \cos \theta\right\} \sin \theta \, d\theta. \tag{7.76}$$

In cases where $W/\tfrac{1}{2}mV^2$ can be neglected, it is seen by comparison of this function with the wave-mechanical result, eq. (7.73) (omitting the $\cos^2$ term) that according to wave-mechanics it appears that the photo-electron has taken on twice the momentum of the incident quantum.

The angle of bipartition, θ_0, can be calculated as follows:

$$\int_0^{2\pi} \int_0^{\theta_0} (1 + 4\beta \cos \theta) \sin^2 \theta \cos^2 \phi \sin \theta \, d\theta \, d\phi$$

$$= \int_0^{2\pi} \int_{\theta_0}^{\pi} (1 + 4\beta \cos \theta) \sin^2 \theta \cos^2 \phi \sin \theta \, d\theta \, d\phi.$$

The integration with respect to ϕ gives the same factor on both sides, so that it can be omitted, and the condition stated as

$$\int_0^{\theta_0} (1 + 4\beta \cos \theta) \sin^3 \theta \, d\theta = \int_{\theta_0}^{\pi} (1 + 4\beta \cos \theta) \sin^3 \theta \, d\theta.$$

Taking advantage of the fact that θ_0 is near $\pi/2$, and hence $\cos \theta_0$ is small, we obtain, as a first approximation

$$\cos \theta_0 = \beta. \qquad (7.77)$$

This important result implies that the bipartition angle is dependent only on the velocity of the ejected photo-electron, which seems to be confirmed by experiment. It also shows by comparison of eqs. (7.71) and (7.77), that the ratio[129]

$$S \equiv \frac{(\cos \theta_0)_{\text{wave mech.}}}{(\cos \theta_0)_{\text{photon theory}}} = 2. \qquad (7.78)$$

It is somewhat doubtful whether this last relation is satisfactorily substantiated by experiment, although there is some evidence of "excess asymmetry," pointed out by E. J. Williams.[130] Without attempting to examine all the known data, we can report some results obtained by Auger and Meyer,[131] which were especially designed to test this point. Using an expansion chamber filled with argon, they observed the values of S shown in Table VII–19. To this may be added the experiment of Lutze,[132] who used x-rays of effective wave-length 0.135 A, and found $\theta_0 = 58°$, which agrees better with wave-mechanical than with photon theories.

Sauter worked over the theory from the wave-mechanical point

---

[129] In Sommerfeld's Wellenmechanischer Ergänzungsband the ratio 9/5 was given. This was due to an error in the application of the theory.

[130] E. J. Williams, Nature **121**, 134 (1928).

[131] Auger and Meyer, Compt. rend. **192**, 672 (1931).

[132] Lutze, Annalen der Physik **9**, 853 (1931).

TABLE VII-19

RATIO OF THE COSINE OF THE OBSERVED ANGLE OF BIPARTITION TO THE COSINE OF
THE ANGLE CALCULATED FROM AN ELEMENTARY FORM OF THE PHOTON THEORY

Effective λ	S
0.87	1.90
0.22	1.56
0.134	1.45

of view, keeping in mind relativity effects which had been neglected by Sommerfeld and Schur. He found that up to a value of β of 0.52 the predicted value of $\cos \theta_0$ was changed only 0.8 per cent from that of the simpler, non-relativistic calculations.

Schur has investigated the problem with particular attention to the L shell. For L shell photo-electrons he finds

$$n(\theta, \phi) = \left\{ 1 + 4\beta \left(1 - \frac{W_L}{h\nu} \right) \cos \theta \right\} \sin^2 \theta \cos^2 \phi$$

$$+ \frac{W_L}{h\nu + 3W_L} \left[1 + \frac{8W_L}{h\nu} \sin^2 \theta \cos^2 \phi + 2\beta \cos \theta \right.$$

$$\left. \times \left\{ 1 + 2 \sin^2 \theta \cos^2 \phi \left(1 + \frac{11W_L}{h\nu} \right) \right\} \right].$$

W_L is here an average of the L ionization energies. The first term of this expression applies to the L_I electrons, and is similar in form to the previous expressions for K electrons. The second part of the expression applies to the $L_{II}L_{III}$ electrons. If we set $\beta = 0$, that is, neglect the momentum of the incident photon, this last part becomes of the form

$$a + b \sin^2 \theta \cos^2 \phi = a + b \cos^2 (E, p).$$

Thus the distribution of these photo-electrons about the electric vector is of a different type from that of K and L_I photo-electrons, and has a spherically symmetrical constituent a. At high frequencies this becomes more and more prominent, and corresponds to the experimental observation that the $L_{II}L_{III}$ distributions are more symmetrical than those from K and L_I.

Sommerfeld[133] calls attention to the fact that the wave-mechani-

[133] A. Sommerfeld, Wellenmechanischer Ergänzungsband, p. 214.

cal treatment is not explicit about the "cause" of the distribution of photo-electron ejection directions about the direction of the electric vector. One obtains only the statistical result, which is the only one important for comparison with observations. The attempts to explain the dispersion by the photon theory over-emphasize the causal aspect of the phenomenon, and use concepts of orbital motions which are not subject to direct experimental test. The non-specificity of the wave-mechanical treatment is typical, and in its use we must relinquish the "Anschaulichkeit," or "ability to be visualized" of the older theories.

CHAPTER VIII

The Interpretation of X-ray Spectra

1. *Gross Features Characteristic of X-ray Emission and Absorption Spectra*

Before the discovery of the diffraction of x-rays by crystals, it had been found by absorption measurements that x-rays, homogeneous in wave-length and characteristic of the target of the tube, are emitted in addition to the general or white radiation. These radiations were most easily observed from secondary radiators, silver, for instance, lying in a range of atomic number in which the phenomenon is readily detected in air with ordinary potentials on the x-ray tube. If a silver plate is placed near an x-ray tube operating at a voltage greater than 25 kv., the measurable secondary x-rays from the plate consist almost entirely of the so-called silver K radiation, the homogeneity of which can be demonstrated by the fact that its absorption coefficient is independent of the amount of filtration to which the beam is subjected. Barkla[1] called the hardest, most penetrating group of x-rays characteristic of an element the K group or series, and in the heavier elements he was able to show that a less penetrating group, the L series, was present. With the advent of x-ray spectrometers, using crystalline diffraction, these groups were rediscovered, and found to consist of x-ray spectrum lines. In addition to the K and L groups, groups called M and N, and a few lines assigned to an O group, have been discovered.[2] It has unfortunately become the custom to speak of these groups of lines as series, i.e., K series, L series, etc. Strictly speaking, only the K group is truly a series; as we shall see, the L group consists of three overlapping series, the M group of 5, etc.

Perhaps the most striking property of these groups is that in a

---

[1] Barkla and Sadler, Phil. Mag. 16, 550 (1908).
[2] *M*-series, Siegbahn, Compt. rend. 161, 787 (1916).
N-series, Dolejsek, Z. Physik 10, 129 (1922).
O-series, Dauvillier, Compt. rend. 183, 656 (1926).

given element, the lines in them occur in a wave-length range which is small compared to the wave-length separation of the groups themselves. This is illustrated in Fig. VIII–1, which shows the x-ray lines of tungsten plotted on a wave-length scale. Within the various groups, the thickness of the lines gives a rough idea of their relative intensities. We notice immediately the wide ranges over which there are no lines characteristic of tungsten.

Another aspect of the x-ray spectra which is of prime importance is discovered by comparing the appearance of the K series, or of the L series, from different radiators. This was first done for the K series in the celebrated researches of Moseley.[3]   A photograph showing the K series lines of the elements 20 Ca to 30 Zn as they appear in an instrument of low resolving power, is shown as Fig. I–27.   It is at once seen that the appearance of the series for these elements is

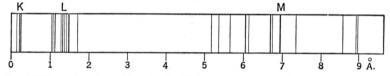

Fig. VIII–1.   Location of lines in the K, L, and M spectra of tungsten on the wave-length scale.

exactly the same, in relative positions and intensities of the lines.   A steady displacement of the entire K spectrum toward shorter wave-lengths takes place as the atomic number increases.   This behaviour is in violent contrast to that of the optical spectra of these elements, which shows distinct evidence of the periodicity which is also displayed in the chemical properties.   This characteristic behaviour is also shown in the L-series,[3] although here there is some wandering of the lines through the pattern from element to element.   Thus for elements of lower atomic number than 82 Pb the strong $L\beta_2$ line lies to the short wave-length side of $L\beta_1$, and for higher atomic numbers it appears on the long wave-length side.

Quantitatively, Moseley found that the square root of the frequency of a typical line in a group is a linear function of the atomic number.   This is illustrated for some of the lines in the K series in Fig. VIII–2.   In this figure, instead of plotting the actual frequency against the atomic number, the conventional method of plotting $\sqrt{\nu/R}$ against Z has been adopted. ν is the wave-number, or recip-

[3] Moseley, Phil. Mag. 6, 26, 1024 (1913), and 27, 703 (1914).

rocal of the wave-length in cm., and R is the Rydberg constant for an atom of infinite nuclear mass; $R = 109{,}737$ cm.$^{-1}$ Between the atomic numbers 20 and 30, the ν/R value of the $K\alpha$ line, which is the

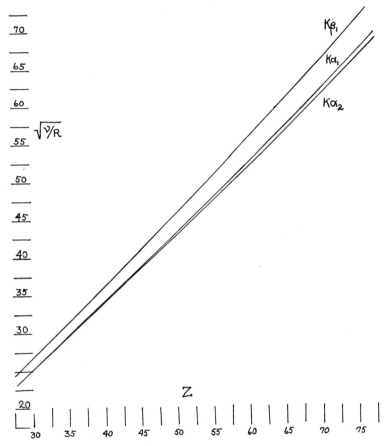

Fig. VIII–2. Moseley diagrams for the lines $K\beta_1$, $K\alpha_1$, $K\alpha_2$ from $Z = 29$ to $Z = 78$.

strongest line appearing in Fig. I–27 may be calculated from the equation

$$\sqrt{\nu/R} = 0.874(Z - 1.13). \tag{8.01}$$

We shall discuss the interpretation of this empirical result in the next section.

It is clear from the positions of the K series of 27 Co and 28 Ni in Fig. I–27 that something more fundamental than the atomic weight controls the frequency of these x-ray lines, since this is one of the places in the periodic system where the atomic weights are in the reverse order of the atomic numbers (27 Co = 58.94, 28 Ni = 58.69). It is also true that in their gross aspects, the x-ray spectra are independent of chemical combination, that is, the x-ray spectrum of a substance such as lead selenide will consist of the lines characteristic of lead and of selenium, and no new spectrum characteristic of the molecule will appear.[4]   One has only to mention a typical case, such as the band spectrum of calcium hydride contrasted with the line spectra of calcium and of hydrogen to realize the contrast between x-ray and optical spectra in this respect.

The first quantitative results on the excitation of x-ray spectra were obtained by Webster.[5]   The experimental procedure consisted in setting the ionization chamber and crystal of a Bragg spectrometer in such a position that the desired x-ray line, if present in the radiation, was diffracted into the chamber.   With the electron current through the x-ray tube held constant, the voltage was increased until the line appeared, signalized by a rapid increase in the rate of change of ionization current with voltage.   When the experiment was performed with an x-ray tube having a rhodium target, and the spectrometer set for the Rh $K\alpha$ line, the result illustrated in Fig. VIII–3 was obtained.   The interpretation of this figure is as follows: below a voltage of about 23.2 kv., the ionization in the chamber is caused by general or white radiation of the wave-length of Rh $K\alpha$, reflected by the crystal into the ionization chamber.   (Strictly speaking, this is only true in the voltage range between 20.1 kv. and 23.2 kv.; below 20.1 kv. the ionization current is caused by radiation scattered into the chamber from the slits, crystal, and so forth, and the natural leak of the insulated system.)   The excitation of the Rh $K\alpha$ line begins at approximately 23.2 kv.   Further experimentation showed that the $K\alpha$ line, and in fact all the lines of the K series of rhodium, were excited at this same potential, and appeared with the same relative intensities as they had at higher voltage.   Some of the spectra obtained with a rhodium target containing a slight amount of ruthenium are shown in Fig. VIII–4.

[4] This illustration was suggested by an experiment performed by G. L. Pearson, Proc. Nat. Acad. Sci. **15**, 658 (1929).

[5] D. L. Webster, Phys. Rev. **7**, 559 (1916).

The wave-length of the Rh $K\alpha$ line is roughly 0.613 A. By Einstein's $h\nu = eV$ relationship, the quantum voltage corresponding to this wave-length is 20.1 kv., a result distinctly lower than the 23.2 kv. observed for its excitation. It is found by experiment that the voltage necessary to excite the K series is greater than the quantum voltage calculated for any line in the series by Einstein's relation. In the L series the lines may be divided into three groups,

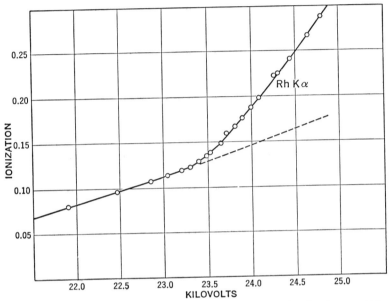

Fig. VIII-3. Excitation of the rhodium $K\alpha$ line by electron bombardment. (After D. L. Webster.) The ionization spectrometer is set to receive the rhodium $K\alpha$ line, and the voltage on the tube gradually increased.

such that for each group the above relationship holds. This kind of excitation is different from that type which appears in some cases in optical spectra, and was first observed by Franck and Hertz.[6] They observed that the strong ultra-violet line λ2536 of mercury was excited in mercury vapor when the energy of the impinging electrons was derived from a potential difference of 4.9 volts, which is just that calculated by Einstein's relation from this wave-length. Similarly the principal series of sodium can be excited line by line

[6] Franck and Hertz, Verh. d. D. Phys. Ges. **15**, 34, 373, 613, 929; **16**, 12, 457, 512 (1914); **18**, 213 (1916).

as the voltage is increased, in contrast to the x-ray case. Many optical lines, however, are not excited when the unexcited atom is bombarded with electrons having the quantum energy of the line; for instance, the first line of the Balmer series, λ = 6563 A, is not radiated from atomic hydrogen when it is subjected to impacts from electrons having the corresponding quantum energy, 1.9 volts.

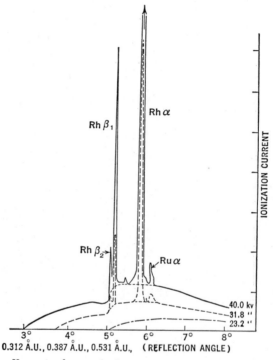

FIG. VIII–4.   K spectra from a rhodium target at various voltages. (After D. L. Webster.)   The relative intensity of the lines does not vary with voltage.

The excitation of characteristic fluorescence radiation from a secondary radiator was investigated even before the days of x-ray spectroscopy by Beatty[7] and by Whiddington,[8] who correctly concluded that in order to excite the K radiation, the incident beam must contain a wave-length shorter than that of any of the K-series lines.   A quantitative investigation with modern apparatus has been

[7] Beatty, Proc. Roy. Soc. Lond. **A 87**, 511 (1912).
[8] Whiddington, Proc. Roy. Soc. Lond. **A 85**, 323 (1911).

made by Allison and Duane.[9]   In these experiments a silver block was placed near an x-ray tube equipped with a tungsten target. Part of the radiation from the silver passed through the slits of an x-ray spectrometer set to receive the $K\alpha$ lines of silver. The ionization current was observed as the voltage on the tube producing the primary radiation was increased, and a curve closely resembling that of Fig. VIII–3 resulted, except that in the present case the ionization current below the critical excitation potential was extremely weak, there being practically no general radiation in the secondary x-rays.   It was found that the fluorescence K radiation of silver was produced when the voltage on the x-ray tube was 25.4 ± 0.15 kv. From our knowledge of the short wave-length limit of the general radiation and the Duane-Hunt law we can calculate that in order to produce the silver fluorescence x-rays the primary beam must contain a wave-length shorter than 0.485 ± 0.003 A, which is less than the shortest wave-length in the silver K series. These phenomena in the excitation of primary and secondary x-rays are closely connected with the absorption of x-rays, which we will now consider.

We will here take up only those aspects of the absorption of x-rays which are of direct importance in the interpretation of x-ray spectra.   In the first place, we note that an element does not selectively absorb radiation of the wave-length of its x-ray lines. If a thin sheet of rhodium is placed in the path of a beam of x-rays of wave-length 0.613 A, there is no critical absorption of this radiation, although as we have seen this is the wave-length of the Rh $K\alpha$ line, approximately.   The absorption coefficient for rhodium in this wave-length region is a monotonic function of wave-length with no unusual features. This is in contrast to the behaviour of sodium vapor, which is practically opaque to radiation of the wave-length of the sodium D lines, with respect to the negligible absorption of radiation of adjacent wave-length.

Instead of single line, or resonance absorption, we have in the x-ray region the well-known critical absorption discontinuities, which have been previously considered in this book. As the wave-length increases, the absorption coefficient suffers a series of abrupt decreases in magnitude, one of which lies in the region of the K series, 3 in the L region, and 5 in the M region. If the absorber is rhodium, such an abrupt change is noted at $\lambda = 0.533$ A, radiation of lesser wave-length being absorbed much more strongly than that of longer wave-

[9] S. K. Allison and W. Duane, Proc. Nat. Acad. Sci. U.S.A. 11, 485 (1925).

length.   A schematic curve showing this effect is given in Fig. IV–7, Chap. IV.   It is this critical absorption wave-length which is connected with the critical excitation voltage by the Einstein relation. Thus we find that o.533 A corresponds to 23.1 kv., which checks within the limit of error with the 23.2 kv. found by Webster as the critical excitation potential of the rhodium K series.

Like the emission spectra, the x-ray absorption spectra, when not considered in great detail, are independent of chemical combination.

2. The Elementary Theory of X-ray Spectra

The gross aspects of x-ray spectra mentioned in the preceding section can be correlated into a theory which had its beginning in the work of Moseley already mentioned, and was qualitatively enlarged by Kossel.[10]   At the time when Moseley's experiments were made, the nuclear atom model had been experimentally established by the work of Rutherford, and Bohr's quantum theoretical interpretation of the hydrogen atom spectrum had appeared.   The fact that these ideas were successfully extended to include the x-ray spectra gave them great support.

Let us first consider the fact that x-ray spectra are independent of chemical combination and do not exhibit gross signs of the periodicity in Mendelejeff's table.   This, combined with the high quantum energies (intermediate between optical spectra and gamma rays) concerned in their production, leads us to postulate that the x-rays come from electrons buried deeply in the electron cloud external to the nucleus.   Chemical effects and optical spectra are concerned with the outermost electrons.   We must assume that in the interior of the atom the arrangement of the electrons is one of the greatest order and regularity, and does not vary in a haphazard or even a periodic manner from element to element, but remains essentially the same, the only varying factor as we ascend the periodic system being the increasing pull of the nucleus as the positive charge augments with each increase in atomic number.

Bohr had shown that in an atom of nuclear charge Z having only one external electron, the energies in the quantized states can be represented by

$$E(n) = -\frac{RhcZ^2}{n^2}\left(\frac{M}{M+m}\right), \; n = 1, 2, 3 \ldots \quad (8.02)$$

[10] Kossel, Verh. dtsch. physik. Ges. **18**, 339, 396 (1916); Physik. Zeitschr. **18**, 240 (1917); Zeitschr. f. Physik **2**, 470 (1920); **1**, 119 (1920).

where

$$R = \frac{2\pi^2 m e^4}{ch^3}. \tag{8.03}$$

In these expressions R is the Rydberg constant for an atom of infinite nuclear mass, and if determined by the extrapolation of experimental spectroscopic data[11] is given by

$$R = 109{,}737.42 \pm 0.06. \tag{8.04}$$

Of course R cannot be calculated with comparable accuracy by means of experiments on the electronic charge, electronic mass, and Planck's constant through eq. (8.03), but within the limits of error with which these can be experimentally measured there is agreement. M is the mass of the nucleus of the atom, and m is the electronic mass. e is the electronic charge in e.s.u., c the velocity of light in vacuo, and h is Planck's constant. n is the so-called total quantum number, which characterizes the quantized state and takes on a series of integral values beginning with unity.

In the emission of a spectrum line, the atom changes from a higher energy state to a lower one, and hence the v/R value of a line in the spectrum, where v is the wave-number, will be given by

$$v/R = Z^2 \left(\frac{M}{M+m}\right)\left(\frac{1}{n_f^2} - \frac{1}{n_i^2}\right). \tag{8.05}$$

In this expression n_i and n_f represent the total quantum numbers of the initial and final states respectively.

In the case of x-ray spectra, for example in the K lines of the elements 20 Ca to 30 Zn, we are not dealing with exactly the case for which eq. (8.05) was devised, namely, a nucleus with one external electron. We may assume that the extra-nuclear electrons which go into the building of these more complicated atoms take up quantum states characterized by different values of the total quantum number n, so that there are K electrons, with $n = 1$, L electrons with $n = 2$, and so on. In this more complex case we cannot hope to proceed exactly according to eq. (8.05) in the calculation of the v/R values of x-ray lines. We expect that a modification of the formula will be necessary, which consists in correcting the nuclear charge for screening, meaning that due to the presence of other external electrons, the

[11] Birge, Phys. Rev. Suppl. 1, 1 (1929).

effective charge attracting the electron to the nucleus is less than Ze. It is customary to make this correction by subtracting a so-called screening constant, σ, from the atomic number, thus writing $(Z - \sigma)$ where Z appears in eq. (8.05). When this empirical correction is introduced, there is no longer any reason to retain the factor $M/(M + m)$ which represents a very small correction due to the motion of the nucleus about the center of mass of the nucleus-electron system, and we will omit it in the subsequent formulae.

Let us assume that the atomic process giving rise to radiation of the wave-length of the $K\alpha$ line involves the transfer of an electron from a state characterized by $n = 2$ to one having $n = 1$. From eq. (8.05) we may then write

$$\left(\frac{\nu}{R}\right)_{K\alpha} = (Z - \sigma)^2 \left(\frac{1}{1^2} - \frac{1}{2^2}\right) = \tfrac{3}{4}(Z - \sigma)^2$$

or

$$\left(\sqrt{\frac{\nu}{R}}\right)_{K\alpha} = 0.866\,(Z - \sigma). \tag{8.06}$$

The approximate numerical agreement of eq. (8.06) with the experimental value 0.874 in eq. (8.01) and its analogous form give very strong evidence of the essential correctness of this rough theory. We shall see however that the screening constant σ introduced here is not simply related to the screening of any individual electron in the atom, but is a complicated function of the constants applicable to the initial and final states. It may further be assumed that the weaker $K\beta$ line which appears in Fig. I–27 is associated with the total quantum numbers 1 and 3, and that L series lines involve in common an energy state characterized by $n = 2$. Approximate numerical agreements may be obtained with experiment through equations similar to (8.06.)

The interpretation of the observed phenomena in the excitation and absorption of x-rays introduces concepts of great importance. Perhaps the most outstanding of these is that only a limited number of electrons characterized by the same total quantum number can exist in an atom. There was nothing in the Bohr theory to suggest such an idea, and it is a result of what is now known as Pauli's exclusion principle.[12]

Anticipating the results to be derived in the next section, we may

[12] W. Pauli, Zs. f. Physik 31, 765 (1925).

assume that in the atoms with which we ordinarily deal in the production of x-ray spectra, the innermost shells, that is, electron groups characterized by $n = 1$ or 2, at least, are filled. In the discussion prior to eq. (8.06), we spoke of the transfer of an L electron to the K shell. But if the K shell is already full, how can such an addition to its quota of electrons be made? The answer, of course, is that no such addition is made, that the necessary condition for the emission of $K\alpha$ is that a vacancy be created in the K shell by the removal of one of the K electrons. Furthermore, in its ejection from the K shell, the K electron being removed cannot stop in the L shell because the L shell is already full. We thus arrive at the explanation of the fact that for the excitation of an x-ray line by cathode ray impact, the impinging electrons must have fallen through a potential difference greater than that which by Einstein's equation corresponds to the wave-length of the line. The incident electrons must have sufficient energy to raise the ejected K electron's energy above that corresponding to any of the completed shells and either deposit it in an incomplete or unoccupied group or remove it to infinity. After the removal of the K electron, the $K\alpha$ line may be emitted as the result of an L to K transfer, and subsequently an L series line may result from the transfer of an M electron to the vacancy in the L shell. Thus the electron transfers giving rise to x-ray lines take place in singly ionized atoms.

We will now consider the application of the combination principle to x-ray spectra. This principle, which may be considered as the foundation stone of spectroscopic theory, may be stated as follows:

For every spectrum there exists a set of terms, small in number in comparison to the number of lines, such that the frequencies of the lines are given by differences between the terms.

It was soon recognized that the terms in the case of the x-ray spectra are the ν/R values corresponding to the critical absorption or excitation frequencies.[13] Thus the initial state for the emission of the $K\alpha$ line corresponds to the energy required to completely remove a K electron from the atom, and the final state to the energy required to remove an L electron. The difference between these two energies is the energy from which by Einstein's relation the wave-length of the $K\alpha$ line may be calculated. An elementary term table including optical and x-ray terms is shown in Fig. VIII-5. The numerical

[13] W. Duane and Kang-Fu-Hu, Phys. Rev. 11, 489 (1918); 14, 369 (1919).

value of any term is arbitrary in the sense that it depends on the choice of some atomic configuration or other which for convenience is assigned the energy content zero. Usually this configuration is one in which one of the electrons of the atom has been removed to infinity.

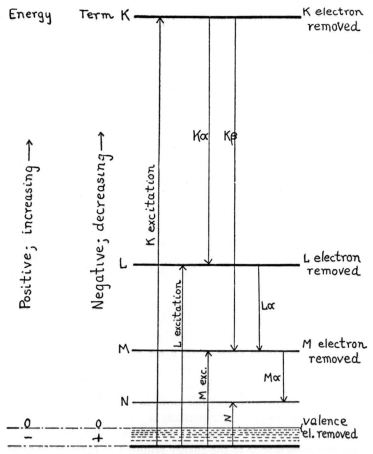

Fig. VIII–5. An elementary x-ray energy level and term diagram, showing the relation of the x-ray terms to the optical terms, which lie below the zero of energy.

With such a choice, negative energies are found for quantized states representing the various stages in the recapture of this electron. In Fig. VIII–5 the zero of energy has been set at a configuration in which the outermost, most loosely held electron of the atom has been removed to infinity. Then all the states in the arc spectrum have negative energies,[14] and the x-ray states have high positive energies. As for the term values, it is common spectroscopic practice to consider arc spectrum terms positive when they lie below the zero of energy, and negative when they lie above this value.[14] On this convention most of the arc terms are positive and all the x-ray terms negative.

If we attempt to give numerical examples of the application of the combination principle based on the elementary x-ray table of Fig. VIII–5, we can only give a poor impression of the accuracy of the principle. In order to give a correct application, we will give the notation assigned to the complete set of x-ray levels and to the observed lines in the K and L series. Different notations have been used by various authors and are summarized in Table VIII–1. A graphical term table showing the complete set of x-ray terms and diagram lines is shown in Fig. VIII–17. The term " diagram lines " used as characteristic of the lines tabulated in Table VIII–1 will be explained later. At present we may state that they are the most prominent and intense lines observed.

3. Pauli's Exclusion Principle and the Building of the Periodic System

Pauli's exclusion principle as applied to atomic structure may be stated as follows:

No two electrons in an atom may exist in such a state that they are characterized by the same set of quantum numbers.

Different sets of quantum numbers are used to describe the electron under different circumstances, in particular, the presence or absence of a magnetic field may make different sets preferable. For our purpose at present we shall consider that set which is useful in what we shall call a " very strong " magnetic field. This is such a strong field that all interactions between electrons in the atom, including the interaction between the spin and orbital momentum of each electron, are insignificant with respect to the interaction of the electron with the field. Such a field for the electrons concerned in x-ray spectra is experimentally unrealizable, nevertheless we may imagine its

---

[14] There are, for instance, negative terms in the optical arc spectrum of calcium. In these terms both valence electrons are excited, and the energy released when both return to the normal state would be more than sufficient to completely remove one of them. These terms have positive energies.

existence.   Under these conditions each electron may be characterized by four quantum numbers, which are

$$n \quad l \quad m_l \quad m_s.$$

TABLE VIII–1

NOTATIONS FOR X-RAY LEVELS AND LINES

A. X-ray Energy Levels

Sommerfeld; This Book	Siegbahn (1924)	Sommerfeld 4 Ed. Atombau	Sommerfeld; This Book	Siegbahn (1924)	Sommerfeld 4 Ed. Atombau
K	K	K	N_I	N_7	N_{11}
L_I	L_3	L_{11}	:	:	:
L_{II}	L_2	L_{21}	N_{VII}	N_1	N_{44}
L_{III}	L_1	L_{22}	O_I	O_5	O_{11}
M_I	M_5	M_{11}	:	:	:
M_{II}	M_4	M_{21}	O_V	O_1	O_{33}
M_{III}	M_3	M_{22}	P_I	P_3	P_{11}
M_{IV}	M_2	M_{32}	:	:	:
M_V	M_1	M_{33}	P_{III}	P_1	P_{22}

B. X-ray Diagram Lines

K Series

Siegbahn; This Book	Sommerfeld	Combina-tions	Siegbahn; This Book	Sommerfeld	Combina-tions
β_2	γ	$K-N_{II}N_{III}$	α_1	α	$K-L_{III}$
β_1	β	$K-M_{III}$	α_2	α'	$K-L_{II}$
β_3	β'	$K-M_{II}$			

L Series

β_5	ζ	$L_{III}-O_{IV, V}$	γ_1	δ	$L_{II}-N_{IV}$
β_7	..	$L_{III}-O_I$	γ_5	..	$L_{II}-N_I$
β_2	γ	$L_{III}-N_V$	β_1	β	$L_{II}-M_{IV}$
β_{15}	γ'	$L_{III}-N_{IV}$	η	η	$L_{II}-M_I$
β_6	..	$L_{III}-N_I$	γ_{14}	..	$L_I-P_{II, III}$
α_1	α	$L_{III}-M_V$	γ_4	ψ	$L_I-O_{II, III}$
α_2	α'	$L_{III}-M_{IV}$	γ_3	χ	L_I-N_{III}
l	ε	$L_{III}-M_I$	γ_2	χ'	L_I-N_{II}
γ_6	ϑ	$L_{II}-O_{IV}$	β_3	ϕ	L_I-M_{III}
γ_8	..	$L_{II}-O_I$	β_4	ϕ'	L_I-M_{II}

n is the so-called total quantum number, which enters into the principal factor giving the binding energy of the electron. It may take on integral values 1, 2, 3. . . .

l is a quantum number expressing the angular momentum in units of $h/2\pi$ possessed by the electron, due, on the older form of the quantum theory, to its orbital motion. We shall carry this terminology over into the modern wave-mechanical theories, and speak of the orbital angular momentum as determined by $lh/2\pi$. l is related to k, the old " azimuthal quantum number " introduced by Sommerfeld to characterize the various elliptic orbits possible under a given n, by the equation $l = k - 1$. Since angular momentum due to the motion of an electric charge is equivalent to magnetic moment, l also gives the orbital magnetic moment in units of Bohr magnetons. l can take on the integral values 0, 1, 2 . . . $(n - 1)$, and may be considered (on the old vector model, see Fig. VIII–7) as the magnitude of a vector l.

m_l represents the projection of the angular momentum l upon the direction of the magnetic field H. The theory of space quantization shows that the application of a magnetic field will cause l to take up orientations with respect to the field such that the magnitude of its projection upon the field takes on the integral values

$$-l < m_l < l$$

among which zero is included. There are $2l + 1$ possible values of m_l for a given l.

m_s is the projection of the electron spin angular momentum vector s upon the magnetic field H. It is an intrinsic property of the electron that it has associated with it an angular momentum of amount $sh/2\pi$, where $s = \frac{1}{2}$. In order to visualize this the electron can be imagined to be spinning like a top about some axis passing through it. We must not, however, take this picture too literally, but must merely use it as a convenient mental image. This amount of angular momentum is associated with one Bohr unit of magnetic moment, and not with one-half unit, as we might expect from the fact that $s = \frac{1}{2}$. The only allowed orientations of the electron spin with respect to the field are such that the magnitude of m_s is $\frac{1}{2}$ or $-\frac{1}{2}$. Orientations of s and l with respect to H for $l = 2$ are shown in Fig. VIII–6, which is constructed according to the wave-mechanics vector model (see the discussion of vector models pertaining to Fig. VIII–7).

These four quantum numbers are sufficient for the application of the Pauli principle to the problem of completed shells in the process of atom building. Let us first ask how many electrons in an atom can have the total quantum number $n = 1$. The possi-

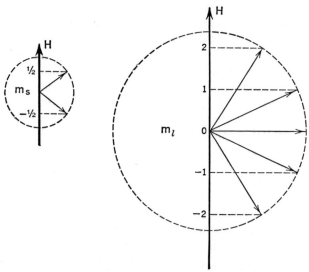

Fig. VIII-6. Orientation of the vectors s and l for $s = \frac{1}{2}$ and $l = 2$ in a very strong magnetic field. As explained later, in the text, the vectors are drawn so that $|l| = \sqrt{l(l+1)}$; $|s| = \sqrt{s(s+1)}$, while m_l and m_s have integral or half integral values differing by unity.

bilities are exhibited in Table VIII-2. It follows that there may be only two K electrons in an atom. In the process of building the periodic system the K shell is full at helium and for all succeeding elements.

TABLE VIII-2

ORIENTATIONS OF K ELECTRONS IN A VERY STRONG MAGNETIC FIELD

n	l	m_l	m_s	Type
I	o	o	$\frac{1}{2}$	$\Big\}\, s$
I	o	o	$-\frac{1}{2}$	

We will next investigate the possible number of electrons for which $n = 2$, that is, L electrons. The possibilities are shown in

Table VIII–3. There are 8 L electrons in all, two having $l =$ o and six having $l =$ 1. The L shell is first completely filled at neon. By a continuation of the process exhibited in Tables VIII–2 and

TABLE VIII–3

Orientations of L Electrons in a Very Strong Magnetic Field

n	l	m_l	m_s	Type
2	o	o	$\frac{1}{2}$	$\left.\vphantom{\begin{array}{c}a\\a\end{array}}\right\} s$
2	o	o	$-\frac{1}{2}$	
2	1	-1	$\frac{1}{2}$	
2	1	-1	$-\frac{1}{2}$	
2	1	o	$\frac{1}{2}$	p
2	1	o	$-\frac{1}{2}$	
2	1	1	$\frac{1}{2}$	
2	1	1	$-\frac{1}{2}$	

VIII–3 it can be shown that there may be 18 M electrons and 32 N electrons. In general the number of electrons in a completed shell of total quantum number n is $2n^2$, which follows from the relation

$$2 \sum_{l=0}^{l=n-1} (2l + 1) = 2n^2.$$

In Tables VIII–2 and VIII–3 the electrons have been classified as belonging to types s or p and we will now explain this nomenclature and extend it. The classification refers to the l values of the electrons, as may be seen from Table VIII–4. Thus the electronic

TABLE VIII–4

Notation for Electrons Based on their l Values

l value....... o   1   2   3   4
Type......... s p d f g

structure of the neutral helium atom may be expressed as $1s^2$. The 1 in this symbol represents the total quantum number of the K shell, and the superscript 2 shows the number of electrons present having $n =$ 1 and $l =$ o. In Table VIII–5 the electronic structures of the rare gases are expressed in this manner.

TABLE VIII-5

ELECTRONIC STRUCTURES OF THE RARE GASES

2 He	$1s^2$					
10 Ne	$1s^2$	$2s^22p^6$				
18 A	$1s^2$	$2s^22p^6$	$3s^23p^6$			
36 Kr	$1s^2$	$2s^22p^6$	$3s^23p^63d^{10}$	$4s^24p^6$		
54 Xe	$1s^2$	$2s^22p^6$	$3s^23p^63d^{10}$	$4s^24p^64d^{10}$	$5s^25p^6$	
86 Rn	$1s^2$	$2s^22p^6$	$3s^23p^63d^{10}$	$4s^24p^64d^{10}4f^{14}$	$5s^25p^65d^{10}$	$6s^26p^6$

4. Some Features of Optical Spectra Appearing in Alkali-like Atoms

In Sec. 2 of this chapter we have indicated in a crude way how the frequency of the $K\alpha$ line may be calculated. The next four sections will be devoted to a more rigorous treatment of this problem, which is, essentially, the calculation of x-ray term values. Let us begin by considering the expression for the energy in a quantized state of an atom consisting of a nucleus of charge Z and one external electron, in the absence of an impressed electric or magnetic field. This is

$$E(n, l, j) = -Rhc\frac{M}{M+m}\left[\frac{Z^2}{n^2} - \frac{\alpha^2 Z^4}{n^3}\left(\frac{3}{4n} - \frac{1}{l+\frac{1}{2}}\right) - \frac{\alpha^2 Z^4 |l| \, |s| \cos(l, s)}{n^3 l(l+1)(l+\frac{1}{2})}\right].$$
(8.07)

In this expression the first term in the brackets is related to the main energy term, which depends on the total quantum number, and arises from the original Bohr treatment of the problem.

The second term in the brackets represents a contribution to the energy from the relativistic change of mass with velocity of the electron. It was derived in the form given here by Gordon [15] although it is analogous to the relativistic correction in the older theory of Sommerfeld. [16] The constant α which appears in the formula is the so-called fine structure constant:

$$\alpha = \frac{2\pi e^2}{hc} = 7.283 \times 10^{-3}.$$
(8.08)

In eq. (8.07) an approximation has been made in that only terms in α^2 have been retained. Terms in higher powers of α are negligible when eq. (8.07) is applied to atoms of small Z, such as hydrogen or

[15] W. Gordon, Zs. f. Physik **48**, 11 (1928).

[16] A. Sommerfeld, Atombau und Spektrallinien, 5th Ed. Bd. 1; Vieweg und Sohn, Braunschweig (1931).

ionized helium, but in the x-ray cases to be considered later, this approximation cannot be made.

The last term in the brackets refers to the contribution to the energy from the interaction of the electron spin with the orbital momentum.[17] The expression $|l|\,|s|\cos(l, s)$ which appears in this term refers to a vector model which is used by spectroscopists in the interpretation of term values, and which we shall proceed to explain briefly.[18] The angular momenta corresponding to the quantum numbers l and s may be represented by vectors l and s. There is an interaction between these vectors, such that one precesses around the other. This is called the " inner precession " of the atom. The total angular momentum vector of the configuration (we will exclude at present the interesting possibility of a contribution from the nucleus) will be the vector sum of l and s, and is commonly represented by j, where only the l and s of one electron are concerned. When two or more electrons contribute to the total angular momentum, it is represented by J. The orientations of the vectors l and s are restricted to those in which j is integral or half integral, and the j values arising from any given l and s must differ by unity.

At the present stage of the use of the vector model, there are two different interpretations of the magnitudes $|l|$, $|s|$, and $|j|$. The first, and older of these, is still used when we wish to predict, from the vector model, the type of term arising from a given configuration. In this interpretation we have, as seems trivial,

$$|s| = s = \tfrac{1}{2}; \quad |l| = l; \quad |j| = j. \tag{8.09}$$

It is known, however, that when the model, with the magnitudes specified in (8.09), is applied to the calculation of energy subdivision of terms, or more specifically, frequency intervals in triplets, Zeeman effect separations in a weak field, etc., it gives a characteristically inaccurate result. These wrong results can be corrected and brought into line with experiment and wave-mechanical theory by using, instead of eqs. (8.09),

$$|s| = \sqrt{s(s + 1)} = \tfrac{1}{2}\sqrt{3}; \quad |l| = \sqrt{l(l + 1)}; \quad |j| = \sqrt{j(j + 1)}. \tag{8.10}$$

We will illustrate the two vector models by Fig. VIII–7, which shows the orientations of the vectors in the case of a single electron when $l = 2$

[17] Heisenberg and Jordan, Zs. f. Physik **37**, 266 (1926).

[18] Pauling and Goudsmit, The Structure of Line Spectra, McGraw-Hill, New York (1930)

and, of course, $s = \frac{1}{2}$. We see that on the old model two terms arise from this configuration, having $j = 3/2$ and $j = 5/2$ respectively, called $^2D_{3/2}$ and $^2D_{5/2}$. The superscript 2 refers to the quantity $2s + 1$, called the multiplicity of the term, giving in this case doublets.

If we wish to calculate the energy difference between the terms $^2D_{3/2}$ and $^2D_{5/2}$, we use the newer form of the vector model. From Fig. VIII–7 we see that

$$|l|\,|s|\cos(l, s) = \tfrac{1}{2}\{j(j + 1) - s(s + 1) - l(l + 1)\}, \quad (8.11)$$

and this expression may be inserted in eq. (8.07).

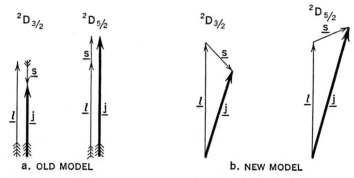

a. OLD MODEL   b. NEW MODEL

FIG. VIII–7. (a) Composition of the vectors s and l for a d-electron to form a ^2D level according to the old vector model. (b) The same vectors in the new vector model, which agrees more closely with wave-mechanical theory.

In atoms consisting of a nucleus and one external electron, eq. (8.07) may be simplified by the following considerations:

$$j = l \pm \tfrac{1}{2} \quad \text{and} \quad s(s + 1) = \tfrac{3}{4}. \quad (8.12)$$

If eqs. (8.11) and (8.12) are substituted in eq. (8.07), it may be separated into two equations, one applicable when $j = l + \frac{1}{2}$, the other when $j = l - \frac{1}{2}$. These equations are:

For $j = l + \frac{1}{2}$

$$E(n, l, j) = - RhcZ^2 \frac{M}{M + m}\left[\frac{1}{n^2} + \frac{\alpha^2 Z^2}{n^4}\left(\frac{n}{l + 1} - \frac{3}{4}\right)\right]. \quad (8.13)$$

For $j = l - \frac{1}{2}$

$$E(n, l, j) = - RhcZ^2 \frac{M}{M + m}\left[\frac{1}{n^2} + \frac{\alpha^2 Z^2}{n^4}\left(\frac{n}{l} - \frac{3}{4}\right)\right]. \quad (8.14)$$

In case $l = 0$ we are to use eq. (8.13). These equations make it clear that in hydrogen and ionized helium, among energy levels of the same n, those of the same j will coincide, although their l values may differ. Thus, although for $n = 3$ there are at first glance five possible energy levels, two having $j = 3/2$ coincide, also two having

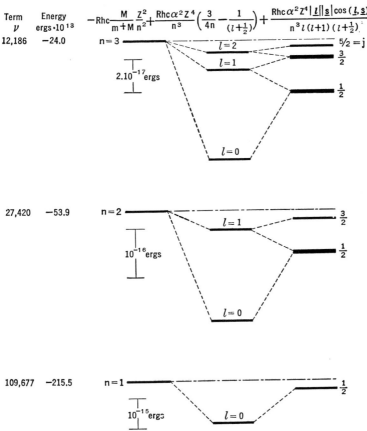

$$-\mathrm{Rhc}\frac{M}{m+M}\frac{Z^2}{n^2} + \frac{\mathrm{Rhc}\,\alpha^2 Z^4}{n^3}\left(\frac{3}{4n} - \frac{1}{(l+\frac{1}{2})}\right) + \frac{\mathrm{Rhc}\,\alpha^2 Z^4 |\underline{l}||\underline{s}|\cos(\underline{l},\underline{s})}{n^3 l(l+1)(l+\frac{1}{2})}$$

Term ν	Energy ergs·10^{13}
12,186	−24.0
27,420	−53.9
109,677	−215.5

Fig. VIII-8. The effect of the various members of the right-hand side of eq. (8.07) on the energy level diagram of the hydrogen atom, for the levels having $n = 1, 2, 3$.

$j = \frac{1}{2}$, leaving only three distinct levels. The effect of the various terms in eq. (8.07) on the hydrogen energy levels for $n = 1, 2, 3$ is shown in Fig. VIII-8.

The same term types which appear in the energy level diagram of Fig. VIII-8 appear in configurations of other atoms in which all the electrons save one are in completed n, l groups according to Sec. 3 of this chapter.   Thus in sodium, for instance, whose electronic structure in the normal state is

$$11\text{Na}\quad 1s^2\quad 2s^2 2p^6\quad 3s^1,$$

the terms which appear in the various stages of binding of the valence electron can be described by the same n, l, j values found applicable to the hydrogen spectrum.   The appearance of the sodium energy level diagram is however quite different because of different relative energy values of the terms.   We shall consider briefly the causes of these similarities and differences.

In the first place, the same term types appear in Na and in H due to the fact that in both cases the only sources of angular momentum (external to the nucleus) are the spin and orbital momentum of a single electron.   The closed groups of K and L electrons in sodium contribute no angular momentum, which is shown by the fact that the preceding atom, neon, has no extra-nuclear angular momentum at all.   Thus in sodium, j, the total angular momentum, is made up of the same s and l combinations as in hydrogen.

The electrons in closed groups in sodium affect the quantitative term values, however, because they screen the nuclear charge.   The valence electron in the normal state of the sodium atom has $n = 3$, $l = 0, j = \frac{1}{2}$.   If the screening by the ten K and L electrons were perfect, we might expect that the valence electron would move in the field of a nucleus of charge $+e$, as in hydrogen.   Actually, however, we find that the wave-number of the term having the values $n = 3$, $l = 0, j = \frac{1}{2}$ in Na is 41,449, whereas the corresponding wave-number in hydrogen is 12,186.   These term values are connected with the energies of quantized configurations in the optical region by the relation

$$\nu(n, l, j) = \frac{1}{hc}\left|E(n, l, j)\right|. \tag{8.15}$$

The large increase of term value in the case of sodium represents a decrease in energy.   This is due to the fact that the effective nuclear charge acting on the valence electron in the normal state is considerably greater than one in electron units.   Quantum mechanical calculations show that the $3s$ electron in sodium has a considerable probability of being found inside the L electrons, and hence in a region of relatively imperfect screening.

The effects of screening are also evident in the relative positions of the other terms having $n = 3$ in sodium and in hydrogen. We shall discuss the terms $3^2P_{\frac{1}{2}}$ $(n, l, j = 3, 1, \frac{1}{2})$, $3^2P_{\frac{3}{2}}$ $(n, l, j = 3, 1, \frac{3}{2})$, $3^2D_{\frac{3}{2}}$ $(n, l, j = 3, 2, \frac{3}{2})$, and $3^2D_{\frac{5}{2}}$ $(n, l, j = 3, 2, \frac{5}{2})$ in

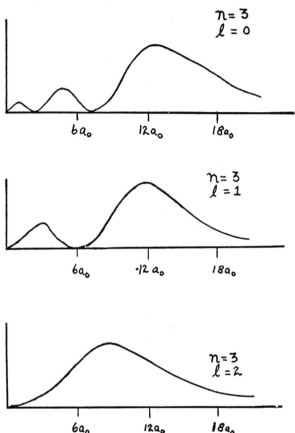

FIG. VIII–9. Probability density distribution curves for various n, l states in hydrogen. (After H. E. White, Phys. Rev. **37**, 1416 (1931).) a_0 is the radius of the first Bohr orbit in hydrogen. The abscissae are distances from the nucleus.

addition to the term $3^2S_{\frac{1}{2}}$ $(n, l, j = 3, 0, \frac{1}{2})$ discussed in the preceding paragraph. In the hydrogen spectrum, we found that the terms $3^2S_{\frac{1}{2}}$ and $3^2P_{\frac{1}{2}}$ coincide, whereas in sodium they have a wave-number separation $\Delta\nu = 16,956.2$. This separation is caused by the fact that the probability of finding the valence electron in a spherical shell at distance r from the nucleus and of radius dr is different in the configurations corresponding to $3^2S_{1/2}$ and $3^2P_{1/2}$. Fig. VIII–9 shows the probability in question for the various configurations of total quantum number 3. Thus the effective nuclear charge is different in Na for $3^2S_{1/2}$ and $3^2P_{1/2}$, causing a separation of these terms, which are coincident in hydrogen. This separation is very great compared to the separation of $3^2P_{1/2}$ and $3^2P_{3/2}$, which makes the appearance of the sodium table quite different from that of hydrogen.

The separation of the terms $3^2P_{1/2}$ and $3^2P_{3/2}$, which is 0.108 wavenumbers in hydrogen, has increased to 17.18 in sodium. In the hydrogen case, the separation of two levels whose n and l values are the same but whose j's are $l + \frac{1}{2}$ and $l - \frac{1}{2}$ respectively may be calculated from eqs. (8.13), (8.14) and (8.15), giving

$$\Delta\nu = \frac{R\alpha^2 Z^4}{n^3 l(l+1)} \qquad (8.16)$$

after omission of the factor $M/(M + m)$. Such pairs of levels are known as spin doublets, and it should be noted that their separation varies as the fourth power of the atomic number, or, more accurately, of the effective nuclear charge. The greatly increased separation of the $3P$ terms in Na is ascribed to the fact that the effective charge acting upon the electron in these configurations is much greater than in hydrogen, due to imperfect screening. We may represent this effect in our equation by introducing a screening constant σ_2, and writing, instead of eq. (8.16)[19]

$$\Delta\nu = \frac{R\alpha^2 (Z - \sigma_2)^4}{n^3 l(l+1)}. \qquad (8.17)$$

Fig. VIII–10 shows the relationship between the sodium and hydrogen atom term tables.

The applicability of this equation to optical spectra may be tested by observations on a series of iso-electronic atoms and ions, often called an iso-electronic sequence. It has become standard notation to express the various stages of ionization of an atom by roman

---

[19] This expression for the spin doublets in many electron atoms is not identical with that used first by Landé (Zs. f. Physik 25, 46 (1924)) and subsequently by other writers, in which the value of the total quantum number is altered. We have used the form of eq. (8.17) because in the x-ray region it is the custom to correct the atomic number instead of the total quantum number.

numerals placed after the symbol for the element. Thus the spectrum of neutral sodium is ascribed to Na I, that of singly ionized

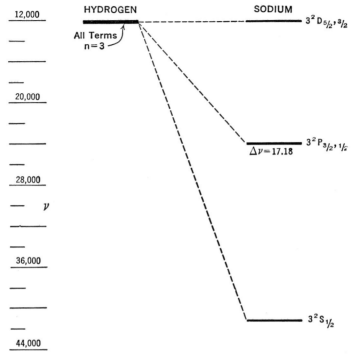

QUALITATIVE, SHOWING FINE STRUCTURE

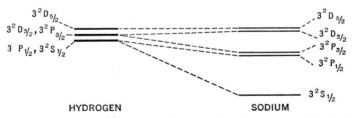

FIG. VIII–10. The relation between the terms of total quantum number 3 in hydrogen and sodium. The apparently different sodium arrangement is attributed to the effects of screening.

sodium (similar to that of neutral neon), to Na II. In this notation, the sequence

$$3 \text{ Li I, } 4 \text{ Be II, } 5 \text{ B III, } 6 \text{ C IV, } 7 \text{ N V, } 8 \text{ O VI}$$

is iso-electronic, having in the lowest energy state the configuration $1s^2 2s^1$. Table VIII–6, taken from Bowen and Millikan,[20] shows the result of application of eq. (8.17) to this sequence, the formula being applied to the separation of the lowest ^2P terms. It is seen that in over a thousand-fold variation in the observed wave-number sep-

TABLE VIII–6

APPLICATION OF EQ. (8.17) TO THE 2^2P TERMS ARISING FROM THE ISO-ELECTRONIC SEQUENCE BEGINNING WITH Li I

Emitter	$\Delta\nu$ Exp.	$(Z-\sigma_2)$	σ_2
3 Li I	0.338 cm^{-1}	0.981	2.019
4 Be II	6.61	2.063	1.937
5 B III	34.4	3.116	1.884
6 C IV	107.4	4.142	1.858
7 N V	259.1	5.162	1.838
8 O VI	533.8	6.184	1.816

aration, the formula gives a value of σ_2 approximately equal to 2, the number of electrons underlying the outermost electron in this case.

5. The Use of the Spin Doublet Formula in X-ray Spectra

Long before data were obtained in optical spectra similar to that displayed in Table VIII–6, it had been known that in the x-ray term table, levels appear whose separation is given by an equation exactly analogous to (8.17), except that the approximation there used in neglecting terms involving higher powers of α^2 is not valid, due to the greatly increased values of Z in the x-ray region.[21] These levels cause the appearance in the x-ray spectrum of lines whose wave-length separation is approximately independent of atomic number. In the K and L groups, the lines showing this effect are listed in Table VIII–7, together with the levels concerned in their emission which exhibit the features characteristic of eq. (8.17).

The constant wave-length difference of the $K\alpha_1$ and $K\alpha_2$ lines, whose wave-number difference is that of the levels $L_{II}L_{III}$, is shown

[20] Bowen and Millikan, Phys. Rev. 24, 209 (1924), also given in Pauling and Goudsmit, The Structure of Line Spectra (1930), p. 62.

[21] A. Sommerfeld, Atombau und Spektrallinien, Friedr. Vieweg und Sohn, Braunschweig, 5te Aufl. Bd. 1 (1931).

TABLE VIII-7

SPIN DOUBLETS IN THE K AND L SERIES

K Series

Lines		Levels
α_1	α_2	$L_{II}L_{III}$
β_1	β_3	$M_{II}M_{III}$

L Series

l	η	$L_{II}L_{III}$
α_2	β_1	$L_{II}L_{III}$
β_6	γ_5	$L_{II}L_{III}$
β_{15}	γ_1	$L_{II}L_{III}$
γ_8	β_7	$L_{II}L_{III}$
β_5	γ_6	$L_{II}L_{III}$
β_4	β_3	$M_{II}M_{III}$
α_1	α_2	$M_{IV}M_{V}$
γ_2	γ_3	$N_{II}N_{III}$
β_{15}	β_2	$N_{IV}N_{V}$

in Table VIII–8, the data in which are taken from Siegbahn, Spektroskopie der Röntgenstrahlen, 2nd Ed. (1931).

TABLE VIII-8

WAVE-LENGTH SEPARATION OF $K\alpha_1\alpha_2$ LINES AS A FUNCTION OF ATOMIC NUMBER

Element	$\Delta\lambda$ in X.U.	Element	$\Delta\lambda$ in X.U.	Element	$\Delta\lambda$ in X.U.
13 Al	2.44	39 Y	4.20	66 Dy	4.72
16 S	2.88	42 Mo	4.27	69 Tu	4.74
20 Ca	3.28	46 Pd	4.36	71 Cp	4.76
23 Va	3.78	49 In	4.42	74 W	4.83
26 Fe	3.94	52 Te	4.54	77 Ir	4.85
29 Cu	3.84	56 Ba	4.56	81 Tl	4.86
32 Ge	3.91	59 Pr	4.65	83 Bi	4.84
35 Br	4.07	63 Eu	4.75	92 U	4.55

The approximate constancy in the wave-length separation of two lines whose wave-number difference is that of two levels whose separation is given by the spin doublet formula can be roughly accounted for as follows. The wave-number difference in question follows the approximate eq. (8.17), or

$$\frac{\Delta\nu}{R} \sim (Z - \sigma_2)^4.$$

But by Moseley's law, which also applies to absorption limits,

$$\frac{\nu}{R} \sim (Z - \sigma_1)^2.$$

By differentiation of the relation $\nu = \lambda^{-1}$, we find

$$|\Delta\lambda| = \frac{1}{\nu^2}\Delta\nu,$$

and setting in this rough calculation $\sigma_1 = \sigma_2$, it results from the preceding three equations that $\Delta\lambda$ is independent of Z, at least in the higher atomic number ranges, when the inaccuracy of our assumption about the equality of the screening constants is less serious.

We shall now discuss the application of the accurate formula of which eq. (8.17) is an approximation, to the $L_{II}L_{III}$ separation. It is a most remarkable fact that this formula, including all the terms in higher powers of α^2, was developed by Sommerfeld on the basis of the older relativistic quantum theory, without wave mechanics or even the pictorial concept of a spinning electron. The more modern basis for the formula rests on Dirac's relativistic theory of the electron, in which its angular momentum appears as a necessary consequence of the fundamental assumptions.[22] The formula in question can be written in a form analogous to that of eqs. (8.13) and (8.14):

For $j = l + \frac{1}{2}$:

$$E(n, l, j) = - Rhc\left[\frac{(Z - \sigma_1)^2}{n^2} + \frac{\alpha^2(Z - \sigma_2)^4}{n^4}\left\{\frac{n}{l + 1} - \frac{3}{4}\right\}\right.$$

$$+ \frac{\alpha^4(Z - \sigma_2)^6}{n^6}\left\{\frac{1}{4}\left(\frac{n}{l + 1}\right)^3 + \frac{3}{4}\left(\frac{n}{l + 1}\right)^2 - \frac{3}{2}\left(\frac{n}{l + 1}\right) + \frac{5}{8}\right\}$$

$$+ \frac{\alpha^6(Z - \sigma_2)^8}{n^8}\left\{\frac{1}{8}\left(\frac{n}{l + 1}\right)^5 + \frac{3}{8}\left(\frac{n}{l + 1}\right)^4 + \frac{1}{8}\left(\frac{n}{l + 1}\right)^3\right.$$

$$\left.\left. - \frac{15}{8}\left(\frac{n}{l + 1}\right)^2 + \frac{15}{8}\left(\frac{n}{l + 1}\right) - \frac{35}{64}\right\} + \cdots\right] \qquad (8.18)$$

[22] Heisenberg and Jordan, Zs. f. Physik **37**, 266 (1926).
W. Gordon, Zs. f. Physik **48**, 11 (1928).
C. G. Darwin, Proc. Roy. Soc. Lond. A **118**, 654 (1928).

For $j = l - \frac{1}{2}$:

$$E(n, l, j) = -Rhc\left[\frac{(Z - \sigma_1)^2}{n^2} + \frac{\alpha^2(Z - \sigma_2)^4}{n^4}\left\{\frac{n}{l} - \frac{3}{4}\right\}\right.$$

$$+ \frac{\alpha^4(Z - \sigma_2)^6}{n^6}\left\{\frac{1}{4}\left(\frac{n}{l}\right)^3 + \frac{3}{4}\left(\frac{n}{l}\right)^2 - \frac{3}{2}\left(\frac{n}{l}\right) + \frac{5}{8}\right\}$$

$$+ \frac{\alpha^6(Z - \sigma_2)^8}{n^8}\left\{\frac{1}{8}\left(\frac{n}{l}\right)^5 + \frac{3}{8}\left(\frac{n}{l}\right)^4 + \frac{1}{8}\left(\frac{n}{l}\right)^3 - \frac{15}{8}\left(\frac{n}{l}\right)^2\right.$$

$$\left.\left. + \frac{15}{8}\left(\frac{n}{l}\right) - \frac{35}{64}\right\} + \ldots\right] \tag{8.19}$$

In applying eqs. (8.18) and (8.19) to the separation of the $L_{\mathrm{II}}L_{\mathrm{III}}$ doublet, we shall assume that eq. (8.18) is to be used for L_{III}, with the values $n = 2$, $l = 1$, $j = 3/2$, and that eq. (8.19) may be applied to L_{II} when the values $n = 2$, $l = 1$, and $j = \frac{1}{2}$ are inserted.[23] Using these values, and solving for $\Delta\nu/R$, we obtain

$$\frac{\Delta\nu}{R} = \frac{\alpha^2(Z - \sigma_2)^4}{2^4}\left[1 + \frac{5}{2}\frac{\alpha^2}{2^2}(Z - \sigma_2)^2 + \frac{53}{8}\frac{\alpha^4}{2^4}(Z - \sigma_2)^4 + \ldots\right].\tag{8.20}$$

Sommerfeld[23] shows that eq. (8.20) may be solved for $(Z - \sigma_2)$ in an approximate manner which gives the result:

$$(Z - \sigma_2)^2 = \left(\frac{4}{\alpha}\sqrt{\frac{\Delta\nu}{R}} - 5\frac{\Delta\nu}{R}\right)\left(1 + \frac{19}{32}\alpha^2\frac{\Delta\nu}{R}\right).\tag{8.21}$$

If this formula is applicable to the separation of $L_{\mathrm{II}}L_{\mathrm{III}}$, we expect that σ_2 will remain constant throughout the region in the periodic system in which the electron shells are sufficiently filled so that no further change in the screening of these inner levels takes place. Table VIII–9, taken from Sommerfeld's book, shows the constancy of σ_2 obtained from eq. (8.21) applied to elements 42 Mo to 92 U. It is seen that the variations of σ_2 about the average value $\sigma_2 = 3.487$

[23] Sommerfeld, Atombau und Spektrallinien, 5te Aufl. Bd. 1 pp. 300–301. We wish here to avoid the implication that an L value of unity can be assigned to these levels. This would mean that in the configuration p^5 from which they arise, the coupling was Russell-Saunders in nature, whereas in Sec. 6 we shall show that by means of rules well tested in optical terms, it can be deduced that eqs. (8.18) and (8.19) can be applied to the x-ray doublet levels regardless of what coupling type exists between the electrons in the underlying configurations.

are entirely random in this range, giving us great confidence in the essential correctness of our procedure.

TABLE VIII–9

THE SCREENING CONSTANT σ_2 FOR THE $L_{II}L_{III}$ DOUBLET

Element	$\Delta\nu/R$	$Z-\sigma_2$	σ_2	Element	$\Delta\nu/R$	$Z-\sigma_2$	σ_2
42 Mo	7.7	38.5	3.5	68 Er	66.81	64.52	3.48
46 Pd	11.57	42.55	3.45	71 Cp	81.11	67.47	3.53
49 In	15.29	45.50	3.50	74 W	98.49	70.52	3.48
52 Te	20.00	48.55	3.45	77 Ir	118.53	73.53	3.47
56 Ba	27.74	52.50	3.50	81 Tl	150.20	77.51	3.49
59 Pr	35.02	55.48	3.52	83 Bi	169.02	79.55	3.45
63 Eu	47.17	59.51	3.49	90 Th	249.37	86.51	3.49
66 Dy	58.24	62.51	3.49	92 U	277.91	88.51	3.49

The separation of other pairs of levels in the x-ray term table can be calculated from the spin doublet formula; some of these are shown in Table VIII–7. Table VIII–10 shows the quantum numbers used in the formula to obtain the separation of these levels, and the screening constants deduced for them.

The behaviour of these screening constants, as exhibited in Table VIII–10, namely, their increase with increasing n, and with increasing

TABLE VIII–10

APPLICATION OF THE SPIN DOUBLET FORMULA TO X-RAY LEVELS

Level	Configuration	n, l, j Values in Eqs. (8.18), (8.19)			σ_2
L_{II}	$2p^5$	2	1	1/2	3.50
L_{III}		2	1	3/2	
M_{II}	$3p^5$	3	1	1/2	8.5
M_{III}		3	1	3/2	
M_{IV}	$3d^9$	3	2	3/2	13.0
M_V		3	2	5/2	
N_{II}	$4p^5$	4	1	1/2	17.0
N_{III}		4	1	3/2	
N_{IV}	$4d^9$	4	2	3/2	24
N_V		4	2	5/2	
N_{VI}	$4f^{13}$	4	3	5/2	34
N_{VII}		4	3	7/2	

l for the same n, is in agreement with our ideas as to atomic structure. The relative nearness of the various shells to the nucleus is clearly shown, and the lesser screening of the lower l values corresponds to the maxima near the nucleus of the distribution functions of Fig. VIII–9 for $l = 0$ and $l = 1$.

We now come to the important question: how can we explain the success of the spin doublet formula when applied to x-ray terms? In the optical region this formula was devised to apply to terms arising from the presence of one electron outside closed shells, while on Kossel's theory the x-ray terms arise from n, l shells lacking one electron of completion. Electrons having the same n and l values are called "equivalent electrons," and from an empirical standpoint we may consider the origin of the x-ray levels obeying the spin doublet formula as a special case of Pauli's "vacancy principle," which applies to equivalent electron configurations. This principle states that from a configuration of z electrons having the same n and l values, the same spectroscopic terms will arise as in a configuration of the same n, l electrons lacking z electrons of completion. Some illustrations of this in the optical region are included in Table VIII–11.

TABLE VIII–11

SOME ILLUSTRATIONS OF PAULI'S VACANCY PRINCIPLE

Atom	Configuration	Lowest Term
5 B I	$1s^2 \ 2s^2 2p$	^2P
9 F I	$1s^2 \ 2s^2 2p^5$	
6 C I	$1s^2 \ 2s^2 2p^2$	^3P
8 O I	$1s^2 \ 2s^2 2p^4$	

The P doublet which arises from the normal state of fluorine is, however, qualitatively different from that of boron, in that it is inverted. In a regular doublet (or, in general, multiplet) the sublevels of lowest j value lie lowest in the term table. In an inverted doublet the highest j values lie lowest. Thus the sodium doublets of Fig. VIII–10, and the hydrogen doublets of Fig. VIII–8 are regular. The x-ray doublets are inverted. Also, considering the various ways in which the angular momenta of the equivalent electrons in an x-ray configuration may couple together, it has yet to be explained why the x-ray doublets follow quantitatively the same separation-formula as do the doublets of an alkali-like atom.

6. The Γ-sum and Permanence Rules Applied to the X-ray Doublets

In an atom having electrons outside closed shells the angular momenta represented by their l and s vectors may couple together in various ways to form J, the total angular momentum of the atom. One type of coupling, called Russell-Saunders[24] coupling, was recognized at an early date because of its similarity to the coupling of the spin of a single electron with its l as in Fig. VIII–7. In this type of coupling the principal interactions are between the s's to form a resultant S, and the l's to form a resultant L. S and L then combine to form their resultant J. Symbolically we write

$$\text{R.S. coupling } \{(s_1, s_2, s_3 \ldots)(l_1, l_2, l_3 \ldots)\} = \{(S)(L)\} = J. \quad (8.24)$$

Another coupling type which may possibly occur is the so-called jj coupling, in which each s couples with the corresponding l to form a resultant j, and these j's couple together to form the final J.

$$jj \text{ coupling } \{(s_1, l_1)(s_2, l_2)(s_3, l_3) \ldots\} = \{(j_1)(j_2)(j_3) \ldots\} = J. \quad (8.23)$$

Figure VIII–11 shows these two coupling types. Between these more or less extreme types, intermediate types may take place. For instance, in the He I spectrum, the (s_1, l_2) interactions are important enough to distort the multiplets considerably from the Russell-Saunders predictions as to the intervals between their components.

The importance of the Γ-sum and permanence rules, as developed by Landé[25] and by Goudsmit[26] lies in the fact that by means of them it is possible to show that the x-ray doublets should be inverted and have their separation given by the spin doublet formula irrespective of the coupling between the electrons left in the incompleted group. We will therefore give a brief explanation of these rules, paying special attention to their application to x-ray spectra.

Let us first introduce the symbol γ, which represents the increase in the energy value of a term due to the interaction between the spin and orbital angular momentum of a single electron. We have already

[24] H. N. Russell and F. A. Saunders, Astrophys. Journ. 61, 38 (1925).
[25] Landé, Zs. f. Physik 19, 112 (1923).
[26] Goudsmit, Phys. Rev. 31, 946 (1928).

had an example of this in the hydrogen atom spectrum in the absence
of a magnetic field; from eq. (8.07) we obtain

$$\gamma = a\,|l|\,|s|\cos{(l, s)} \qquad (8.24)$$

where

$$a = Rhc\,\frac{M}{M + m}\,\frac{\alpha^2 Z^4}{n^3 l(l + 1)(l + \tfrac{1}{2})}. \qquad (8.25)$$

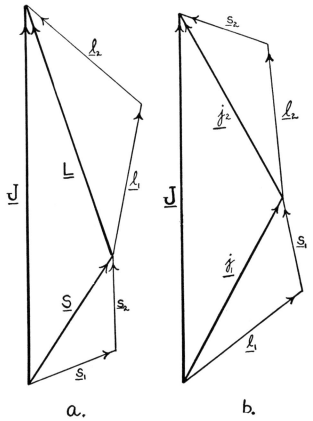

Fig. VIII-11. (a) Schematic illustration of Russell-Saunders coupling of two
electrons. (b) Schematic illustration of jj coupling of two electrons.

Equation (8.24) also gives the γ-value in the absence of a magnetic
field for the arc spectrum of the alkalis, but in this case we would
use instead of eq. (8.25) for a, the value

$$a = Rhc\,\frac{\alpha^2(Z - \sigma_2)^4}{n^3 l(l + 1)(l + \tfrac{1}{2})}. \qquad (8.25a)$$

At present we are more interested in the γ values for electrons in a very strong magnetic field, as defined in Sec. 3 of this chapter, and illustrated for a d-electron in Fig. VIII–6. The value of γ in this case is also due to the precession of s about l which remains as a small contribution to the energy. Equation (8.24) can be used, except that now the angle between l and s is not constant. We have in such a case to speak of an average value of cos (l, s) and it can be shown that here

$$\overline{\cos (l, s)} = \cos (s, H) \cos (l, H).\qquad(8.26)$$

But from Fig. VIII–6,

$$\cos (s, H) = m_s/|s|; \quad \cos (l, H) = m_l/|l|\qquad(8.27)$$

and use of these values in eq. (8.24) gives

$$\gamma = am_s m_l.\qquad(8.28)$$

We shall now define Γ as the sum of all the γ values for the individual electrons in a given orientation with respect to the magnetic field. Thus, in a very strong field

$$\Gamma = \sum_i \gamma_i = \sum_i a_i m_{s_i} m_{l_i}.\qquad(8.29)$$

Let us now consider M, which in our very strong field we will define as the algebraic sum of all the m_s and m_l in a given orientation:

$$M = \sum_i (m_{s_i} + m_{l_i}).\qquad(8.30)$$

In a configuration of several electrons, a given value of M may arise through more than one orientation with respect to the field, and we shall denote the sum of the Γ values for all the orientations leading to the same value of M as $(\Sigma\Gamma)_M$.

To illustrate these ideas, we shall calculate the possible values of M and $(\Sigma\Gamma)_M$ arising from a configuration of five p electrons oriented in a very strong magnetic field, this being, on Kossel's theory, the configuration responsible for the $L_{II}L_{III}$ energy levels. We are guided here by Pauli's exclusion principle, which greatly restricts the possible number of orientations. The permitted arrangements are shown in Table VIII–12, together with their M values.

TABLE VIII–12

ORIENTATIONS OF A p^5 CONFIGURATION IN A VERY STRONG MAGNETIC FIELD

Orientation Number	m_{l_1}	m_{l_2}	m_{l_3}	m_{l_4}	m_{l_5}	m_{s_1}	m_{s_2}	m_{s_3}	m_{s_4}	m_{s_5}	M
1	1	1	0	0	-1	$\frac{1}{2}$	$-\frac{1}{2}$	$\frac{1}{2}$	$-\frac{1}{2}$	$\frac{1}{2}$	$3/2$
2	1	1	0	0	-1	$\frac{1}{2}$	$-\frac{1}{2}$	$\frac{1}{2}$	$-\frac{1}{2}$	$-\frac{1}{2}$	$1/2$
3	-1	-1	0	0	1	$\frac{1}{2}$	$-\frac{1}{2}$	$\frac{1}{2}$	$-\frac{1}{2}$	$\frac{1}{2}$	$-1/2$
4	-1	-1	0	0	1	$\frac{1}{2}$	$-\frac{1}{2}$	$\frac{1}{2}$	$-\frac{1}{2}$	$-\frac{1}{2}$	$-3/2$
5	-1	-1	1	1	0	$\frac{1}{2}$	$-\frac{1}{2}$	$\frac{1}{2}$	$-\frac{1}{2}$	$\frac{1}{2}$	$1/2$
6	-1	-1	1	1	0	$\frac{1}{2}$	$-\frac{1}{2}$	$\frac{1}{2}$	$-\frac{1}{2}$	$-\frac{1}{2}$	$-1/2$

Table VIII–13 shows the γ values of the electrons and the Γ values of the various orientations of Table VIII–12. The calculations are greatly simplified in that we are dealing with equivalent electrons, which all have the same n and l, and hence the same a value by eq. (8.25a).

TABLE VIII–13

γ AND Γ VALUES OF A p^5 CONFIGURATION IN A VERY STRONG MAGNETIC FIELD

Orientation Number	γ_1	γ_2	γ_3	γ_4	γ_5	Γ
1	$\frac{1}{2}a$	$-\frac{1}{2}a$	0	0	$-\frac{1}{2}a$	$-\frac{1}{2}a$
2	$\frac{1}{2}a$	$-\frac{1}{2}a$	0	0	$\frac{1}{2}a$	$\frac{1}{2}a$
3	$-\frac{1}{2}a$	$\frac{1}{2}a$	0	0	$\frac{1}{2}a$	$\frac{1}{2}a$
4	$-\frac{1}{2}a$	$\frac{1}{2}a$	0	0	$-\frac{1}{2}a$	$-\frac{1}{2}a$
5	$-\frac{1}{2}a$	$\frac{1}{2}a$	$\frac{1}{2}a$	$-\frac{1}{2}a$	0	0
6	$-\frac{1}{2}a$	$\frac{1}{2}a$	$\frac{1}{2}a$	$-\frac{1}{2}a$	0	0

From Table VIII–12 it is seen that four numerically distinct M values arise, namely, $M = -3/2,\ -1/2,\ 1/2,\ 3/2$. Table VIII–14 shows the computation of the corresponding Γ-sums.

TABLE VIII–14

VALUES OF $(\Sigma\Gamma)_M$ FOR A p^5 CONFIGURATION IN A VERY STRONG MAGNETIC FIELD

M	$-3/2$	$-1/2$	$1/2$	$3/2$
$\Gamma\ \Big\{$	$-\frac{1}{2}a$	0 $\frac{1}{2}a$	$\frac{1}{2}a$ 0	$-\frac{1}{2}a$
$(\Sigma\Gamma)_M$	$-\frac{1}{2}a$	$\frac{1}{2}a$	$\frac{1}{2}a$	$-\frac{1}{2}a$

We now wish to consider what will happen if we decrease the strength of the magnetic field to zero. As this process goes on, the interactions of the spin and orbital momenta of the electrons will become more and more important, until in the so-called " weak field " stage these vectors form the resultant J which precesses about H. These stages are shown for Russell-Saunders and for jj coupling in Fig. VIII–12. In this process there is no change in the number of terms arising from a given configuration. There are by Table VIII–12 six distinct orientations in the very strong field. As we decrease the field strength, the energy values of four of these terms coalesce to a limit which is a term having $J = 3/2$, and two of them approach a term having $J = \frac{1}{2}$, leaving in the limiting case of zero field only two distinct terms.

The Γ-permanence rule states that for a given configuration (i.e., $2p^5$) the $(\Sigma\Gamma)_M$ values are independent of the strength of the magnetic field. This rule may be verified by assuming a certain coupling for which Γ values may be computed, and calculating the sums involved at various field strengths.[26a] In the weak field orientations of the p^5 configuration under consideration at present, we see that the M values may be grouped into two runs,[26b] $-3/2, -1/2, 1/2,$ $3/2$ and $-1/2, 1/2$. These correspond to two values of J; $3/2$ and $1/2$, and we desire to find the Γ values for these J's. This can be accomplished by the use of the Γ-sum rule, which states that the sum of the Γ values for terms of the same J arising from a given configuration is independent of the coupling. In the present simple case not more than one term of the same J value appears from the configuration; we have no Γ sums for constant J, and hence the full generality of the Γ-sum rule is not apparent. This simplicity, however, allows us to obtain uniquely the Γ values for the two states; in more general cases only the sum of the Γ values for all the terms of the same J may be obtained. Let $\Gamma_{\frac{1}{2}}$ and $\Gamma_{\frac{3}{2}}$ be the Γ values of the states $J = 1/2$ and $J = 3/2$ respectively. The Γ-sum rule then tells us that these values will be independent of the coupling, and this statement is of paramount importance in understanding the fact that the spin doublet formula applies to the x-ray levels throughout the

---

[26a] This computation is carried out for a triplet D term in a weak and a strong field in Pauling and Goudsmit, The Structure of Line Spectra, p. 159, Table X.

[26b] In changing the strength of the field the M value of the term is conserved. In a weak field, a term characterized by $M = 3/2$, is reached by a continuous change in energy of the very strong field term whose $M = 3/2$.

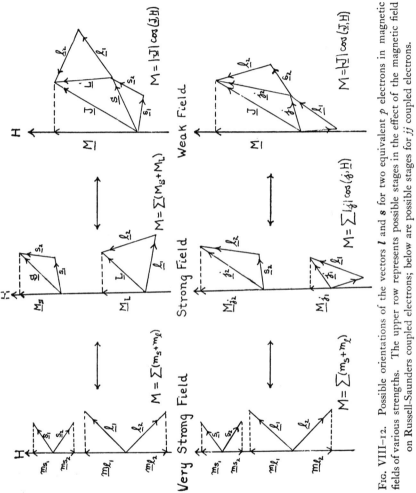

Fig. VIII-12. Possible orientations of the vectors **l** and **s** for two equivalent p electrons in magnetic fields of various strengths. The upper row represents possible stages in the effect of the magnetic field on Russell-Saunders coupled electrons; below are possible stages for jj coupled electrons.

periodic system. In Table VIII–15 is shown a weak field table analogous in form to Table VIII–14.

TABLE VIII–15

$(\Sigma\Gamma)_M$ Values for the Terms $J = 3/2, 1/2$ in a Weak Field

$M=$	$-3/2$	$-1/2$	$1/2$	$3/2$
$J=3/2$	$\Gamma_{3/2}$	$\Gamma_{3/2}$	$\Gamma_{3/2}$	$\Gamma_{3/2}$
$J=1/2$		$\Gamma_{1/2}$	$\Gamma_{1/2}$	
$(\Sigma\Gamma)_M$	$\Gamma_{3/2}$	$\Gamma_{3/2}+\Gamma_{1/2}$	$\Gamma_{3/2}+\Gamma_{1/2}$	$\Gamma_{3/2}$

By application of the Γ permanence rule to Tables VIII–14 and VIII–15, which means equating the $(\Sigma\Gamma)_M$ values, we obtain

$$\Gamma_{3/2} = -\tfrac{1}{2}a, \qquad \Gamma_{1/2} = a. \tag{8.31}$$

From these Γ values, which will remain unchanged from a weak field to zero field, we can calculate the energy separation of the two terms with $J = 3/2$ and $J = 1/2$. This will be

$$\Delta E = \Gamma_{1/2} - \Gamma_{3/2} = 3a/2. \tag{8.32}$$

By eq. (8.17) we have seen that the separation of the doublet terms produced in an alkali-like atom is

$$\Delta E = Rhc \frac{\alpha^2(Z - \sigma_2)^4}{n^3 l(l + 1)}.$$

If the electron has $l = 1$ (a p-electron), this expression may be written (since $l + 1/2 = 3/2$)

$$\Delta E = \frac{3}{2} \frac{Rhc\alpha^2(Z - \sigma_2)^4}{n^3 l(l + 1)(l + \tfrac{1}{2})}$$

or by eq. (8.25a)

$$\Delta E = 3a/2$$

in exact agreement with eq. (8.32). Thus by the application of laws well tested in optical spectroscopy, we have shown that the $L_{II}L_{III}$ separation, arising from a p^5 configuration, should have a separation obeying exactly the same law as does the separation of a ^2P term in the optical spectrum of an alkali.

Equations (8.31) give us also another property of the x-ray terms, namely their inverted character. Note that the shift of the n, l

term, symbolized by $\Gamma_{3/2}$, is a negative one, $-\tfrac{1}{2}a$. This means that the $J = 3/2$ term lies deeper in the term table than does $J = 1/2$, in contrast to the sodium arc spectrum. This is illustrated in Fig. VIII–13.

This discussion of the separation of the terms arising from a p^5 configuration may be extended to d^9 and f^{13} configurations, which in the x-ray diagram give rise to $M_{IV}M_V$, $N_{IV}N_V$, and to $N_{VI}N_{VII}$, respectively. In these cases it may also be shown that, irrespective of coupling, inverted doublet terms will arise whose energy separation is subject to the same formula which governs the ^2D and ^2F separations in alkali-like emitters.

The generality of the above discussion is particularly satisfactory in view of the fact that there is reason to believe that the coupling

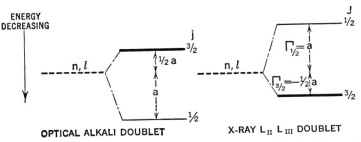

Fig. VIII–13. Illustration of the effect of eq. (8.31) on the original n, l term of an x-ray doublet, and the inversion of the resulting multiplet with respect to an alkali doublet.

may not be the same in the inner shells of light and of heavy atoms. In light atoms the Russell-Saunders type is probably approximated, whereas in heavy atoms the preponderating nuclear pull makes the electrons more and more independent of each other, in which case the interaction of each s with its l predominates, and we approach the jj type. Various authors have assigned term symbols to x-ray levels patterned after those applicable to alkali atoms, thus, $K \sim 1^2S_{1/2}$, $L_I \sim 2^2S_{1/2}$, $L_{II} \sim 2^2P_{1/2}$, $L_{III} \sim 2^2P_{3/2}$, etc. This is only appropriate (at least for the levels other than K, L_I, M_I, N_I, etc., where there can be no question of coupling since only one electron is involved in the underlying configuration) in case the coupling is Russell-Saunders, in which there is a meaning to the L and S vectors implied in the notation. The question as to whether, in the unexcited atom, it is permissible to speak of 2 L_{II} electrons and 4 L_{III} electrons known as Stoner[27] sub-groups, also turns upon this point. In Russell-Saunders coupling there is no significance to such a sub-division, whereas in jj coupling such a classification is permitted.

7. Screening Doublets and Screening Constants in X-ray Spectra

In 1920 Hertz[28] announced the discovery of a new type of regularity in the x-ray energy level diagram. If the levels L_I, L_{II}, and L_{III} are plotted on a Moseley diagram ($\sqrt{\nu/R}$ against Z) the L_{II} and L_{III} levels diverge as the square of the corrected atomic number increases, as we see from eq. (8.17). Hertz noted that on the same diagram the L_I and L_{II} levels run parallel, preserving a constant $\Delta\sqrt{\nu/R}$ separation independent of atomic number. This is shown in Fig. VIII–14.

For the explanation of this behaviour we must consider the interpretation of the level L_I. The preceding two sections of this chapter have developed the hypothesis that the levels L_{II} and L_{III} arise from the configuration $2p^5$. According to Table VIII–3, there are two electrons with $n = 2$ whose l value is zero. Hence we may ascribe L_I to the configuration $2s^1$. The J value is made up entirely by the spin of the remaining electron, hence $J = \frac{1}{2}$. In the hydrogen atom the term with $n = 2$, $l = 0$, $j = \frac{1}{2}$, $2^2S_{\frac{1}{2}}$, coincides with $2^2P_{\frac{1}{2}}$, as we see from Fig. VIII–8. In an alkali, such as 11 Na, we find the $^2S_{\frac{1}{2}}$ and $^2P_{\frac{1}{2}}$ terms of the same total quantum number having a separation enormous compared to that of the corresponding $^2P_{\frac{1}{2}}$ and $^2P_{\frac{3}{2}}$, due to the effect of screening on orbits of different l values. In the x-ray region the separation of the analogous $L_I L_{II}$ levels is also due to the effect of screening, but here it may even be smaller than the $L_{II} L_{III}$ separation which, as we have seen, increases as the fourth power of the effective atomic number. Thus in uranium, the $L_I L_{II}$ separation is 59.9 ν/R units, whereas the $L_{II} L_{III}$ separation in the same units is 278.5.

In addition to the $L_I L_{II}$ separation, such screening doublets arise between the levels $M_I M_{II}$, $M_{III} M_{IV}$, $N_I N_{II}$, $N_{III} N_{IV}$, $N_V N_{VI}$, etc. In each case we are dealing with adjacent levels arising from configurations of equivalent electrons whose l values differ by unity. The

[27] E. C. Stoner, Phil. Mag. **48**, 718 (1924).

J. D. Main-Smith, Chemistry and Atomic Structure, D. Van Nostrand, New York (1924).

[28] G. Hertz, Zs. f. Physik **3**, 19 (1920).

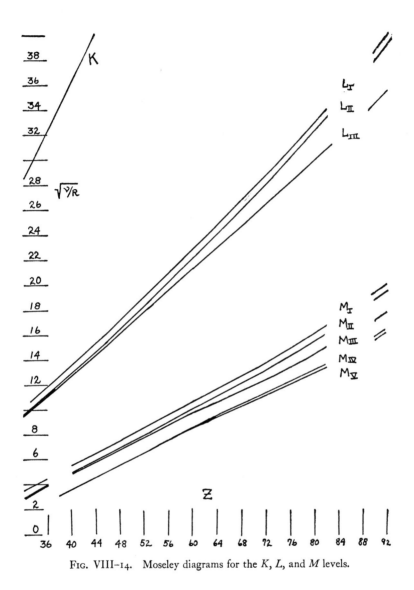

FIG. VIII-14.   Moseley diagrams for the K, L, and M levels.

interpretation of these separations is found by writing out the appropriate expressions from eqs. (8.18) and (8.19). For the levels L_I, M_I, M_{III}, N_I, N_{III}, and N_V we have

$$E(n, l, j) = -Rhc \frac{(Z-\sigma_1)^2}{n^2} - Rhc\alpha^2 \frac{(Z-\sigma_2)^4}{n^4} \left(\frac{n}{l+1} - \frac{3}{4} \right) - \cdot \cdot \quad (8.33)$$

and for the levels L_{II}, M_{II}, M_{IV}, N_{II}, N_{IV}, N_{VI} we have

$$E'(n', l', j') = -Rhc \frac{(Z-\sigma_1')^2}{n'^2} - Rhc\alpha^2 \frac{(Z-\sigma_2')^4}{n'^4} \left(\frac{n'}{l'} - \frac{3}{4} \right) - \cdot \cdot \cdot \quad (8.34)$$

Using the relation

$$\frac{\nu}{R} = \left| \frac{E(n, l, j)}{Rhc} \right|$$

and taking the square root, we obtain from (8.33)

$$\sqrt{\frac{\nu}{R}} = \frac{Z - \sigma_1}{n} + \frac{\alpha^2}{2n^3} \frac{(Z - \sigma_2)^4}{Z - \sigma_1} \left(\frac{n}{l+1} - \frac{3}{4} \right) \quad (8.35)$$

and an analogous expression from eq. (8.34). If now we solve for the $\Delta\sqrt{\nu/R}$ difference of a screening doublet, we have $n = n'$ and $l' = l + 1$, so that there results

$$\Delta\sqrt{\frac{\nu}{R}} = \frac{\sigma_1' - \sigma_1}{n} + \frac{\alpha^2}{2n^3} \left(\frac{n}{l+1} - \frac{3}{4} \right) \left\{ \frac{(Z-\sigma_2)^4}{Z-\sigma_1} - \frac{(Z-\sigma_2')^4}{Z-\sigma_1'} \right\}. \quad (8.36)$$

The second term in the right-hand member of eq. (8.36) may be neglected in a rough calculation, whence

$$\Delta\sqrt{\frac{\nu}{R}} = \frac{\Delta\sigma_1}{n}. \quad (8.37)$$

Our conceptions of the unvarying character from element to element of the structure of the inner parts of the atom lead us to expect that the difference $\Delta\sigma_1$ will be independent of Z, hence the behavior of the screening doublets is explained. Sommerfeld[29] has discussed the effect of retaining the term in α^2 in eq. (8.36). We may make

[29] Sommerfeld, Atombau und Spektrallinien, 5. Aufl. Bd. 1, pp. 305-310.

this correction by defining a "reduced" term value as follows, from eq. (8.33):

$$\left(\frac{\nu}{R}\right)_{\text{red.}} = \left(\frac{\nu}{R}\right) - \frac{\alpha^2}{n^4}(Z - \sigma_2)^4\left(\frac{n}{l+1} - \frac{3}{4}\right) = \frac{(Z - \sigma_1)^2}{n^2}. \quad (8.38)$$

This reducing process, if applied to the terms whose difference follows the spin doublet formula, has the effect of producing the same reduced term from both of them. In other words, they are reduced to their parent n, l level analogous to the level which would be obtained from eq. (8.07) if the third term in the bracketed part were not present. Thus for the reduced terms we may properly speak of the screening doublet as existing between L_I and $L_{II}L_{III}$, or between $N_{IV}N_V$ and $N_{VI}N_{VII}$, etc. For these reduced terms, eq. (8.36) should be strictly accurate. We may reduce all terms except L_I, M_I, N_I, etc., by using values of σ_2 from Table VIII–10. When this is done, and σ_1 values calculated by (8.38), we find that for $M_{II}M_{III}$, $M_{IV}M_V$, $N_{II}N_{III}$, $N_{IV}N_V$ and $N_{VI}N_{VII}$, $\Delta\sigma_1$ is independent of Z, as exhibited in the curves of Fig. VIII–15.

We cannot obtain values of σ_2 for the terms L_I, M_I, N_I from the spin doublet equation; they have, however, been found by the following method. The observed terms for these levels are reduced, using various assumed values of σ_2 until one is found which makes the $\Delta\sigma_1$ values independent of Z. In this way the following values of σ_2 have been found: L_I, 2.0; M_I, 6.8; N_I, 14. It is an interesting fact, as yet unexplained, that the $\Delta\sigma_1$ values obtained in this way are approximately integral multiples of 0.57.

Let us consider for a moment the difference between the screening constants σ_1 and σ_2 for a given level. By a comparison of Fig. VIII–15 and Table VIII–10 it is seen that σ_1 is larger than σ_2 and that while σ_2 is independent of atomic number, σ_1 increases as Z increases. The difference between σ_1 and σ_2 has been ascribed by Bohr and Coster[30] to the fact that while σ_1 includes the screening effects of the electrons in shells internal and external to the shell in question, σ_2 concerns the internal screening only. These statements cannot be true in a highly precise sense, since due to the interpenetration of the shells, no sharp distinction between internal and external shells is possible.

The simplest numerical calculation of the external screening effect

[30] Bohr and Coster, Zs. f. Phys. **12**, 342 (1923).

due to a given outer shell would be based on the concept of the uniform distribution of the charge of the z electrons in that shell on a sphere of radius ρa_0, a_0 being the radius of the first Bohr orbit in

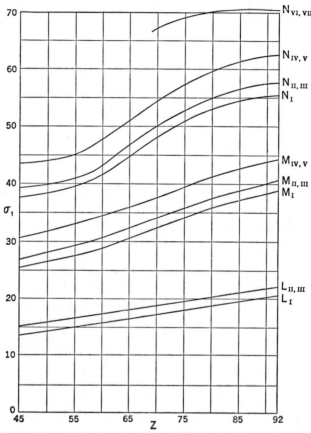

FIG. VIII–15. The screening constant σ_1 as a function of atomic number. (From Sommerfeld, Atombau und Spektrallinien, p. 309 (5th Ed.).

hydrogen. The work required to bring an electron from infinity to this shell would be

$$\frac{z e^2}{\rho a_0}$$

and the main term in the energy of the screened electrons would be

$$E(n) = - Rhc \frac{(Z - \sigma_1)^2}{n^2} = - Rhc \frac{(Z - \sigma_0)^2}{n^2} + \sum_i \frac{z_i e^2}{\rho_i a_0} \qquad (8.39)$$

in which σ_0 represents the effect of screening by levels internal to the one in question. If such a calculation is made, it is not found that σ_0 and σ_2 entirely agree, indicating the approximate nature of the considerations. From eq. (8.39), however, we see that the contribution to the external screening of a single electron is greater in a shell of smaller than in one of larger radius. This explains the sudden increase in the slope of the σ_1 against Z curve for the M and N levels near atomic number 57 (Fig. VIII–15). At $Z = 47$, where the curves begin, added electrons go into $5s$ or $5p$ shells, but at the beginning of the rare earths, at 57 La, electrons begin to enter the $4f$ shells, which are presumably of smaller effective radius.[31]

8. *X-ray Energy Level Diagrams; the Selection Rules and Exceptions to Them*

The configuration p^5 is the only unclosed group in the normal state of 10 Ne II and 18 A II. After the remarkable analysis of the Ne I spectrum by Paschen,[32] Meissner[33] made the important discovery that the series found by Paschen converge to two different limits, which thus are the normal levels of Ne II. Grotrian[34] realized that these two limits are really the $L_{II}L_{III}$ terms of neon, which are inverted, and showed that the wave-number separation, 780 cm.$^{-1}$, could be satisfactorily explained by Sommerfeld's formula (eqs. (8.18), (8.19)). This was probably the first direct connection found between the optical and x-ray terms of a given element.

Fig. VIII–16 shows an analogous case, the convergence of the optical terms of A I to two limits which arise from the configuration $3p^5$, and are the $M_{II}M_{III}$ levels of argon.[35]   In this figure the zero of energy and of wave-number is chosen for the configuration $3p^5$ in

[31] The following papers deal with various aspects of the problem of calculation of x-ray term values:

G. Wentzel, Zs. f. Physik **6**, 84 (1921); Zs. f. Physik **16**, 46 (1923); Ann. der Physik **76**, 803 (1925).

L. Pauling, Zs. f. Physik **40**, 344 (1926); Proc. Roy. Soc. London. **A 114**, 181 (1927).

A. Sommerfeld and G. Wentzel, Zs. f. Physik **7**, 86 (1921).

A. Sommerfeld, J. O. S. A. **7**, 503 (1923).

Braunbek, Zs. f. Physik **63**, 154, 718 (1930).

Vrkljan, Zs. f. Physik **71**, 403 (1931).

[32] F. Paschen, Ann. der Physik **60**, 405 (1919); **63**, 201 (1920).

[33] K. W. Meissner, Ann. d. Physik **58**, 333 (1919).

[34] W. Grotrian, Zs. f. Physik **8**, 116 (1921).

[35] W. Grotrian, Zs. f. Physik **40**, 10 (1926).

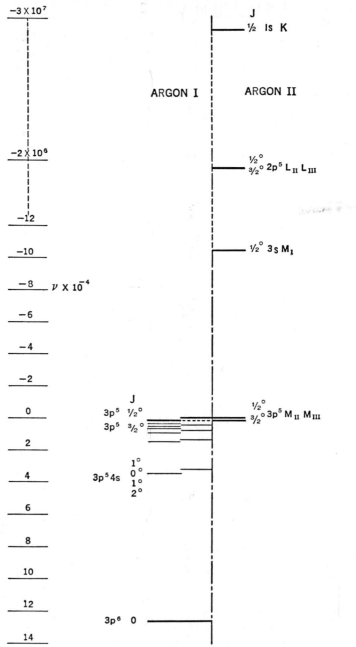

FIG. VIII–16. Optical and x-ray terms of argon. Only a few of the known optical levels are shown, namely, those arising from $3p^5ms$.

628

such an orientation that it gives rise to a term whose $J = 3/2$. Only a few of the known optical terms are shown, those included belonging to the configurations $3p^5ms$; $m = 4, 5, 6. \ldots$ The J values of these terms are given, and a superscript o added to indicate odd terms, the significance of which will be explained presently. Terms on the left hand of the center vertical line belong to Argon I; the x-ray terms on the right belong to Argon II.[36] The energy values of the optical levels are negative, with the exception of $3p^5$, $J = \frac{1}{2}^o$, and by eq. (8.15) the corresponding optical terms have positive wave-numbers. According to this convention, the x-ray terms have positive energies and negative wave-numbers.

Fig. VIII–17 shows the complete x-ray energy level diagram for a heavy element, indicating the transitions giving rise to lines in the K, L, M groups. In this figure no attempt is made to plot the energy values to scale. On the extreme right only the J values of the terms are given, since we have shown that the properties of the levels can be explained without assuming any coupling type. The strict interpretation of the symbol $2^2P_{\frac{1}{2}, \frac{3}{2}}$ applied to the L_{III} level would mean that the l vectors of the five p-electrons were coupled to form a resultant $L = 1$, as indicated for two electrons in Fig. VIII–11a. More probably the coupling for these x-ray levels is intermediate between the type illustrated in Figs. VIII–11a and VIII–11b, and the L has little or no significance.

It is seen that in Fig. VIII–17 not all combinations of the x-ray terms appear as spectrum lines, which is an example of the working of the selection principles. In every spectrum, the terms may be divided into two great classes, called even and odd. In spectra in which the configuration underlying the level is unknown, this assignment can nevertheless usually be made from the experimental data. If the configuration is known, the term is even if the sum of the l values of the electrons is even, and odd if this sum is odd. Thus the L_{II} and L_{III} levels are odd, with $\Sigma l = 5$; the $M_{IV}M_V$ levels are even, with $\Sigma l = 18$. The selection rules for x-ray spectra may be stated as follows:

(a) Only transitions between odd and even terms occur, no two even or odd terms combine.[37]

(b) Permitted transitions involve $\Delta J = 1, 0,$ or -1.

[36] The inclusion of the x-ray terms in the first spark spectrum was clearly indicated by R. T. Birge, Phys. Rev. **29**, 922 (1927).

[37] This method of stating the x-ray selection rules is not new, having been invented by Coster, who classified the terms with the letters a or b, such that only the ab combinations occur. If the coupling is Russell-Saunders, a rule equivalent to this is that $\Delta L = \pm 1$.

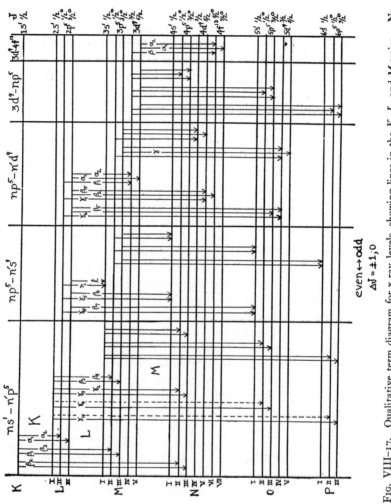

FIG. VIII-17. Qualitative term diagram for x-ray levels, showing lines in the K, L, and M series. No attempt has been made to plot the energy levels to scale.

The above rules are well known in optical spectra. In addition to these rules, lines in which n does not change are very weak or absent. This apparent rule does not operate in optical spectra, the sodium D lines, $3^2S_{1/2}-3^2P_{1/2, 3/2}$ showing $\Delta n = 0$. If the transitions $L_I-L_{II}L_{III}$ exist in uranium, the lines should be found in the region of its M-series, and are not observed.[38] It has been suggested that the failure to observe these lines is connected with the ν^4 factor which appears in the intensity of radiation from a dipole (eq. (8.45)), and is taken over into the quantum mechanical theory of spectral intensities. Thus the frequency of the radiation resulting from the $L_I-L_{II}L_{III}$ transitions in question is so much smaller than that due to other possible transitions having L_I as initial state (i.e., $L\beta_3$, $L\beta_4$) that the intensity is negligible. In the very soft x-ray region, lines have been discovered which are attributed to the transitions $N_{IV}-N_{VI}$ and $N_V-N_{VI, VII}$.[39] Here the difference in the frequencies of possible transitions from the initial state is not so great as in the example previously cited.

Although the selection rules given account for the great majority of the observed x-ray lines, exceptions to them have been observed. These lines are always of low intensity compared to the more prominent diagram lines. In their investigation of the relative intensities in the tungsten L spectrum Allison and Armstrong[40] found that the ratio of the intensity of the forbidden lines $L\beta_9$ and $L\beta_{10}$ (L_I-M_V, L_I-M_{IV}) to the line $L\beta_3$ (L_I-M_{III}) is about 0.04 at 30.7 kv. in 74W. The line $L\beta_3$ is however one of the weaker L group lines, having at 30.7 kv. an intensity relative to $L\alpha_1$ ($L_{III}-M_V$) of only approximately 0.08. Ross[42b] has estimated that the intensity of the forbidden line $K\beta_5$ in 42 Mo and 45 Rh ($K-M_{IV, V}$) is of the order of 1/1000 of that of $K\alpha_1$ ($K-L_{III}$), although in 46 Pd the corresponding fraction seems to be nearer 1/250. Idei[41] has recently given a discussion of these lines, based upon his measurements in the K and L series, and most of the data in Table VIII–16 are taken from his report.

In the K series, a line is found in elements up to and including 29 Cu which was at first thought to be $K\beta_2$ ($K-N_{II}N_{III}$) because of its analogous position to that occupied by this line in heavier elements.

[38] D. Coster, Phil. Mag. 43, 1070; 44, 546 (1922).

[39] S. Idei, Nature 123, 643 (1929).

J. Thibaud, Compt. Rend. 188, 1394 (1929).

[40] S. K. Allison and A. Armstrong, Phys. Rev. 26, 714 (1925).

[41] S. Idei, Sci. Rep. Tohoku Imperial University I, 19, 559 (1930); 19, 641 (1930)

However, according to our ideas of the building of the periodic system, electrons do not enter the $N_{II}N_{III}$ shells below 31 Ga. Idei has shown that below 29 Cu the line in the position considered here corresponds closely to the transition $K-M_{IV}M_V$, a forbidden transition. He has therefore called this line $K\beta_5$. Beuthe[42] has measured a weak K series line up to 39 Y which is probably the extension of this line even after a regular $K-N_{II}N_{III}$ transition becomes possible. New

TABLE VIII–16

EXCEPTIONS TO THE SELECTION PRINCIPLES IN THE K AND L GROUPS

K group

Transition	Symbol	Type of Exception	Remarks
$K-M_{IV}M_V$	$K\beta_5$	Even-even	Found from 23 V to 51 Sb.
$K-N_{IV}N_V$	$K\beta_4$	Even-even	In 41 Cb, 42 Mo, 47 Ag, 51 Sb, called δ by Ross.

L group

Transition	Symbol	Type of Exception	Remarks
L_I-M_{IV}	$L\beta_{10}$	Even-even	From 73 Ta to 92 U
L_I-M_V	$L\beta_9$	Even-even	From 73 Ta to 92 U
$L_I-N_{IV, V}$	$L\gamma'_{2, 3}$	Even-even	May be a spark line.
L_I-N_V	$L\gamma_{11}$	Even-even	In 74 W and 90 Th.
$L_{II}-N_{VI}N_{VII}$	Lv	Odd-odd	In 74 W, 77 Ir, 92 U.
$L_{II}-M_{III}$	$L\beta_{17}$	Odd-odd	β_{11} (Dauvillier)
$L_{III}-N_{VI}N_{VII}$	Lu	Odd-odd	73 Ta to 92 U
$L_{III}-M_{II}$	Lt	Odd-odd	73 Ta to 92 U.
$L_{III}-M_{III}$	Ls	Odd-odd	73 Ta to 92 U.

lines in the K group have been discovered by Duane,[42a] using a high resolving power photographic spectrometer; Ross,[42b] using a double spectrometer, and Carlsson,[42c] using a crystal of mica bent around the surface of a cylinder. Carlsson, working with molybdenum and silver targets, found evidence of the lines $K\beta_4$ and $K\beta_5$ listed in Table VIII–16, and found satisfactory agreement

[42] Beuthe, Zs. f. Physik **60**, 603 (1930).
[42a] W. Duane, Phys. Rev. **37**, 1017 (1931); Proc. Nat. Acad. Sci. **18**, 63 (1932).
[42b] P. A. Ross, Phys. Rev. **39**, 536 (1932); **39**, 748 (1932); **43**, 1036 (1933).
[42c] Carlsson, Zeits. f. Physik **80**, 604 (1933).

between calculated and observed frequencies on the postulated transitions. Ross worked in 42 Mo, 45 Rh, 46 Pd, 47 Ag, 41 Cb and 51 Sb. He found the lines δ and β_4, which are probably identical with β_4 and β_5 of Table VIII–16 respectively. In addition, he found a line called by him β_5, of wave-length only slightly shorter than β_1, which was not detected by Carlsson.

The lines $L\beta_9$ and $L\beta_{10}$ are probably the most intense lines violating the selection principles in the L group. The violations of the selection principles observed in x-rays are similar to those known in optical spectra, the observed combinations of ^2S and ^2D terms in the sodium and potassium arc spectra (even–even or $\Delta l = 2$) being one of the numerous possible examples.[43]

Siegbahn[44] has pointed out that in certain cases there is evidence that the x-ray critical absorption limits correspond to removal of an electron from an inner shell to an outer incomplete shell or optical level, rather than to infinity, and that in these cases we must apply the selection principles in absorption. Sandström[45] has shown that in the elements 73 Ta to and including 79 Au the frequency of the L_{III} absorption limit coincides with that of the line $L\beta_5$ (L_{III}–$O_{IV, V}$). The O shells of the final state are unfilled in this region of the periodic system. If the absorption act consists in the removal of the electron to infinity, we should, by Fig. VIII–17, have

$$(\nu/R)_{L_{II}} - (\nu/R)_{L\beta_1} = (\nu/R)_{M_{IV}}$$

and

$$(\nu/R)_{L_{III}} - (\nu/R)_{L\alpha_1} = (\nu/R)_{M_V}.$$

When the most precise measurements of these quantities[45a] are used in the attempt to verify these relationships, however, discrepancies larger than the experimental error are found. This is probably due

[43] References to articles dealing with lines arising from violations of the selection principles, other than those already given, are:

Coster, Phil. Mag. (6), **43**, 1070 (1922).

Rogers, Proc. Camb. Phil. Soc. **21**, 430 (1922–23).

Crofutt, Phys. Rev. **24**, 9 (1924).

Eddy and Turner, Proc. Roy. Soc. Lond. A **114**, 605 (1927).

Auger and Dauvillier, Compt. rend. **176**, 1927 (1923).

[44] M. Siegbahn, Zs. f. Physik **67**, 567 (1931).

[45] A. Sandström, Zs. f. Physik **66**, 784 (1930).

[45a] L group lines. S. Idei, Sci. Rep. Tohoku Imperial University **19**, 559 (1930).

M absorption limits. E. Lindberg, Zs. f. Physik **54**, 632 (1929).

L absorption limits. A. Sandström, Zs. f. Physik **65**, 632 (1930).

to the fact that the L and M limits in question do not represent removal of the electron to infinity, and because of the selection rules the electron removed from the L limits in question must go to a different outer level than is possible for an electron ejected from the pertinent M levels. This leaves room for a so-called " combination defect," which would be the energy difference between the outer levels to which the L and M electrons are ejected. Siegbahn further shows that such a " defect " does not occur when the equation

$$(\nu/R)_{L_{\text{III}}} - (\nu/R)_{L\beta_2} + (\nu/R)_{M_{\text{III}}-N_{\text{V}}} = (\nu/R)_{M_{\text{III}}}$$

is tested, due to the fact that electrons ejected from L_{III} and M_{III} could go to the same outer level.

9. Effects Leading to a Possible Fine-structure of the X-ray Levels

In the interpretation of the x-ray term diagram given here, we have so far assumed that the only source of angular momentum in the atom is the incomplete group which on Kossel's theory is the configuration underlying the x-ray term. It was with this assumption in mind that argon was chosen in Fig. VIII–16 for the construction of a term table containing both optical and x-ray terms. In most atoms this will not be the case, for instance in a potassium atom in potassium vapor which happens to have one $2p$ electron removed, there is in addition to the J values of the remaining $2p^5$ configuration a non-neutralized source of angular momentum in the spin of the outer $4s$ electron. We have seen that the J values arising from $2p^5$ will be the same as those of a single p electron. Terms arising from s, p configurations are known in many optical spectra, notably those of the alkaline earths. Four terms having $J = 0, 1, 1, 2$ arise, which in Russell-Saunders coupling may be classified as a triplet ($^3P_{012}$) and a singlet ($^1P_1$), the singlet-triplet interval being large compared to the spread of the triplet.

In view of this fact, we may well ask: why does not this triplet-singlet structure appear in the x-ray levels of potassium? An immediate but trivial reply to this query is that the x-ray spectra are not obtained from gaseous, but from solid potassium, in which we can no longer speak of the valence electron as in an optical orbit. The principle of the question still remains, however, for we can cite the case of the rare earths, which have an incomplete $4f$ shell, yet whose

L levels have the common doublet structure. The explanation of this is that the doublet structure of the higher energy x-ray terms is only very slightly perturbed by the interaction with the angular momentum of the outer, much more loosely bound electrons. Russell-Saunders coupling undoubtedly does not apply between the angular momenta arising from $2p^5$ in potassium, and that from the outer $4s$ electron. We would on the other hand have (J, s) coupling, in which it is proper to speak of the interaction between the resultant J's from the $2p^5$ configuration and the s of the valence electron.

An interesting and analogous case may be seen in Fig. VIII–18 which shows the terms arising from configurations $1s^2$ $2s^2 2p$ ms, where $m = 3, 4, 5. \ldots$ These configurations occur in the arc spectrum of carbon, C I.[46] The terms arising from $1s^2$ $2s^2$ $2p$, which is the configuration of the lowest state of C II, are $^2P_{\frac{1}{2}}$ and $^2P_{\frac{3}{2}}$. The figure enables us to follow the effect upon these terms of the various stages of binding of the outer s electron. We see that at first the P levels are only slightly perturbed, each one being split into two components whose separation is small compared to that of the P levels of the ion. It is here that we may speak of (j, s) coupling between the $2p$ electron and the outer s electron. As the value of m decreases, the type of coupling gradually changes to Russell-Saunders, and we approach a separation of the four terms into the typical singlet and triplet.

To return to the x-ray case, we may expect in the configuration $2p^5 4s$ of the potassium atom under discussion as an example, only a very slight splitting of each doublet level into two levels, and no radical departure from the doublet structure, as shown in the example in the preceding paragraph. Similarly the K level of potassium in the vapor state, configuration $1s$ $4s$, should be double $(^1S_0, {}^3S_1)$, but the separation should be a minute fraction of the energy of either of these states. In the K and L groups such a fine structure of x-ray lines has not been observed, due probably more to the large natural widths of the lines themselves than to lack of resolving power. This splitting may, however, contribute to the measured total line widths.

[46] Data from Bacher and Goudsmit, Atomic Energy States, McGraw-Hill, New York (1932).

Quantum mechanical calculations on similar cases have been made by W. V. Houston, Phys. Rev. 33, 297 (1929), and tested by Condon and Shortley, Phys. Rev. 35, 1342 (1930).

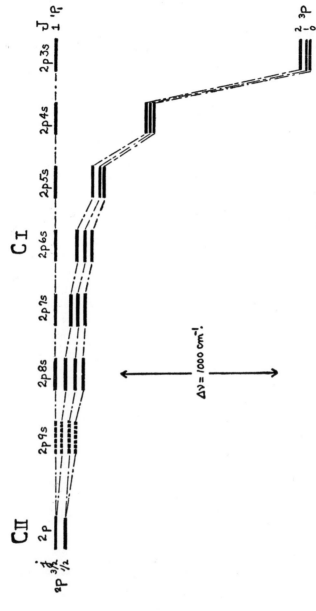

FIG. VIII-18. Transition from Russell-Saunders to (j, s) coupling in terms in the spectrum of carbon arising from the configurations $1s^2 \, 2s^2 2p \, ms$, where $m = 3, 4, 5 \dots$.   The typical singlet-triplet structure appearing on the right changes to a modified doublet as the outer electron is removed.

In the M series of the rare earths, van der Tuuk[47] investigated some of the stronger lines in the hope of finding evidence of higher multiplicities due to the interaction with the angular momenta of the incompleted $4f$ shell. He found that the compound doublet $M\alpha_1$, $M\alpha_2$, $M\beta_1$ ($M_{IV, V}-N_{VI, VII}$) in these elements is an unresolved multiplet whose structure changes from element to element, and although quantitative proof cannot be attained, it seems reasonable to assume that the effect is due to the interactions under consideration.

Another possibility is the so-called hyperfine structure of x-ray levels, due to the presence of nuclear magnetic moments. In many cases it has been shown that optical hyperfine structures, in the bismuth spectrum, for example, can be explained by the assignment of an angular momentum to the nucleus of the atom. Breit[48] has made some calculations of the expected order of magnitude of this effect for a nucleus having an angular momentum of $(9/2)$ $(h/2\pi)$ on the K levels of the heaviest elements. He found that a splitting of the K level into two components should result, with an energy difference of 22 electron-volts. In molybdenum the same nuclear angular momentum would cause a split in the K level of only 0.9 electron volts. Since the half-width at half maximum of the molybdenum $K\alpha_1$ line is 3.6 volts, the possibility of detecting this separation, if it exists in molybdenum, seems remote.

10. *Experimental Data on the Relative Intensities of X-ray Lines*

Measurements of the relative intensities of x-ray lines have been made by the photographic method, by means of the ionization chamber, and by the use of the Geiger counter. In all these methods, there is little difficulty in obtaining reliable results on the relative intensities of two lines of small wave-length separation, i.e., $K\alpha_1\alpha_2$ or $L\alpha_1\alpha_2$. As the separation of two lines increases, the corrections which must be applied become increasingly difficult to calculate accurately. We have discussed the methods and corrections in another place (p. 492), and merely give here the results and some discussion of their interpretation. It may be said, however, that the fundamental work of many observers, showing that the energy expended in producing a pair of ions is independent of the wave-length of the

[47] J. H. van der Tuuk, Zeits. f. Physik **44**, 737 (1927). The idea that such higher multiplicities should arise in x-ray spectra had already been propounded by Coster and Mulder, Zeits. f. Physik **38**, 264 (1926), Coster and Druyvesteyn, Zs. f. Physik **40**, 765 (1927), and van der Tuuk, Zs. f. Physik **41**, 326 (1927).

[48] G. Breit, Phys. Rev. **35**, 1447 (1930).

x-rays entering the ionization chamber, and the tests of the ionization chamber method carried out by Allison and Andrew,[48a] and by Williams[49] show that within the wave-length range from 0.6 to 2.3 A this method, with fairly obvious and readily calculable corrections, leads to correct values of the relative intensities.

K series.—The experiments of D. L. Webster[5] on the excitation of *K* series lines, previously considered in this chapter, show that the relative intensities of these lines are not a function of the voltage, and that all the lines are connected with a single excitation limit. This simplifies the measurement and interpretation of the relative intensities of these lines.

In 1920, Duane and Stenstrom[50] measured the relative ionization currents produced by the *K* series lines of tungsten. These were not corrected in any way, but due to the small absorption of the radiation in the chamber, the intensities in question are very roughly given by the results, which are the only *K* series measurements available on tungsten. They are

Line............	$K\alpha_2$	$K\alpha_1$	$K\beta_1$	$K\beta_2$
Intensity........	50	100	35	15

Other intensity measurements in the *K* series have been made by Duane and Hu,[51] Duane and Patterson,[52] Zacek and Siegbahn,[53] Allison and Armstrong,[54] and by Woo,[55] using fluorescence radiation. The range of atomic numbers in which these experiments were performed has been completely covered in the work of Meyer[56] and of Williams,[49] and only the data in these latter researches will be presented here. We may mention, however, that Allison and Armstrong succeeded in resolving the narrow Mo $K\beta_1K\beta_3$ doublet in the fifth order from calcite, and found

Line............	$K\beta_1$	$K\beta_3$
Intensity........	2	1

[48a] S. K. Allison and V. J. Andrew, Phys. Rev. **38**, 441 (1931).

[49] J. H. Williams, Phys. Rev. **44**, 146 (1933).

[50] Duane and Stenström, Proc. Nat. Acad. Sci. **6**, 477 (1920).

[51] Duane and Hu, Phys. Rev. **14**, 369 (1919).

[52] Duane and Patterson, Proc. Nat. Acad. Sci. **6**, 518 (1920); **8**, 85 (1922).

[53] Zacek and Siegbahn, Ann. der Physik **71**, 187 (1923).

[54] Allison and Armstrong, Phys. Rev. **26**, 701; 714 (1925).

[55] Woo, Phys. Rev. (2), **28**, 427 (1926).

[56] H.-T. Meyer, Wissenschaftliche Veröffentlichungen aus dem Siemens-Konzern **7**, 108 (1929).

showing that we have here the same intensity ratio as in the $K\alpha_1\alpha_2$ doublet.

H.-T. Meyer has by a photographic photometric method measured the relative intensities in the K series from 23 Va to 49 In. The values given by him are uncorrected for absorption in the target, and hence may be taken as the relative intensities at the surface of the target. In obtaining the relative intensities of lines widely separated in wavelength, among other corrections, Meyer corrected for the varying fraction of the radiation absorbed in the silver bromide of the photographic plate.

Williams has made measurements on the K series lines from 24 Cr to 52 Te, using the ionization chamber method. He chose such gases that any fluorescence radiation produced in them by the x-rays was completely absorbed before reaching the walls of the chamber, and corrected his observations for the fraction of the direct beam absorbed in the length of the chamber, the absorption in the air path, in the windows of the x-ray tube and ionization chamber, and for the variation of the coefficient of reflection of the crystal with wave-length. The results of these two investigations are given in Table VIII–17. The doublet $K\beta_1\beta_3$ was not resolved in these researches. Due probably to the higher resolving power used in the photographic method, Meyer was able to follow the line β_2 to elements below 30 Zn. In this region we have seen in Sec. 7 of this chapter that this line is probably due to the forbidden transition $K-M_{IV}M_V$ and is represented by $K\beta_5$. The variation in the ratio β_1/α_1 and β_2/α_1 with atomic number is shown in Figs. VIII–19 and VIII–20.

In order to obtain data on the relative transition probabilities of these lines, correction must be made for absorption in the target. This correction is very difficult to calculate with high accuracy (p. 86). A rough calculation may be made assuming that the rate of loss of kinetic energy of the impinging electrons as a function of depth of penetration of the target, and that the probability of ionizing the K shell as a function of electron velocity, are known. J. H. Williams has carried out such a calculation, assuming the validity of the Thomson-Whiddington law and using an empirical ionization function found by Webster, Hansen, and Duveneck.[57] The correction to be applied to the intensity ratio β_1/α_1 as measured at the surface of the target varied from a factor of 0.97 in 24 Cr to 1.00 in 52 Te, thus being in most cases within the experimental error. Recent work of F. J

[57] Webster, Hansen, and Duveneck, Phys. Rev. **43**, 839 (1933).

TABLE VIII–17

RELATIVE INTENSITIES OF K SERIES LINES AT THE TARGET SURFACE

Element	α_2/α_1		β_1/α_1		β_2/α_1	
	Meyer	Williams *	Meyer	Williams	Meyer	Williams
23 Va	0.521	....	0.205	....	0.0048	
24 Cr	0.506	0.515	0.210	0.179	0.0066	
25 Mn	0.549	....	0.224	....	0.0034	
26 Fe	0.491	0.500	0.182	0.167	0.0026	
27 Co	0.532	0.497	0.191	0.160	0.0023	
28 Ni	0.476	0.495	0.171	0.187	0.0020	
29 Cu	0.460	0.497	0.158	0.200	0.0015	
30 Zn	0.489	0.503	0.185	0.207	0.0019	0.0036
31 Ga	0.506	....	0.216			
32 Ge	0.507	0.499	0.228	0.240	0.0046	0.0132
33 As	0.492	....	0.217	....	0.0069	
34 Se	0.503	....	0.210	....	0.0107	
35 Br	0.509	....	0.222	....	0.0173	
37 Rb	0.493	....	0.230	....	0.0262	
38 Sr	0.486	0.503	0.218	0.274	0.0272	0.0416
39 Y	0.500	....	0.233	....	0.0319	
40 Zr	0.491	0.502	0.219	0.274	0.0328	0.0450
41 Cb	0.497	0.498	0.214	0.279	0.0332	0.0490
42 Mo	0.506	0.499	0.233	0.279	0.0348	0.0517
44 Ru	0.511	0.501	0.233	0.293	0.0396	0.0563
45 Rh	0.512	0.503	0.253	0.279	0.0397	0.0578
46 Pd	0.523	0.500	0.248	0.290	0.0414	0.0613
47 Ag	0.517	0.499	0.240	0.290	0.0422	0.0617
48 Cd	0.538	0.499	0.261	0.297	0.0418	0.0642
49 In	0.518	0.499	0.217	0.296	0.0365	0.0647
50 Sn	....	0.498	....	0.296	....	0.0702
51 Sb	....	0.503	....	0.310	....	0.0708
52 Te	....	0.497	....	0.306	....	0.0735

* In J. H. Williams' original paper values of the ratio are given to four significant figures; only the first three are given here.

Williams[58] has shown that the rate of loss of kinetic energy specified by the Thomson-Whiddington law is too great, which would increase the depth of penetration over that calculated by J. H. Williams, but on the other hand the calculation neglects the effects of diffusion which reduce the depths of penetration. The calculated correction also

[58] E. J. Williams, Proc. Roy. Soc. Lond. A **130**, 310 (1930).

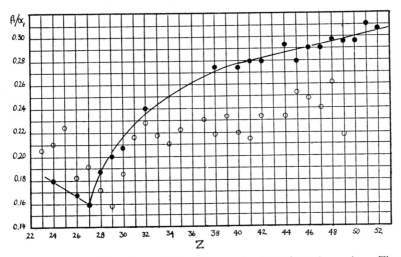

FIG. VIII–19. The intensity ratio $K\beta_1/K\alpha_1$ as a function of atomic number. The open circles are observations of H.-T. Meyer by a photographic method; the solid circles are the ionization chamber results of J. H. Williams.

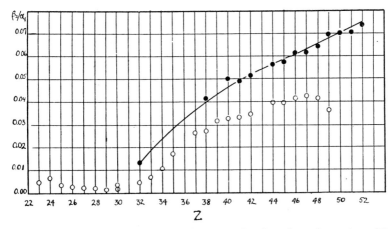

FIG. VIII–20. The intensity ratio $K\beta_2/K\alpha_1$ as a function of atomic number. The open circles are data obtained by H.-T. Meyer by a photographic method, the solid circles are points obtained by J. H. Williams. Below atomic number 31 it is believed that another transition, $K\beta_5$, replaces $K\beta_2$.

neglects the production of characteristic radiation in the target by photo-electric action of the general radiation which is also excited by the incident electrons. However it seems that the ratios in Table VIII–17 may be considered as values to which eq. (8.46) may be applied within an error of less than 5 per cent.

L series.—The difficulties in connection with measurement and interpretation of results of L group lines are considerably greater than for the K series. The L series of a given element covers a relatively large wave-length range (in 92 U from 0.57 to 1.06 A), and the lines are connected with three excitation limits rather than with one. Thus the relative intensities of the L group lines corresponding to different limits will vary with voltage.[59]   Because of the wide wave-length spread, early intensity measurements by Duane and Patterson,[60] and by Allison and Armstrong[61] attempted only to compare lines of small wave-length separation, and announced results only for the α,- β,- and γ-groups separately. Some of the results of these earlier investigations will be quoted in connection with the question of relative intensities of x-ray multiplets.

A. Jönsson[62] was the first to give results on the intensities of lines throughout the L series, to correct for absorption, and to attempt to deduce relative transition probabilities from the measurements. His work was carried out on 74 W and 78 Pt with the use of a Geiger counter to detect the radiation. Allison[63] has measured the relative intensities in the L spectra of 90 Th and 92 U, using the ionization chamber method. Hicks[64] measured the relative intensities in the 73 Ta L spectrum, using the ionization chamber method, but later realized that his results were in error due to improper construction of his chamber, such that ions formed in the vicinity of the entrance window were not collected. He then corrected his earlier results by estimating the error involved. Andrew[65] has

[59] D. L. Webster and H. Clark, Proc. Nat. Acad. Sci. U. S. A. **3**, 181 (1917).

D. L. Webster, Proc. Nat. Acad. Sci. U. S. A. **6**, 26 (1920).

F. C. Hoyt, Proc. Nat. Acad. Sci. U. S. A. **6**, 639 (1920).

[60] Duane and Patterson, Proc. Nat. Acad. Sci. **6**, 518 (1920); **8**, 85 (1922).

[61] Allison and Armstrong, Phys. Rev. **26**, 714 (1925).

[62] A. Jönsson, Zeits. f. Physik **36**, 426 (1926).

[63] Allison, Phys. Rev. **30**, 245 (1927); **32**, 1 (1928).

[64] Hicks, Phys. Rev. **36**, 1273 (1930); **38**, 572 (1931). Photographic data on the relative intensities of the tantalum L series lines have been published by M. Bötzkes, Zeitschr. f. Physik **89**, 667 (1934).

[65] V. J. Andrew, Phys. Rev. **42**, 591 (1932).

measured the relative intensities of the strong lines $L\alpha_1$, β_2, β_1, γ_1 in 73 Ta, 74 W, 77 Ir, and 78 Pt. His results are probably somewhat more reliable in that he used an ionization chamber whose action had been tested,[48] and a calcite crystal whose coefficient of reflection for the different wave-lengths was known.[66] To reduce the effect of roughness of the target in absorbing the rays, the targets were optically polished to a mirror-like surface, and operated at electron currents of one milliampere or less to avoid pitting.

At the present stage of intensity measurements, the relative intensities at the surface of the target, and at a known constant voltage, may be deduced with comparative certainty from the measured ionization currents. The problem of calculating the transitions probabilities and statistical weights of initial and final states from these results is much more complicated and the correct solution is much less certain. In Table VIII–18 are given relative intensities at the target surface at known voltages. Probably because of the low resolving power used, Allison was unable to detect the lines γ_4 and γ_5 in 90 Th and 92 U, and their intensities are listed as 0 with respect to α_1 in the table. These transitions, however, actually take place, as they have been photographed by Dauvillier[67] and by Idei.[68]

Various methods have been used in attempting to calculate transition probabilities and statistical weights from intensities at the target surface. In the work of Allison on thorium and uranium, of Jönsson on tungsten and platinum, and of Hicks on tantalum, no attempt was made to correct for absorption in the target. A correction factor was applied to the intensities which, if it accomplished its purpose, would give the intensity ratios approached as the voltage is indefinitely increased. This was done by using an empirical formula for the intensity of a line emitted from a thick target first proposed by Webster and Clark.[69] Jönsson,[70] in work on the L group of 42 Mo, 45 Rh, 46 Pd, and 47 Ag applied a correction intended to take account of the target absorption and at the same time give the relative intensities which the lines would have if the probabilities of the impinging electrons giving up to the atom the energies requisite

[66] S. K. Allison, Phys. Rev. **41**, 1 (1932).
[67] A. Dauvillier, Journal de Physique **3**, 221 (1922).
[68] S. Idei, Sci. Rep. Tohoku Imp. Univ. I, **19**, 559 (1930).
[69] D. L. Webster and H. Clark, Phys. Rev. **11**, 433 (1918).
[70] A. Jönsson, Zeitschr. f. Physik **41**, 801; **43**, 845 (1927); **46**, 383 (1928).

for the production of the states L_I, L_{II}, and L_{III} were all equal. This procedure will not necessarily yield the same corrected intensities as that first mentioned, aside from the question of target absorption, for, according to the classical theory the probability of removal of a bound electron by a very high speed impinging electron is inversely

TABLE VIII–18 *

RELATIVE INTENSITIES OF L GROUP LINES AT THE TARGET SURFACE

Line	Transition	73 Ta	74 W			77 Ir	78 Pt		90 Th	92 U
		30.6 kv. Hicks	30.0 kv. Andrew	20.0 kv. Jönsson	30.0 kv. Andrew	30.0 kv. Andrew	20.0 kv. Jönsson	30.0 kv. Andrew	31.8 kv. Allison	52.8 kv. Allison
l	$L_{III}-M_I$	3.6	....	3.2	......	....	3.4	....	3.6	2.4
α_2	$L_{III}-M_{IV}$	11.0	....	11.5	......	....	11.4	....	12.0	11.0
α_1	$L_{III}-M_V$	100	100	100	100	100	100	100	100	100
η	$L_{II}-M_I$	1.1	....	1.0	......	....	1.0	....	1.1	0.83
β_6	$L_{III}-N_I$	......	....	1.0	......	....	1.5	....	1.4	1.6
β_2	$L_{III}-N_V$	20	21.2	20.0	22.6	23.8	22.7	24.4	26	28
β_4	L_I-M_{II}	5.4	....	3.6	......	....	3.0	......	......	3.2
β_7	$L_{III}-O_I$	0.4	....	......	......	....	......	......	0.4	0.4
β_5	$L_{III}-O_{V, IV}$	......	....	0.2	......	....	......	....	} 38	6.4
β_1	$L_{II}-M_{IV}$	51	54.2	40.8	54.1	52.8	34.8	51.0		40.5
β_9	L_I-M_V	0.4	....	0.5						
β_{10}	L_I-M_{IV}	......	....	0.5						
β_3	L_I-M_{III}	6.8	....	5.7	......	......	4.8	....	1.8	3.3
γ_5	$L_{II}-N_I$	0.5	....	0.32	......	......	......	......	0	0
γ_1	$L_{II}-N_{IV}$	10	10.9	7.2	12.1	12.4	7.6	11.8	8.5	9.7
γ_2	L_I-N_{II}	1.7	....	1.03	......	......	......	......	0.81	1.1
γ_3	L_I-N_{III}	2.3	....	1.40	......	......	......	......	} 3.1	1.1
γ_6	$L_{II}-O_{IV}$	0.2	....	0.2	......	......	......	......		1.8
γ_4	$L_I-O_{II, III}$	0.7	....	0.41	......	......	......	......	0	0

* In interpreting this table, it should be noted that the various observers have worked at different voltages, and that the L group relative intensities are a function of voltage. Further, all results except those of Andrew are uncorrected for variation of coefficient of reflection of calcite with wave-length.

proportional to the binding energy. In calculating this correction, Jönsson assumed the classical ionization function developed by J. J. Thomson[71] and used by Rosseland,[72] and the Thomson-Whiddington law[73] of loss of energy of the cathode rays in the target. Andrew[65] made a similar correction to his intensities, assuming the classical ionization function, and also made the calculation for the

[71] J. J. Thomson, Phil. Mag. **23**, 449 (1912).
[72] S. Rosseland, Phil. Mag. **45**, 65 (1923).
[73] R. Whiddington, Proc. Roy. Soc. **86**, 360 (1912).

TABLE VIII-19

CORRECTED INTENSITIES OF L GROUP LINES

		42 Mo J	45 Rh J	46 Pd J	47 Ag J	73 Ta H	73 Ta An R	73 Ta An W	74 W J	74 W An R	74 W An W	77 Ir An R	77 Ir An W	78 Pt J	78 Pt An R	78 Pt An W	90 Th A	92 U A
l	$L_{III}-M_I$	...	...	3.4	4.1	3.6	...	...	3.2	...	...	...	...	3.4	...	...	3.6	3.4
α_2	$L_{III}-M_{IV}$	13	13	12	12	11	...	...	11.5	...	...	...	...	11.4	...	...	12	11
α_1	$L_{III}-M_V$	100	100	100	100	100	100	100	100	100	100	100	100	100	100	100	100	100
η	$L_{II}-M_I$	...	...	2.0	2.2	1.2	...	...	1.3	...	...	...	...	1.5	...	...	1.8	1.0
β_6	$L_{III}-N_I$	...	...	...	...	...	...	...	1.0	...	...	...	...	1.5	...	...	1.4	1.6
β_2	$L_{III}-N_V$	8	13	13	21	20	20.7	20.3	20	21.6	21.1	23.0	22.9	23	23.4	23.8	26	28
β_4	L_I-M_{II}	9.9	7.9	6.4	5.8	6.4	...	...	5.2	...	...	...	...	5.2	...	...	...	4.1
β_7	$L_{III}-O_I$	...	...	...	...	0.4	...	...	...	...	...	...	...	...	...	...	0.4	0.4
β_5	$L_{III}-O_V$	...	...	...	...	...	...	...	0.2	...	...	...	...	...	...	...	} 62	6.4
β_1	$L_{II}-M_{IV}$	62	61	59	59	57	69.9	72.3	52	69.8	73.0	72.2	76.5	51	70.6	75.0		49.4
β_9	L_I-M_V	...	...	...	...	0.5	...	...	...	...	...	...	...	...	...	...	...	...
β_{10}	L_I-M_{IV}	...	...	...	...	0.5	...	...	...	...	...	...	...	...	...	...	...	...
β_3	L_I-M_{III}	14.2	12.1	10.0	9.4	7.4	...	...	8.2	...	...	...	...	8.2	...	...	3.3	4.2
γ_2	L_I-N_{II}	...	...	...	...	2.0	...	...	1.5	...	...	...	...	...	...	...	1.5	1.5
γ_3	L_I-N_{III}	...	...	...	...	2.7	...	...	2.0	...	...	...	...	...	...	...	...	1.4
γ_1	$L_{II}-N_{IV}$	6.8	7.7	12	12	11	14.8	15.2	9	16.4	17.0	17.6	18.5	11	17.0	17.9	14	12
γ_5	$L_{II}-N_I$	...	...	...	...	0.6	...	...	0.4	...	...	...	...	...	...	...	0	0
γ_6	$L_{II}-O_{IV}$	...	...	...	...	0.2	...	...	0.3	...	...	...	...	...	...	...	...	2.2
γ_4	$L_{II}-O_{III}$	...	...	...	...	0.8	...	...	0.6	...	...	...	...	...	...	...	0	0

$J \sim$ Jönsson; $H \sim$ Hicks; An $\sim$ Andrew; A $\sim$ Allison. In the results of Andrew, R signifies that the correction was calculated assuming Rosseland's theory; W, assuming the empirical function of Webster. As explained in the text, the type of correction applied by Andrew, and by Jönsson in 42 Mo to 47 Ag is not the same as in the other cases.

empirical function found by Webster and his associates.[74]   These corrected intensities are collected in Table VIII–19.

M Series.—Experiments on the relative intensities of lines in the *M* group have been carried out by K. Molin[75] using both the Geiger counter and ionization chamber methods.   Due to the high absorption of these relatively soft x-rays, and the tendency of strong diagram lines in the *M* series to be accompanied by satellites, no great accuracy is claimed for this work.   The most trustworthy results were obtained for the ratio $(M\alpha_1 + M\alpha_2)/M\beta_1$, representing the transitions $(M_V-N_{VI, VII})/(M_{IV}-N_{VI})$.   This observed ratio varied from 1.7 in 73 Ta to 1.3 in 79 Au.

11. *Interpretation of Relative Intensities in X-ray Spectra*

Various authors have suggested that the so-called sum rules of Burger and Dorgelo should apply to the relative intensities of x-ray multiplets.[76]   A definition of a multiplet, adequate for the description of the simple types appearing in x-ray spectra[77] is as follows: A multiplet is a group of lines whose initial states arise from a single configuration, and whose final states likewise arise from another single configuration.   Thus in the *L* series, the lines $L\alpha_1$, α_2, β_1 constitute a multiplet arising from $2p^5L_{II}L_{III}$ and $3d^9M_{IV}M_V$.   A simpler type arises when one of the configurations produces only one level, thus $K\alpha_1\alpha_2$, $L\beta_3\beta_4$, $L l\eta$, are simple doublets, a special case of multiplets.

We have in eq. (4.01) the expression for the rate of radiation of energy from an oscillating electron, which shows that this rate is

---

[74] Reference 57.   In Table VIII–19 the corrected results given by Andrew using Webster's function have been multiplied by the ratio

$$\{(\text{energy of sub-level})/(\text{energy of } L_{III})\}^2$$

in order to approach the classical theory prediction for the relative excitation of two levels of different energy by a high-speed electron.

[75] K. Molin, Diss. Upsala (1927); Ark. Mat. Astro. och Fys. Stockholm, A, **21**, 20, 22 (1929).

[76] Dorgelo, Phys. Zeitschr. **26**, 756 (1925).

Coster, Naturwiss. **12**, 724 (1924); Physica **4**, 337 (1924).

Coster and Goudsmit, Naturwiss. **13**, 11 (1925).

Sommerfeld, Ann. der Physik **76**, 284 (1925).

[77] In optical spectra arising from Russell-Saunders coupling of two or more electrons, this definition would lead to a more general idea than is usually implied when the word multiplet is used.

proportional to the square of the acceleration. Let the equation of the motion be

$$z = P \cos 2\pi\tilde{\nu}t, \qquad (8.40)$$

where P is the amplitude, $\tilde{\nu}$ the frequency, and t the time. By differentiation, it is seen that

$$a \equiv \frac{d^2z}{dt^2} = - 4\pi^2 P\tilde{\nu}^2 \cos 2\pi\tilde{\nu}t \qquad (8.41)$$

and from eq. (4.01) we find

$$\frac{dw}{dt} = - \frac{32}{3} \frac{\pi^4 e^2 P^2 \tilde{\nu}^4}{c^3} \cos^2 2\pi\tilde{\nu}t. \qquad (8.42)$$

The electron is making many oscillations per second, and we desire to find the average rate of loss of energy over a cycle, which will be

$$\overline{\frac{dw}{dt}} = \frac{1}{T} \oint \frac{dw}{dt} dt \qquad (8.43)$$

where $T = 1/\tilde{\nu}$ is the period of the simple harmonic motion. Substitution of eq. (8.42) in eq. (8.43) and integration leads to

$$\overline{\frac{dw}{dt}} = - \frac{16\pi^4 e^2}{3c^3} \tilde{\nu}^4 P^2. \qquad (8.44)$$

This result has previously been obtained in eq. (2.06), Chap. II. Thus on the classical theory if there are N atoms each having a simple harmonic oscillator radiating the frequency $\tilde{\nu}$, the intensity of the line will be

$$I = \left| \sum \overline{\frac{dw}{dt}} \right| = \frac{16\pi^4 e^2}{3c^3} N\tilde{\nu}^4 P^2. \qquad (8.45)$$

In the endeavor to translate this expression into the quantum theory of radiation, we may consider that the line in question is radiated as the result of a transition from an initial state i to a final state f, and has the frequency $\tilde{\nu}(i,f)$. We then consider the quantity N_i, the number of atoms in the initial state. This will depend on two factors. One of them we may call F_i, which represents the probability that the atom will receive from the energy sources available, energy enough to put it into the state i. In purely thermal excitation, the factor

F has the familiar Boltzmann form. The other factor is the so-called statistical weight g_i of the state, which we may interpret as the number of different orientations of the underlying electron configuration which give rise to the state.

In place of the amplitude P in eq. (8.45), the new mechanics introduces a matrix component which we may call $P(i, f)$, which is the amplitude of a virtual harmonic oscillator having the frequency $\tilde{\nu}(i, f)$ of the line emitted in the transition $i \rightarrow f$. Thus we have

$$I(i, f) \sim \tilde{\nu}^4(i, f) F_i g_i P^2(i, f). \qquad (8.46)$$

The previously mentioned Burger-Dorgelo rule applies to relative values of the quantities $g_i P^2(i, f)$ of the lines in a multiplet. In a form sufficiently general to be applied to the simple multiplet types appearing in x-ray spectra, the rule is:

Imagine the separation of the sub-divisions of either the initial or final state reduced to zero. The sums of the quantities $g_i P^2(i, f)$ for the lines whose frequencies would then be identical are proportional to the statistical weights of the unreduced states.

The statistical weight of a term characterized by the quantum number J is $2J + 1$. We have seen an example of this in Sec. 5 of this chapter, where four very strong field terms approach coincidence to give L_{III} ($J = 3/2$, $2J + 1 = 4$), and two combine to give L_{II} ($J = \frac{1}{2}$, $2J + 1 = 2$).

A very simple example of the application of the Burger-Dorgelo rule is the calculation of the relative intensities of $K\alpha_1(K-L_{\text{III}})$ and $K\alpha_2(K-L_{\text{II}})$. Here there are no subdivisions of the initial K state, hence the reducing process described in the rule is not necessary. The quantities $P^2(i, f)$ are then simply proportional to the statistical weights of L_{III} and L_{II}, giving

$$P^2(K\alpha_1)/P^2(K\alpha_2) = 2/1. \qquad (8.47)$$

Since the lines have the same initial state the statistical weight disappears in the ratio; also the F's are the same. Since the lines are close together in frequency, the $\tilde{\nu}^4$ factor is not important, and we may expect eq. (8.47) to give the intensity ratio without further corrections. The lines $K\beta_1\beta_3$, and in the L group $L\gamma_2\gamma_3$, $L\beta_3\beta_4$, may be similarly treated.

Let us consider the application of the rule to the compound doublet

$L\alpha_1\alpha_2\beta_1$, whose transitions are indicated in Fig. VIII–21. Imagine the interval $M_{IV}M_V$ closed; then the rule gives

$$\frac{g_{L_{III}}P^2(\alpha_1) + g_{L_{III}}P^2(\alpha_2)}{g_{L_{II}}P^2(\beta_1)} = \frac{g_{L_{III}}}{g_{L_{II}}} = \frac{2}{1}. \qquad (8.48)$$

If we now imagine the $L_{II}L_{III}$ interval closed, we obtain

$$\frac{g_{L_{III}}P^2(\alpha_2) + g_{L_{II}}P^2(\beta_1)}{g_{L_{III}}P^2(\alpha_1)} = \frac{g_{M_{IV}}}{g_{M_V}} = \frac{2}{3} \qquad (8.49)$$

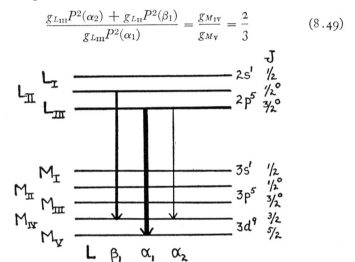

FIG. VIII–21.   The transitions of the L group multiplet $L\beta_1$, $L\alpha_1$, $L\alpha_2$.

and from the preceding two equations we may deduce

$$g_{L_{III}}P^2(\alpha_1) : g_{L_{III}}P^2(\alpha_2) : g_{L_{II}}P^2(\beta_1) = 9 : 1 : 5. \qquad (8.50)$$

By this method the values appearing in Table VIII–20 were deduced.

In some cases it is certain that the ratios of Table VIII–20 may be interpreted as the relative intensities of the lines without further consideration. We have seen that this is so for the $K\alpha_1\alpha_2$ doublet. The same considerations may be applied to the doublet $K\beta_1\beta_3$ and in the L group $L\alpha_1\alpha_2$, $L\beta_2\beta_{15}$. We see that the predicted intensity ratios in these cases are in agreement with experiment.[78]

Experimental results have been obtained in the L group which definitely disagree with the predicted ratios of Table VIII–20. The

[78] The relative intensities of $L\beta_2$: $L\beta_{15}$ have been measured by Allison, Phys. Rev. **34**, 176 (1929) and found to be 11 : 1 in 92 U, which is within the rather large experimental error in agreement with the predicted 9 : 1 ratio.

TABLE VIII-20

THEORETICAL RELATIVE VALUES OF $g_i P^2(i, f)$ FOR SOME X-RAY MULTIPLETS

K Group

$\alpha_1 : \alpha_2$	$2 : 1$
$\beta_1 : \beta_3$	$2 : 1$

L Group

$\gamma_3 : \gamma_2$	$2 : 1$
$\beta_3 : \beta_4$	$2 : 1$
$l : \eta$	$2 : 1$
$\beta_6 : \gamma_5$	$2 : 1$
$\beta_7 : \gamma_8$	$2 : 1$
$\alpha_1 : \alpha_2 : \beta_1$	$9 : 1 : 5$
$\beta_2 : \beta_{15} : \gamma_1$	$9 : 1 : 5$
$\beta_5 : \gamma_6$	$2 : 1$

M Group

$\alpha_1 : \alpha_2 : \beta_1$	$20 : 1 : 14$

lines in question are the doublets having the initial state L_I. Here the F_i and g_i factors are the same for both lines, and the $\bar{\nu}^4$ differences are negligible. The two doublets $\gamma_3\gamma_2$ and $\beta_3\beta_4$ should therefore have the intensity ratio $2 : 1$. Table VIII–21 shows the measured results, whose accuracy leaves something to be desired; but which clearly show a departure from the theory.

TABLE VIII-21

MEASURED INTENSITY RATIOS OF $L\gamma_3\gamma_2$; $L\beta_3\beta_4$ *

Element	$L\gamma_3 : L\gamma_2$	$L\beta_3 : L\beta_4$	Element	$L\gamma_3 : L\gamma_2$	$L\beta_3 : L\beta_4$
42 Mo	....	1.43	74 W	1.33	1.58
45 Rh	....	1.52	76 Os	....	1.67
46 Pd	....	1.56	78 Pt	....	1.60
47 Ag	....	1.61	82 Pb	....	1.38
50 Sn	....	1.43	83 Bi	....	1.49
73 Ta	1.35	1.26	92 U	0.93	1.03

* Data on 50 Sn from A. Jönsson, Zeitschr. f. Physik 41, 801 (1927); on 76 Os, 82 Pb, 83 Bi, from Allison, Phys. Rev. 34, 7 (1929).

We now come to the very interesting case of the compound doublets $L\alpha_1\alpha_2\beta_1$ and $L\beta_2\beta_{15}\gamma_1$. Here the factors F_i and $\bar{\nu}_i$ of eq. (8.46) cannot be neglected, because the probabilities of having the atom in the state L_{II} or in L_{III} after removal of an electron are not equal, and the frequency difference between L_{II} and L_{III} makes the separation of $\alpha_2\beta_1$ and $\beta_{15}\gamma_1$ very large (in 92 U the energy separation is about 3760 volts, or 22 per cent of the L_{III} energy).

Let us first consider the results in Table VIII–19, which have been corrected with the intent of giving the limiting ratios approached by the lines as the voltage is raised. By inspection of the Table, it is seen that the intensity ratios thus obtained fit fairly well with the theoretical ratios of the quantities $g_iP^2(i,f)$ of Table VIII–20. Thus, for instance, in 74 W Jönsson found for $\alpha_1 : \alpha_2 : \beta_1 = 100 : 11.5 : 52$, and Allison in 92 U found $100 : 11 : 49.5$, whereas the $g_iP^2(i,f)$ ratios in Table VIII–20 are $100 : 11 : 56$. We may remark here that if the values of β_1 were corrected for the variation of coefficient of reflection of calcite with wave-length, experimental values even nearer $100 : 56$ for $\alpha_1 : \beta_1$ would result. But from eq. (8.46) there is no reason to expect that these intensity ratios should give the $g_iP^2(i,f)$ ratios as they apparently do. In the first place, if the $\bar{\nu}^4$ correction were made, the value of β_1 would be decreased by a factor 0.568 in 74 W and 0.390 in 92 U, completely disrupting the agreement. On the other hand, there is no reason to believe that the factors $F_{L_{II}}$ and $F_{L_{III}}$ are equal, even in the limit of high velocity of the impinging electrons. If the classical theory were adequate in this case, we would have $F_i \sim (E_i)^{-1}$ where E_i is the energy transferred to the atom when it is left in the state i. If this factor is applied, the intensity of β_1 should be raised by the ratio $(E_{L_{II}})/(E_{L_{III}})$, or 1.13 in 74 W and 1.22 in 92 U. Thus the total factor to be applied to the β_1 line is 0.642 in 74 W and 0.476 in 92 U, which would produce ratios of $100 : 11.5 : 33.4$ and $100 : 11 : 23.5$, showing for the α_1/β_1 ratio a large departure from Table VIII–20.

The results of Andrew and of Jönsson on elements 42 Mo to 47 Ag in Table VIII–19 have been corrected in a different manner, and purport to represent the relative intensities which the lines would have if the probabilities of the impinging electrons giving up to the atom the energies requisite for the production of the states L_{II} and L_{III} were equal. In eq. (8.46) this corresponds to values of F_i the same for lines α_1, α_2, β_1, hence to obtain $g_iP^2(i,f)$ values the $\bar{\nu}^4$ correction alone should be applied, but the resulting ratios are also not in agreement with Table VIII–20.

Thus we have the disturbing fact that the corrections to the observed intensities demanded by eq. (8.46) destroy an agreement which is present when the data are treated in a very naive fashion. We must conclude that the question is at present in an unsatisfactory state. The same problem arises, of course, whenever the initial states of a multiplet have a separation given by the spin doublet formula, i.e., the doublet $L l \eta$, $L \beta_6 \gamma_5$, etc.[78a]

The variation of the relative intensities of the lines with atomic number is also a subject of interest. In certain cases we can observe the increase in intensity of a line as the electron population of the final state increases. Qualitative estimates have been made by the

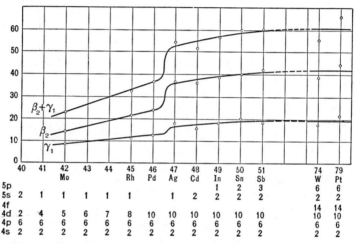

	40	41	42 Mo	43	44	45 Rh	46 Pd	47 Ag	48 Cd	49 In	50 Sn	51 Sb		74 W	79 Pt
5p										1	2	3		6	6
5s	2	1	1	1	1	1		1	2	2	2	2		2	2
4f														14	14
4d	2	4	5	6	7	8	10	10	10	10	10	10		10	10
4p	6	6	6	6	6	6	6	6	6	6	6	6		6	6
4s	2	2	2	2	2	2	2	2	2	2	2	2		2	2

FIG. VIII–22.   The ordinates of the figure are intensities of the lines $L \beta_2$ and $L \gamma_1$ in per cent of $L \beta_1$, from observations by Jönsson.

visual examination of photographic plates, but we shall give here only examples in which quantitative measurements have been taken. The first of these is seen in Fig. VIII–20, showing the intensity ratio $K \beta_2 / K \alpha_1$ with atomic number. The transition for $K \beta_2$ is K–$N_{II}N_{III}$, and according to spectroscopic evidence the $N_{II}N_{III}$ levels are first filled at 32 Ge. It is interesting to note that in this region the intensity of $K \beta_2$ is practically zero, and increases with increasing atomic

[78a] Since this was written, discussions of this point by Bethe, Handbuch der Physik 2nd Ed.Vol. 24 (1933), and by Bötzkes, Zeitschr. f. Physik 89, 667 (1934) have appeared. Bethe calls attention to the fact that the life-times of the states involved probably enter, and Bötzkes attempts to account for the discrepancy by assigning different Auger coefficients (fluorescence yields) to the states involved.

number. The increase with decreasing atomic number is attributed, as we have seen, to another line ($K\beta_5$).

The lines $L\beta_2$ and $L\gamma_1$ represent the transitions L_{III}-N_V and L_{III}-N_{IV} respectively. According to spectroscopic evidence the N_VN_{IV} shells are full at 46 Pd. Fig. VIII–22 shows the intensity of these lines relative to $L\beta_1(L_{II}$–$M_{IV})$ as observed by Jönsson.[79] The

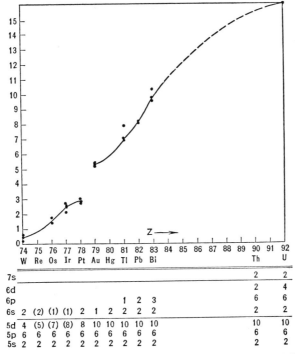

Fig. VIII–23. The ordinates of this figure are ratios of the intensity of $L\beta_5$ to $L\beta_1$ expressed in per cent.

line $L\beta_1$ should be expected to show no anomalous behaviour in this region since the M_{IV} shell is filled at the much lower element 29 Cu. The sudden increase of intensity of these lines between 46 Pd and 47 Ag marks the completion of the $N_{IV}N_V$ shell as it exists in the solid elements.

Figure VIII–23 shows an analogous case observed by Allison,[80]

[79] A. Jönsson, Zs. f. Physik **41**, 221 (1927).

[80] S. K. Allison, Phys. Rev. **32**, 1 (1928); **34**, 7 (1929).

illustrating the completion of the $O_{IV}O_V$ shells at 78 Pt. Here the intensity of $L\beta_5$ (L_{III}–$O_{IV}O_V$) is compared to $L\beta_1$ as the atomic number increases.

Some theoretical attempts have been made to calculate the ratio of the sum of the intensities of the lines in a given x-ray multiplet to the corresponding sum for another multiplet. In the L series such ratios would be, for instance, $(\alpha_1 + \alpha_2 + \beta_1) : (l + \eta) : (\beta_3 + \beta_4)$.[81] It has been supposed that such ratios can be calculated by a simple extension of the method used by Schrödinger[82] for the hydrogen atom spectrum; however, the x-ray case is really more complicated, because here the possibility exists of internal absorption of the radiation. Because of the unsatisfactory agreement with experiment we will not discuss these attempts here. F. C. Hoyt,[83] using the old quantum theory, attempted a similar calculation.

12. *Non-diagram Lines*

Weak lines are observed in x-ray spectra whose frequencies cannot be expressed as differences of any of the terms of Fig. VIII–17, and which are therefore called non-diagram lines. The presence of such lines was first established by Siegbahn and Stenström[84] in the K spectra of the elements 24 Cr to 32 Ge. These lines are often close to strong diagram lines and hence are frequently referred to as satellites. Due to a theory of their origin, which supposes that their initial and final states arise in atoms from which two inner electrons have been removed, they are also sometimes called x-ray spark lines, although to conform to optical use such terms would lie in the second spark spectrum, and be characterized by the numeral III.

Five well defined satellites of the $K\alpha$ group have been found in elements 11 Na to 32 Ge. They lie on the high frequency side of the group, and in order of increasing frequency are called α', $\alpha_3\alpha_4$, $\alpha_5\alpha_6$. The line $K\alpha_3$ appears to be complex,[85] and Ford[86] has measured the wave-length of a higher frequency component α_3' in the elements 13 Al to 17 Cl. The lines $\alpha_5\alpha_6$ have been separated in the elements 11 Na to 14 Si, and observed as a diffuse doublet in 15 P and 16 S.

[81] G. Wentzel, Naturwiss. **14**, 621 (1926).

[82] Schrödinger, Ann. d. Physik **80**, 437 (1926).

[83] F. C. Hoyt, Phil. Mag. **46**, 135 (1923).

[84] Siegbahn and Stenström, Physik. Zeitschr. **17**, 48; 318 (1916).

[85] Bäcklin, Zeitschr. f. Physik **33**, 547 (1925).

[86] Ford, Phys. Rev. **41**, 577 (1932), also Du Mond and Hoyt, ref. 98.

In the $K\beta$ group satellites are also found, but the differing notations used by various authors limit the value of any general statement concerning them. Figure VIII–24 shows the relative positions of the lines in the K group of aluminium.[87]

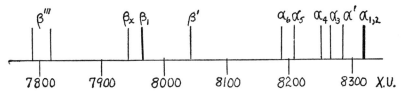

FIG. VIII–24. Lines in the K group of aluminium on a wave-length scale.

In the L series, the stronger lines have satellites in the region approximately below atomic number 50 in the periodic system. Here the satellites are much more difficult to resolve from the parent line

[87] Papers other than those already mentioned which deal with measurements of K series non-diagram lines are:

Siegbahn, Ann. der Physik **59**, 56 (1919).

Hjalmar, Zeitschr. f. Physik **1**, 489 (1920).

Hjalmar, Phil. Mag. **41**, 675 (1921); Zeitschr. f. Physik **7**, 341 (1921).

Dauvillier, Compt. Rend. **174**, 443 (1922).

Dolejsek, Compt. Rend. **174**, 441 (1922).

Siegbahn, Zeitschr. f. Physik, **9**, 68 (1922).

Siegbahn and Dolejsek, Zeitschr. f. Physik **10**, 159 (1922).

Lindh and Lundquist, Arkiv. Mat. Astro. och Fys. **18**, 14, 3 (1924).

Lundquist, Zeitschr. f. Physik **33**, 901 (1925).

Seljakow and Krassnikow, Zeitschr. f. Physik **33**, 601 (1925).

Bäcklin, Zeitschr. f. Physik **38**, 215 (1926).

Druyvesteyn, Zeitschr. f. Physik **43**, 707 (1927).

Ortner, Wiener Ber. 2a, **136**, 369 (1927).

Wetterblad, Zeitschr. f. Physik **42**, 603; 611 (1927).

Druyvesteyn, Dissertation, Groningen (1928).

Eriksson, Zeitschr. f. Physik **48**, 360 (1928).

Dolejsek and Felcakova, Nature **123**, 412 (1929).

v. Friesen, Zeitschr. f. Physik **58**, 781 (1929).

Beuthe, Zeitschr. f. Physik **60**, 603 (1930).

Deodhar, Nature **125**, 777 (1930).

Idei, Sci. Rep. Tohoku Imp. Univ. I, **19**, 551 (1930).

Kawata, Mem. Coll. Sci. Kyoto Imp. Univ. A **13**, 383 (1930).

Richtmyer and Ramburg, Phys. Rev. **35**, 661 (1930).

Richtmyer and Taylor, Phys. Rev. **36**, 1044 (1930).

Wennerlof, Ark. Mat. Astr. och Phys. A **22**, 8 (1930).

Deodhar, Proc. Roy. Soc. Lond. A **131**, 633 (1931).

than in the K series.   The presence of such non-diagram line, was shown by Coster[88] in the elements 37 Rb to 51 Sb, and Thoraeus[89] has found them from 29 Cu to 35 Br.   Recently an investigation of the satellites of $L\alpha_1$, $L\beta_1$, and $L\beta_2$ from 37 Rb to 50 Sn has been carried out by F. K. Richtmyer and R. D. Richtmyer.[90]   Five, and in some cases seven satellites of $L\alpha_1$ were found, four of $L\beta_1$, and five of $L\beta_2$.   In addition, evidence was found of a continuous spectrum extending toward shorter wave-lengths from the parent line.

In the M series, non-diagram lines close to the strong lines $M\alpha_1$ (M_V-N_{VII}), $M\beta$ ($M_{IV}-N_{VI}$) and $M\gamma$ ($M_{III}-N_V$) were first reported by Hjalmar.[91]   Lindberg[92] has also measured M series satellites, and recently Hirsh[93] has reported on the satellites from 70 Yb to 92 U.   Four satellites of $M\alpha$ were found, and three of $M\beta$.   Indications of a continuous spectrum accompanying the satellites of $M\alpha$ and $M\beta$ in 90 Th and 92 U are observed.

The first theoretical attempt to explain the presence of these non-diagram lines was made by Wentzel.[94]   He assumed that the lines were the result of single electron jumps in atoms having two or more inner electrons removed.   As we have seen, the terms of the ordinary x-ray diagram arise from atoms lacking one inner electron.   In the early form of the theory, the various L and M sub-levels were considered unseparated, hence the notation of Table VIII-5 is too specific for the description of the underlying electronic configurations, and we shall need to devise a simpler one.   The symbol K already represents the term arising from the absence of one K electron; let K^{II} represent the term arising from the absence of both K electrons.   Similarly L^{III} represents a term arising from the removal of three L electrons.

Wentzel's assignment of terms to the five $K\alpha$ satellites is shown in Table VIII-22.   Although fundamentally the idea proposed by Wentzel for the explanation of these satellites is probably correct, it seems proven that the particular assignment of initial and final states

[88] D. Coster, Phil. Mag. **43**, 1088, 1105 (1922).

[89] Thoraeus, Phil. Mag. **2**, 107 (1926).

[90] F. K. and R. D. Richtmyer, Phys. Rev. **34**, 574 (1929).

   R. D. Richtmyer, Phys. Rev. **38**, 1802 (1931).

[91] Hjalmar, Zeitschr. f. Physik **1**, 439 (1920); **15**, 65 (1923).

[92] Lindberg, Zeitschr. f. Physik **50**, 82 (1928); **57**, 797 (1929).

[93] Hirsh, Phys. Rev. **38**, 914 (1931).

[94] G. Wentzel, Ann. d. Physik **66**, 437 (1921); Zeitschr. f. Physik **31**, 445 (1925).

which he gave cannot be maintained. The evidence for this state-ment has been summarized by F. K. Richtmyer.[95]

TABLE VIII-22

WENTZEL'S ASSIGNMENT OF INITIAL AND FINAL STATES TO α-GROUP SATELLITES IN THE K SERIES

Satellite	Initial State	Final State	Satellite	Initial State	Final State
$K\alpha'$	KM	LM	$K\alpha_5$	KL^{II}	L^{III}
$K\alpha_3$	KL	L^{II}	$K\alpha_6$	$K^{II}L$	KL^{II}
$K\alpha_4$	K^{II}	KL			

Let us consider the possible methods by which a double ionization of the atom might take place. There are, for the present purposes, three such processes:

(1) An atom in the target loses an inner electron by an impact from the cathode ray electrons. Subsequently, and before this inner loss is replaced, the atom is again struck and another inner electron is removed.

(2) In one encounter with a cathode ray electron, two inner electrons are removed.

(3) A singly ionized atom, by the process discovered by Auger,[96] ejects a second electron instead of emitting a photon corresponding to an x-ray diagram line.

The third process may be dropped from consideration as a possi-bility in the production of the state K^{II}, since the quantum energy of none of the x-ray lines is sufficient to eject a second K electron. If the K^{II} state is produced by process (1), it is very difficult to under-stand how lines having this as an initial state have any appreciable intensity. Due to the very short lifetime of x-ray states (on the order of magnitude of 10^{-16} seconds), and the small density of electrons in the cathode ray beam compared to that of atoms in the target, the probability that an atom excited to the K state would remain in that condition until struck by another electron and excited to K^{II} is much too small to explain the observed relative intensity of satellites

[95] F. K. Richtmyer, J. Frankl. Inst. 208, 325 (1929).
[96] P. Auger, Journ. de Physique et le Radium 6, 205 (1925). See also H. R. Robin-son, Nature 118, 224 (1926); Phil. Mag. 4, 763 (1927).

to diagram lines. Allison and Armstrong[97] estimated the intensity of $K\alpha_3\alpha_4$ to $K\alpha_1$ as less than $1 : 100$ in 29 Cu; DuMond and Hoyt[98] estimate from a comparison of areas the intensity ratio $K\alpha_3 : K\alpha_1$ in 29 Cu as $1 : 120$. We are left with the conclusion that if the K^{II} state occurs in the term table of the non-diagram lines, it must be produced by process (2), that is, simultaneous removal of two K electrons.

We can, however, test the assumption that process (2) is the correct one by measuring the excitation voltages of the non-diagram lines. The energy necessary to remove both K electrons must be slightly greater than twice the amount necessary to remove the first K electron, and hence the critical excitation voltage of $K\alpha_4$ must be at least twice as great as that of $K\alpha_1$, according to Wentzel's scheme. Bäcklin[98a] has examined this question experimentally in the K spectrum of aluminium. The K excitation of 13 Al takes place at 1550 volts; therefore the line $K\alpha_4$ should not appear below 3.1 kv., whereas $K\alpha_3$ should be excited at slightly over 1.55 kv. At a voltage of 2.90 ± 0.05 kv. Bäcklin found both $K\alpha_3$ and $K\alpha_4$, and in the same intensity ratio as at higher voltages.

A similar experiment was performed by Druyvesteyn[87] on the $K\alpha_3\alpha_4$ lines of 23 V. Here the single K excitation occurs at 5.45 kv. and the non-diagram lines under consideration could be detected at 6.45 ± 0.1 kv.

Working at high resolving power with a double crystal spectrometer, Du Mond and Hoyt[98] found that the $K\alpha_3\alpha_4$ lines appeared at a voltage less than 200 greater than that at which the $K\alpha_1\alpha_2$ doublet is excited in copper, namely 8.86 kv.

Druyvesteyn[87] has modified Wentzel's theory in such a manner that it is not necessary to suppose the loss of two electrons from an n, l shell. The assignments of Druyvesteyn for some K group satellites are shown in Table VIII–23; his interpretations of L group satellites will not be discussed here. Druyvesteyn gives the following method of calculation in testing his theory of the origin of $K\beta'''$. Let $(E_{KL})_Z$ be the energy of an atom of atomic number Z from which a K and an L electron have been removed, then to a close approximation,

$$(E_{KL})_Z = (E_K)_Z + (E_L)_{Z+1}, \tag{8.51}$$

[97] S. K. Allison and A. H. Armstrong, Phys. Rev. 26, 714 (1925).
[98] Du Mond and Hoyt, Phys. Rev. 36, 799 (1930).
[98a] E. Bäcklin, Zeitschr. f. Physik 27, 30 (1924).

TABLE VIII–23

DRUYVESTEYN'S ASSIGNMENT OF INITIAL AND FINAL STATES TO X-RAY NON-DIAGRAM
LINES IN THE K GROUP

Parent Line	Satellite	Initial State	Final State
$K\alpha_1$	$K\alpha'$	$1s\ 2s$	$2s\ 2p^5$
$K\alpha_1$	$K\alpha_3,\ \alpha_4$	$1s\ 2p^5$	$2p^4$
$K\alpha_1$	$K\alpha_5,\ \alpha_6$	$1s\ 2p^4$	$2p^3$
$K\beta_1$	$K\beta'''$	KL	LM

since the removal of a K electron is practically equivalent to increasing the pull on the L electrons by augmenting the nuclear charge one proton unit. Also

$$(E_{LM})_Z = (E_L)_Z + (E_M)_{Z+1}. \qquad (8.52)$$

Now for the diagram line K_{β_1}, we have, to the approximation at which we are working,

$$(h\tilde{\nu})_{\beta_1} = (E_K)_Z - (E_M)_Z \qquad (8.53)$$

and by Table VIII–23

$$h\tilde{\nu}_{\beta'''} = (E_{KL})_Z - (E_{LM})_Z. \qquad (8.54)$$

Combination of these four equations gives

$$(h\tilde{\nu}_{\beta'''} - h\tilde{\nu}_{\beta_1})_Z = [(E_L)_{Z+1} - (E_L)_Z] - [(E_M)_{Z+1} - (E_M)_Z], \qquad (8.55)$$

so that the frequency difference between the satellite and its parent line can be roughly computed in terms of known energy levels of atoms of atomic numbers Z and $Z + 1$. Table VIII–24 gives the observed and computed values for elements 13 Al to 26 Fe. The line $K\beta'''$ has been resolved into two components in 13 Al, 14 Si, and 15 P. In the first column of the computed values, the E_L is taken as the average of the $L_{II}L_{III}$ values, in the other computed column, E_L is taken as the energy of L_I.

Although the agreement here is fairly good, Druyvesteyn has not presented data to support his assignments of initial and final states to the $K\alpha$ group satellites. Furthermore the M levels of these relatively light elements are not known with high precision, and thus a certain indefiniteness is possible in the computed values.

TABLE VIII-24

Computation (Eq. (8.55)) and Observation of the Position of $K\beta'''$

Element	Observed $\Delta\nu/R$ $K\beta_1 K\beta'''$		Computed $\Delta\nu/R$ $K\beta_1 K\beta'''$	
			$L_{II}L_{III}$	L_I
13 Al	1.79	2.23	1.82	2.34
14 Si	2.07	2.74	2.11	2.63
15 P	2.38	2.97	2.40	2.92
16 S		2.97	2.70	3.22
17 Cl		3.27	2.97	3.49
19 K		3.59	3.55	4.07
20 Ca		3.83	3.84	4.36
21 Sc		3.77	3.53	4.05
22 Ti		3.72	3.73	4.25
23 V		3.92	3.95	4.47
24 Cr		4.00	4.16	4.68
25 Mn		4.34	4.38	4.90
26 Fe		4.69	4.58	5.10

F. K. Richtmyer[95] has suggested another explanation of the satellites, based on the idea of double electron jumps. Consider a doubly ionized atom, having lost one electron from an inner shell i (K or L), and one from an outer shell o. Then a double jump may occur in which the inner vacancy is filled from a shell of higher total quantum number, and the outer vacancy filled, perhaps from a valence electron. The emitted quantum may be expressed as follows:

$$h\tilde{\nu}_s = h\tilde{\nu}_i + h\tilde{\nu}_o, \qquad (8.56)$$

where $\tilde{\nu}_s$ is the frequency of a satellite of the line whose frequency is $\tilde{\nu}_i$. Since $\tilde{\nu}_o$ is the frequency of a soft x-ray line, we may expect $\tilde{\nu}_o$ to be a linear function of atomic number by Moseley's law, and hence

$$\sqrt{\nu_s - \nu_i} = \text{linear function of } Z. \qquad (8.57)$$

Richtmyer shows that in many cases this relation holds, and indeed may be used to establish the parent line of a given satellite. On the other hand, Idei,[87] considering the same data, concluded that $(\nu_s - \nu_i)$ itself is a linear function of atomic number, which casts some doubt on the unique significance of the relationship found by Richtmyer. The presence of a continuous spectrum in the region of the satellites could, however, be readily explained on Richtmyer's suggestion, as the filling of the outer vacancy by captured electrons bringing various amounts of kinetic energy.

Langer[99] has proposed the possibility that the five $K\alpha$ satellites may arise from $(1s\,2s) \rightarrow (2s\,2p^5)$ and $(1s\,2p^5) \rightarrow 2p^4$. The configuration $1s\,2s$ will give rise to two terms, $^1S_0$ and $^3S_1$, both of which are even. $2s\,2p^5$ will give rise to four terms, which, if Russell-Saunders coupling is applicable, may be divided into $^1P_1$ and $^3P_{012}$, and a similar set will arise from $1s\,2p^5$. The number of terms arising from $2p^4$ is limited by Pauli's exclusion principle, since we are dealing with equivalent electrons, and only $^1D_2$, $^1S_0$, $^3P_{012}$ occur in Russell-Saunders coupling. Table VIII–24 gives the assignment of the five possible transitions between these states (neglecting the possibility of intercombination lines) to the five $K\alpha$ satellites, according to Langer and to Wolfe.[100]

TABLE VIII–24

ASSIGNMENT OF LEVELS TO THE $K\alpha$ SATELLITES ACCORDING TO LANGER AND TO WOLFE

Langer	Satellite	Wolfe
$1s\,2s\,^1S \rightarrow 2s\,2p^5\,^1P$	$K\alpha'$	$1s\,2p^5\,^1P \rightarrow 2p^4\,^1S$
$1s\,2p^5\,^3P \rightarrow 2p^4\,^3P$	$K\alpha_3$	$1s\,2s\,^3S \rightarrow 2s\,2p^5\,^3P$
$1s\,2s\,^3S \rightarrow 2s\,2p^5\,^1S$	$K\alpha_4$	$1s\,2s\,^1S \rightarrow 2s\,2p^5\,^1P$
$1s\,2p^5\,^1P \rightarrow 2p^4\,^1S$	$K\alpha_5$	$1s\,2p^5\,^3P \rightarrow 2p^4\,^3P$
$1s\,2p^5\,^1P \rightarrow 2p^4\,^1D$	$K\alpha_6$	$1s\,2p^5\,^1P \rightarrow 2p^4\,^1D$

Wolfe has supported his assignments by a calculation of the frequencies to be expected using Slater's[101] method of computing interaction energies, which assumes Russell-Saunders coupling. The calculations were carried out for 19 K, and the contributions to the energy from the interchange of the electron spins proved to be large compared to the spin-orbit interaction energy, which justifies the assumption that large deviations from Russell-Saunders coupling do not occur. Table VIII–25 shows the extent of the numerical agreement.

[99] Langer, Phys. Rev. **37**, 457 (1931).
[100] H. C. Wolfe, Phys. Rev. **43**, 221 (1933).
[101] Slater, Phys. Rev. **34**, 1293 (1929).

TABLE VIII–25

COMPUTED AND OBSERVED FREQUENCIES FOR $K\alpha$ SATELLITES IN POTASSIUM

Line	ν/R Observed	ν/R Calculated	Line	ν/R Observed	ν/R Calculated
$K\alpha'$	245.05	245.05	$K\alpha_5$	....	246.38
$K\alpha_3$	245.56	245.63	$K\alpha_6$	....	246.15
$K\alpha_4$	245.69	245.53			

When the assignment is made in the manner of Table VIII–24, according to Wolfe, the $K\alpha_3$ and $K\alpha_5$ lines involve transitions between triplet states, and should be diffuse, which agrees with the experiments. Also in this assignment, the initial configuration of $K\alpha_3$ and $K\alpha_4$, $1s\,2s$, is different from that of the other lines, which may explain their greater intensity and persistence to higher atomic numbers.

Sawada[102] has extended the ideas of Langer and made assignments of initial and final states to satellites of the $K\beta$ group.

13. *Structure of Absorption Edges, and Chemical Effects in X-ray Spectra*

In certain cases it is known that the absorption coefficient of a substance for x-rays does not increase in a uniform manner with increasing wave-length up to a critical absorption limit, and then undergo a discontinuous decrease. The question of the width of absorption limits themselves will be taken up elsewhere; here we shall discuss the " uneven " variations of the absorption coefficient with wave-length in a region (some 200 volts wide in some cases) whose low frequency limit is the main critical absorption edge. Figure VIII–25 is a photometer tracing of the transmission absorption spectrum of a copper foil in the region of the 29 Cu K limit, obtained by Coster and Veldkamp.[103] Here the phenomenon in question is clearly indicated at the short wave-length side of the K absorption limit.

In 1920 Kossel[10] pointed out that such a structure of the absorption limit might be expected from his theory of the origin of x-ray spectra. It is not necessary that in an absorption act the ejected

[102] M. Sawada, Kyoto Coll. Sci. Mem. **15**, 43 (1932).
[103] Coster and Veldkamp, Zeitschr. f. Physik **70**, 306 (1931).

electron be removed to infinity, it is only necessary that it be displaced to the first unfilled group which it may occupy.   If there are no incomplete inner groups, the electron may come to rest in various optical orbits.   On this idea the absorption jump of shortest wavelength would represent removal to infinity, longer wave-length limits being associated with removal to unoccupied outer orbits.   Such a structure could not cover a region of more than a few tens of volts, at the most.

In some cases of the absorption of x-rays by monatomic gases and vapors, structures of this simple type have been detected.   We may mention especially the work of Coster and van der Tuuk[104] on the K absorption edge of argon.   They were able to estimate the energy values of the possible states in which the electron could stop from the known optical levels of potassium, since the field outside an argon atom ionized in the K shell should resemble that of a potassium atom. Hanawalt[105] investigated absorption by gaseous 80 Hg, 30 Zn, 36 Kr, and 54 Xe.   In these cases all the extended structures found could be interpreted on Kossel's ideas.

In certain cases, however, these secondary structures cover regions representing some hundreds of volts energy, and Kossel's interpretation

[104] Coster and van der Tuuk, Zeitschr. f. Physik **37**, 367 (1926).

[105] J. D. Hanawalt, Phys. Rev. **37**, 715 (1931).

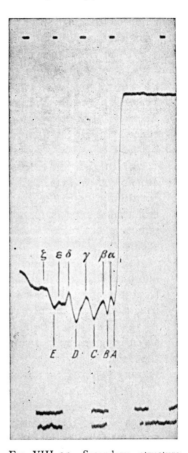

FIG. VIII–25.   Secondary structure of the K absorption edge of copper after Coster and Veldkamp. The uppermost line represents the zero reading of the microphotometer; the third curve from the top is taken through a section of the plate exposed to only scattered and fluorescence radiation; the bottom curve is taken through an unexposed portion of the plate. The direction of increasing wave-length is from left to right.

cannot be adequate. Kievit and Lindsay,[106] who have made extensive experimental investigations into the nature of the secondary structure in the elements 20 Ca to 31 Ga, have attributed the phenomenon to the ejection of two or more electrons by the absorption of a single quantum, and attempted to correlate their observations with ejection from known outer levels of the atoms. This theory does not, however, explain the absence of such a structure in monatomic vapors, nor does it account for a temperature effect on the structure observed by Hanawalt.[107]

Kronig[108] has proposed quite a different theory for the extended structure and lists the following as significant experimental facts:

(1) In addition to the previously mentioned results on monatomic gases, Hanawalt[105] has found that in some cases of polyatomic gases (Se_8, AsH_3) only a secondary structure of the monatomic type is found, whereas in other polyatomic gases a structure extending several hundred volts from the main edge occurs.

(2) Such an extended structure is in general found in crystalline materials, notably metals in the solid state. As the distance from the principal edge increases, the separation of adjacent irregularities in the absorption increases.

(3) Hanawalt[107] showed that as the temperature is raised, a given irregularity is displaced toward the principal edge, and at the same time smoothed out, the entire secondary structure tending to disappear as the temperature increases.

(4) Coster and Veldkamp found that the per cent variation of the absorption coefficient in the region on the short wavelength side of the K limit is about twice as great in 29 Cu as in 30 Zn at room temperature.

Kronig bases his explanation on some results of the application of wave-mechanics to the motion of electrons in crystalline substances, where a periodic potential function may be used. Bloch[109] and others have shown that in such a case not all possible kinetic energies

[106] Kievit and Lindsay, Phys. Rev. 36, 648 (1930). See also B. B. Ray, Zeitschr. f. Physik 55, 119 (1929).

[107] J. D. Hanawalt, Zeitschr. f. Phys. 70, 293 (1931).

[108] R. de L. Kronig, Zeitschr. f. Physik 70, 317 (1931).

[109] F. Bloch, Zeitschr. f. Physik 52, 555 (1928).

are permitted for an electron traversing the lattice. If the electron is proceeding parallel to one of the crystallographic axes, the possible kinetic energy spectrum consists of permitted and forbidden zones of finite width, which have been quantitatively investigated for some simple potential function forms.[110]   As the kinetic energy increases, the permitted zones become broader than the forbidden zones, approaching the state where the traversing electron may have any given kinetic energy. If we define a reference level of potential in the crystal such that the average potential referred to this level vanishes, the higher forbidden energy zones, which are quite narrow, practically coincide with the values

$$E(n) = \frac{n^2 h^2}{8md^2} \qquad (8.58)$$

where n is an integer, h the Planck constant, m the electronic mass, and d the interatomic (in simple crystals the interplanar) distance. Davisson and Germer[111] and Rupp[112] have shown that these forbidden zones are detectable at kinetic energies of hundreds of volts, since a maximum of reflection of incident electrons from the crystal is observed when the incident kinetic energy coincides with that of one of the forbidden zones.

Applying this to the phenomena under consideration, we may interpret the absorption discontinuity of longest wave-length as corresponding to an absorption act in which the electron is moved to the first possible, unoccupied level. In the over-simplified one-dimensional case, where all photo-electrons are ejected parallel to a crystallographic axis, an absorption band should extend to the short wave-length side of this edge, containing finite intervals in which the absorption vanishes, coinciding with the forbidden zones, since no photo-electrons may be ejected having the forbidden kinetic energies. In a later paper Kronig[113] has shown that even when it is considered that photo-electrons may be ejected in all possible

[110] M. J. V. Strutt, Ann. der Physik **86**, 319 (1928).
   P. M. Morse, Phys. Rev. **35**, 1310 (1930).
   R. de L. Kronig and W. G. Penney, Proc. Roy. Soc. Lond. A **130**, 449 (1931).
[111] Davisson and Germer, Phys. Rev. **30**, 705 (1927); Proc. Nat. Acad. Sci. **14**, 317, 619 (1928).
[112] E. Rupp, Annalen der Physik **5**, 453 (1930); Zeitschr. f. Physik **61**, 587 (1930) and previous papers.
[113] R. de L. Kronig, Zeitschr. f. Physik **75**, 191 (1932).

directions, there remains an effect which would cause the observed irregularities in the absorption coefficient.

The fact that the intervals between irregularities are greater toward higher frequencies is explained by eq. (8.58), since as n increases the forbidden zones are spaced farther and farther apart.

The disappearance of the extended structure as the temperature rises is explained as due to an increase in d of eq. (8.58). Further, the progress of the electron through the crystal is deflected by more frequent encounters with atoms due to their increased thermal agitation, which decreases the sharpness of the effect. The more marked effect observed in 29 Cu than in 30 Zn at room temperature may be considered as due to the fact that this temperature is nearer the melting point of Zn than of Cu.

Some confirmation of the dependence of eq. (8.58) on the reciprocal of the square of the lattice constant has been obtained from the work of Lindsay,[114] who investigated the extended structure of the K limit of potassium in the crystals KCl, KBr, and KI, whose lattice constants are 3.14, 3.29 and 3.53 A respectively. He found that the structures in these cases were qualitatively quite similar, but spaced roughly inversely as the squares of the lattice constants, as predicted by eq. (8.58). Confirmation along similar lines has been obtained by Coster and Veldkamp,[114a] who have investigated the extended structure of the K edge of Cu, and the L_{III} edges of 78 Pt and 79 Au. These metals crystallize in the face-centered cubic system, and when the separations of the edges have been multiplied by the square of the lattice constant, the observed structures agree closely. The structures near the 26 Fe and 30 Zn limits were found to be quite different, however, since iron is body centered cubic and zinc hexagonal.

An indication of the treatment to be given polyatomic gases, considering them as intermediates between the monatomic state and solids, has been presented by Kronig.[115] As yet unexplained by these considerations is the fact that the 30 Zn structure has been observed to persist to within 20° C. of its melting point, whereas the iron structure has vanished at 600° C.; also that under similar cir-

---

[114] G. A. Lindsay, Zeitschr. f. Physik 71, 735 (1931).
[114a] Coster and Veldkamp, Zeitschr. f. Physik 70, 306 (1931).
[115] R. de L. Kronig, Zeitschr. f. Physik 75, 468 (1932).

cumstances the structure near a K limit is more pronounced than that near an L limit.[116]

Although, as we have seen in Sec. 1 of this chapter, the x-ray spectra are to a first approximation independent of chemical combination of the emitting or absorbing atom, yet slight changes in both the emission and absorption spectrum have been found and attributed to chemical effects. Bergengren[117] was the first to demonstrate an effect of chemical combination on the absorption spectrum. He investigated the K absorption limit of phosphorus in various allotropic modifications, and found slight variations in the wave-length of the edge. A large amount of experimental work on the effect of chemical combinations on the wave-length of the K absorption edge has been done by Lindh.[118] In his investigations of chlorine compounds, he found that there is in general a structure to the limit, which in various compounds extends over an energy range of the order of 20 volts. The most important generalization about this structure is that it is the same in all chlorine compounds of the same chlorine valence. Thus there is a characteristic pattern for all chlorides, all chlorates, and all perchlorates. Among the monovalent chlorine

[116] Other papers, not previously mentioned, dealing with these effects, are:
Nishina, Phil. Mag. **49**, 521 (1925).
Lindsay and Van Dyke, Phys. Rev. **28**, 613 (1926).
Lindsay and Voorhees, Phil. Mag. **6**, 910 (1928).
J. M. Nuttall, Phys. Rev. **31**, 742 (1928).
Coster and Wolf, Nature **124**, 230 (1929).
H.-T. Meyer, Wiss. Veroff. a. d. Siemens Konzern **7**, 108 (1929). Some of the results reported by Meyer are in conflict with the general facts summarized by Kronig.
Ray and Mahanti, Zeitschr. f. Physik **54**, 534 (1929).
Deodhar, Nature **125**, 776 (1930).
S. Idei, Sci. Rep. Tohoku Imp. Univ. **19**, 653 (1930).
A. E. Lindh, Zeitschr. f. Physik **63**, 106 (1930).
Sandström, Nature **128**, 759 (1931).
In a recent paper by V. P. Barton and G. A. Lindsay, Phys. Rev. **46**, 362 (1934) it is shown that the structure of the K absorption edge of Ca in aragonite and calcite is not the same, which agrees with Kronig's theory since the two crystals are different. However in four other cases, in which a given crystal contains two metals, the structures were found to be different, which indicates that the crystal lattice is not the only factor governing the fine structure.
[117] Bergengren, Zeitschr. f. Physik **3**, 247 (1920); Compt. rend. **171**, 624 (1920).
[118] A. E. Lindh, Zeitschr. f. Physik **6**, 303 (1921); **31**, 210 (1925); Compt. rend. **172**, 1175 (1925); Dissertation, Lund (1923); Arkiv. Mat. Astro. och Fysik **18**, 14 (1924).

compounds, HCl is found to be an exception, and also Cl_2 itself has a distinctive pattern.

Stelling,[119] however, using higher dispersion than Lindh, found changes in the K absorption limit of chlorine in various chlorides, depending on the nature of the metal atom in the compound. He also detected an effect apparently due to water of crystallization. In chlorates and perchlorates Stelling found no dependence of the limit upon the metal atom in the compound, agreeing with Lindh. The K absorption of chlorine in many organic compounds has been investigated by Aoyama, Kimura, and Nishina.[120]

Lindh[118] has also carried out extensive investigations on 16 S and 15 P in various compounds. The sulfides were found to differ in the wave-length of the main absorption edge of sulfur, the shortest being that for ZnS, 5.0053 A, the longest that for Cr_2S_3, 5.0117 A. Many previous discrepancies were clarified when Chamberlain[121] showed that often the x-rays themselves change the composition of the absorbing material. She found that iodic acid and potassium permanganate are reduced by the action of x-rays, and showed that part of the structure of the K absorption edges of 22 Ti to 25 Mn in higher oxides as observed by Coster[122] was undoubtedly due to the presence of the free metal, formed by reduction of the compound.[123]

Pauling[124] has discussed the theoretical interpretation of shifts of the critical absorption wave-length with chemical combination, following the previous treatment by Fajans,[125] who attributed the effect largely to deformation of the ions in a crystal lattice. Pauling has considered the various factors which may affect the energy necessary to remove an electron from an ion in a crystal. In the first place, we must consider the fact that the work required to remove an electron is influenced by the external screening exerted by adjacent

[119] O. Stelling, Z. anorg. allg. Chemie, 131, 1023, 48 (1927); Chem. Ber. 60, 650 (1927); Zeitschr. f. Physik 50, 506, 626 (1928); Naturwiss. 17, 689 (1929).

[120] Aoyama, Kimura and Nishina, Zeitschr. f. Physik 44, 810; 46, 150 (1927).

[121] K. Chamberlain, Phys. Rev. 26, 525 (1925).

[122] Coster, Zeitschr. f. Physik 25, 83 (1924).

[123] Chemical effects in the L absorption spectra have been observed by:
J. G. Tandberg, Ark. Mat. Astro. och Fysik 18, 14 (1924).
Jönsson, Zeitschr. f. Physik 35, 387 (1926).
The K absorption of vanadium in various compounds has been investigated by Hendricks and Wyckoff, J. Physical Chem. 31, 703 (1927).

[124] L. Pauling, Phys. Rev. 34, 954 (1929).

[125] K. Fajans, Zeitschr. f. Physik 50, 531 (1928).

ions in the vicinity of the parent ion. This effect will differ with the sign of the ion; in a positive ion the external screening of surrounding negatives will facilitate removal of an electron and vice versa. The effect will furthermore be inversely proportional to the distance between the ions. Then the crystal itself will have an electron affinity which will aid in the process of photo-ionization. Pauling shows that this affinity may be calculated from the specific diamagnetic susceptibility, and the effect of screening of adjacent ions is calculable in crystals as simple in form as the alkali halides. The shifts of the K absorption edge of Cl in LiCl, NaCl, KCl, RbCl can thus be estimated, and agree well with theory, but NH_4Cl, CsCl, CuCl and AgCl do not show agreement.

The different behaviour of a cation with respect to the effect of outer screening is shown in the negligible variations of the wavelength of the K absorption edge of potassium in KF, KCl, KBr, and KI. For a positive ion, the sum of the effects of external screening and crystal electron affinity is important, and by calculation it results that in the cited series this sum does not materially change, the external screening effect decreasing as fast as the crystal infinity increases.

Lindh and Lundquist[126] were the first to discover an effect of chemical combination on x-ray line spectra. They investigated the $K\beta_1$ line of 15 P, 16 S and 17 Cl in various compounds. With Ag_2S on Cu, Fe, and Al anticathodes, different positions and relative intensities of the $K\beta_1$ and $K\beta_x$ (a satellite of $K\beta_1$) resulted. Wetterblad[127] investigated the $K\beta$ group of 11 Na, 12 Mg and 13 Al, and of these elements in their oxides, and found differences. It is not surprising that such effects occur in this range of the periodic system, for here the electrons in the M shell, which by transitions to the K shell cause emission of lines in the β group, are the valence electrons, and partake in chemical combination.

The interpretation of the results is made difficult by the probability that the action of the cathode rays alters the chemical compounds which are originally put on the target.

Ray[128] and Bäcklin[129] showed that the wave-length of the

126 A. E. Lindh and O. Lundquist, Ark. Mat. Astro. och Fysik 18, Nos. 14, 34, 35 (1924).

127 Wetterblad, Zeitschr. f. Physik 42, 603, 611 (1927).

128 B. B. Ray, Phil. Mag. 49, 168 (1925).

129 Bäcklin, Zeitschr. f. Physik 33, 547 (1925); 38, 215 (1926). See also G. B Deodhar, Proc. Roy. Soc. Lond. A 131, 647 (1931).

$K\alpha_1\alpha_2$ doublet of 16 S depends on the particular sulfate in which the sulfur is found; thus in the series $CaSO_4$, $MgSO_4$, K_2SO_4, $BaSO_4$ a progressive shift toward shorter wave-lengths takes place, which amounts to as much as 3 X.U. from the position of the doublet in the pure element on an aluminium target. Similar shifts are found in the $K\alpha_1\alpha_2$ doublet in 13 Al, 14 Si and 15 P, and a chemical effect on the $K\alpha_3\alpha_4$ spark lines has also been established, the lines appearing much broader in $BaSO_4$ on an aluminium target than in sulfur itself on an aluminium target.

In order to avoid as far as possible the danger of dissociating the compounds whose x-ray spectrum is under investigation, Faessler[130] and Valasek[131] have used special x-ray tubes in which the method of excitation is wholly, in the case of Faessler, and to a large part in the case of Valasek, by fluorescence. Both authors investigated the K spectrum of 16 S in various compounds and were able to detect effects due to chemical combination. Svensson[132] has attempted to study the reactions of sulfur with different metals by the changes in x-ray wave-lengths produced.

In the region of very soft x-rays, such as the K lines of 4 Be, it is definitely known that the lines are much broader from a solid than from a gaseous source.[133] Houston[134] has discussed this effect, and attributed it to the fact that in a solid, particularly a metal, the energies which the outer electrons of an atom may have are not strictly limited to certain discrete values by the quantum conditions. It is these outer electrons which, falling into the vacancy in the K shell, cause the emission of the $K\alpha$ line, and hence this line may be a broad band, the components of which are not resolved.

Houston has studied the distribution of intensity in the $K\alpha$ line of 4 Be, as predicted by the free electron model of Pauli and of Sommerfeld.[135] He finds that the energies of the outer electrons are so distributed that the $K\alpha$ line of beryllium should have a sharp short wave-length edge, and a linear slope extending to softer wave-lengths

[130] Faessler, Zeitschr. f. Physik 72, 734 (1931).
[131] Valasek, Phys. Rev. 43, 612 (1933).
[132] Svensson, Zeitschr. f. Physik 75, 120 (1932).
  Other recent papers are:
  Owen and Williams, Proc. Roy. Soc. Lond. A 132, 282 (1931).
  Yoshida, Inst. Physical Chem. Research Tokyo Sci. Rep. 421, 298 (1933).
[133] M. Soderman, Zeitschr. f. Physik 65, 656 (1930).
[134] W. V. Houston, Phys. Rev. 38, 1797 (1931).
[135] W. Pauli, Zeitschr. f. Physik 41, 81 (1927); A. Sommerfeld, ibid., 47, 1 (1928).

for some 18 A (the wave-length of the line is about 117 A). Thus the full width of the line at half maximum should be roughly 9 A, which agrees well with that observed by Sodermann, although the observation does not show a sharp short wave-length edge.

Using the bound electron model of Bloch[109] in which the electron is initially attached to a particular atom, but can easily jump to an adjacent one, under the action of an external field, Houston finds that a sharp short wave-length edge is not predicted, but that a width somewhat less than that observed results. In these calculations the spread of the K level was neglected, since it is certainly relatively small.

Glocker and Renninger[136] have investigated the shape of the $K\alpha$ line of carbon in graphite, diamond, and carborundum. In each case the line is asymmetrical, being steeper on the short than on the long wave-length side. The full width of the line at half maximum is progressively less in graphite, diamond and carborundum, and varies from about 1.6 A to 0.9 A. The wave-length of carbon $K\alpha$ is approximately 44.5 A. In the case of the diamond a weak line appears adjacent to $K\alpha$ on the long wave-length side. The shape of the line in the various crystals is discussed in connection with the treatment by Hund[137] of the energy states in crystals of the diamond type, a development of which is outside the scope of this book.

[136] Glocker and Renninger, Naturwiss. 20, 122 (1932).
Renninger, Zeitschr. f. Physik 78, 510 (1932).
Glocker, Physikalische Zeitschr. 24, 963 (1932).
[137] Hund, Zeitschr. f. Physik 74, 1 (1932).

CHAPTER IX

SOME ACCURATE METHODS OF X-RAY WAVE-LENGTH MEASUREMENT
AND THEIR RESULTS

1. *The Correction of Bragg's Equation for the Effects of the Index of Refraction of the Crystal*

In the treatment of the diffraction of x-rays by a perfect crystal, we found that a rigorous solution of the problem leads to the conclusion that the greatest intensity in the diffraction pattern is not observed in a direction making the glancing angle θ_0 with the face of the crystal, where θ_0 is defined by

$$\sin \theta_0 = n\lambda/2d, \qquad (9.01)$$

λ being the wave-length in air. The maximum intensity of the diffraction pattern occurs at glancing angles greater than θ_0, and this effect is usually called the influence of the refractive index on Bragg's equation. The accurate measurement of x-ray wave-lengths by crystal diffraction necessitates a knowledge of the magnitude of this effect. It is possible by elementary methods to treat the problem in a manner which will give the correct index of refraction correction provided Darwin's diffraction pattern of a perfect crystal represents the actual diffraction pattern. Darwin's approximation consists in neglecting absorption in the crystal, or, in other words, using only the real part of the complex number which in the more complete theory gives rise to the index of refraction and the absorption. In the case of the diffraction of Mo $K\alpha$ from calcite, the difference between the correction to be calculated here and the correction demanded by the more complete dispersion theory is on the order of a tenth of a second of arc, which is within the limit of experimental measurement.[1] For longer wave-lengths (greater absorption) the

---

[1] This may be seen from an examination of Fig. VI-5, Chap. VI. If the elementary theory to be developed here were strictly accurate, the curve of the figure would be symmetrical about the ordinate at $l = 0$. Actually the center of gravity lies slightly toward negative values of l, and the extent of this effect is the difference between the complete and elementary theories. The difference is clearly greater for longer wave-lengths as may be seen from Fig. VI-6, Chap. VI.

difference is greater, but in no case in which accurate wave-length measurements from crystals have been made does it become large compared to the total correction for index of refraction. With this justification, then, we will proceed with the elementary derivation of the corrections to be applied to Bragg's equation.

We have seen in the chapter on dispersion theory that the index of refraction for x-rays traversing matter is less than unity, and that the unit decrement for the more commonly used wave-lengths is of

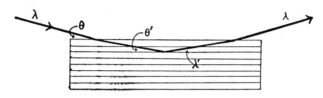

Fɪɢ. IX–1. The x-rays are bent away from the normal on entering the crystal. If one assumes that the Bragg law may be strictly applied to the quantities λ' and θ' inside the crystal, it is possible to derive in an elementary manner the index of refraction correction.

the order of 10^{-6}. Thus a beam entering the crystal will be bent away from the normal, as shown in Fig. IX–1. Let

$\lambda \sim$ wave-length of the x-rays in air,

$\theta \sim$ glancing angle in air,

$\lambda' \sim$ wave-length in the crystal,

$\theta' \sim$ glancing angle in the crystal.

Let us first investigate the relation between λ and λ'. The index of refraction is the ratio of the phase velocity of the waves in the air (v) and in the crystal (v'):

$$\mu = v/v'. \qquad (9.02)$$

The frequency in the air and in the crystal is the same, hence since $\mu < 1$ and $v' > v$, the wave-length in the crystal must be the longer, and

$$\mu = \lambda/\lambda', \qquad (9.03)$$

also

$$\mu = (\cos \theta)/(\cos \theta') \qquad (9.04)$$

and

$$n\lambda' = 2d \sin \theta', \qquad (9.05)$$

since we may assume that the reflections by which the diffracted beam is made up occur inside the crystal medium, after the ray has been bent upon entrance. We will also use δ, the unit decrement of the index of refraction, defined by

$$\mu = 1 - \delta. \tag{9.06}$$

The elimination of μ and of the primed quantities from the eqs. (9.03) to (9.06) gives directly the result

$$n\lambda = 2d \left(1 - \frac{2\delta - \delta^2}{\sin^2 \theta} \right)^{\frac{1}{2}} \sin \theta. \tag{9.07}$$

If we expand the radical and neglect terms in powers of δ higher than the first, we obtain the standard form

$$n\lambda = 2d \left(1 - \frac{\delta}{\sin^2 \theta} \right) \sin \theta. \tag{9.08}$$

In this equation θ is the observed glancing angle, obtained directly from the experiment.

The value of the correction term in parentheses in eq. (9.08) changes with order, and hence there is an apparent change of wave-length with order if the uncorrected formula is used. We now derive a formula which will enable us to calculate δ from measurements of the apparent wave-lengths in two different orders, n_1 and n_2. We will have the equations

$$n_1\lambda = 2d \left(1 - \frac{\delta}{\sin^2 \theta_1} \right) \sin \theta_1, \tag{9.09}$$

$$n_2\lambda = 2d \left(1 - \frac{\delta}{\sin^2 \theta_2} \right) \sin \theta_2. \tag{9.10}$$

Now let λ_1 and λ_2 be the apparent wave-lengths obtained in the two orders by simply substituting the observed values of θ in the uncorrected Bragg equation. They will be

$$\lambda_1 = (2d \sin \theta_1)/n_1, \tag{9.11}$$

$$\lambda_2 = (2d \sin \theta_2)/n_2. \tag{9.12}$$

We wish to solve the above four equations for δ in terms of measurable quantities. Since the difference between λ_1 and λ_2 is minute compared to either λ_1 or λ_2, we will set $\lambda_1 = \lambda_2 = \bar{\lambda}$ everywhere in the solution except in the term $(\lambda_1 - \lambda_2)$, where $\bar{\lambda}$ may be taken as either λ_1 or λ_2 or some average of them. The indicated solution gives

$$\delta = \frac{\lambda_1 - \lambda_2}{\bar{\lambda}} \frac{n_2{}^2}{n_2{}^2 - n_1{}^2} \sin^2 \theta_1, \qquad (9.12a)$$

which is known as Stenström's formula. In 1919 Stenström[2] observed that the apparent wave-length of Mo $L\beta_1$, 5.167 A, changed with order when reflected from a sugar crystal, and explained the effect using the above formula, thus obtaining the first measurement of the index of refraction for x-rays.

We will now indicate the method of derivation of a formula giving the actual angular correction to be applied to the observed angle of diffraction in order to calculate the true wave-length in air by the Bragg equation. This means that we shall express the difference $\theta - \theta_0$ in terms of δ, where θ_0 is defined by eq. (9.01). It should be clear to the reader that θ_0 does not appear in Fig. IX–1 and may be defined in words as that angle, which used with the simple Bragg equation, will give the correct wave-length in air. From Fig. IX–1 it easily follows that, to quantities of the order of magnitude of δ,

$$\theta - \theta' = \delta \cot \theta, \qquad (9.13)$$

and from eqs. (9.01) and (9.05) it follows that to the same approximation

$$\theta' - \theta_0 = \delta \tan \theta. \qquad (9.14)$$

Combination of these last two equations gives the desired result, namely,

$$\theta - \theta_0 = \delta \sec \theta \operatorname{cosec} \theta. \qquad (9.15)$$

Equation (9.15) was first derived by Darwin[3] in 1914, five years before the technique of x-ray spectroscopy was sufficiently advanced to detect the effects which it predicts. It corresponds to the shift of the ordinate of symmetry of Fig. VI–7, Chap. VI, from the angle θ_0.

To summarize the discussion of index of refraction corrections, and to orient the reader with respect to their order of magnitude, some calculations of the quantities involved are given in Table IX–1. The calculations summarized in this table are made on the following basis:

$$\delta = 2.03 \times 10^{-6}, \lambda = 0.708 \times 10^{-8} \text{ cm., } \sin \theta_1 = 0.11684.[4]$$

[2] W. Stenström, Dissertation, Lund (1919).
[3] C. G. Darwin, Phil. Mag. **27**, 315 (1914), p. 318.
[4] δ-value from C. C. Hatley, Phys. Rev. **24**, 486 (1924).

TABLE IX-1

EFFECT OF THE REFRACTIVE INDEX ON THE REFLECTION OF Mo $K\alpha_1$ FROM THE CALCITE
CLEAVAGE FACES

Order	Correction to Observed Wave-length	$\theta - \theta_0$
1	-107×10^{-14} cm.	3.60 sec.
2	$- 29$	1.84
3	$- 13$	1.28
4	$- 7$	1.02
5	$- 5$	0.88

2. Constants and Conventions Used in the Precision Measurement of X-ray Wave-lengths by Crystalline Diffraction

At present there are two main methods of measuring x-ray wave-lengths, namely by crystalline diffraction, and by diffraction from a ruled grating.   In this section we shall treat the first of these methods. In the crystalline method it is essential to calculate the wave-length (forgetting for the moment the index of refraction corrections of the preceding section) from the equation

$$n\lambda = 2d \sin \theta. \qquad (9.16)$$

Experimentally we can measure θ, but the equation contains two other unknowns besides λ, namely n and d.   The proper interpretation of n and d in rock-salt was discovered in Bragg's analysis of this crystal. If we take the reflection from the cleavage or (100) planes and call $n = 1$ for the reflection observed with the smallest value of θ, then d is one-half the length of the edge of a cube containing four molecules of NaCl.   This distance can be calculated from a knowledge of the atomic weights W of sodium and chlorine, Avogadro's number N, and the density of rock-salt ρ, and is given by

$$d_{100} = \frac{1}{2} \sqrt[3]{\frac{4(W_{Na} + W_{Cl})}{\rho N}}. \qquad (9.17)$$

From the data available in 1913, Moseley[5] calculated from an equation similar to (9.17)

$$d_{100} = 2.814 \times 10^{-8} \text{ cm.} \qquad (9.18)$$

[5] Moseley, Phil. Mag. 26, 1024 (1913).

It is of interest to note that from eq. (9.17) the value of d, and hence that of λ, depends on the value of the Avogadro number and on the density. N, however, depends on the value of the electronic charge so that fundamentally λ depends on e and ρ. The discussion at this point is complicated by two experimental facts:

(a) It has been found in x-ray spectroscopic work that rock salt is not the best crystal to use, since it often gives false lines and is far from being perfect. Calcite has been found much more satisfactory.

(b) The accuracy with which the glancing angle θ can be measured is much greater than that with which d is known, because of the uncertainty in the value of e.

Let us discuss the second point first, and illustrate it by tabulating some of the data on calcite. Table IX–2 gives the results of some recent determinations of the density of calcite.

TABLE IX–2

SOME RECENT DETERMINATIONS OF THE DENSITY OF CALCITE AT 18° C

Author

2.7102±0.0004	Defoe and Compton, Phys. Rev. **25**, 618 (1925)
2.71026	Bearden, Phys. Rev. **38**, 1389 (1931)
2.71003	Tu, Phys. Rev. **40**, 662 (1932)

The largest difference here is 0.00023, and hence the largest per cent deviation is 0.0085.

Let us compare the accuracy of some recent determinations of the angle of reflection of Mo $K\alpha_1$ from calcite in the first order at 18° C.; Table IX–3.

TABLE IX–3

SOME RECENT DETERMINATIONS OF θ FOR Mo $K\alpha_1$ FROM CALCITE IN THE FIRST ORDER AT 18° C

θ	θ in Seconds	Author
6° 42′ 35.4″	24155.4	Larsson, Phil. Mag. **3**, 1136 (1927)
6° 42′ 36.0″	24156.0	Compton,* Rev. Sci. Inst. **2**, 365 (1931)
6° 42′ 35.3″	24155.3	Bearden, Phys. Rev. **38**, 1389 (1931)
6° 42′ 35.5″	24155.5	Tu, Phys. Rev. **40**, 662 (1932)

* The result of Compton was corrected by J. H. Williams, Phys. Rev. **40**, 636 (1932).

In Table IX–3 the greatest variation is 0.7 second, or 0.0029 per cent. By comparison of the variations in ρ and θ of Tables IX–2 and IX–3 it is seen that the uncertainty in the value of ρ is roughly three times that in the glancing angle. Since the value of the grating space depends on the cube root of the density, the uncertainty in d due to that in ρ is one third of the uncertainty in ρ, hence the uncertainty in the calculated wave-length due to errors in ρ and θ measurements is nearly the same, and on the order of 0.003 per cent.

However, in the calculation of d from ρ, the value of the electronic charge is involved. In 1929 Birge[6] estimated that the most probable value of e from Millikan's work is

$$e = (4.770 \pm 0.005) \times 10^{-10} \text{ e.s.u.} \qquad (9.19)$$

Thus the error in e from this source may be as large as 0.1 per cent, or some 36 times the error in θ. The error in λ may then be some 12 times as great from the uncertainty in e as it is from that in θ. The difficulty in reducing a measurement of glancing angle to an absolute wave-length of comparable accuracy is thus evident.

This relatively large uncertainty in the value of e makes it apparent why the index of refraction correction has been neglected in the preceding discussion. From an inspection of the value of $\theta - \theta_0$ in Table IX–1 and the value of θ in Table IX–3 it is seen that in the reflection of Mo $K\alpha_1$ from calcite in the first order the angle correction amounts to some 0.015 per cent. Thus the total index of refraction correction is less than the uncertainty introduced through the error in e, and any errors in the value of δ will make corrections in the absolute wave-length which at present are unimportant, if the calculation is being carried out from a measured glancing angle.

Perhaps the most satisfactory method of tabulating the results of spectroscopic measurement on x-ray lines by means of crystals would be to give the angles of reflection from calcite, and not make the relatively inaccurate wave-length calculation. This method has not been adopted, however, and wave-lengths have been tabulated which are based on an arbitrary and assumed value of d. Following the paper of Moseley,[5] Siegbahn defined the grating space of rock salt to be

$$d_{\text{NaCl}} = 2.81400 \text{ A at } 18° \text{ C.} \qquad (9.20)$$

At this time the accuracy of measurement was not sufficient to

[6] R. T. Birge, Phys. Rev. Suppl. 1, 1 (1929).

require index of refraction corrections, so that it was not necessary to specify the order of reflection to which the above d is applicable. Siegbahn then made a determination of the grating space of calcite in terms of that of rock salt, by comparing the glancing angles for the same wave-length from both crystals in the first order. If the uncorrected Bragg equation is used, it is easily seen that

$$d_1 = d_{\mathrm{NaCl}} \frac{\sin \theta_{\mathrm{NaCl}}}{\sin \theta_1}, \qquad (9.21)$$

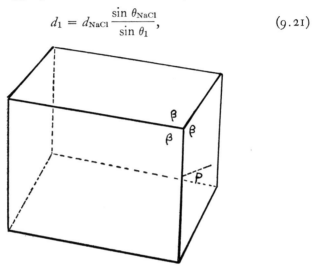

Fig. IX–2. Schematic representation of the cleavage unit of the calcite structure. β is an obtuse angle, and the axis of symmetry passes through this corner. p is the perpendicular distance between faces.

where d_1 is the calcite grating space in the first order and θ_1 the glancing angle of the wave-length from calcite in the first order. From the result of his measurements, Siegbahn found

$$d_1 = 3.02904 \text{ A.} \qquad (9.22)$$

d can also be independently calculated from a measurement of the density of calcite, but because of the non-cubic character of the crystal the calculation of the grating space from the density is more complicated than in the case of rock salt. The smallest rhombohedron of calcite having faces parallel to the cleavage planes and containing an integral number of $CaCO_3$ molecules contains four molecules. This unit is shown in Fig. IX–2. It is not the true unit cell of calcite, since the true unit contains two molecules and does not have faces parallel to the calcite cleavage.

This so-called cleavage unit is a rhombohedron, having a trigonal axis of symmetry and a characteristic angle β between its edges. The measurement of this angle is essential to the computation of the grating space of calcite from density measurements. It can be shown that this measurement can be made with sufficient accuracy to make the uncertainty in this angle a negligible factor in the computation of d. Beets,[7] by x-ray methods, obtained the value $\beta = 101° 55.1' \pm 0.2'$ at 20° C. Let V be the volume of this cleavage unit, and p the perpendicular distance between opposite faces. From solid geometry it may be shown that the expression for V is

$$V = \frac{(1 + \cos \beta)^2 p^3}{(1 + 2 \cos \beta) \sin \beta} \equiv \Phi(\beta) p^3. \qquad (9.23)$$

Since the unit contains four molecules of $CaCO_3$,

$$V = 4M/N\rho \qquad (9.24)$$

where M is the molecular weight of calcite, N the Avogadro number, and ρ the density. From the preceding equations a solution for p is readily obtained. The arrangement of the molecules in this unit is such that a plane identical in atomic composition with one of the boundary planes occurs at a distance $\frac{1}{2}p$ through the unit. Thus $d = \frac{1}{2}p$ or finally

$$d = \sqrt[3]{\frac{M}{2N\rho\Phi(\beta)}}. \qquad (9.25)$$

Table IX-4 gives some recent determinations of d from density measurements. From the results it is clear that the conventional

TABLE IX-4

SOME RECENT DETERMINATIONS OF d FROM DENSITY MEASUREMENTS FOR CALCITE
AT 18° C

d	Value of e Used	Observer *
3.029	4.774×10^{-10}	Defoe and Compton
3.0281	4.768	Bearden
3.0294	4.770	Tu

* The references are the same as in Table IX-2.

[7] H. N. Beets, Phys. Rev. **25**, 624 (1925).

value of eq. (9.22) is within the limit of error in agreement with values obtained from the density of calcite and from the oil-drop e.

If all precision wave-length determinations are made in the first order from calcite, the arbitrary value of d_1 of eq. (9.22) will enable us to tabulate wave-lengths using the uncorrected Bragg equation for their calculation. If, however, precision measurements are made in higher orders of reflection, and the same d_1 is used, the index of refraction effect will cause an apparent variation of λ with order, if calculations are made using the uncorrected Bragg law. It is necessary therefore to define a set of d's for the various orders which will take care of this variation. Fortunately it may be shown that if the wave-lengths used are far from any critical absorption wave-lengths of the crystal, such a set of d's is independent of wave-length.

To show this, we proceed from eq. (9.08), from which it is seen that if we define a set of d's such that

$$d_n = d\left(1 - \frac{\delta}{\sin^2 \theta}\right) \qquad (9.23)$$

and use these in the calculation of wave-lengths by the simple Bragg formula, apparent variations with order will not occur. From eq. (4.46) we know that in regions on the short wave-length side of any of the natural frequencies of a substance

$$\delta = \frac{n_e e^2 \lambda^2}{2\pi m c^2}, \qquad (9.24)$$

where n_e is the number of electrons per cubic centimeter. Using the uncorrected Bragg equation to express λ^2 in terms of d, θ, and n, it is seen that eq. (9.23) may be written

$$d_n = d\left(1 - \frac{2d^2 n_e e^2}{\pi m c^2 n^2}\right). \qquad (9.25)$$

Thus in the wave-length ranges under consideration, the d_n values are independent of wave-length. In Table IX-5 is given a list of defined d_n values for the various orders of reflection from calcite.

TABLE IX-5

VALUES OF d_n AT 18° FOR CALCITE USED IN THE COMPUTATION OF WAVE-LENGTHS

d_1	3.02904 A	d_3	3.02940 A	d_5	3.02943 A
d_2	3.02934	d_4	3.02942	:	:
				d	3.02945

It is the limiting value of d_n, namely $d = 3.02945$ A, which the density determinations must check if the values in Table IX–5 are to agree entirely with density measurements. From Table IX–4 it is seen that Tu's value agrees more closely with the assumed d_n's than do the other results there tabulated.

If the wave-length to be measured is greater than twice the grating space of calcite, the Bragg law shows us that diffraction from calcite cannot take place, and some crystal of greater grating space must be used. Table IX–6 gives the first order d's for some of the crystals used in x-ray spectroscopy.

TABLE IX–6

GRATING CONSTANTS FOR VARIOUS CRYSTALS IN THE FIRST ORDER, AND EXPANSION
COEFFICIENTS (α)

Crystal	Plane	d_1	α
Calcite..........	Cleavage	3.02904 A	1.02×10^{-5}
Gypsum.........	Cleavage	7.57907	3.78×10^{-5}
Mica...........	Cleavage	9.92758	1.53×10^{-6}
Quartz..........	Prism	4.24492	1.04×10^{-5}
Rock salt........	(100)	2.81400	4.0×10^{-5}
Sugar...........	(100)	10.57	

From Siegbahn, Spektroskopie der Röntgenstrahlen 2d Ed. (1931).

If the temperature changes, the crystal will expand or contract, and the angle at which a given wave-length is reflected will change. By differentiation of the Bragg law with respect to a temperature change δT, it is easily shown that

$$\frac{\delta \theta}{\delta T} = -\frac{1}{d}\frac{\delta d}{\delta T}\tan \theta. \qquad (9.26)$$

The definition of the linear expansion coefficient α of a crystal in a direction perpendicular to the planes in question gives

$$\alpha \equiv \frac{1}{d}\frac{\delta d}{\delta T}. \qquad (9.27)$$

Hence the temperature correction to be applied to the observed angle of diffraction may be written

$$\delta \theta = -\alpha \delta T \tan \theta \qquad (9.28)$$

where δT is the variation of the temperature from 18° C. This correction is applied directly to the observed glancing angle. Some values of the expansion coefficient α are shown in Table IX–6. The temperature correction is under ordinary circumstances very small, and elaborate precautions for temperature control are unnecessary.

3. *Three Methods for Absolute Measurement of the Bragg Angle for an X-ray Line*

In this section no attempt will be made to give an exhaustive treatment of all the methods which have been used in precision

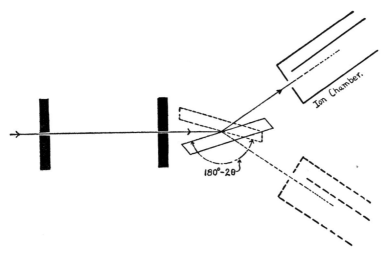

Fig. IX–3. The essentials of a measurement of glancing angle with the single crystal ionization spectrometer.

measurements of x-ray wave-lengths. Three representative methods are described, which have been used for absolute determination of the glancing angle of Mo $K\alpha_1$ from calcite.

The Bragg Ionization Spectrometer.—The very early experiments of the Braggs on x-ray spectra were performed with the ionization spectrometer, but shortly afterward the photographic x-ray spectrometer was developed, and because of its greater simplicity of operation and its adequacy when wave-lengths, not intensities, are required, became the most commonly used instrument for measurement of x-ray spectra. Some accurate measurements have been carried out on the ionization spectrometer, however, largely due to the advances in technique made by Duane at Harvard University. The essentials of an ionization spectrometer are indicated in Fig. IX–3. S_1 and S_2 are two slits limiting the horizontal divergence of the beam, and for precision measurements are so adjusted that this maximum divergence $2\alpha_m$ is about 3 minutes of arc. If w_1 and w_2 are the slit widths, and L is the distance between them, α_m may be computed from the equation

$$2\alpha_m = (w_1 + w_2)/L. \qquad (9.29)$$

The vertical divergence of the beam, due to the height of the slits, introduces an error into the measurement of θ which depends on the square of the maximum vertical divergence. This source of error tends to make the observed angles of diffraction too large. The magnitude of corrections for this effect, which in low orders seldom exceeds a small fraction of a second of arc, will be discussed under the theory of the double spectrometer.

In adjusting the instrument, it is convenient to speak of a central ray, which is the ray passing through the geometrical centers of the two slit apertures. This ray must pass through the center of the focal spot of the x-ray tube and over the axis of rotation of the crystal, and when the ionization chamber is in its zero position, should pass through the center of the aperture in front of the chamber, and along its axis. The crystal is so adjusted that its face lies in the axis of rotation of the spectrometer, but if its face lies parallel to this axis, great precision in the horizontal adjustment is not necessary.

The process of making a measurement of glancing angle is as follows:

(1) A rough determination of the zero position of the crystal is made by optical methods, and the crystal is then turned to a position in which the glancing angle of the central ray upon it is approximately that of the line whose angle is to be measured.

(2) The ionization chamber (which must be capable of separate movement about the axis) is set so that it registers the maximum ionization current obtainable from the crystal in this position.

(3) The crystal is then moved in small angular steps (5 seconds of arc) through the region in which the line is reflected, and the ionization chamber moved with it in such a way that the angular steps of the chamber are twice those of the crystal. In this way the reflected beam always passes through the same portion of the window.

(4) The ionization currents obtained for the various settings are then plotted against the angular settings of the crystal, and the center of the curve determined, which should coincide with the peak.

(5) The crystal is rotated through approximately the angle $180° - 2\theta$, and steps (3) and (4) repeated. The angle between the centers of the two peaks thus found gives the exact value of $180° - 2\theta$.

The ionization spectrometer method is characterized by directness and simplicity, in that all measurements are made directly on the angular scale of the instrument. High precision in the horizontal adjustment of the crystal is unnecessary, and no linear distances need be measured.

One disadvantage lies in the relatively low resolving power. In order to reach the resolving power easily attainable by photographic methods, the slits must be made so narrow that the power of the x-ray beam passing through them becomes too small for convenient measurement. Furthermore a source of high potential must be used which will give operation of the x-ray tube under constant conditions.

For precision work the accuracy of the angular scale should be such that a difference of angle of a second of arc can be read. Two microscopes are used, one 180° from the other, and both are read for each setting. The average of the angle read on both microscopes contains no error due to a possible eccentricity of the scale.

The Photographic Method.—By far the largest number of precision measurements of the glancing angles of x-ray lines have been carried out by photographic methods, due to their relative simplicity. Many types of photographic spectrometers have been designed but only one will be described here, the so-called " tube spectrometer " of Siegbahn and Larsson.[8]

Figure IX–4, from the paper of Larsson, shows the principle of operation of the instrument. The tube from which the instrument gets its name is placed directly behind the slits and extends to the photographic plate P. The slit is made very narrow (in comparison to the widths used with the ionization spectrometer), in many experiments about 0.002 cm. The width of the impression on the photographic plate is primarily that of the slit. The crystal, whose reflecting face is represented in two positions by the dashed lines in

---

[8] A. Larsson, Phil. Mag. **3**, 1136 (1927).

the figure, is mounted so that its face lies in the axis of the spectrometer. This is accomplished by an auxiliary apparatus and can be done

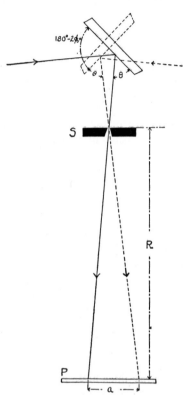

with an error of less than 0.002 mm. The angular positions of the crystal can be read on an accurately divided circular scale. With the crystal in position 1 (solid lines) the line whose glancing angle is to be determined is exposed on the plate. The position of the crystal with respect to the plate is read off accurately on the divided circle by means of the microscopes. The crystal is then turned to position 2 (dotted lines), which is so chosen that when the x-ray line is photographed, the impression on the plate falls in the immediate proximity (about half a millimeter) of the impression obtained in position 1. The linear distance between the lines is involved in computing the glancing angle, and by having the lines close together errors due to unevenness in the photographic plate, shrinkage in the emulsion, etc., are largely eliminated. Position 2 of the crystal

FIG. IX-4. The essentials of the tube spectrograph of Siegbahn and Larsson.

is read off by means of the microscopes. The angular difference between positions 1 and 2 is

$$180° - 2\phi_0 = 180° - 2(\theta \pm \Delta\theta). \qquad (9.30)$$

The small angle $2\Delta\theta$ is determined by measuring with a travelling microscope the distance between the lines on the plate, a, from

$$2\Delta\theta = a/R, \qquad (9.31)$$

where R is the distance from the photographic plate to the slit. According to the figure, the x-ray tube must be swung about the axis of the instrument through an angle of approximately 4θ to change from position 1 to position 2. In actual practice, the x-ray tube is left fixed and the entire spectrometer rotated. This angle through which the spectrometer is rotated does not enter into the calculation of the glancing angle.

In the photographic method it is not necessary to have a constant potential applied to the x-ray tube as in the ionization methods. Also, measurements of wave-lengths emitted by powdered substances rubbed on the target are possible, in spite of the fact that the intensities of the lines vary due to disappearance of the powder. In a strict sense, the impressions on the photographic plate are not straight lines, but are conic sections, formed by the intersection of the plane of the photographic plate with a cone of rays reflected at the Bragg

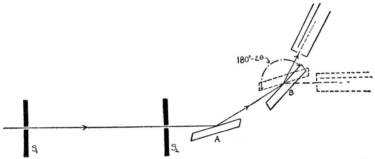

Fig. IX–5. Measurement of the glancing angle by the double spectrometer method.

angle from the crystal. Practically, this effect is not important because of the small slit heights employed. In any case, either the minimum or maximum distance between the two " lines " should be measured.

The Double Spectrometer Method.—In this method the resolving power of the Bragg ionization spectrometer is increased until it becomes slightly greater (roughly by a factor $\sqrt{2}$) than that attainable in the same order and using the same crystal planes in the photographic method.

The essential experimental feature is that the reflection takes place from two crystals in series, as indicated by Fig. IX–5. It has become customary to call the crystal on which the x-rays first fall crystal A, the second crystal, crystal B. In a measurement of a glancing angle, the accurate measurements are made on crystal B.[9] Crystal A is set

[9] A. H. Compton, Rev. Sci. Insts. U.S.A. **2**, 365 (1931).

so that the line in question is reflected from it in the first order.   The position of crystal A need not be determined with great accuracy, since the slits S_1 S_2 can be wide.   As will be seen later, the resolving power is independent of the width of the slits, that is, the width of the peaks obtained on rotation of crystal B, called " rocking curves," does not depend on the horizontal divergence of the beam incident upon crystal A.   The diffracted beam from crystal A passes over the axis about which B is turned.   Crystal B is placed so that the spectrometer is in the (1, -1) position, that is, the reflecting surface of B is parallel to that of A, both crystals reflecting in the first order.   The

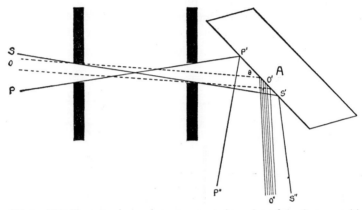

Fɪɢ. IX–6.   This illustrates in an elementary way the action of the first crystal in a double spectrometer.   The radiation incident on the crystal contains a wide range of wave-lengths and is divergent.   In the diffracted beam, $O'O''$ represents radiation of wave-length corresponding to the Bragg angle θ.

diffracted beam from B passes into the ionization chamber, and the angular position of the peak or center of the rocking curve is determined.   Crystal B and the ionization chamber are then turned until the instrument is in the (1, 1) position, with both crystals reflecting in the first order, but the face of B not parallel to that of A.   The angular setting for the peak of the rocking curve[10] in this position is noted, and then the angle between the two positions of crystal B is $180° - 2\theta$.

Fig. IX–6 shows in a simple way the reason for the increase in

[10] In this book the term rocking curve is applied to peaks obtained by rotation of crystal B whether or not the instrument is in a parallel position.   Some authors restrict the term to the curve obtained in parallel positions only.

resolving power. A much more detailed discussion of the theory of the instrument will be given later. The figure is an analysis of the beams incident on and reflected by crystal A, the width of the slits being enormously exaggerated. The entire beam incident upon A is divergent, and contains all the wave-lengths emitted from the x-ray tube. The entire beam reflected from crystal A is also divergent, but, because of the Bragg law, the different wave-lengths are sorted out into parallel bundles. Thus the ray $S'S''$ has a different wave-length from that of the ray $P'P''$. $O'O''$ shows the width of a monochromatic bundle of rays coming from the region near O on the target. These have all been selected as to wave-length by the action of the crystal, and constitute, in the elementary treatment considered here, a monochromatic, non-divergent beam. Thus for each wave-length crystal A acts as a pair of slits of zero width, and the resolving power is raised to the point where it is limited merely by the width of single crystal diffraction patterns as discussed in Chap. VI.

Richtmyer[11] has investigated the Mo $K\alpha$ doublet with the single

TABLE IX-7

THE BRAGG ANGLE FOR THE REFLECTION OF Mo $K\alpha_1$ FROM CALCITE BY VARIOUS METHODS

Method	θ	λ $(d_1 = 3.02904\,\text{A})$	Author
Bragg Ionization Spectrometer...........	6° 42′ 36.4″	0.707862 A	Allison and Armstrong (1925)
Photographic Tube Spectrometer...........	6° 42′ 35.4″	0.707833 A	Larsson (1927)
Double Crystal Spectrometer..........	6° 42′ 36.0″	0.707850	Compton (1931)
	6° 42′ 35.5″	0.707836	Tu (1932)
	6° 42′ 35.3″	0.707830	Bearden (1931)

References:

Allison and Armstrong, Phys. Rev. **26**, 701 (1925). In a strict sense the measurements of Allison and Armstrong cannot be compared with the others because they were made in the 3rd, 4th and 5th orders only. The angle in this table is the first order angle consistent with their results.

Larsson, Phil. Mag. **3**, 1136 (1927).

A. H. Compton, Rev. Sci. Insts. U.S.A. **2**, 365 (1931).

Tu, Phys. Rev. **40**, 662 (1932).

Bearden, Phys. Rev. **38**, 1389 (1931).

[11] F. K. Richtmyer, Phys. Rev. **26**, 724 (1925).

crystal ionization spectrometer, using two slits each 0.0025 cm. wide and 38 cm. apart. In the first order from calcite, the full width at half maximum of Mo $K\alpha_1$ corresponded to 0.67 X.U. Such narrow slits necessitate a high power input to the x-ray tube in order to obtain appreciable intensity. With the double spectrometer in the (1, 1) position, using 5 milliamperes and 35 kv. in the x-ray tube, rocking curves for Mo $K\alpha_1$ are obtained whose wave-length width is 0.29 X.U. The comparison illustrates the advantage of the latter instrument.

Table IX–7 gives the results obtained on the glancing angle of Mo $K\alpha_1$ from calcite in the first order by these various methods. The remarkable agreement between the different methods shows that this angle belongs to the most accurately known constants of physics.

4. *X-ray Wave-lengths from Ruled Gratings*

We have seen in Chap. I that at sufficiently small glancing angles, x-rays are totally reflected from polished surfaces,[12] due to the fact that the index of refraction is less than unity. It was shown that the critical angle, greater than which no total reflection can take place, is

$$\theta_m = \sqrt{2\delta} \qquad (9.32)$$

where δ is the unit decrement of the refractive index. In his original experiments, Compton found that about 91 per cent of the primary beam reappeared in the totally reflected beam, and it was soon suggested that it should be possible to obtain grating spectra of x-rays, by reflecting them from ruled gratings at glancing angles within the region of total reflection.[13] The first successful spectra were obtained by Compton and Doan.[14] The elementary theory of the grating at large angles of incidence (small glancing angles) is readily developed, and some points of the discussion given here follow the treatment of J. Thibaud.[15]

In Fig. IX–7, the reflecting face of the grating lies along the line AB, and a is the linear distance between two adjacent rulings. Two rays incident at the glancing angle θ and diffracted at the glancing

---

[12] A. H. Compton, Phil. Mag. **45**, 1121 (1923).
[13] N. Carrara, N. Cimento **1**, 107 (1924).
[14] Proc. Nat. Acad. Sci. **11**, 598 (1926).
[15] J. Thibaud, Journal de Physique **8**, 13 (1927).

angle $\theta + \alpha$ are shown. The condition for a maximum of interference is an integral number of wave-lengths path difference, or

$$n\lambda = PB - RA = a\{\cos \theta - \cos (\theta + \alpha)\}. \qquad (9.33)$$

In this case negative values of n have physical significance, the corresponding glancing angles of diffraction lying between the plane of the grating and the totally reflected ray. This means that for negative values of n we also have negative values of α. An approximate equation of considerable usefulness is obtained by expanding eq. (9.33), and taking account of the fact that the angles α and θ are small. We thus obtain

$$n\lambda = a(\alpha\theta + \tfrac{1}{2}\alpha^2). \qquad (9.34)$$

An instructive comparison of the results of this glancing angle method and the conventional method of using the plane grating,

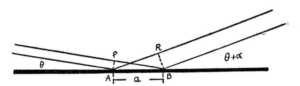

FIG. IX–7. Diffraction of x-rays from a ruled grating. a is the grating space. The reflected beam is not shown.

which involves approximately normal incidence of the radiation, may be made as follows. Consider two identical gratings, one illuminated by a beam normal to its surface, the other by a beam tangent to its surface. These gratings will then diffract the same wave-length λ through the angles α_1 and α_2 respectively, for which one may write, supposing them small, and limiting the discussion to the first order:

Normal incidence: $n\lambda = a(\sin i - \sin \alpha_1)$ in general; for
$i = 0°$, if α_1 is small
$$\alpha_1 = \lambda/a.$$

Grazing incidence: Setting $\theta = 0$ in eq. (9.34), we obtain, in the first positive order
$$\alpha_2 = \sqrt{2\lambda/a}.$$

Let us now investigate the dispersion of the grating in these two cases. We have:

Normal incidence: $D_1 \equiv d\alpha_1/d\lambda = 1/a$.

Grazing incidence: From differentiation of eq. (9.34) we obtain

$$D_2 \equiv d\alpha_2/d\lambda = \frac{n}{a\sqrt{\theta^2 + (2n\lambda/a)}}$$

$$= \frac{n}{a(\alpha_2 + \theta)}. \qquad (9.35)$$

In the first positive order this becomes

$$D_2 = 1/\sqrt{2\lambda a}.$$

From these equations it may be shown that the dispersion for the cases under consideration is greater for the case of tangential than for normal incidence. For instance, for $\lambda = 1860$ A, a tangential grating of 200 lines per millimeter gives the same dispersion in the first positive order as does a grating of 730 lines per millimeter used normally, and at 500 A, a tangential grating of 570 lines per millimeter is equivalent to a 2400 line per millimeter grating used normally. It should be noted, however, that when the grating is used tangentially, the dispersion is not normal, that is, it is a function of wave-length, increasing with decreasing λ.

From eq. (9.35) it may be concluded that in negative orders, having negative values of α, the dispersion is greater than in the corresponding positive order. This apparent advantage of the negative orders is however offset by a relatively greater divergence of the diffracted beam. Since in the wave-length regions in which the tangential grating is used lenses are not available to produce parallel incident wave-fronts, the sharpness of the diffracted maxima is concerned with the relative divergence of the incident and diffracted beams for a given wave-length. Let $d\theta$ be the angular divergence of the incident beam, and $d(\alpha + \theta)$ that of the diffracted beam. From eq. (9.34) we find

$$(\alpha + \theta) = \sqrt{2n\lambda/a + \theta^2} \qquad (9.36)$$

and

$$\frac{d(\alpha + \theta)}{d\theta} = \frac{\theta}{\sqrt{(2n\lambda/a) + \theta^2}} = \frac{\theta}{\theta + \alpha}. \qquad (9.37)$$

For positive orders eq. (9.37) shows that the divergence of the diffracted beam must be less than that of the incident. For negative orders, however, the diffracted beam is more diffuse than the incident. This disadvantage overshadows any possible benefit to be obtained from increased dispersion, and positive orders are generally used in experimental work.

Because of the importance of the problem of the measurement of x-ray wave-lengths by ruled gratings, many authors have discussed possible sources of error. The first to receive notice is due to the fact that the incident x-ray beam does not consist of parallel wave-fronts, and because of the lack of lenses the diffraction phenomena are of the Fresnel rather than the Fraunhofer type. Porter[16] calculated the correction to be applied in cases in which the grating to plate and target to grating distances are the same. Stauss[17] has also considered this problem, and solved it for the more general case in which these two distances are not necessarily equal. He finds that an observed wave-length must be multiplied by the factor

$$1 + \frac{3X^2}{20\{(\theta + \alpha)^2 - \theta^2\}} \left[\frac{(\theta + \alpha)^2}{l_2^2} - \frac{\theta^2}{l_1^2} \right] \qquad (9.38)$$

where θ and α have the significance of Fig. IX–7, X is the length of the grating, l_1 the distance from the source to the center of the grating, and l_2 that from the grating to the impression on the photographic plate. The effect of divergence in a plane through the source and the central ruling of the grating, that is, vertical divergence, has also been considered. As we shall see later, divergence corrections are negligible in all actual experiments thus far carried out.

Fagerberg[18] has discussed the effect of periodic errors in the ruling engine on absolute wave-length measurements, and also of an error such that the spacing varies continuously and monotonically along the grating. If the variation of the latter type is linear, that is, the distance between rulings is a linear function of the distance from one end of the grating, no correction need be made to the observed wave-length, for the central ray of the divergent or convergent diffracted bundle of rays will make the diffraction angle $\theta + \alpha$ which would occur if a perfect grating, having a uniform spacing equal to the average spacing of the imperfect grating, were used. In the case of

[16] Porter, Phil. Mag. 5, 1067 (1928).
[17] Stauss, Phys. Rev. 34, 1601 (1929).
[18] S. Fagerberg, Zeitschr. f. Physik 62, 457 (1930).

a periodic error, whose period is often the pitch of the screw, more important corrections may enter. The width of the region of the grating used in x-ray work is seldom more than 2 or 3 mm. If the pitch of the screw of the ruling engine is 1 mm., only 2 or 3 periods may occur in the effective length of the grating. This source of error may be avoided by using gratings ruled in such a manner that a great many periods lie within the 3 mm. region,[19] or by using several different gratings and averaging the results.[20]

Compton[21] has discussed possible sources of error in grating measurements of x-rays and has given an elementary but general proof that the effect of penetration of the material of the grating by the x-rays and the consequent effect of the refractive index in changing the direction of the path in the material can have no effect on the validity of eq. (9.33). Eckart[22] has pointed out that the same argument may be used to dismiss questions arising as to the effect of multiple scattering, and of the shadows cast on one ruling by its neighbors. Eckart has given a very general derivation of the diffraction equation, which includes the above-mentioned effects, and the possible effect of surface waves, similar to those arising from total reflection at a plane surface. The result of the derivation is that the ordinary grating formula, eq. (9.33), should be adequate to represent the positions of the diffraction maxima. In view of these results, there seems little reason to doubt the validity of x-ray wave-length measurements by ruled gratings.

5. Results of Grating Measurements of X-ray Wave-lengths; the Determination of e

The problem of determination of the wave-length of x-rays with ruled gratings is primarily the problem of the measurement of the small angles θ and $\theta + \alpha$ of Fig. IX-7. The grating constant a of eq. (9.33) offers no such uncertainties as does the value of d in Bragg's equation, since the number of lines per mm. can actually be counted with a microscope, or the grating can be calibrated by the use of visible light of known wave-length. Table IX-8 gives some of the results obtained. The results in the table are selected from the many grating measurements of wave-length because they have

---

[19] Siegbahn and Magnusson, Zeitschr. f. Physik **62**, 435 (1930).
[20] J. A. Bearden, Phys. Rev. **37**, 1210 (1931).
[21] A. H. Compton, J. Frankl. Inst. **208**, 605 (1929).
[22] C. Eckart, Phys. Rev. **44**, 12 (1933).

been used for the determination of the electronic charge, as explained later.

TABLE IX–8

COMPARISON OF WAVE-LENGTHS MEASURED BY RULED GRATINGS AND BY CRYSTALS

Observer	Line	λ_g Grating	λ_c Crystal	$\lambda_g - \lambda_c$ in Per Cent
Bäcklin.............	Mo $L\alpha_1$	5.402 A	5.3950 A	+0.13
	Mo $L\beta_1$	5.174	5.1665	+0.15
	Al $K\alpha$	8.333	8.3205	+0.16
	Mg $K\alpha$	9.883	9.8690	+0.14
Cork...............	Mo $L\alpha_1$	5.4116	5.3950	+0.31
	Mo $L\beta_1$	5.1832	5.1665	+0.33
Bearden............	Cu $K\alpha$	1.54172	1.5387	+0.20
	Cu $K\beta_1$	1.39225	1.3894	+0.20
	Cr $K\alpha$	2.29097	2.2859	+0.22
	Cr $K\beta_1$	2.08478	2.0806	+0.22

References:

E. Bäcklin, Inaugural dissertation, Uppsala (1928).
J. M. Cork, Phys. Rev. **35**, 1456 (1930).
J. A. Bearden, Phys. Rev. **37**, 1210 (1931).

Column 4 of Table IX–8 gives values of the wave-length λ_c determined from crystalline diffraction. These wave-lengths have been calculated with the conventional values of d, which in the case of calcite, are given in Table IX–5. In the case of the $K\alpha$ lines of copper and chromium, the resolving power of the crystal is sufficient to separate them, whereas the ruled grating spectra show the doublet as a single line. In these cases the wave-length given in the table as the crystal wave-length is $\lambda_1 + \frac{1}{3}\Delta\lambda$, where λ_1 is the wave-length of $K\alpha_1$ and $\Delta\lambda$ is the wave-length separation of the doublet. This choice is made because of the fact that $K\alpha_2$ is one-half as intense as $K\alpha_1$, although in the unresolved photographic doublet the exact wave-length to be taken will depend on the blackness of the impression. Column 5 shows that in all the experiments the grating wave-lengths exceed the crystal wave-lengths by a few tenths of a per cent. If we assume that the grating wave-lengths are correct, this must mean that the conventional values of d are too small.

The most uncertain constant entering eq. (9.25) for the computation of d is N, the Avogadro number, and the principal uncertainty in N is due to the possible error in the value of the electronic charge. It is therefore reasonable to use the measurements as a determination of the charge on the electron. Let us consider the three equations

$$d = \sqrt[3]{\frac{M}{2N\rho\Phi(\beta)}}$$

$$n\lambda = 2d\left(1 - \frac{\delta}{\sin^2\theta}\right)\sin\theta$$

$$Q = Ne.$$

In these equations λ is the wave-length in air, which presumably is correctly obtained from ruled grating measurements. Q is the value

TABLE IX-9

EVALUATION OF e FROM EQ. (9.39)

Constant	Source
$Q = 2.89260 \times 10^{14}$ esu/gm. equiv.	Birge, Phys. Rev. Suppl. **1**, 1 (1929).
$\rho = 2.71024$ gm./cm³.,	Average of Table IX-2
$\Phi(\beta) = 1.09594$	Bearden, Phys. Rev. **38**, 2089 (1931)
$M = 100.078$ gm./mol.	Birge, Phys. Rev. Suppl. **1**, 1 (1929).
δ values	Larsson, Thesis, Uppsala (1929)
θ values	Siegbahn, Spektroskopie der Röntgenstrahlen (1931)

Author	Line	λ	δ	θ	$e \times 10^{10}$	Author's Own Estimate
Bäcklin.....	Mo $L\alpha_1$	5.402 A	1.03×10^{-4}	62° 56′ 31″	4.793	4.793
	Mo $L\beta_1$	5.174	9.42×10^{-5}	58° 31′ 15″	4.795	
Cork........	Mo $L\alpha_1$	5.4116	1.03×10^{-4}	62° 56′ 31″	4.818	4.8162
	Mo $L\beta_1$	5.1832	9.42×10^{-5}	58° 31′ 15″	4.820	
Bearden.....	Cu $K\alpha$	1.54172	8.80×10^{-6}	14° 42′ 50″	4.802	
	Cu $K\beta_1$	1.39225	7.18×10^{-6}	13° 15′ 31″	4.803	4.806
	Cr $K\alpha$	2.2859	19.43×10^{-6}	22° 10′ 06″	4.806	
	Cr $K\beta_1$	2.0806	16.13×10^{-6}	20° 05′ 12″	4.803	

e from Millikan's oil drop expt.: 4.770×10^{-10} esu. (Birge, loc. cit.)

of the Faraday, in electrostatic units of charge per gram equivalent, and the other symbols have the meanings previously assigned in this chapter. If we solve these equations for e, eliminating d and N, we obtain

$$e = \frac{n^3 \lambda^3 Q \rho \Phi(\beta)}{4M[1 - \delta/\sin^2\theta]^3 \sin^3 \theta}. \tag{9.39}$$

Thus a grating measurement of wave-length of an x-ray line, combined with a determination of the glancing angle θ in the nth order from a crystal of known structure and density allows the evaluation of the electronic charge from well-known fundamental physical constants. Table IX–9 gives values of the quantities involved for calcite which have been used in this chapter, and shows the resulting values of e. The measurements of Bäcklin on Mg $K\alpha$ and Al $K\alpha$ which appear in Table IX–8 have not been put in Table IX–9, since the wave-lengths of these lines are too great to be diffracted by calcite, which is used as the reference crystal. Bäcklin's own estimate of the best value of e from his experiments, appearing in the right-hand column of the table, includes values of e calculated from these lines.

6. Discussion of the Value of e

Because the x-ray values of e are uniformly greater than the oil-drop method value, the possible errors in the x-ray method have received considerable attention.

The effect of divergence of the x-ray beam, as calculated by Porter and by Stauss in eq. (9.38), has been shown to be negligible in the experiments of Bearden and of Bäcklin. Stauss[23] calculated that in earlier experiments of Bearden[24] the divergence introduces a correction of some thousandths of a per cent, depending on the width X of the grating used. Bäcklin[25] has himself shown that the corrections to his work from this cause are negligible.

Another class of possibilities is concerned with the conjecture that the value of ρ obtained from macroscopic density measurements is not that value which should be inserted in eq. (9.39) to obtain the value of e. For instance it is known (Chap. VI, Sec. 9) that in the first order from a perfect crystal of calcite, the diffracted x-ray beam

[23] H. E. Stauss, Phys. Rev. **34**, 1604 (1929).
[24] J. A. Bearden, Proc. Nat. Acad. Sci. **15**, 528 (1929).
[25] E. Bäcklin, Nature **125**, 239 (1931).

is made up from a layer of the crystal only some 5×10^{-5} cm. deep. It is at first thought conceivable that the spacing of these planes near the surface might be different from that in the interior of the crystal due to some effect analogous to surface tension, or due to some unknown cause. The experiments of Allison and Armstrong[26] in higher order reflections, compared to first order results, however, give strong evidence that such an effect does not exist. Table IX–10 gives the results of glancing angle measurements of Mo $K\alpha_1$ reflected by calcite cleavage planes in the first, third, fourth and fifth orders. The first order results are from Larsson.[27] The order of magnitude of the depth of penetration into the crystal increases with increasing order, and may be estimated from the primary extinction coefficient μ_e as calculated from eq. (6.55), Chap. VI, which is applicable to the σ-polarized component only but which is sufficiently accurate for our purpose. Approximate values of F/Z in the various orders, for use in eq. (6.55), may be obtained from a paper by Allison and Williams.[28] From Table IX–10 it is seen that a comparison of the wave-lengths

TABLE IX–10

COMPARISON OF WAVE-LENGTH MEASUREMENTS OF Mo $K\alpha_1$ IN VARIOUS ORDERS OF REFLECTION FROM CALCITE

$\delta = 1.82 \times 10^{-6}$

d_n Values from Table IX–5

Order	F/Z	μ_e (Eq. 6.55)	Half-depth of Penetration		λ	$\dfrac{\lambda_n - \lambda_1}{\lambda}$
			Cm.	Planes	A	Per Cent
1	0.52	1.4×10^4	5×10^{-5}	1.6×10^3	0.707831	
3	0.19	1.8×10^3	4×10^{-4}	1.3×10^4	0.707902	0.01
4	0.18	1.2×10^3	6×10^{-4}	2×10^4	0.707850	0.003
5	0.10	5.5×10^2	1.2×10^{-3}	4×10^4	0.707840	0.001

[26] S. K. Allison and A. H. Armstrong, Phys. Rev. **26**, 701 (1925). The results quoted in Table IX–10 of this book in the third, fourth, and fifth orders of reflection are taken from Table I of this paper. The observations in the paper on glancing angles were changed to λ values, uncorrected for index of refraction, by the use of the simple Bragg formula with $d = 3.028$ A. These values appear in column 6 of Table I in the reference. In order to correct these to the conventional basis used in this chapter, each " wave-length " in column 6, Table I of the reference has been multiplied by the ratio $d_n/3.028$ A, where the d_n values are obtained from Table IX–5 of this chapter.

[27] A. Larsson, Phil. Mag. **3**, 1136 (1927).

[28] S. K. Allison and J. H. Williams, Phys. Rev. **35**, 1476 (1930).

in the first and fifth orders, where the penetration into the crystal has increased by a factor of 25, shows a difference of only 0.0013 per cent, which is within the experimental error. If there is any difference in the effective density at the crystal surface and in the interior, it is very difficult to explain these results.

Another possibility is that the crystal may have minute gaps or crevices in its structure, such that the measured density is less than the effective value to be used in eq. (9.39). In the first place, one may remark[29] that such an effect, if corrected for, would increase the discrepancy between the x-ray and the oil-drop values of e, rather than be in the direction to reconcile them. Furthermore the work of Tu, to be discussed below, makes the existence of such an effect doubtful.

Zwicky[30] has proposed a theory of the structure of perfect crystals which requires that there be periodic variations in the grating space in the crystal along a direction normal to the planes. This period would be of the order of 10^{-6} cm. The superposition of such a long period on the interplanar spacings of 10^{-8} cm. would not affect the relative positions of diffraction maxima and would have negligible effects on their intensity. It might possibly be true, however, that the macroscopic density is not the effective density in such a case. The experiments of Tu,[31] mentioned previously, bear upon this point. Tu has measured the density of samples of calcite, rock salt, potassium chloride, and diamond crystals, and at the same time measured with precision the glancing angle of reflection of Mo $K\alpha_1$ from them. We may assume an arbitrary value of e, regardless of whether or not it is the true one, and proceed to calculate the grating space of calcite from the observed density by eq. (9.25). Using this value of d as a standard, we may then calculate the d values of the other crystals in two ways. One of these ways is illustrated by eq. (9.21), namely, the relative d's are inversely proportional to the sines of the glancing angles. The second way is to calculate the d value from the density, through a formula similar to eq. (9.25), and using the same arbitrary value of e which was used for calcite. Actually Tu used a value of N (Avogadro's number) of 6.064×10^{23}, which is given by Birge (1929) as consistent with an e value of 4.770×10^{-10} e.s.u. The results are shown in Table IX–11. The agreement

[29] A. H. Compton, J. Frankl. Inst. **208**, 605 (1929).
[30] Zwicky, Phys. Rev. **40**, 63 (1932).
[31] Y. C. Tu, Phys. Rev. **40**, 662 (1932).

TABLE IX–11

Tu's Results on d-values Calculated from Observations of θ and of ρ

Crystal	Density 18° C.	d from θ	d from ρ	$\dfrac{d_\rho - d_\theta}{d_\rho}$, Per Cent
Calcite..........	2.71003 ±0.00005	....	3.02940	
Rock salt........	2.16418 ±0.00014	2.81387	2.81418	+0.011
KCl.............	1.98930 ±0.00014	3.13990	3.13889	−0.032
Diamond (0.89 K).	3.5141 ±0.0001	3.55966 (2d)	3.55942	−0.007
Diamond (1.78 K).	3.5142 ±0.0001	3.55956	3.55938	−0.005

between the d values from relative values of glancing angles, and from density measurements with an assumed e for such widely different crystals makes it difficult to maintain the hypothesis that cavities or secondary structure affect the x-ray method of determination of e.

In spite of the investigations into the theory of the diffraction grating applied to x-rays it may yet be true that there is some unknown correction to be made, and that the ruled grating wave-length determinations are in error. Bearden[32] has attempted to obtain a value of λ by an independent method, namely, by measuring the index of refraction of a substance and computing the wave-length by the dispersion formula, assuming a value of e/m.

From eq. (4.80), Chap. IV, we have, when the wave-length is shorter than any of the resonating wave-lengths of the medium

$$\delta_q = \frac{2\pi e^2}{m\omega_q^2}\, n_q\, \frac{1}{x^2}\left[1 + \frac{ln(x^2 - 1)}{x^2} - \frac{2\pi\gamma}{x^3}\right]. \qquad (9.40)$$

In this equation δ_q is the contribution to the unit decrement of the

[32] J. A. Bearden, Phys. Rev. 39, 1 (1932).

refractive index from electrons in the medium whose resonating wave-length λ_q is given by $2\pi c/\omega_q$. n_q is the number of such q electrons per cubic centimeter; $x^2 = \omega^2/\omega_q{}^2$, where the incident wave-length $\lambda = 2\pi c/\omega$.

In Sec. 10 of Chap. IV we have seen that there is some evidence that γ is roughly 4×10^{-4} in the x-ray region. If z_q is the number of electrons per molecule, M the molecular weight, N the Avogadro number and ρ the density, we have

$$n_q = \frac{\rho N}{M} z_q = \frac{\rho Q z_q}{Me}, \qquad (9.41)$$

where Q is the value of the Faraday in electrostatic units per gram-molecule. Solved for λ, eq. (9.40) becomes

$$\lambda = \sqrt{\frac{\delta}{\dfrac{e}{m}\dfrac{\rho Q}{2\pi Mc^2}[z_K(1 + x_K{}^{-2}ln(x_K{}^2 - 1) + Z_M - z_K]}}. \qquad (9.42)$$

In this expression Z_M is the number of electrons per molecule. The equation is written in a form suitable to the assumption that there is only one type of electron, the K electrons of one of the atoms in the molecule, whose natural frequencies need be taken into account. The term in γ has been dropped, which assumes that the incident frequency is sufficiently far from the critical absorption frequency.

Bearden has used this equation in connection with measurements of the index of refraction of quartz for Cu $K\alpha$, Cu $K\beta$, Mo $K\alpha$ and Mo $K\beta$. λ, of course, appears in the right hand member of the equation, through x, but the expression is not sensitive to slight changes in the λ-value on this side of the equality. The distinction between Millikan's oil-drop value of e and the x-ray value involves a change of λ of eq. (9.39) of some 0.2 per cent, and it is somewhat doubtful whether the accuracy of the dispersion theory is sufficient to warrant confidence in the value of λ from eq. (9.42) to this extent. We may mention the following points, which have not been thoroughly discussed: (a) The dispersion theory neglects the effect of the polarization of the medium on the field of an oscillator in the medium (see footnote 22, Chap. IV). (b) In the revised theory of x-ray dispersion the distribution of virtual oscillators is made as if the absorption coefficient varied as λ^3, whereas it is known experimentally that this coefficient is not accurately 3. Another questionable point is the value to be inserted for z_K in eq. (9.42). This has to do with the question of the oscillator strength. It is known that the proper value of z_K is not 2 for the two K electrons of an atom, but is somewhat less. Hönl[33] has published theoretical calculations which show that the oscillator strength of the K electrons should be represented in 14 Si by the factor 1.53 rather than 2. Larsson[34] found approximately 1.5 for 14 Si, and Prins[35] 1.3 for Fe. Theoretically the oscillator strength should be a function of the atomic number.

Table IX–12 shows some calculations of λ values from eq. (9.42), using Bearden's data on the index of refraction from his experiments

TABLE IX–12

CALCULATION OF X-RAY WAVE-LENGTHS FROM INDEX OF REFRACTION MEASUREMENTS. EQ. (9.42)

Constants	Source
$e/m = c \times 1.761 \times 10^7$ esu/gram.	Birge, Phys. Rev. **40**, 228 (1932).
$c = 2.99796 \times 10^{10}$ cm./sec.	Birge, Phys. Rev. Suppl. **1**, 1 (1929)
$\rho = 2.6485$ gm./cm.^{3} (SiO$_2$)	Bearden, Phys. Rev. **39**, 1 (1932).
$Q = 2.89260 \times 10^{14}$ esu/gm. mol	Birge, Phys. Rev. Suppl. **1**, 1 (1929).
$M = 60.06$ gm./mol	International Critical Tables
$\lambda_K = 6.731 \times 10^{-8}$ cm. (14 Si)	Lindh, Zeitschr. f. Physik **31**, 210 (1925)
$Z_M = 30$ electrons per molecule	

Line	$\delta \times 10^6$ Obs.	z_K	$\lambda_r \times 10^8$	$\lambda_\theta \times 10^8$	$\lambda_c \times 10^8$
Cu $K\alpha$	8.553	2.0	1.539	1.542	1.539
Cu $K\alpha$	8.553	1.3	1.541	1.542	1.539
Cu $K\alpha$	8.553	1.8	1.539	1.542	1.539
Cu $K\alpha$	8.553	1.53	1.540	1.542	1.539
Cu $K\beta$	6.971	1.53	1.391	1.392	1.389
Mo $K\alpha$	1.805	1.53	0.7096	0.7109	0.7093
Mo $K\beta$	1.432	1.53	0.6324	0.6328	0.6314

on quartz. It is assumed that the two K-electrons of silicon are the only electrons in the SiO$_2$ molecule whose natural frequencies need be considered. The values of λ calculated from eq. (9.42) are given in column 4 under λ_r. The first four rows show the effect of different values of the oscillator strength on the computed λ_r of Cu $K\alpha$. If we adopt the value $z_K = 1.53$ due to Hönl as the most reliable, the last

[33] H. Hönl, Zeitschr. f. Physik **84**, 1 (1933).
[34] A. Larsson, Thesis, Uppsala (1929).
[35] J. A. Prins, Zeitschr. f. Phys. **47**, 479 (1928).

four rows give the best computed values of λ_r. It is known that the conventional crystal wave-lengths λ_c agree well with the densities when the oil-drop value of e is used, so that one can see whether the refraction wave-length determination favors the oil-drop or the x-ray value of e by noting whether it agrees better with λ_c or λ_g. It is seen that the result is indecisive, the α lines agreeing better with the crystal wave-length, the β lines better with the grating values. In his own calculations, Bearden came to the conclusion that his refraction measurements agreed best with the conventional x-ray wave-lengths, and thus favored the oil-drop value of e. With the values used for the constants in Table IX–12 it is seen, however, that such is not the case.[35a]

Shiba[36] has discussed the most probable values of e, e/m, and h, and has come to the conclusion that these are

$$e = (4.803 \pm 0.004) \times 10^{-10} \text{ esu.}$$

$$e/m = (1.7605 \pm 0.001) \times 10^7 \text{ emu./gm.}$$

$$h = (6.624 \pm 0.007) \times 10^{-27} \text{ ergs} \times \text{sec.}$$

His value of e is thus essentially the x-ray value. Shiba points out that the error in the oil-drop method may lie in the value of the viscosity of air used in the calculation. In 1917 Millikan[37] adopted the value $(1822.6 \pm 0.04\%) \times 10^{-7}$ cgs. units, which is the value obtained by Harrington,[38] who used the method of rotating cylinders. Van Dyke[39] by the same method found a value of 1822.1×10^{-7}. The capillary tube method has given consistently higher results,[40] and Shiba shows that if the true value of the viscosity of air is

[35a] J. A. Bearden and C. H. Shaw, Phys. Rev. **46**, 759 (1934) have recently reported new measurements on the index of refraction of quartz for Cu $K\alpha_1$, and found the value $\delta = (8.553 \pm 0.005) \times 10^{-6}$. Using the best values of the fundamental constants available to them, they conclude that the wave-length computed by the dispersion theory agrees best with the ruled grating wave-lengths, and they recalculate the results given in Table IX–12 with the same conclusion, which is contrary to Bearden's previous conclusion.

[36] K. Shiba, Sci. Pap. Inst. Phys. Chem. Research, Tokyo **19**, 97 (1932).

[37] R. A. Millikan, Phil. Mag. **34**, 1 (1917).

[38] Harrington, Phys. Rev. **8**, 738 (1916).

[39] Van Dyke, Phys. Rev. **21**, 250 (1923).

[40] 1835.6×10^{-7} Gille, Ann. der Phys. **48**, 799 (1915).
     1827.3   Markwell, Phys. Rev. **8**, 479 (1916).
     1833   Wagstaff, Phil. Mag. **45**, 84 (1923).
     1849   Markowski, Ann. der Phys. **14**, 742 (1904).
     1850   Robert, Phil. Mag. **23**, 250 (1912).

1831.2 $\times$ 10^{-7} cgs. units at 23° C., as he deems probable, the oil-drop value of e is (4.803 $\pm$ 0.010) $\times$ 10^{-10}, which removes the discrepancy between Millikan's result and the results by the x-ray method.

Birge[41] has given a comprehensive treatment of the most probable values of the fundamental physical constants. In his most recent article he has extended a method devised by Bond[42] for the simultaneous calculation of the values of e, e/m, and h which are in best accord with the various experimental methods of measuring them or their inter-relations. Relationships between h and e are given by experimental results on ionization potentials, on the critical excitation wave-length in the photo-electric effect, on the Stefan-Boltzmann constant, the Wien-Planck constant, and from the electron diffraction wave-length. Birge concludes that the value of e which best fits the data from these measurements confirms the oil-drop rather than the x-ray value of e. A value of e/m consistent with any adopted values of e and h may be obtained from the expression for the Rydberg constant. Shiba has also considered this method of obtaining values of e and h, and although the resultant value of e in his treatment lies, as does Birge's, nearer the oil-drop than the x-ray value, he concludes, contrary to Birge, that this is not of significance. Birge in 1932 recommended the following values:

$$e = (4.7688 \pm 0.0040) \times 10^{-10} \text{ esu.}$$

$$e/m = (1.7611 \pm 0.0009) \times 10^7 \text{ emu./gm.}$$

$$h = (6.5443 \pm 0.0091) \times 10^{-27} \text{ erg} \times \text{sec.}$$

In view of the careful consideration which has been given of possible sources of error in the x-ray method of evaluation of e, and the failure to find any such sources, it seems that the values of e in Table IX–9 cannot arbitrarily be discarded as numerically too high. At the present time, however, there does not exist a sufficiently large group of physicists favorable to either value of e to warrant a definite decision between them.

7. The Measurement of h by X-ray Methods

We have seen that the short wave-length limit λ of the general radiation emitted from an x-ray tube operated at constant voltage is given by the relation

$$eV' = hc/\lambda, \tag{9.43}$$

[41] R. T. Birge, Phys. Rev. Suppl. **1**, 1 (1929); Phys. Rev. **40**, 228 (1932).
[42] W. N. Bond, Phil. Mag. **10**, 994 (1930); **12**, 632 (1931).

where e is the charge on the electron in esu, V' is the potential difference through which the electrons fall in esu, h is Planck's constant,
and c the velocity of light.

An experimental determination of the limiting wave-length and
the voltage on the tube will therefore give a relation between h and e.
If we determine λ by reflection from a crystal, we must use the Bragg
Law and an equation similar to eq. (9.25). The measurements have
not as yet been made with sufficient precision to warrant an index of
refraction correction, so that we will omit it and use merely the
uncorrected Bragg equation. This gives

$$he^{-\frac{4}{3}} = \frac{2pqV \sin \theta}{10^{-8}c^2} \sqrt[3]{\frac{M}{2\rho Q \Phi(\beta)}}. \tag{9.44}$$

p and q in this expression are factors each very near unity which have
to do with the calibration of the international volt (V) in terms of
the electromagnetic unit. Birge[43] has shown that the value of the
product pq is 1.0005. The remaining symbols have previously been
defined in this chapter.

Measurements of the limiting wave-length of the general radiation
have been carried out by many experimenters,[44] but only the measurements of Duane, Palmer and Chi-Sun Yeh, and of Feder will be
discussed here. In the experiments of Duane and his collaborators,
the voltage on the x-ray tube was supplied by a storage battery and
was 24,413 volts in all determinations. The voltage was measured
by observing the current through a calibrated, wire-wound resistance
of some 6×10^6 ohms. The voltage being kept constant, the calcite
crystal was moved in steps $\Delta\theta$, and the ionization chamber in corresponding steps $2\Delta\theta$ through the angular region in which the minimum
wave-length was expected to appear in the first order. At angular
settings nearer the direct beam than corresponds to the Bragg angle
of the limiting wave-length, observed ionization currents are due to

[43] R. T. Birge, Phys. Rev. Suppl. 1, 1 (1929).
[44] Duane and Hunt, Phys. Rev. 6, 166 (1915).
A. W. Hull, Phys. Rev. 7, 156 (1916).
D. L. Webster, Phys. Rev. 7, 599 (1916).
Blake and Duane, Phys. Rev. 10, 624 (1917).
A. Müller, Arch. des Sciences 46, 63 (1918).
C. T. Ulrey, Phys. Rev. 11, 401 (1918).
E. Wagner, Ann. d. Physik 57, 401 (1918); Jahrb. der Radioakt. 16, 190 (1919).
Duane, Palmer and Chi-Sun Yeh, Proc. Nat. Acad. Sci. 7, 237 (1921).
H. Feder, Ann. d. Physik 5, 1, 497 (1929).

radiation diffusely scattered by the crystal, and to natural leak of the electrical apparatus. At larger angles, the general radiation is super-posed upon this background, and by extrapolation an angular reading is found at which this first appears. Readings are taken on both sides of zero as described in the part of Sec. 3 of this chapter dealing with wave-length measurements by means of the Bragg ionization spectrometer. Due to the horizontal divergence of the x-ray beam, a slight correction must be added to the observed value of θ. Roughly

TABLE IX–13

DETERMINATIONS OF $he^{-5/3}$ BY DUANE, PALMER AND YEH AND BY FEDER. EQ. (9.44)

Constant	Source
$pq = 1.0005$	Birge, Phys. Rev. Suppl. 1, 1 (1929)
$c = 2.99797$ cm./sec.	Birge, ibid.
$M = 100.078$ cm./mol ($CaCO_3$)	Birge, ibid.
$M = 58.46$ gm./mol (NaCl)	Landolt Bornstein Tb. I Ergz. Bd.
$Q = 2.89270 \times 10^{14}$ esu	Birge, loc. cit.
$\rho = 2.71024$ gm./cm.^{3} ($CaCO_3$)	Average, Table IX–2
$\rho = 2.16418$ gm./cm.^{3} (NaCl)	Tu, Phys. Rev. 40, 662 (1932)
$\Phi(\beta) = 1.09594$ ($CaCO_3$)	Bearden, Phys. Rev. 38, 2089 (1931)
$\Phi(\beta) = 1.00000$ (NaCl)	

DUANE, PALMER, AND YEH. ($CaCO_3$)

θ	V	$he^{-5/3}$
$4°$ $47'$ $30''$	24,413	1.7600×10^{-14}
$4°$ $47'$ $36''$	24,413	1.7606
$4°$ $47'$ $44''$	24,413	1.7614
$4°$ $47'$ $33''$	24,413	1.7603

$(1.7606 \pm 0.0009) \times 10^{-14}$

FEDER. (NaCl)

θ	V	$he^{-5/3}$	θ	V	$he^{-5/3}$
$-15°$ $52'$	8000	1.7535×10^{-14}	$16°$ $16.5'$	7815	1.7556
$15°$ $53.5'$	8013	1.7590	$-16°$ $17.7'$	7808	1.7564
$-15°$ $10'$	8375	1.7566	$-15°$ $32.5'$	8185	1.7582
$15°$ $06'$	8415	1.7574	$15°$ $31.5'$	8190	1.7574
$-14°$ $17.5'$	8872	1.7558	$14°$ $00.5'$	9045	1.7553
$14°$ $14'$	8918	1.7579	$-14°$ $01.5'$	9040	1.7564
$16°$ $36'$	7660	1.7514	$-13°$ $31.5'$	9362	1.7553
$-16°$ $50.5'$	7550	1.7563	$13°$ $29.5'$	9388	1.7560
$-17°$ $21.5'$	7345	1.7568			
$17°$ $16'$	7385	1.7573			

$(1.7563 \pm 0.0009) \times 10^{-14}$
uncorrected.

this correction is the angle α in eq. (9.29), but due to the non-uniformity in the emissivity of the focal spot the foot of the general radiation curve is not linear, and the exact amount of the correction is difficult to estimate. Thus, considering this factor alone, minimum glancing angle determinations at large angles are apt to be more accurate than at small angles. In the experiments of Duane, Palmer, and Yeh, this correction was estimated to be less than one part in 300.

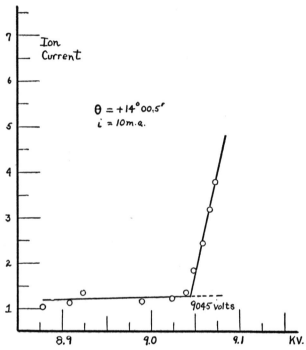

Fig. IX–8.   An isochromat obtained by Feder in his measurement of *h*. The wavelength in question first appears in the spectrum at 9045 volts.

In the work of Feder, an ionization spectrometer was also used, but in this case the crystal was left stationary and the voltage changed on the tube until the lowest voltage was found at which the x-ray beam contained wave-lengths which could be diffracted at the known angle. The cleavage planes of a rock salt crystal were used. The zero position of the crystal was located by keeping the voltage constant and observing symmetric general radiation curves on both sides of the incident beam. The final experiments appearing in Table IX–13 are grouped so that pairs correspond to approximately equal positions (+ and −) on both sides of the direct beam.   Table IX–13 shows the results of Feder and those of Duane, Palmer, and Yeh.   In the latter case the angles themselves have been corrected for the divergence of the beam.   In Feder's data the uncorrected, observed angles are given.   Feder estimates that this correction, together with another for his voltage measurements, calls for an addition of 0.45 parts per thousand to his average result.   We thus obtain the results in Table IX–14.   These values agree closely with the estimates of the value of h from x-ray measurements made by Ladenburg in 1933.[45]

TABLE IX–14

DETERMINATION OF h BY MEANS OF X-RAYS

Author	$he^{-4/3} \times 10^{14}$	$h \times 10^{27}$ $(10^{10}e = 4.7688 \pm 0.004)$	$h \times 10^{27}$ $(10^{10}e = 4.803 \pm 0.004)$
Duane, Palmer, Yeh	1.7606±0.0009	6.5595±0.009	6.6223±0.009
Feder.............	1.7571±0.0009	6.5465±0.009	6.6092±0.009

Kirkpatrick and Ross[45a] have recently investigated the limit of the continuous spectrum using a double crystal spectrometer.   In this work no angles were measured.   The spectrometer was set on the maximum of the Ag $K\alpha_1$ line in the (1, 1) position of calcite, and the voltage was lowered until no reflected radiation was observed in the ionization chamber.   The glancing angle for Ag $K\alpha_1$ is known with great accuracy from the measurements made in Siegbahn's laboratory, and has the value $5° 17' 13.7'' \pm 0.4''$.   The resolving power of the double spectrometer is so high that the correction for slit width which appears in the previous determinations is negligible.   Corrections to the measured voltage were made for the following effects:

(a) The potential drop along the hot filament due to the heating current (about −3 volts);

(b) The average thermal energy of the thermo-electrons emitted from the filament (about 0.2 volt);

(c) The work function of tungsten, which means that in entering the target material the electrons were speeded up about 4.5 volts.

[45] R. Ladenburg, Handb. der Physik, J. Springer, Berlin, Bd. XXIII (1933).
[45a] Kirkpatrick and Ross, Phys. Rev. 45, 454 (1934).

The measurements on the continuous spectrum were made on radiation from a commercial tungsten target tube because it was found that in tubes not very thoroughly baked out deposits on the target changed the slope of the intensity versus voltage curve near the short wavelength limit.

From eleven determinations, the value of the quantum voltage corresponding to the wave-length of the Ag $K\alpha_1$ line was found to be $(2.20875 \pm 0.00015) \times 10^4$ international volts, which when substituted in eq. (9.44) together with the value of the glancing angle gives a value of $he^{-5/3}$ of $(1.7654 \pm 0.002) \times 10^{-14}$, using the constants for calcite at the head of Table IX–13. The authors discuss the previous work on the problem and come to the conclusion that a correction should be applied to the work of Duane, Palmer and Yeh which brings their result within 0.07 per cent of that of Feder. The result of Feder lies within 0.04 per cent of that of Kirkpatrick and Ross, so that after this correction has been made, the three results lie very close together. From the value of Kirkpatrick and Ross, the value of h is

$$h = 6.544 \times 10^{-27} \quad \text{if} \quad e = 4.7688 \times 10^{-10}$$

$$h = 6.607 \times 10^{-27} \quad \text{if} \quad e = 4.803 \ \times 10^{-10}.$$

Kirkpatrick and Ross point out that if their determination of $he^{-5/3}$ is combined with determinations of h/e by independent methods, such as the determination of the photo-electric threshold, an estimate of the value of e may be obtained which may indicate whether the oil-drop or the x-ray value should be preferred. From data on the photo-electric effect, they estimate

$$h/e = 1.3720 \times 10^{-17} \text{ erg sec./e.s.u.}$$

and we have

$$h/e^{2/3} = 1.7564 \times 10^{-17} \text{ erg sec./(e.s.u.)}^{2/3}.$$

Solving these two equations for e gives the value 4.766×10^{-10}, which favors the result obtained by the oil-drop method. There is some doubt, however, as to the accuracy with which h/e can be measured by the photo-electric effect.

8. *General Theory of the Double Spectrometer*

In Sec. 3 of this chapter the double crystal ionization spectrometer was mentioned as an instrument adaptable to precision measurements of absolute glancing angles. Its advantage over the single crystal ionization spectrometer was there stated as principally due to the greater resolving power attained. In a general way it may be said that this increase is caused by the selective action of the first crystal upon the incident beam, in that monochromatic constituents of it are diffracted in parallel bundles in the beam leaving the crystal. We will now investigate in more detail the action of the instrument, and attempt a definition of its resolving power.

X-ray spectrometers in which the reflection takes place from two crystals in series were used at an early date in the attempt to measure the coefficient of reflection from a single crystal. Among the experimenters were A. H. Compton,[46] Bragg, James, and Bosanquet,[47] Davis and Stempel,[48] and Wagner and Kulenkampff.[49] The recent vogue of the double spectrometer may be said to date from the realization that the instrument is capable of high resolving power. Although an expression for the dispersion in anti-parallel positions is given in the paper of Wagner and Kulenkampff, these positions were not consciously exploited until the work of Davis and Purks,[50] and independently, Ehrenberg and Mark,[51] who first made a theoretical attempt to understand the shape of the curves obtained from rotation of crystal B in the various positions of the instruments.

The theory of the double spectrometer has been discussed by Schwarzschild,[52] Spencer,[53] Laue[54] and recently by L. P. Smith.[54a] Many of the ideas in the presentation given here were first developed by these authors.

Assumptions as to the Experimental Arrangement.—We shall develop equations for the spectrometer keeping in mind the method of operation in which the rocking curves are obtained from the rotation of the second crystal alone. Later we shall show how the equations are to be applied in case both crystals are rotated. We shall assume that the two axes of rotation of the crystals lie in a vertical plane, and are accurately parallel. It is also necessary that the crystal planes

[46] A. H. Compton, Phys. Rev. 10, 95 (1917).

[47] Bragg, James, and Bosanquet, Phil. Mag. 41, 309; 42, 1 (1921).

[48] Davis and Stempel, Phys. Rev. 17, 608 (1921); Phil. Mag. 45, 463 (1923).

[49] Wagner and Kulenkampff, Ann. d. Physik, 68, 369 (1922).

[50] Bergen Davis and H. Purks, Proc. Nat. Acad. Sci. 13, 419 (1927).

[51] Ehrenberg and Mark, Zeitschr. f. Physik 42, 807, 823 (1927).

[52] M. Schwarzschild, Phys. Rev. 32, 162 (1928).

[53] R. C. Spencer, Phys. Rev. 38, 618 (1931).

[54] A. von Laue, Zeitschr. f. Physik 72, 472 (1931).

[54a] L. P. Smith, Phys. Rev. 46, 343 (1934).

which are reflecting lie parallel to these axes. The discussion is applicable to cases in which the reflection takes place from a crystal surface, and is not adequate for cases in which there is transmission through a crystal slab. The crystal on which the x-rays first fall we will call crystal A; the second crystal, crystal B.

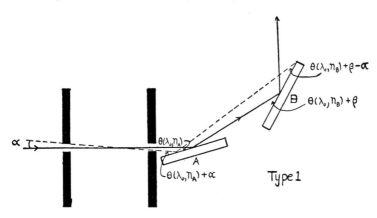

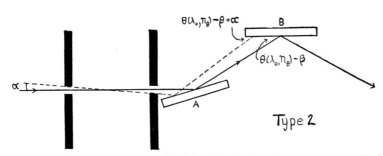

Fig. IX-9. The two main types of positions in the double spectrometer. α is the horizontal divergence.

Definitions.—The positions of the two crystals fall into two major classes, which are:

Positions of Type 1: The rays incident on crystal A and leaving from crystal B are on the same side of the ray between the crystals.

Positions of Type 2: The rays incident on crystal A and leaving from crystal B are on opposite sides of the ray between the crystals. These positions are shown in Fig. IX–9.

Central Ray: The central ray is a ray passing through the geometrical center of the slit apertures.

Vertical Divergence, ϕ: The vertical divergence of a ray is the angle made with its projection on a plane perpendicular to the axes of the instrument (a horizontal plane). It is not necessary to define what is meant by positive and negative values of ϕ since the functions appearing in the instrument are symmetrical with respect to rays lying above or below the horizontal plane.

Horizontal Divergence, α: The horizontal divergence of a ray is the angle made with its projection on a vertical plane containing the

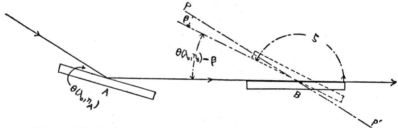

Fig. IX–10. This illustrates the conventions adopted here as to the zero position of crystal B, and the sense of a positive rotation of B. If the reflecting surface of B lies in the line PP', the central ray makes the characteristic angle $\theta(\lambda_o, n_B)$ with it. A positive deviation β from this position is illustrated.

central ray. A positive value of α indicates that the glancing angle made by the ray on crystal A is greater than that made by the central ray, and vice versa.

Parallel Positions: The parallel positions are important special cases of positions of Type 2 in which the reflecting faces of the two crystals lie in parallel planes.

Angular Positions of Crystal B: We shall define the zero or fundamental reference position of crystal B as an angular setting in which the central ray reflected from crystal A is parallel to the surface of B, and crystal B lies on the same side of ray AB as does crystal A. This is shown in Fig. IX–10. A positive angular displacement of B of amount ζ is defined as a rotation of B in a counter-clockwise direction through angle ζ. Thus from $\zeta = 0$ to $\zeta = \pi/2$, crystal B passes through positions of Type I, and from $\zeta = \pi/2$ to $\zeta = \pi$, the positions are of Type 2. Let $\theta_0(\lambda_0, n_B)$ represent the angle θ_0 obtained from eq. (9.01) corresponding to the wave-length λ_0 when crystal B is reflecting in the order n_B. Corresponding to $\theta_0(\lambda_0 n_B)$ there will be an angle $\theta(\lambda_0 n_B)$ given by

$$\theta(\lambda_0, n_B) = \theta_0(\lambda_0, n_B) + \delta \sec \theta_0 \operatorname{cosec} \theta_0.$$

The reflection of a given wave-length λ_0 from crystal B will then take place through certain small ranges of ζ, which in positions of Type 1

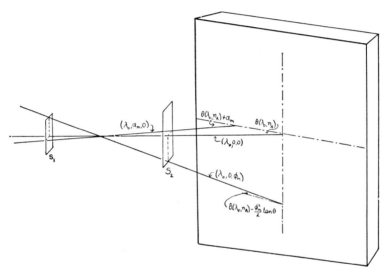

Fig. IX-11. A ray incident upon the first crystal may be designated by the three symbols (λ, α, ϕ). The figure shows the glancing angles made by the rays $(\lambda_0, \alpha_m, 0)$ and $(\lambda_0, 0, \phi_m)$ when the glancing angle of the central ray $(\lambda_0, 0, 0)$ is $\theta(\lambda_0, n_A)$.

lie close to the values $\zeta = \theta(\lambda_0, n_B)$, and in positions of Type 2 near the values $\zeta \Rightarrow \pi - \theta(\lambda_0, n_B)$. It will be convenient to speak of the deviations of crystal B from these characteristic angles, and the deviations which it is necessary to consider are in all cases so small that an ambiguity as to which value of $\theta(\lambda_0, n_B)$ the deviation is measured from will never arise.

The angular deviation of crystal B from one of these characteristic positions will be represented by β. A positive value of β in positions of Type 1 means $\zeta > \theta(\lambda_0, n_B)$; in positions of Type 2 it means $\zeta > \pi - \theta(\lambda_0, n_B)$. It is noticed in Fig. IX-10 that we have drawn the instrument in positions of Type 1 in such an orientation that successive deviations of the incident radiation are counter-clockwise in sense. If the instrument is set so that these deviations in positions of Type 1 are in the opposite sense, certain conventions as to the sense of rotation of crystal B to pass from shorter to longer wave-lengths are reversed.

A ray in the beam incident upon crystal A may be characterized by three quantities (λ, α, ϕ), giving its wave-length, and horizontal and vertical divergence respectively. Let us find the glancing angle of such a ray on crystal A in terms of α and ϕ. Let us suppose that crystal A is set in such an angular position that the central ray, which has $\alpha = \phi = 0$, makes the glancing angle $\theta(\lambda_0, n_A)$. We may think of λ_0 as some characteristic wave-length in the incident radiation, corresponding to the center of a spectrum line or an absorption limit. It may be readily shown from Fig. IX–11 that, if the angles α and ϕ are small, the required expression for the glancing angle of ray (λ, α, ϕ) on crystal A is

$$\theta(\lambda_0, n_A) + \alpha - \tfrac{1}{2}\phi^2 \tan \theta(\lambda_0, n_A). \qquad (9.45)$$

We wish now to find the deviation of this glancing angle from the angle $\theta(\lambda, n_A)$ which is the reference angle corresponding to λ in the n_Ath order. We have

$$\theta(\lambda, n_A) = \theta(\lambda_0, n_A) + (\lambda - \lambda_0) \frac{\partial}{\partial \lambda_0} \theta(\lambda_0, n_A). \qquad (9.46)$$

The deviation in question is then the actual glancing angle of eq. (9.45) minus the reference angle of eq. (9.46), or

$$\alpha - \tfrac{1}{2}\phi^2 \tan \theta(\lambda_0, n_A) - (\lambda - \lambda_0) \frac{\partial}{\partial \lambda_0} \theta(\lambda_0, n_A). \qquad (9.47)$$

If crystal A has a diffraction pattern approaching that predicted for a perfect crystal, and the deviation of eq. (9.47) is more than a few seconds of arc, the intensity of reflection of ray (λ, α, ϕ) from crystal A will be very small, but we shall not neglect the fact that at least theoretically, each ray (λ, α, ϕ) incident on crystal A is reflected to some (in general very minute) extent.

Let us now consider the glancing angle made by ray (λ, α, ϕ) on crystal B, after its reflection from crystal A. This will depend on the type of position in which the spectrometer is operating.

Positions of Type 1: Let crystal B be placed at angular deviation β from a position in which the glancing angle of the central ray upon it is $\theta(\lambda_0, n_B)$. The glancing angle of the central ray upon it is then $\theta + \beta$. From a study of Fig. IX-9 it may be seen that the glancing angle of the ray (λ, α, ϕ) is

(Type 1) $\theta(\lambda_0, n_B) + \beta - \alpha - \frac{1}{2}\phi^2 \tan \theta(\lambda_0, n_B)$.

The deviation of this glancing angle from the angle $\theta(\lambda, n_B)$ is

(Type 1) $\beta - \alpha - \frac{1}{2}\phi^2 \tan \theta(\lambda_0, n_B) - (\lambda - \lambda_0) \dfrac{\partial}{\partial \lambda_0} \theta(\lambda_0, n_B).$ (9.49)

Positions of Type 2: Again, let crystal B be set so that its angular deviation is β from a position where the glancing angle of the central ray upon it is $\theta(\lambda_0, n_B)$. Then the glancing angle of the central ray upon crystal B is $\theta(\lambda_0, n_B) - \beta$, and the glancing angle made by the ray (λ, α, ϕ) is

(Type 2) $\theta(\lambda_0, n_B) - \beta + \alpha - \frac{1}{2}\phi^2 \tan \theta(\lambda_0, n_B)$.

The deviation of the glancing angle of this ray from the angle $\theta(\lambda, n_B)$ is

(Type 2) $-\beta + \alpha - \frac{1}{2}\phi^2 \tan \theta(\lambda_0, n_B) - (\lambda - \lambda_0) \dfrac{\partial}{\partial \lambda_0} \theta(\lambda_0, n_B).$ (9.49a)

In general, then, we may write for the deviation of the glancing angle of the ray (λ, α, ϕ) on crystal B from the angle $\theta(\lambda, n_B)$ when the crystal is set so that its angular deviation is β from a position where the central ray makes the glancing angle $\theta(\lambda_0, n_B)$ the expression

$$\pm \beta \mp \alpha - \frac{1}{2}\phi^2 \tan \theta(\lambda_0, n_B) - (\lambda - \lambda_0) \dfrac{\partial}{\partial \lambda_0} \theta(\lambda_0, n_B).$$ (9.50)

Upper signs, Type 1; lower signs, Type 2.

Let us now consider the power in an element of the beam incident on crystal A. This element will consist of radiation having wavelengths between λ and $\lambda + d\lambda$, and will have the horizontal and vertical divergences $d\alpha$ and $d\phi$ in the neighborhood of the values α and ϕ. The power in such an elementary beam may be written

$$G(\alpha, \phi) J(\lambda - \lambda_0) d\alpha d\lambda d\phi.$$

In this expression the function G will in general arise from considerations of the geometry of the instrument, that is, the shape of the slit apertures, the distribution of intensity in the focal spot, etc. The function J gives the distribution of energy in the incident spectrum.

When this element of the incident beam is diffracted from crystal A, the power in the diffracted beam depends on the deviation of the glancing angle from the angle $\theta(\lambda, n_A)$. This dependence will be given by the single crystal diffraction pattern function, which we shall call the C function. If the crystals are perfect, this C function should have the shape of the I function of eq. (6.48), Chap. VI, but we will not assume this to be the case at present. Thus the power in the elementary beam after diffraction from crystal A may be written

$$G(\alpha, \phi)J(\lambda - \lambda_0)C_A[\alpha - \tfrac{1}{2}\phi^2 \tan \theta(\lambda_0, n_A)$$

$$- (\lambda - \lambda_0)(\partial/\partial\lambda_0)\theta(\lambda_0, n_A)]d\alpha d\lambda d\phi. \qquad (9.50a)$$

After diffraction of this element of the beam from crystal B, we will obtain, on integration, the entire intensity reflected from crystal B as

$$P'(\beta) = \int_{-\phi_m}^{\phi_m} \int_{\lambda_{\min.}}^{\lambda_{\max.}} \int_{-\alpha_m}^{\alpha_m} G(\alpha, \phi)J(\lambda - \lambda_0)$$

$$C_A[\alpha - \tfrac{1}{2}\phi^2 \tan \theta(\lambda_0, n_A) - (\lambda - \lambda_0)(\partial/\partial\lambda_0)\theta(\lambda_0, n_A)]$$

$$C_B[\pm\beta\mp\alpha-\tfrac{1}{2}\phi^2 \tan \theta(\lambda_0, n_B)-(\lambda-\lambda_0)(\partial/\partial\lambda_0)\theta(\lambda_0, n_A)]d\alpha d\lambda d\phi. \quad (9.51)$$

Upper signs, Type 1; lower signs, Type 2.

In writing this expression, we have assumed that the range of wave-lengths covered in any rocking curve is so small that the variation of the functions C with wave-length can be neglected. This is the general equation of the instrument, from which the properties and the shapes of the various types of rocking curves may be deduced. The term " rocking curve " as used here means the ionization versus position curve obtained by the rotation of crystal B about its own axis in any position of the instrument (not merely parallel positions). The limiting values of α and ϕ are α_m and ϕ_m respectively. If the two slits are rectangular apertures, of equal width w and height h, separated by the distance L, then $\alpha_m = w/L$ and $\phi_m = h/L$. The limits of λ in any practical case cannot extend farther than the limits of the range of wave-lengths reflected by crystal A, which depend on the horizontal divergence of the beam incident on A.

Some elementary properties of the instrument may be deduced from eq. (9.51) by considering the limiting case in which the diffraction patterns of the two crystals are so narrow that no appreciable contribution to the function $P'(\beta)$ occurs except when the arguments of both C functions are zero. This corresponds to the elementary treatments in which it is assumed that there is a perfectly discrete Bragg angle for any incident wave-length λ. Such an assumption is of course, unphysical, and eq. (9.51) shows that in such a case no power would be diffracted from a divergent incident beam at any position. Nevertheless, the dispersion of the instrument may be obtained by this method, which gives the two equations

$$\alpha - \tfrac{1}{2}\phi^2 \tan \theta(\lambda_0, n_A) - (\lambda - \lambda_0)(\partial/\partial\lambda_0)\theta(\lambda_0, n_A) \qquad = 0$$

$$\pm \beta \mp \alpha - \tfrac{1}{2}\phi^2 \tan \theta(\lambda_0, n_B) - (\lambda - \lambda_0)(\partial/\partial\lambda_0)\theta(\lambda_0, n_B) = 0$$

Elimination of α between these two expressions leads to

$$\beta - \frac{\phi^2}{2}\{\tan \theta(\lambda_0, n_A) \pm \tan \theta(\lambda_0, n_B)\}$$

$$-(\lambda - \lambda_0)\left\{\frac{\partial\theta(\lambda_0, n_A)}{\partial\lambda_0} \pm \frac{\partial\theta(\lambda_0, n_B)}{\partial\lambda_0}\right\} = 0. \qquad (9.52)$$

Let us now introduce the symbol D, defined by

$$D = \frac{\partial\theta(\lambda_0, n_A)}{\partial\lambda_0} \pm \frac{\partial\theta(\lambda_0, n_B)}{\partial\lambda_0}. \qquad \begin{array}{l} \text{Type 1} \\ \text{Type 2} \end{array} \qquad (9.53)$$

Carrying out the differentiations by the use of the Bragg law, we find

$$D = \frac{n_A}{2d \cos \theta(\lambda_0, n_A)} \pm \frac{n_B}{2d \cos \theta(\lambda_0, n_B)} \qquad (9.54)$$

or

$$D = \frac{1}{\lambda_0}\{\tan \theta(\lambda_0, n_A) \pm \tan \theta(\lambda_0, n_B)\}. \qquad (9.55)$$

Substitution of eqs. (9.54) and (9.55) in eq. (9.52) gives

$$\beta = \tfrac{1}{2}D\lambda_0\phi^2 + D(\lambda - \lambda_0). \qquad (9.56)$$

The dispersion of the double crystal spectrometer when crystal B alone is rotated, is naturally defined as $d\beta/d\lambda$, and from eq. (9.56) we see

$$\text{Dispersion} = d\beta/d\lambda = D.$$

From eq. (9.54) it is seen that in positions of Type 2, where $n_B > n_A$, the dispersion is negative. This means that the sense of rotation of crystal B to pass from shorter to longer wave-lengths is clockwise in the arrangement of Fig. IX–10. Where D is positive, counter-clockwise rotation of crystal B increases the wave-length reflected. As previously mentioned, these statements are only correct as to sign in the arrangement of Fig. IX–10, where successive deviations of the beam in positions of Type 1 are counter-clockwise.

Allison and Williams[55] have devised a notation useful in describing arrangements of the double spectrometer based on eq. (9.54). The method advocated is to state the wave-length for which the spectrometer is set (λ_0), and then the numbers n_A and n_B, with the convention that n_B is negative in positions of Type 2. Thus the symbol Mo $K\alpha_1$ (1, 1) means that the spectrometer is set to reflect Mo $K\alpha_1$ in the first order from both crystals, and that the crystals are set in a Type 1 position (anti-parallel). In the case under consideration, the dispersion is given by

$$D = \{d \cos \theta(\text{Mo } K\alpha_1, 1)\}^{-1} \sim 68.57 \text{ sec./X. U.} \qquad (9.57)$$

which is twice the value of the dispersion of a single crystal spectrometer at Mo $K\alpha_1$ in the first order. The symbol Mo $K\alpha_1$ (1, −1) means both crystals reflecting in the first order, but in a position of Type 2. The dispersion is zero in the position under consideration, which is one in which the reflecting faces are parallel.[56]

9. *Theory and Experiment in Parallel Positions of the Double Spectrometer*

The so-called parallel positions of the double spectrometer are, as we have seen, characterized by being positions of Type 2 in which D is zero. They thus have the notation $(n, -n)$. Let us assume that the C functions of the two crystals are identical, and thus that

---

[55] S. K. Allison and J. H. Williams, Phys. Rev. **35**, 149 (1930).

[56] If we consider the radiation monochromatic, all of wave-length λ_0, then eq. (9.56) becomes

$$\beta = \tfrac{1}{2}D\lambda_0\phi^2.$$

Since ϕ can take on all values from o to $\phi_m = h/L$, it results that the maximum value of β at which λ_0 can be reflected is

$$(\tfrac{1}{2}D\lambda_0 h^2)/L^2.$$

This was deduced by Schwarzschild, loc. cit., and called the extent of the geometric rocking curve. It does not seem advantageous to separate the geometrical and physical properties of the instrument as he did, at least in this respect, because in most experiments ϕ is small enough so that ϕ^2 is of the order of the width of the diffraction pattern, so that our assumption of width zero, on which eq. (9.56) was deduced, is not valid.

$C_A = C_B = C$. Furthermore we have $\theta(\lambda_0, n_A) = \theta(\lambda_0, n_B) = \theta$, so that eq. (9.51) simplifies to

$$P'(\beta) = \int_{-\phi_m}^{\phi_m} \int_{\lambda_{min}}^{\lambda_{max}} \int_{-\alpha_m}^{\alpha_m} G(\alpha, \phi) J(\lambda - \lambda_0)$$

$$C[\alpha - \tfrac{1}{2} \phi^2 \tan \theta - (\lambda - \lambda_0)(\partial\theta/\partial\lambda_0)]$$

$$C[\alpha - \beta - \tfrac{1}{2} \phi^2 \tan \theta - (\lambda - \lambda_0)(\partial\theta/\partial\lambda_0)] d\alpha d\lambda d\phi. \quad (9.58)$$

In interpreting this expression it is necessary to have in mind the characteristics of the functions C, J, and G. If the crystals are at all nearly perfect, C is negligibly small everywhere except in a very narrow range of its argument close to zero. This range is of the order of magnitude of the width of the single crystal diffraction pattern, and in good crystals, this is a few seconds of arc, or, in radian measure, 10^{-5}. This very important width thus becomes a standard of comparison, and by the terms "very narrow" or "very close to," we will, in this discussion, mean within the order of the diffraction pattern width.

In the cases in question here, the function $G(\alpha, \phi)$ can be considered as the product of two functions:

$$G(\alpha, \phi) = G_1(\alpha) G_2(\phi). \quad (9.59)$$

The functions G_1 and G_2 are finite in the range of argument of some minutes of arc, as this is the usual extent of the maximum horizontal and vertical divergence of the beam. Thus these functions are finite over a range of argument some 10^{-3} radian units wide, or perhaps one hundred times the range over which the C functions are finite. In most cases, however, the term $\tfrac{1}{2} \phi^2 \tan \theta$ is very small, that is, of diffraction pattern width order.

With these considerations in mind, we can deduce from eq. (9.58) some characteristic properties of the rocking curves obtained in parallel positions by rotation of crystal B, that is, of the function $P'(\beta)$.

(1) The effective values of α for any monochromatic constituent of the beam of wave-length λ lie very close to the value $(\partial\theta/\partial\lambda_0)(\lambda - \lambda_0)$, for if this were not so, the argument of the first C function would be large, and the function negligibly small. This is what is spoken of in the elementary discussion as the action of crystal A of separating the beam into monochromatic parallel bundles.

(2) The function $P'(\beta)$ can be appreciably different from zero

only over a very narrow range of β. For, consider the possibility that β might be large. If this were so, in order for the second C function in eq. (9.58) to be of appreciable value, $\alpha - (\partial\theta/\partial\lambda_0)(\lambda-\lambda_0)$ would have to be large, in order to have the argument sufficiently small. But if $\alpha - (\partial\theta/\partial\lambda_0)(\lambda - \lambda_0)$ is large, then the first C function of eq. (9.58) becomes negligible, and therefore the entire integrand function. Thus the parallel position rocking curves have widths comparable to those of the diffraction pattern of a single crystal.

(3) The effective wave-length range reflected by crystal B is at any position β independent of β, and covers the relatively large range

$$\lambda = \lambda_o \pm \frac{\partial\lambda_o}{\partial\theta}\, \alpha_m. \qquad (9.60)$$

This may be shown as follows. For a very small value of β, it is sufficient that $\alpha - (\partial\theta/\partial\lambda_0)(\lambda - \lambda_0)$ be small for appreciable values of the integrand product to be obtained. This condition is satisfied by values of λ close to the value $\lambda = \lambda_o + (\partial\lambda_o/\partial\theta)\alpha$ and since the range of α is $-\alpha_m < \alpha < \alpha_m$ we deduce the above. Thus in a parallel position, the beam entering the ionization chamber from crystal B at any position on the rocking curve contains effective contributions from every wave-length reflected from crystal A. This is another way of stating that the dispersion is zero.

Let us consider the integration of eq. (9.58) with respect to α. We are to imagine holding the variables λ, ϕ, β, constant, and considering the entire integrand as a function of α. We have seen that the only pertinent values of α under these conditions lie in a very narrow range near $(\partial\theta/d\lambda_0)(\lambda - \lambda_0)$. The change in the slowly varying function $G_1(\alpha)$ of eq. (9.59) through this narrow range of α can be neglected, and we can write

$$G_1(\alpha) = G_1\left\{(\lambda - \lambda_0)\,\frac{\partial\theta}{\partial\lambda_0}\right\}. \qquad (9.61)$$

Furthermore, the angular range in which important values of α are found (if λ and ϕ are constant) is some seconds of arc, while the range of α as given by the limits of the integral is $2\alpha_m$, which will be some minutes of arc. Therefore the limits of the α-integration may be extended to $\pm\infty$ without affecting the value of the integral. If a wave-length is chosen such that the important values of α lie very near one " side " of the incident beam, that is, near $\pm\alpha_m$, then the

G_1 function is nearly zero and the contribution to the function $P'(\beta)$ unimportant. When the limits of the α-integration have been extended to $\pm \infty$, we may avail ourselves of a useful theorem, applicable when F is finite and continuous everywhere, which says,

$$\int_{-\infty}^{\infty} F(\alpha)d\alpha = \int_{-\infty}^{\infty} F(\alpha - a)d\alpha, \qquad (9.62)$$

where a is any constant. Thus we may add or subtract any constant to α in the integration without changing the result. Let

$$\frac{2\delta l}{\sin 2\theta_0} = \alpha - \frac{\phi^2}{2}\tan\theta - \frac{\partial\theta}{\partial\lambda}(\lambda - \lambda_0),$$

where l is the new variable to replace α. We may identify this l with the variable defined in eq. (6.49a), Chap. VI, and interpret the change partially as a change in the unit of angle, the angular deviation corresponding to the entire argument of the C function now being measured in an angular unit which is $2\delta/\sin 2\theta_0$ radians. We may then write eq. (9.58) as follows:

$$P'(\beta) = \frac{2\delta}{\sin 2\theta_0} \int_{\lambda_0 - (\partial\lambda_0/\partial\theta)\alpha_m}^{\lambda_0 + (\partial\lambda_0/\partial\theta)\alpha_m} \int_{-\phi_m}^{\phi_m} G_1\left\{\frac{\partial\theta}{\partial\lambda_0}(\lambda - \lambda_0)\right\}$$
$$G_2(\phi)J(\lambda - \lambda_0)d\phi d\lambda \int_{-\infty}^{\infty} C(l)C(l - \beta)dl,$$

or

$$P'(\beta) = K \int_{-\infty}^{\infty} C(l)C(l - \beta)dl. \qquad (9.63)$$

The constant K is proportional to the power of the heterogeneous beam incident on crystal A. We have thus reached the very important result that the shape of the rocking curve in parallel positions is independent of the width or the height[57] of the slits, and of the spectral energy distribution function of the radiation used.

The rocking curves $P'(\beta)$ may be obtained experimentally. The question then arises: is it possible to deduce from the experimental results the form of the function $C(l)$, and thus prove or disprove the validity of the diffraction pattern deduced from the theory of diffraction by a single crystal? The question has been answered by

[57] This assumes that the spectrometer is adjusted correctly as specified in the preceding section. Schwarzschild, loc. cit., has made an estimate of the effect produced when the crystal faces do not lie in the axes of rotation.

Laue,[58] who found that such a solution is not uniquely possible.   It can be shown that the curve $P'(\beta)$ must have an ordinate about which it is symmetrical, whether or not there is such an ordinate for $C(l)$.   For, making use of the theorem of eq. (9.62), let us replace l in eq. (9.63) by $l + \beta$.   We then find

$$P'(\beta) = K \int_{-\infty}^{\infty} C(l)C(l-\beta)dl = K \int_{-\infty}^{\infty} C(l+\beta)C(l)dl = P'(-\beta), \quad (9.64)$$

which proves the point.   If we assume that $C(l)$ has an ordinate of symmetry it is possible to calculate $C(l)$ from $P'(\beta)$, but this assumption defeats the purpose, which is to obtain $C(l)$ directly from experiment without additional assumptions.   It also follows that if the observed curves in parallel positions do not have an ordinate of symmetry, we must conclude that the diffraction patterns of crystals A and B are not identical.

Thus we are checkmated in an attempt to discover the shape of the single crystal diffraction pattern functions from experimental rocking curves in the parallel position of the double spectrometer. In view of this, the procedure has been to assume some function $C(l)$; calculate the resulting function $P'(l)$, and compare it with the experimental curve.   In the remaining paragraphs of this section we shall assume that the function $C(l)$ is that calculated for a perfect crystal, namely, $C(l) = I'(l)$ of eq. (6.50), Chap. VI, or, if the absorption can be neglected, $C(l) = I^D((l)$ of eq. (6.51).   We shall show how the various features of the parallel position rocking curves may be calculated if these single crystal diffraction patterns are assumed.

In Sec. 11 of Chap. VI we have indicated that the parallel positions of the double spectrometer have been used for measuring the so-called coefficient of reflection, R.   From an experimental standpoint, R may be defined as the ratio of the area under the rocking curve to the power obtainable from the beam incident on crystal B from crystal A.   Other aspects of the rocking curve which are of interest are (1) the per cent reflection $P(o)$, which is defined as the ratio of the maximum ionization current obtainable from crystal B to that obtained from the diffracted beam from crystal A, and (2) the angular half width at half maximum, w, which is the angular range through which crystal B must be turned to reduce the power entering the ionization chamber to one-half its maximum value.

[58] Laue, Zeitschr. f. Physik 72, 472 (1931).

It is convenient to consider a rocking curve $P(\beta)$ whose ordinates are normalized by each being the ratio of the power obtained from crystal B at the position β to that incident on B. Thus

$$P(\beta) = \frac{P'(\beta)}{K \int_{-\infty}^{\infty} I'(l)dl}. \qquad (9.65)$$

The integral in the denominator of this expression is obtained from integration of expression $(9.50a)$. The double crystal coefficient of reflection, commonly called merely the coefficient of reflection R, is then the area under the $P(\beta)$ curve if the angular deviations β are expressed in radians.

We must consider at this point the effects of polarization of the x-ray beam. Most of these rocking curve measurements are made by having the angle θ and the wave-length λ_0 correspond to some x-ray spectrum line. Characteristic x-ray lines emitted from a target are known to be unpolarized, so that we shall set up equations applicable to the case in which the beam incident on crystal A is unpolarized. The procedure is then to consider the beam as composed of two components, plane polarized at right angles, and each containing half the incident power. The σ-component is considered to be so polarized that its electric vector lies in a plane perpendicular to the plane of incidence on the crystal, that is, the electric vector lies in the vertical plane. The electric vector of the π-component lies in a horizontal plane. We must now distinguish between the diffraction pattern functions applicable to the σ- and π-components. Equation (9.65) becomes

$$P(\beta) = \frac{\int_{-\infty}^{\infty} I_\sigma'(l)I_\sigma'(l-\beta)dl + \int_{-\infty}^{\infty} I_\pi'(l)I_\pi'(l-\beta)dl}{\int_{-\infty}^{\infty} I_\sigma'(l)dl + \int_{-\infty}^{\infty} I_\pi'(l)dl}. \qquad (9.66)$$

In the general case, where the absorption in the crystal cannot be neglected, and Prins' I' function must be used (eq. (6.50), Chap. VI), the method of calculation of the σ- and π-component single crystal diffraction patterns is shown in eqs. (6.53) and (6.54), Chap. VI. If the absorption in the crystals can be neglected, so that Darwin's simplified single crystal diffraction pattern function may be used, eq. (9.66) may be entirely expressed in terms of the σ-component function. If the second term in the right hand member of eq. (6.54a), Chap. VI, is divided in numerator and denominator by $\cos 2\theta_0$, and then compared with the first term, it is seen that

$$I_\pi^D(l) = I_\sigma^D(l \sec 2\theta_0).$$

We recall that the angular unit in which l is measured is $2\delta/\sin 2\theta_0$ radians. If we adopt the smaller angular unit $2\delta/\tan 2\theta_0$ we can make calculations for the π-component using the function I_σ^D, and then after integration restore our result to the angular scale on which l is measured by multiplication by $\cos 2\theta_0$. Thus we obtain, for Darwin's function,

$$P(\beta) = \frac{\displaystyle\int_{-\infty}^{\infty} I_\sigma^D(l)I_\sigma^D(l-\beta)dl + \cos 2\theta_0 \int_{-\infty}^{\infty} I_\sigma^D(l)I_\sigma^D(l-\beta \sec 2\theta_0)dl}{(1 + \cos 2\theta_0)\displaystyle\int_{-\infty}^{\infty} I_\sigma^D(l)dl}.$$

$$(9.67)$$

It is shown in the derivation of eq. (6.59), Chap. VI that the integral appearing in the denominator of the above expression is $8F/3Z$ if the angular unit is $2\delta/\sin 2\theta_0$. An expression for $P(0)$, the per cent reflection, can be obtained by setting $\beta = 0$ in the preceding equation, giving

$$P(0) = \frac{\displaystyle\int_{-\infty}^{\infty} [I_\sigma^D(l)]^2 dl}{\displaystyle\int_{-\infty}^{\infty} I_\sigma^D(l)dl} = 0.80. \qquad (9.68)$$

Thus if Darwin's equation for the diffraction pattern can be applied, the per cent reflection is independent of the polarization, wavelength, or glancing angle. It should be emphasized that this is not the case under the more general Prins diffraction pattern function, and in this case $P(0)$ must be found by setting $\beta = 0$ in eq. (9.66). The numerical value indicated in eq. (9.68) was found by graphical integration of the numerator function. The early investigators using the double crystal spectrometer expected to obtain $P(0) = 1.00$, due to the region of 100 per cent reflection in Darwin's diffraction pattern. This expectation is seen to be due to an incomplete analysis of the operation of the instrument.

The double crystal coefficient of reflection, R, is numerically equal to the area under the $P(\beta)$ curve when the angular unit is the radian. Thus the general expression for R is

$$R = \frac{2\delta}{\sin 2\theta_0} \frac{\displaystyle\int_{-\infty}^{\infty} \int_{-\infty}^{\infty} I_\sigma{'}(l)I_\sigma{'}(l-\beta)dld\beta + \int_{-\infty}^{\infty} \int_{-\infty}^{\infty} I_\pi{'}(l)I_\pi{'}(l-\beta)dld\beta}{\displaystyle\int_{-\infty}^{\infty} I_\sigma{'}(l)dl + \int_{-\infty}^{\infty} I_\pi{'}(l)dl}$$

where the angular values of l and β are measured in units of $2\delta/\sin 2\theta_0$.

If we investigate one of the double integrals appearing in the numerator of the preceding expression, we see that it can be considerably modified.[58a] Taking the first of these integrals, let us replace the variable β by a new variable γ, where

$$\gamma = l - \beta; \quad d\gamma = -d\beta.$$

We then have

$$\int_{-\infty}^{\infty} \int_{-\infty}^{\infty} I_\sigma{'}(l)I_\sigma{'}(l-\beta)dld\beta = \int_{+\infty}^{-\infty} \int_{-\infty}^{\infty} I_\sigma{'}(l)I_\sigma{'}(\gamma)dl(-d\gamma)$$

$$= \int_{-\infty}^{\infty} \int_{-\infty}^{\infty} I_\sigma{'}(l)I_\sigma{'}(\gamma)dld\gamma = \left[\int_{-\infty}^{\infty} I'(l)dl\right]^2$$

so that we obtain

$$R = \frac{2\delta}{\sin 2\theta_0} \frac{\left[\displaystyle\int_{-\infty}^{\infty} I_\sigma{'}(l)dl\right]^2 + \left[\displaystyle\int_{-\infty}^{\infty} I_\pi{'}(l)dl\right]^2}{\displaystyle\int_{-\infty}^{\infty} I_\sigma{'}(l)dl + \int_{-\infty}^{\infty} I_\pi{'}(l)dl}. \tag{9.69}$$

If we are content with Darwin's approximation, which is very useful for the purpose of obtaining rapidly a rough estimate of the coefficient of reflection to be expected, a further simplification is possible, due to the fact that

$$\int_{-\infty}^{\infty} I_\pi{}^D(l)dl = \cos 2\theta_0 \int_{-\infty}^{\infty} I_\sigma{}^D(l)dl.$$

Thus eq. (9.69) becomes

$$R = \frac{2\delta}{\sin 2\theta_0} \frac{1 + \cos^2 2\theta_0}{1 + \cos 2\theta_0} \int_{-\infty}^{\infty} I_\sigma{}^D(l)dl.$$

[58a] The following property of these integrals was pointed out to the authors by Carl Eckart.

From the considerations leading to eq. (6.59), Chap. VI, it is shown that

$$\int_{-\infty}^{\infty} I_\sigma^D(l)dl = (8/3)FZ^{-1}$$

so that we obtain

$$R = \frac{16}{3} \frac{1 + \cos^2 2\theta_0}{1 + \cos 2\theta_0} \frac{F}{Z} \frac{\delta}{\sin 2\theta_0}$$

or

$$R = 2 \frac{1 + \cos^2 2\theta_0}{(1 + \cos 2\theta_0)^2} R_c, \qquad (9.70)$$

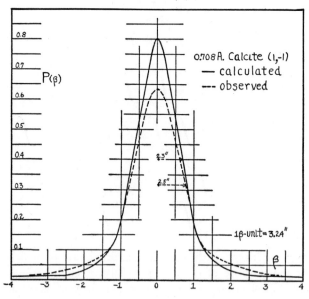

Fig. IX-12. Calculated and observed rocking curves for Mo $K\alpha_1$ $(1, -1)$ from calcite. The single crystal diffraction pattern curve from which the calculated curve of this figure was computed is Fig. VI–5, Chap. VI.

in which R_c is given by eq. (6.59), and is the single crystal coefficient of reflection.

The third important characteristic of these parallel position rocking curves is their half width at half maximum. We are unable to derive any simple formula applicable to this quantity from the shape of the single crystal diffraction pattern, but it is relatively easy to obtain an approximate result. The width will in general be greater than the half width at half maximum of the single crystal diffraction pattern, but the increase in width depends on the glancing angle (polarization) and the absorption in the crystal in a complicated manner. The straightforward method of calculation is to find $P(o)$ from eq. (9.66) and then find the value of β corresponding to the ordinate $\frac{1}{2}P(o)$.

In case the absorption can be neglected and Darwin's approxima-- tion used, some estimate of the half width at half maximum to be

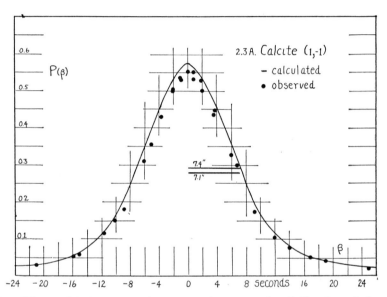

Fig. IX–13. Calculated and observed rocking curves for Cr $K\alpha_1$ (1, −1) from calcite. The corresponding single crystal diffraction pattern curves are shown in Fig. VI–6, Chap. VI.

expected can be made from the following considerations. The half width at half maximum w_c of Darwin's diffraction pattern (Fig. VI–7, Chap. VI) is never more than 6 per cent greater than the half width of the region of 100 per cent reflection for the σ-component. As the glancing angle is increased in the range below 45°, the increase falls off from 6 per cent to zero. If we limit our considerations to the small glancing angle range (below 10°), we may write, from eq. (6.52), Chap. VI,

$$w_c = 1.06\Delta\theta/2 = 2.13\delta F Z^{-1} \operatorname{cosec} 2\theta_o.$$

Calculation[59] of the shape of the crystal B rocking curve from eq.
(9.67) shows that w, the half width at half maximum of the parallel
position rocking curve is given by

$$w = 2.80FZ^{-1} \operatorname{cosec} 2\theta_0$$

so that

$$w = 1.32w_c. \tag{9.71}$$

It is emphasized that eq. (9.71) can be used only if Darwin's treatment is applicable, and then only at small glancing angles. At
larger glancing angles the ratio w/w_c becomes less than 1.32.

Figures IX–12 and IX–13 show calculated and observed rocking
curves for Mo $K\alpha_1(1, -1)$ and Cr $K\alpha_1(1, -1)$ from the cleavage
faces of calcite. The single crystal diffraction patterns used in these
calculations are shown in Figs. VI–5 and VI–6, Chap. VI. Table

TABLE IX–15

RESULTS OBTAINED BY ALLISON AND BY PARRATT ON w AND $P(o)$ FOR CALCITE SPECI-
MENS AT VARIOUS WAVE-LENGTHS IN THE $(1, -1)$ POSITION

Line	λ	Calcites V		Calcites III		Calcites II		Calculated	
		w Sec.	100 $P(o)$	w Sec.	100 $P(o)$	w Sec.	100 $P(o)$	w Sec.	100 $P(o)$
W $K\alpha_1$	208.6 X.U.	7.2	28	2.3	35	4.2	33	0.64	80
Ag $K\alpha_1$	558.3	7.0	34	2.2	59	3.8	48		
Mo $K\alpha_1$	707.8	7.2	33	2.6	63	3.9	52	2.3	80
Ir $L\beta_1$	1155	8.1	37	4.1	64	4.8	59		
Cu $K\alpha_1$	1537	7.8	46	4.9	62	5.6	61	4.9	69
Fe $K\alpha_1$	1932	9.9	42	6.2	58	6.8	54		
Cr $K\alpha_1$	2285	9.3	42	7.1	55	7.7	52	7.5	58
U M_IO_{III}	2299	......	......	......	......	7.5	51	7.4	58
U M_IN_{III}	2745	......	......	......	......	9.1	43		
U $M_{III}O_{IV, V}$	2941	......	......	......	......	9.1	39	8.6	44
U $M_{III}O_I$	3114	......	......	......	......	9.2	57	8.7	69
U $M_{III}N_{IV}$	3514	......	......	......	......	13.0	57		
U $M\beta$	3708	......	......	......	......	14.2	58		
U $M\alpha$	3902	......	......	......	......	15.2	58	15.0	67
U $M_{III}N_I$	4322	......	......	......	......	18.6	58		
U M_VN_{III}	4937	......	......	......	......	23.7	51	23.5	60

[59] Such a calculation is mentioned by Allison, Phys. Rev. **38**, 203 (1931), eq. 12,
but the value given there must be considered inaccurate.

IX–15 shows the results of measurements by Allison[60] and by Parratt[61] on the (1, −1) rocking curves of calcite at various wavelengths. Data on the values of R observed in these experiments are

TABLE IX–16

RESULTS OF RICHTMYER, BARNES, AND MANNING ON THE EFFECT OR POLISHING AND ETCHING OF A PAIR OF CALCITES

λ	Position	w Before Treatment	w After First Polishing and Etching	w After Second Polishing and Etching
0.15 A	(1, −1)		2.2 sec.	1.4 sec.
0.20	(1, −1)	4 to 7 sec.	2.8	1.4
0.20	(2, −2)	1.6	1.7	0.82
0.40	(1, −1)	2.3	3.2	1.8

TABLE IX–17

PARALLEL POSITION ROCKING CURVES

Crystal	Wavelength	Position	w sec.	$P(0) \times 100$	$R \times 10^5$	Observer
Calcite (100)	Mo $K\alpha$	(1, −1)	3.0			A. and W.
		(2, −2)	0.9			
		(3, −3)	0.95			
		(4, −4)	1.1			
		(5, −5)	1.2			
Calcite (100)	Ag $K\alpha$	(1, −1)	3.3	30.6	2.25	K. and R.
Diamond (111)	Mo $K\alpha$	(1, −1)	3.2			E. and M.
Topaz (001)	Mo $K\alpha$	(6, −6)	2.6			M. and S.
NaCl (100)	Ag $K\alpha$	(1, −1)	87	17.7	18.2	
Rochelle Salt (001)	Ag $K\alpha$	(1, −1)	3.5	6.3	0.25	K. and R.
Rochelle Salt (001)	Ag $K\alpha$	(2, −2)	1.5	1.0	0.02	
Barite (001)	0.574 A	(1, −1)	390	1.7	7.32	

References.

Allison and Williams, Phys. Rev. 35, 1476 (1930).
Kirkpatrick and Ross, Phys. Rev. 43, 586 (1933).
Ehrenberg and Mark, Zeitschr. f. Physik 42, 807 (1927).
Mark and von Susich, Zeitschr. f. Physik 65, 253 (1930).

[60] S. K. Allison, Phys. Rev. 41, 1 (1932).
[61] L. G. Parratt, Phys. Rev. 41, 561 (1932).

given in Table VI–6, Chap. VI. It is noticed that better agreement with the theory of a perfect calcite crystal is obtained for the longer wave-lengths; the observed values for W $K\alpha$ (0.208 A) showing no agreement with prediction. An interesting discovery in this direction has been made by Richtmyer, Barnes, and Manning,[62] who found that by successive polishing and etching of calcite the observed rocking curve widths became smaller and smaller in the short wave-length region, and furthermore did not vary over different parts of the crystal surface. Their results are given in Table IX–16. It thus appears that polishing with subsequent etching may possibly produce surfaces which have the characteristics of those of a perfect crystal even for these relatively short wave-lengths. Other experimental data on parallel position rocking curves are given in Table IX–17.

10. *Theory and Experiment in Positions* (n, n)

All positions of the double spectrometer other than parallel positions are characterized by finite dispersion, and may belong to either Type 1 or Type 2. We shall not attempt to discuss all such positions, but will discuss those characterized by the symbol (n, n), being positions of Type 1 in which both crystals are reflecting in the same order. Among these positions we shall especially treat the $(1, 1)$ position, in which much experimental work has been done. We have $n_A = n_B$ $= n$, $C_A = C_B = C$, $\theta(\lambda_0, n_A) = \theta(\lambda_0, n_B) = \theta$, so that our general eq. (9.51) becomes

$$P'(\beta) = \int_{-\phi_m}^{\phi_m} \int_{\lambda_{\min}}^{\lambda_{\max}} \int_{-\alpha_m}^{\alpha_m} G(\alpha, \phi) J(\lambda - \lambda_0) C \left\{ \alpha - \frac{\phi^2}{2} \tan\theta - (\lambda - \lambda_0) \frac{\partial\theta}{\partial\lambda_0} \right\}$$

$$C \left\{ \beta - \alpha - \frac{\phi^2}{2} \tan\theta - (\lambda - \lambda_0) \frac{\partial\theta}{\partial\lambda_0} \right\} d\alpha d\lambda d\phi. \quad (9.72)$$

The remarks concerning the nature of the functions G, J, and C made in the discussion of eq. (9.58) in the preceding section are still applicable, and keeping them in mind we can deduce some of the characteristics of the ionization current curves obtained by rotation of crystal B. We will, as before, consider that the term $\frac{1}{2}\phi^2 \tan\theta$ is comparable in magnitude to the angular width of a single crystal diffraction pattern.

---

[62] Richtmyer, Barnes, and Manning, Phys. Rev. **44**, 311 (1933).

(1) By the same argument as used in parallel positions, it may be shown that for any given λ, the effective values of α lie very close to the value

$$\alpha = (\lambda - \lambda_0) \frac{\partial \theta}{\partial \lambda_0}. \qquad (9.73)$$

(2) In contrast to the parallel positions, however, we can show that in the present case $P'(\beta)$ can have appreciable values at values of β large compared to the width of the single-crystal diffraction pattern. For, if in the C function of eq. (9.72) applicable to crystal B, β has a large value, it must follow that $\alpha + (\lambda - \lambda_0)$ $(\partial \theta / \partial \lambda_0)$ is large in order that the argument of the function be small. This does not preclude the possibility, however, that $\alpha - (\lambda - \lambda_0)(\partial \theta / \partial \lambda_0)$ be small, and that the value of the first C function be appreciable. Thus it is only necessary to establish the proper relation between λ and β in order to have appreciable intensity observed.

(3) The effective values of λ for a given value of β are very near those given by

$$\beta = 2 \frac{\partial \theta}{\partial \lambda_0} (\lambda - \lambda_0). \qquad (9.74)$$

This must be true, because the argument of the second C function of eq. (9.72) may be written

$$\left\{ \beta - 2 \frac{\partial \theta}{\partial \lambda_0} (\lambda - \lambda_0) \right\} - \left\{ \alpha - (\lambda - \lambda_0) \frac{\partial \theta}{\partial \lambda_0} \right\} - \frac{\phi^2}{2} \tan \theta.$$

Since the third term of this expression is by hypothesis small, the second must be small also, or else the first C function of eq. (9.72) will be approximately zero. Therefore the first bracketed term must also be very small, or else the second C function will be zero, which establishes the point.

This means, therefore, that if crystal B is set at a position such that the deviation of the glancing angle of the central ray upon it from the angle θ is β, the two crystals select from the incident x-ray beam a very narrow band of radiation with wave-lengths lying very near the value

$$\lambda = \lambda_0 + \tfrac{1}{2} \frac{\partial \lambda_0}{\partial \theta} \beta. \qquad (9.76)$$

If appreciable intensity does not result at this setting, the interpretation is either that at the value of λ given by eq. (9.76) the function $J(\lambda - \lambda_0)$ is small (in other words, there is very little energy in the incident beam at this wave-length), or that at the value of α called for by eq. (9.73) the value of $G(\alpha, \phi)$ is small (in other words, the spectrometer is working far over on one " side " of the horizontally divergent incident beam). Thus if the latter possibility is avoided the rocking curves will to some extent give the function $J(\lambda - \lambda_0)$ or the spectrum of the incident radiation.

In order to obtain an idea of the extent to which the incident spectrum is reproduced in the rocking curve, we may imagine monochromatic radiation and inquire into the shape of the (n, n) rocking curve. Such curves can never be experimentally observed, but their predicted nature is of considerable importance. We may suppose that all the radiation has the wave-length λ_0, and set $J(0) = 1$. From eq. (9.73) it results that the effective values of α are very near zero, and the effective range of α minute compared to the limits $\pm \alpha_m$ imposed by the horizontal divergence. Hence, as in the previous section, for this monochromatic curve, the limits of integration with respect to α can be extended to $\pm \infty$. Equation (9.74) then gives

$$P'(\beta) = \int_{-\phi_m}^{\phi_m} \int_{-\infty}^{\infty} G(\alpha, \phi) C(\alpha - \tfrac{1}{2}\phi^2 \tan \theta)$$

$$C(\beta - \alpha - \tfrac{1}{2}\phi^2 \tan \theta) d\alpha d\phi. \quad (9.76)$$

It is instructive to note that the effect of vertical divergence, that is, the term $\tfrac{1}{2}\phi^2 \tan \theta$ cannot be made to disappear from eq. (9.76) by adding an arbitrary constant to α, as was the case in the treatment of parallel position rocking curves. Thus the slit height has an effect on the (n, n) curves but not on the $(n, -n)$ curves. Let us nevertheless for the moment assume that this effect can be neglected in eq. (9.76); we then have

$$P'(\beta) = \int_{-\infty}^{\infty} C(\alpha) C(\beta - \alpha) d\alpha, \quad (9.77)$$

in which a factor of proportionality has been omitted. We may at once demonstrate the interesting fact, that, in contrast to the parallel position curves, eq. (9.63), the function of eq. (9.77) does not have an ordinate of symmetry unless $C(l)$ has such an ordinate. For consistency, we will replace α by l and omit the constant factor depending on the difference in the units in which α and l are measured. Let us replace l by $l + \frac{1}{2}\beta$. This gives

$$P'(\beta) = \int_{-\infty}^{\infty} C(l)C(\beta - l)dl = \int_{-\infty}^{\infty} C(l + \tfrac{1}{2}\beta)C(\tfrac{1}{2}\beta - l)dl,$$

and by replacing l by $l - \frac{1}{2}\beta$ in the expression for $P'(-\beta)$, we obtain

$$P'(-\beta) = \int_{-\infty}^{\infty} C(l)C(-\beta - l)dl = \int_{-\infty}^{\infty} C(l - \tfrac{1}{2}\beta)C(-\tfrac{1}{2}\beta - l)dl.$$

Now unless the C function is symmetrical, so that $C(l + \frac{1}{2}\beta) = C(-l - \frac{1}{2}\beta)$ and $C(l - \frac{1}{2}\beta) = C(\frac{1}{2}\beta - l)$ we cannot set $P'(\beta) = P'(-\beta)$ in the above expression. Thus if Prins' unsymmetrical single crystal diffraction patterns are correct, the monochromatic anti-parallel rocking curve will also not be symmetrical. The effect is to shift the center of gravity of the curve toward smaller glancing angles. Thus the center of gravity of the curve will not occur at a value of β at which the glancing angle of the central ray upon the crystal is $\theta_0 + \delta \sec \theta_0 \csc \theta_0$, but will occur at a smaller value of β. This means that, if the Prins' theory is correct, the application of the ordinary index of refraction correction to a precision determination of the glancing angle by the double spectrometer overcorrects the observed angle, if we omit consideration of the slit height. This is the background in the discussion in the first paragraph of Sec. 1 of this chapter.

On the other hand, when the effect of slit height is considered, it is found that it tends to shift the center of gravity of the mono-chromatic rocking curve in the direction of larger glancing angles, thus counteracting the effect of lack of symmetry in the single crystal pattern.

The results of calculation of two such curves for perfect calcite crystals have been given by Allison[63] and are shown in Fig. IX–14. The calculations for these curves were made for the $(1, 1)$ position of calcite for the Cu $K\alpha_1$ wave-length, 1.537 A. In order to make such a calculation it is necessary to assume some form for the function $G(\alpha, \phi)$. The form assumed was

$$G(\alpha, \phi) = G_1(\alpha)G_2(\phi) = \left(1 - \left|\frac{\alpha}{\alpha_m}\right|\right)\left(1 - \left|\frac{\phi}{\phi_m}\right|\right). \tag{9.78}$$

[63] S. K. Allison, Phys. Rev. **44**, 63 (1933).

The single crystal diffraction pattern curves used are those given by Prins' formula, with $\delta = 8.735 \times 10^{-6}$, $\beta = 1.85 \times 10^{-7}$, corresponding to a linear absorption coefficient of 208, and the variation of the scattering power with angle of Ca, C, and O is that indicated in Table VI–2, Chap. VI. The shift of the center of gravity of the curve corresponding to eq. (9.76) toward larger glancing angles with

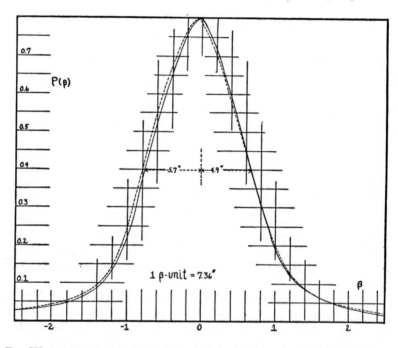

Fig. IX–14. The dotted curve is computed by eq. (9.77) for the wave-length 1.53 A (Cu $K\alpha_1$). It therefore represents the computed monochromatic rocking curve in (1, 1) of calcite, uncorrected for vertical or horizontal divergence. The solid curve is calculated from eqs. (9.76) and (9.78), and shows the effect of slit height on the dotted curve. The assumed values for α_m and ϕ_m were both 4×10^{-3}, which corresponds to two square slits, 2 mm on a side, 50 cm apart.

respect to the uncorrected monochromatic curve computed from eq. (9.37) is clear. Furthermore, if any correction is made to the observed glancing angle after correction for index of refraction (subtraction of the angle $\theta - \theta_0 = \delta \sec \theta_0 \operatorname{cosec} \theta_0$) this correction should be a positive one since the effect of asymmetry of the single crystal diffraction pattern over-balances the geometric correction for slit height. This positive correction is a matter of a few tenths of a second of arc.

Let us briefly investigate the nature of the curve which some authors have called the purely geometric rocking curve. Retaining the assumption of monochromatic radiation, let us imagine that crystal B is set in a position corresponding to the deviation β. Working from eq. (9.76) we see that the effective values of α and ϕ lie near those obtained by the solution of the simultaneous equations

$$\alpha - \tfrac{1}{2}\phi^2 \tan \theta = 0$$

$$\beta - \alpha - \tfrac{1}{2}\phi^2 \tan \theta = 0$$

which means that the effective values lie near the values

$$\left. \begin{aligned} \alpha &= \tfrac{1}{2}\beta \\ \phi &= \sqrt{\beta \cot \theta} \end{aligned} \right\} . \qquad (9.79)$$

Now in the case of Fig. IX–14, for instance, where $\theta = 14° 41'$, a value of β of 10^{-5} requires that the effective values of ϕ lie in a region about $\pm 6.2 \times 10^{-3}$. While some of these effective values may be less than $\phi_m = 4 \times 10^{-3}$ and contribute to the power in the beam reflected from crystal B, it is clear that the ionization current obtainable from this position will be reduced due to the falling off in the function $G_2(\phi)$ at the higher ϕ values demanded. The required α values are in the neighborhood of 5×10^{-6} and the value of the function $G_1(\alpha)$ will not be essentially different from its maximum value which occurs at $G_1(0)$. Thus the range of β over which appreciable intensity results from the monochromatic rocking curves is limited in a geometric sense primarily by the height of the slits.

Let us imagine that the values of ϕ_m are made so large that appreciable power occurs in the reflected beam at values of β large compared to single crystal diffraction pattern widths. This means that the slits are so high that $\phi_m{}^2 \tan \theta \gg w_c$. If we push this process to the limit we will attain a condition in which the monochromatic rocking curve will be governed by geometrical considerations alone. For it will in the limit be true that the variation of the slowly varying function $G_2(\phi)$ over the effective range of ϕ at any given β will be negligible, and we may replace $G_2(\phi)$ in eqs. (9.78) and (9.76) by

$G_2(\sqrt{\beta \cot \theta})$, and long before this limit has been reached we may replace $G_1(\alpha)$ by $G_1(\tfrac{1}{2}\beta)$. We thus obtain from eq. (9.76)

$$P'(\beta) = G_1(\tfrac{1}{2}\beta)G_2(\sqrt{\beta \cot \theta})$$

$$\int_{-\infty}^{\infty}\int_{-\infty}^{\infty} C\left(\alpha - \frac{\phi^2}{2}\tan\theta\right) C\left(\beta - \alpha - \frac{\phi^2}{2}\tan\theta\right) d\alpha d\phi. \quad (9.80)$$

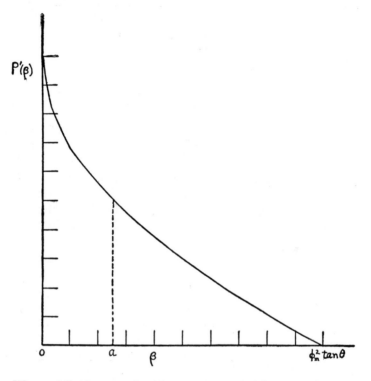

FIG. IX-15. A limiting type of rocking curve approached for monochromatic x-rays in an (n, n) position as the slit height is increased. The solid curve of Fig. IX-14 is an intermediate stage in the transition from the dotted curve of Fig. IX-14 to this purely "geometric" rocking curve.

The double integral in this expression will be a constant, independent of β, since for any given value of β, by eqs. (9.79) values of α and ϕ may be found which produce the argument zero for each C function. In the ordinary case we will have $\sqrt{\beta \cot \theta} \ll \tfrac{1}{2}\beta$, and hence the function G_2 will control the geometrical rocking curve shape. Using the form of G_2 in eq. (9.78) one obtains

$$P'(\beta) = \left(1 - \left|\frac{\sqrt{\beta} \cot \theta}{\phi_m}\right|\right). \qquad (9.81)$$

This curve is shown as Fig. IX–15. Various estimates may be made of the effective abscissa to which this curve corresponds. If we select an abscissa a, such that an ordinate through it divides the curve into two parts of equal area, we find

$$a = \tfrac{1}{4}\phi_m^2 \tan \theta,$$

which is somewhat larger than the correction calculated by Compton[64] and corrected by Williams.[65]

The discussion given here shows, however, that in any actual determination of absolute glancing angle with the double spectrometer, the geometric correction for slit height is probably quite meaningless. For no experiments are likely to be performed with slits so high that the monochromatic rocking curve would take the form of Fig. IX–15, and for ordinary slit heights the correction is of the order of magnitude of the effect produced by the supposed lack of symmetry of the single crystal diffraction pattern, and in the opposite direction. The best procedure would thus seem to be to limit the slit height until the value of $\tfrac{1}{4}\phi^2 \tan \theta$ is less than half a second of arc and make no geometric correction to the observed angle.

It is useful to have some criterion of the resolving power of a spectroscopic instrument, and an arbitrary definition of resolving power has been proposed by Allison[66] for x-ray spectrometers. Let us consider two wave-lengths near together in the spectrum whose monochromatic rocking curves are given by eq. (9.76) and Fig. IX–14. We shall suppose that two such wave-lengths may be detected as separate if the separation of their maxima is equal to their full width at half maximum. The full width at half maximum of the monochromatic rocking curves in the (n, n) positions, supposing that the slit height effect is small, will be very close to the full width at half maximum of the corresponding $(n, - n)$ curves, or $2w$. If $\delta\lambda$ is the

[64] A. H. Compton, Rev. Sci. Insts. **2**, 365 (1931).
[65] J. H. Williams, Phys. Rev. **40**, 636 (1932).
[66] S. K. Allison, Phys. Rev. **38**, 203 (1931).

smallest wave-length separation detectable, then the resolving power is

$$\frac{\lambda}{\delta\lambda} = \frac{D\lambda}{2w},$$ (9.82)

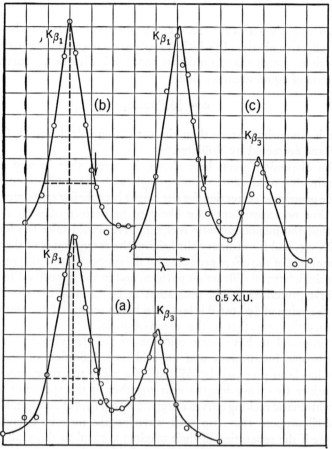

FIG. IX–16. The Mo $K\beta_1\beta_3$ doublet in (2, 2) from calcite. (After Allison and Williams.)

where D is defined by eq. (9.54). If $w = 2.6''$ as in Table IX–15 for Mo $K\alpha_1$ (1, − 1) for crystals III, then the resolving power for this wave-length in the (1, 1) position is about 9300. Defined in this way the resolving power in the (2, 2) position of good calcites may be as high as 55,000. Fig. IX–16 shows rocking curves of Mo $K\beta_1\beta_3$

obtained in the $(2, 2)$ position. The wave-length separation of these two lines is about 0.57 X.U. and their wave-length about 631 X.U., so that if the two lines were strictly monochromatic, a resolving power of only 1100 would suffice for their separation. Thus the high theoretical resolving power of the instrument is rendered ineffective by the large natural width of the lines. Allison[66] has discussed the resolving power attainable by photographic methods in x-ray spectroscopy, and has shown that the resolving power of the double spectrometer in a position (n, n) is roughly $\sqrt{2}$ times that attainable photographically from the same crystal in the order n. This had previously been stated by Valasek.[67]

Du Mond and Hoyt[68] have called attention to the difficulty mentioned in the discussion following eq. (9.75), namely, that if crystal B is rotated leaving crystal A stationary, in a position of finite dispersion, the effective values of α vary, and if the range of motion of B is sufficiently large, a " geometric " intensity curve, due to slit widths, inhomogeneity in the focal spot, or in the reflecting surface of the crystals, may be superimposed on, and distort, the spectrum which it is desired to study. This difficulty may be avoided by rotating both crystals A and B to pass from one wave-length to another. If the axes of rotation of A and B are fixed relative to each other, the x-ray tube must be moved relative to them in this process, and Du Mond has constructed a spectrometer of this type. If the axis about which crystal B rotates can itself move about the axis of A, the x-ray tube can maintain a fixed position in this process of "double rotation." This method has been carried out by Allison.[69]

Suppose that crystals A and B are set in an (n, n) position so that the deviation of the glancing angle of the central ray upon them from the angle θ is in each case γ. Then it is not difficult to show that the power in the beam diffracted from crystal B into the ionization chamber is given by

$$P'(\gamma) = \int_{-\phi_m}^{\phi_m} \int_{\lambda_{\min}}^{\lambda_{\max}} \int_{-\alpha_m}^{\alpha_m} G(\alpha, \phi) J(\lambda - \lambda_0)$$

$$C[\gamma + \alpha - \tfrac{1}{2}\phi^2 \tan \theta - (\lambda - \lambda_0)(\partial \theta_0/\partial \lambda)]$$

$$C[\gamma - \alpha - \tfrac{1}{2}\phi^2 \tan \theta - (\lambda - \lambda_0) \partial \theta_0/\partial \lambda] \, d\alpha d\lambda d\phi. \quad (9.83)$$

[67] Valasek, Phys. Rev. 36, 1523 (1930).
[68] Du Mond and Hoyt, Phys. Rev. 36, 1702 (1930).
[69] S. K. Allison, Phys. Rev. 44, 63 (1933).

Let us recall that for the entire integrand function to have an appreciable value, the argument of each of the C functions must be very small, of diffraction pattern width. We shall suppose the term $\frac{1}{2}\phi^2 \tan \theta$ to be of the order of the diffraction pattern width. If γ be large compared to this width, examination of the arguments of the C functions shows that appreciable intensity can result only if

$$\gamma \doteq (\lambda - \lambda_0) \frac{\partial \theta_0}{\partial \lambda}$$

and

$$\alpha \doteq 0.$$

Thus for any value of γ, the effective values of α lie near zero, in contrast to the single rotation method.

By an argument exactly similar to that used in the derivation of eq. (9.56) it can be shown that the dispersion in double rotation is half that in single rotation, or

$$\frac{d\gamma}{d\lambda} = \frac{1}{2}D.$$

The resolving power, however, is the same as for single rotation, since double rotation would produce monochromatic rocking curves half as wide as those obtained by single rotation.

11. *Double Spectrometer Measurements of the Widths of Spectrum Lines*

The range of wave-lengths in a so-called " monochromatic " x-ray spectrum line is so great that rocking curves in positions of finite dispersion are always wider than the predicted monochromatic curves. Thus with Cu $K\alpha_1$ in the (1, 1) position of calcite, a rocking curve of 41 seconds full width at half maximum is obtained, instead of the width of 10 seconds of the curve of Fig. IX–14. Thus the finite dispersion curves must be considered as approximations to the form of the function $J(\lambda - \lambda_0)$ of eq. (9.72). Allison[69] has investigated experimentally the effect of changing the slit height and width on the Cu $K\alpha_1$ (1, 1) curves, and found that changes in α_m from 2.2×10^{-3} to 6.2×10^{-3} and in ϕ_m from 4.0×10^{-3} to 1×10^{-2} have no appreciable influence.

In the early work on the double spectrometer, Ehrenberg and Mark[70] attempted to calculate the correction to be applied to the

[70] W. Ehrenberg and H. Mark, Zeitschr. f. Physik **42**, 807 (1927).

observed width in a position of finite dispersion in order to obtain the true wave-length width of the line. They assumed that the functions C and J were all of Gaussian error curve shape, which is, in the case of C contrary to the predictions of the single crystal diffraction pattern, and in the case of J, contrary to the theory of the shape of a spectrum line (classical shape, eq. (4.27), Chap. IV). The only justification of the assumption is that the function is amenable to analytical treatment and perhaps not too far removed from the real functions in question, so that a correction can be calculated. In the application of eq. (9.72) to a spectrum line, we shall assume that the line is so narrow that values of α of the order of α_m are not significant, and thus extend the limits of integration of α and λ to $\pm \infty$. Neglecting effects due to slit height, and making the Gaussian error curve assumption, eq. (9.72) becomes

$$P'(\beta) = \int_{-\infty}^{\infty} \int_{-\infty}^{\infty} \exp\left[- \frac{(ln2)}{w_\lambda^2} (\lambda - \lambda_0)^2 \right]$$
$$\exp\left\{ - \frac{(ln2)}{w_c^2} \left[\alpha - \frac{\partial\theta}{\partial\lambda_0} (\lambda - \lambda_0) \right]^2 \right\}$$
$$\exp\left\{ - \frac{(ln2)}{w_c^2} \left[\beta - \alpha - \frac{\partial\theta}{\partial\lambda_0} (\lambda - \lambda_0) \right]^2 \right\} d\alpha d\lambda. \quad (9.84)$$

Here w_λ is the linear half width at half maximum of the assumed Gaussian error curve shaped line, and w_c the angular half width at half maximum of the assumed Gaussian error curve shaped single crystal diffraction pattern. This expression may be integrated by ordinary methods, with the result that $P'(\beta)$ is itself a Gaussian error curve function, and if w_β is its half width at half maximum,

$$w_\beta = \sqrt{2w_c^2 + D^2 w_\lambda^2}.$$

It may also be shown that the same results hold true in positions of Type 2, including parallel positions, where $D = 0$, which means that w, the parallel position width, is related to w_c by $w = w_c\sqrt{2}$. Thus for positions (n, n) we may write

$$w_\lambda = D^{-1}\sqrt{w_\beta^2 - 2w_c^2}. \quad (9.85)$$

If eq. (9.84) is set up for the general case (n_A, n_B), where the single crystal diffraction pattern half widths at half maximum are w_A and w_B in the orders n_A and n_B respectively, one obtains

$$w_\lambda = D^{-1}\sqrt{w_\beta^2 - w_A^2 - w_B^2}. \quad (9.86)$$

From eq. (9.85) it may be shown that the correction in per cent to be applied to the observed value of w is about $50\ w^2/w_\beta^2$. Thus in the study of Cu $K\alpha_1$ from calcite in the $(1, 1)$ and $(1, -1)$ positions one finds $w_\beta = 20$ sec.; $w = 5$ sec., hence the correction to be applied according to the method of Ehrenberg and Mark is about 3 per cent.

Due to the fact that the observed rocking curves definitely depart from the Gaussian error curve shape, and thus that the method of correction of Ehrenberg and Mark must be considered very artificial, some experimenters have made no correction at all to their observed widths. This omission is further justified by the smallness of the correction, which is close to the accuracy with which the observed widths can be measured. In attempts to measure the width of the W $K\alpha_1$ line from calcite, Barnes and Palmer[71] found that a method of correction in which w was directly subtracted from w_β gave more consistent results when rocking curves for the line were obtained in several orders.

TABLE IX–18

ALLISON AND WILLIAMS' RESULTS ON THE WIDTH OF Mo $K\alpha_1$; $K\alpha_2$

Mo $K\alpha_1$

Position	D in Sec. per X.U.	Half Width at Half Max. Corr.
$(1, -2)$	-35.748	0.154 X.U.
$(2, -1)$	35.748	0.168
$(1, 1)$	68.572	0.155
$(1, -3)$	-74.777	0.148
$(1, 2)$	104.32	0.139
$(2, 1)$	104.32	0.138
$(2, 2)$	140.07	0.136
$(1, 3)$	143.34	0.135
	Weighted average,	0.147
	Mo $K\alpha_2$	
$(1, 1)$	68.572	0.169
$(1, 2)$	104.36	0.151
	Weighted average,	0.161

[71] Barnes and Palmer, Phys. Rev. **43**, 1050 (1933).

The experimental data on widths of x-ray lines is presented in several tables. Table IX–18 shows results obtained by Allison and Williams[72] on the width of Mo $K\alpha_1$ in various positions of a calcite double crystal spectrometer. There is no evidence of asymmetry in the Mo $K\alpha_1$ or $K\alpha_2$ lines. The observed widths were corrected by eq. (9.86), using the parallel position results of Table IX–17. A small geometrical correction was also applied, in an incorrect manner, as pointed out by Spencer.[72a] The effect of voltage on the width of Mo $K\alpha_1$ from 25 to 50 kv. was also studied, and no change in width detected. Table IX–19 shows results on the full width at half maximum, $\Delta\lambda$, of Mo $K\alpha_1$ obtained by various observers. The results of Valasek quoted in this table were not obtained by the double spectrometer. A single crystal photographic method was used with a very narrow slit behind the crystal and a large distance

TABLE IX–19

FULL WIDTH OF Mo $K\alpha_1$ AT HALF MAXIMUM, $\Delta\lambda$

Authors	Crystal	Orders	$\Delta\lambda$ X.U.	Remarks
Ehrenberg and Mark (1927)	Diamond (111)	(1, 1)	0.41	Corr. for (1, −1) width
Ehrenberg and von Susich (1927)	Calcite (100)	(1, 1)	0.38	Corrected
Mark and von Susich (1930)	Calcite (100)	(2, 2)	0.326	Corrected
Mark and von Susich (1930)	Topaz (001)	(6, 6)	0.288	Corrected
Allison and Williams (1930)	Calcite (100)	Many	0.294	Corrected
Valasek (1930)	Calcite (100)	(1)	0.26	Photographic *
Spencer (1931)	Calcite (100)	(2, 2)	0.281	Uncorrected
Allison (1933)	Calcite (100)	(1, 1)	0.29	Uncorrected

* The correction to be applied to the photographic measurements of Valasek (Phys. Rev. **36**, 1523 (1930)) has been criticized (Phys. Rev. **38**, 203 (1931)). According to the method of correction advocated, Valasek's results for Mo $K\alpha_1$ should be nearer 0.38 X.U.

to the photographic plate. Table IX–20 shows the results on the wave-length width of Cu $K\alpha_1$ and Cu $K\alpha_2$ obtained by various observers. Fig. IX–17 shows curves of the Cu $K\alpha$ doublet obtained by Spencer[73] in the (2, 2) position of calcite. Table IX–21 shows collected results on the $K\alpha$ lines of elements from 20 Ca to 74 W.

[72] Allison and Williams, Phys. Rev. **35**, 1476 (1930).
[72a] R. C. Spencer, Phys. Rev. **38**, 618 (1931).
[73] R. C. Spencer, Phys. Rev. **38**, 630 (1931).

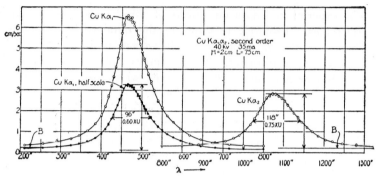

FIG. IX–17. Rocking curves of Cu $K\alpha_1$, α_2 (2, 2) from calcite obtained by Spencer. The asymmetry of the lines is clearly shown.

TABLE IX–20

WIDTHS OF THE Cu $K\alpha$ DOUBLET

Cu $K\alpha_1$

Author	Orders	Full Width at Half Maximum	Remarks
		X.U.	
Ehrenberg and von Susich (1927)......	(1, 1)	0.70	Corrected for (1, −1) width.
Purks (1928)........	(1, 1)	0.63	Crystals probably unreliable; uncorrected.
Valasek (1930)......	(1),(2)	0.38	Photographic spectrometer; corrected, but method doubtful.
Spencer (1931).....	(2, 2)	0.60	} Uncorrected; "universal" spectrometer.
	(1, 1)	0.61	
	(1, 1)	0.69	Uncorrected; old type spectrometer.
Allison (1933)........	(1, 1)	0.58	Uncorrected.

Cu $K\alpha_2$

Purks (1928)........	(1, 1)	0.63	As above.
Spencer (1931)......	(2, 2)	0.75	Uncorrected; universal.
Allison (1933)........	(1, 1)	0.77	Uncorrected.

L. G. Parratt, Phys. Rev. **46**, 749 (1934), has investigated the width and shape of Cu$K\alpha_1$ with etched quartz crystals which were prepared by Bozorth and Hayworth, Phys. Rev. **45**, 821 (1934). The reflections were taken from the (11.0) planes, and these have from 2 to 4 times the resolving power of calcite. Parratt found the full width at half maximum to be 0.48 X.U. which seems to indicate that in calcite the correction for resolving power is larger than previously suspected.

TABLE IX–21

FULL WIDTHS AT HALF MAXIMUM OF THE $K\alpha$ DOUBLET

Element	Line	Wave-length in X.U.	$\Delta\lambda$ X.U.	$\Delta\nu/R$	ΔV Volts	Observer
20 Ca	$K\alpha_2$	3354.95	1.504	0.125	1.69	
	$K\alpha_1$	3351.69	1.60	0.130	1.76	
22 Ti	$K\alpha_2$	2746.81	1.43	0.172	2.33	
	$K\alpha_1$	2743.17	1.22	0.148	2.00	
23 Va	$K\alpha_2$	2502.13	1.35	0.197	2.67	
	$K\alpha_1$	2498.35	1.15	0.167	2.26	Parratt
24 Cr	$K\alpha_2$	2288.91	1.30	0.225	3.05	
	$K\alpha_1$	2285.03	1.08	0.188	2.55	
25 Mn	$K\alpha_2$	2101.49	1.22	0.253	3.43	
	$K\alpha_1$	2097.51	1.10	0.228	3.09	
26 Fe	$K\alpha_2$	1936.012	1.18	0.273	3.70	
	$K\alpha_1$	1932.076	1.02	0.249	3.37	
26 Fe	$K\alpha_2$	1936.012	1.06	0.26	3.5	
	$K\alpha_1$	1932.076	1.00	0.24	3.3	Allison
27 Co	$K\alpha_2$	1789.19	0.95	0.27	3.7	
	$K\alpha_1$	1785.29	0.81	0.23	3.1	
28 Ni	$K\alpha_2$	1685.35	0.88	0.293	3.96	Parratt
	$K\alpha_1$	1654.50	0.72	0.238	3.23	
28 Ni	$K\alpha_2$	1685.35	0.82	0.26	3.6	
	$K\alpha_1$	1654.50	0.64	0.21	2.9	
29 Cu	$K\alpha_2$	1541.232	0.77	0.30	4.0	
	$K\alpha_1$	1537.395	0.58	0.22	3.0	
30 Zn	$K\alpha_2$	1436.03	0.58	0.26	3.5	
	$K\alpha_1$	1432.17	0.51	0.23	3.1	
32 Ge	$K\alpha_2$	1255.21	0.46	0.27	3.7	Allison
	$K\alpha_1$	1251.30	0.43	0.25	3.4	
38 Sr	$K\alpha_2$	877.61	0.36	0.43	5.8	
	$K\alpha_1$	873.45	0.35	0.42	5.7	
40 Zr	$K\alpha_2$	788.51	0.35	0.51	6.9	
	$K\alpha_1$	784.30	0.33	0.49	6.6	
41 Cb	$K\alpha_2$	748.89	0.31	0.51	6.9	
	$K\alpha_1$	744.65	0.33	0.54	7.4	
42 Mo	$K\alpha_2$	712.015	0.32	0.56	7.7	Allison-Williams
	$K\alpha_1$	707.831	0.29	0.53	7.2	
44 Ru	$K\alpha_2$	646.06	0.29	0.63	8.6	
	$K\alpha_1$	641.74	0.29	0.64	8.7	Allison
45 Rh	$K\alpha_2$	616.37	0.29	0.70	9.4	
	$K\alpha_1$	612.02	0.29	0.70	9.5	

TABLE IX–21—*Continued*

Element	Line	Wave-length in X.U.	$\Delta\lambda$ X.U.	$\Delta\nu/R$	ΔV Volts	Observer
46 Pd {	$K\alpha_2$	588.63	0.29	0.76	10.3	}
	$K\alpha_1$	584.27	0.28	0.75	10.1	
47 Ag {	$K\alpha_2$	562.67	0.29	0.83	11.3	} Allison
	$K\alpha_1$	588.28	0.28	0.82	11.1	
74 W	$K\alpha_1$	208.56*	0.15	3.14	42.5	Barnes-Palmer

* J. H. Williams, Phys. Rev. **40**, 791 (1932), other wave-lengths from Siegbahn, Spektroskopie der Röntgenstrahlen (1931).

References to width measurements.

L. G. Parratt, Phys. Rev. **44**, 695 (1933).
S. K. Allison, Phys. Rev. **44**, 63 (1933).
Allison and Williams, Phys. Rev. **35**, 1476 (1930).
Barnes and Palmer, Phys. Rev. **43**, 1050 (1933).
F. K. Richtmyer and S. W. Barnes, Phys. Rev. **46**, 352 (1934), have found the following full widths at half maximum of the W K lines, in volts: α_2, 43.3; α_1, 43.0; β_3, 50.0; β_1, 48.6; γ_2, 37.0; γ_1, 37.0; δ_2, 34.0; δ_1, 34. The last two lines represent transitions from $O_{II}O_{III}$ to K. They also report additional evidence in favor of the method of correction of Barnes and Palmer.[71]

The widths given in Table IX–21 for the elements 20 Ca to 26 Fe depend to some extent on the observer's estimate of a probable shape for the lines $K\alpha_1$ and $K\alpha_2$, since these are so broad that they overlap, and the minimum between them is above the adjacent background. In the case of the width of W $K\alpha_1$ the observed rocking curve widths have been corrected in a somewhat arbitrary manner.

The $K\alpha$ lines of the lighter elements (20 Ca to 29 Cu) are definitely asymmetrical, the effect consisting in a flaring out of the line toward longer wave-lengths. If an ordinate be drawn through the peak of the line, at half maximum a greater part of the width lies to the longer wave-length side. The ratio of the widths has been called the index of asymmetry. At Ca this index was found to be about 1.15 for the $K\alpha_1$ line, and with increasing atomic number it increases to the value 1.65 at 26 Fe. From here on it falls to unity, being about 1.4 for Cu $K\alpha_1$.

Table IX–22 shows data obtained on the full width at half maximum of certain L series lines. In this table older values of L series

TABLE IX-22

FULL WIDTHS AT HALF MAXIMUM OF CERTAIN L SERIES LINES

Element	Line	Wave-length in X.U.	Transition	$\Delta\lambda$ X.U.	$\Delta\nu/R$	ΔV Volts	Observer
47 Ag	$L\alpha_1$	4145.6	$L_{III}-M_V$	4.5	0.24	3.2	Spencer
74 W	$L\alpha_1$	1473.36	$L_{III}-M_V$	1.26	0.73	7.2	
	$L\beta_1$	1279.17	$L_{II}-M_{IV}$	0.94	0.73	7.1	
	$L\beta_2$	1242.03	$L_{III}-N_V$	1.38	0.90	10.1	
	$L\gamma_1$	1096.30	$L_{II}-N_{IV}$	1.01	0.88	10.4	
77 Ir	$L\alpha_1$	1348.47	$L_{III}-M_V$	1.19	0.77	8.1	
	$L\beta_1$	1155.40	$L_{II}-M_{IV}$	0.82	0.75	7.6	
	$L\beta_2$	1132.97	$L_{III}-N_V$	1.17	0.91	11.3	
	$L\gamma_1$	988.76	$L_{II}-N_{IV}$	0.92	0.93	11.6	
78 Pt	$L\alpha_1$	1310.33	$L_{III}-M_V$	1.17	0.79	8.4	
	$L\beta_1$	1117.58	$L_{II}-M_{IV}$	0.80	0.77	7.9	
	$L\beta_2$	1099.74	$L_{III}-N_V$	1.14	0.93	11.6	
	$L\gamma_1$	955.99	$L_{II}-N_{IV}$	0.84	0.91	11.3	
79 Au	$L\alpha_1$	1273.77	$L_{III}-M_V$	1.13	0.76	8.6	Williams (2)
	$L\beta_1$	1081.28	$L_{II}-M_{IV}$	0.79	0.78	8.3	
	$L\beta_2$	1068.01	$L_{III}-N_V$	1.06	0.92	11.4	
	$L\gamma_1$	924.61	$L_{II}-N_{IV}$	0.79	0.92	11.4	
81 Tl	$L\alpha_1$	1204.93	$L_{III}-M_V$	1.11	0.83	9.4	
	$L\beta_1$	1012.99	$L_{II}-M_{IV}$	0.74	0.81	8.9	
	$L\beta_2$	1008.22	$L_{III}-N_V$	1.00	0.95	12.2	
	$L\gamma_1$	865.71	$L_{II}-N_{IV}$	0.74	0.95	12.2	
82 Pb	$L\alpha_1$	1172.58	$L_{III}-M_V$	1.05	0.84	9.5	
	$L\gamma_1$	838.01	$L_{II}-N_{IV}$	0.70	0.95	12.3	
83 Bi	$L\alpha_1$	1141.50	$L_{III}-M_V$	1.03	0.85	9.8	
	$L\beta_1$	950.02	$L_{II}-M_{IV}$	0.70	0.84	9.6	
	$L\beta_2$	953.24	$L_{III}-N_V$	0.90	0.95	12.1	
	$L\gamma_1$	811.43	$L_{II}-N_{IV}$	0.67	0.96	12.5	
92 U	$L\alpha_1$	908.74	$L_{III}-M_V$	0.88	0.97	13.1	
	$L\alpha_2$	920.62	$L_{III}-M_{IV}$	0.99	1.06	14.4	
	$L\beta_1$	718.51	$L_{II}-M_{IV}$	0.60	1.06	14.3	
	$L\beta_2$	753.07	$L_{III}-N_V$	0.74	1.19	16.1	
	$L\beta_3$	708.79	L_I-M_{III}	0.76	1.39	18.8	
	$L\beta_4$	746.4	L_I-M_{II}	1.45	2.38	32.0	Williams (1)
	$L\beta_5$	724.85	$L_{III}-O_V$	0.50	0.87	11.9	
	$L\beta_6$	786.79	$L_{III}-N_I$	0.97	1.43	19.4	
	$L\gamma_1$	613.59	$L_{II}-N_{IV}$	0.48	1.17	15.9	
	$L\gamma_2$	603.86	L_I-N_{II}	1.14	2.85	39.0	
	$L\gamma_3$	597.11	L_I-N_{III}	0.94	2.40	32.0	
	$L\gamma_6$	593.4	$L_{II}-O_{IV}$	0.47	1.21	16.4	

Spencer, Phys. Rev. 38, 630 (1931).
Williams, (1), Phys. Rev. 40, 791 (1932); (2), Phys. Rev. 45, 71 (1934).

line widths obtained by Ehrenberg and von Susich[74] and by Allison[75] have been omitted. Molin[76] has made estimates of the widths of the more intense M lines of 74 W, 77 Ir, 78 Pt, and 79 Au, using a single crystal ionization spectrometer. These are shown in Table IX–23.

TABLE IX–23

M series Line Widths According to Molin

Element	Line	Wave-length in X.U.	Transition	$\Delta\lambda$ X.U.	$\Delta\nu/R$	ΔV Volts
74 W	$M\alpha_1$	6969	$M_V–N_{VII}$	7.1	0.133	1.8
	$M\beta$	6743	$M_{IV}–N_{VI, VII}$	6.6	0.132	1.8
	$M\gamma$	6076	$M_{III}–N_V$	18	0.444	6.0
77 Ir	$M\alpha_1$	6249	$M_V–N_{VII}$	7.7	0.180	2.5
	$M\beta$	6025	$M_{IV}–N_{VI, VII}$	6.5	0.163	2.2
	$M\gamma$	5490	$M_{III}–N_V$	23	0.695	9.5
78 Pt	$M\alpha_1$	6034	$M_V–N_{VII}$	5.8	0.145	2.0
	$M\beta$	5816	$M_{IV}–N_{VI} N_{VII}$	5.3	0.143	1.9
79 Au	$M\alpha_1$	5838	$M_V–N_{VII}$	6.8	0.182	2.5
	$M\alpha_2$	5842	$M_V–N_{VI}$	6.4	0.171	2.5
	$M\beta$	5135	$M_{IV}–N_{VI, VII}$	18	0.622	8.5
	$M–$	6241	$M_{III}–N_I$	32	0.749	10.0

Williams[77] found that the uncorrected shape of the rocking curve obtained for U $L\alpha_1$ could be fairly well represented by the classical theory prediction for the shape of a spectrum line, eq. (4.27), Chap. IV. The observed curve differed markedly from a Gaussian error curve shape, which had previously been noted by Spencer[73] for the Mo $K\alpha_1$ line shape. A. Hoyt[78] has found that the formula

$$J(\lambda - \lambda_0) = \frac{a}{1 + (\lambda - \lambda_0)^2/w_\lambda{}^2}$$

represents the shape of the rocking curves obtained in positions of finite dispersion satisfactorily. a is proportional to the maximum

[74] Ehrenberg and von Susich, Zeitschr. f. Phys. **42**, 823 (1927).

[75] S. K. Allison, Phys. Rev. **34**, 176 (1929).

[76] K. Molin, Diss. Uppsala (1927). Values in Table IX–23 from Siegbahn, Spektroskopie der Röntgenstrahlen (1931).

[77] J. H. Williams, Phys. Rev. **40**, 791 (1932).

[78] A. Hoyt, Phys. Rev. **40**, 477 (1932).

ordinate of the line, and w_λ is the half width at half maximum. When expressed in frequencies instead of wave-lengths, this empirical formula becomes indistinguishable from eq. (4.27), and hence Hoyt's results confirm those of Williams.

Few generalizations of any value have as yet been made about the existing data on line widths. In the L series it seems to be true that the lines showing the largest energy widths involve initial and final states arising from configurations in which an electron has been removed from what, in the older quantum theory, is an orbit of high eccentricity. It is a curious and interesting fact that L series lines of approximately the same wave-length as the Cu $K\alpha$ lines show none of the asymmetry which is characteristic of the K lines.[78a] The data given here do not include observations made by Jönsson[79] on the relative widths of certain L series lines in the region 42 Mo to 51 Sb.

The results of this work on line widths and shapes by means of the double spectrometer undoubtedly give us good approximations to the true values, but a more rigorous method of treating the experimental data is much to be desired. We have simply assumed that the corrections to be applied are small, without a very clear idea of their magnitude. L. P. Smith[79a] has attacked the problem from a mathematical view-point in a paper too recent to be adequately discussed here. He has shown that although any one rocking curve, either in parallel or in anti-parallel positions, is not uniquely resolvable into its component curves, it is nevertheless possible to compute the curve $J(\lambda - \lambda_0)$ from a sufficiently large number of curves in various positions. In his development the line shape can be computed from results in the $(1, -1)$, $(2, -2)$, $(1, 1)$, $(2, 2)$, $(1, 2)$ and $(2, 1)$ positions. An application to actual rocking curves has not as yet been carried out.

[78a] Added to proof. Richtmyer and Barnes, Phys. Rev. **45**, 754 (1934) and subsequently, have investigated L series line widths and absorption limit widths in 79 Au. L absorption widths have also been studied by W. H. Zinn, Phys. Rev. **46**, 659 (1934) and by H. Semat, Phys. Rev. **46**, 688 (1934). Richtmyer and Barnes attempt to deduce the widths of absorption limits from one measured absorption limit width and measurements on line widths. They consider the line width as the sum of the widths of the absorption limits representing the initial and final states. This relation will result if the lines and limits have the shape given by eq. (4.27), Chap. IV, and is obtained by an integral using this function but otherwise analogous to eq. 9.84.

[79] A. Jönsson, Zeitschr. f. Physik **41**, 221 (1927); **46**, 383 (1928).

[79a] L. P. Smith, Phys. Rev. **46**, 343 (1934).

Smith also calls attention to the fact that in the discussion of the single crystal diffraction pattern the spread of the diffracted beam from an incident parallel, monochromatic beam on a stationary crystal has not been treated. In perfect crystals the spread is presumably small compared to the angular range through which the crystal may be turned and reflect the radiation.

12. *Focussing X-ray Spectographs*

The problem of concentrating the diffracted rays from a monochromatic, divergent beam of x-rays at a point in order to gain intensity has been considered from the earliest days of x-ray spectroscopy.[80] Some of the principles in the construction of such an instrument have been discussed by Du Mond and Kirkpatrick[81] in a description of the multicrystal spectrograph designed by them, which will be mentioned later. We will discuss here the design adopted by Mlle. Cauchois and successfully used by her.[82] The construction necessitates the bending of a thin crystal section (of mica, gypsum, or quartz) so that it becomes part of a cylindrical surface. Fig. IX–18 represents a cross-section of this cylinder perpendicular to its axis. The radius of the cylinder is R. The crystal sheet may be thought to extend from M to N, and divergent x-rays are incident from above. The radiation is transmitted through the sheet, and diffracted by prominent transverse crystal planes. Let us assume for the moment that these crystal planes are normal to the surface. Consider a wave-length λ_0 in the incident beam, whose Bragg angle is θ_0. A ray of this wave-length is incident at point N of the diagram, and the diffracted ray is NN'. The same wavelength in the incident beam is diffracted from point A along AA'. As the point of incidence on the bent crystal moves along the arc MN it is seen from the diagram that the envelope of the diffracted rays is the circle of radius $R \sin \theta_0$, centered at the axis of the cylinder. Let ω be the polar angle of the point of incidence on the crystal.

[80] M. de Broglie, Compt. rend. **158**, 944 (1914).
    Dardord, Journ. de Physique et le Radium **3**, 218 (1922).
[81] Du Mond and Kirkpatrick, Rev. Sci. Insts. **1**, 88 (1930). Du Mond and Watson, Phys. Rev. **46**, 316 (1934), have announced the completion of a bent crystal spectrograph constructed of quartz, which they found to give much sharper lines than did the mica which they had previously tried.
[82] Y. Cauchois, Journal de Physique **3**, 320 (1932).

It is seen that the equations of the envelope in parametric form are

$$x = R \sin \theta_0 \cos \left\{ \omega + \left(\frac{\pi}{2} - \theta_0 \right) \right\}$$

$$y = R \sin \theta_0 \sin \left\{ \omega + \left(\frac{\pi}{2} - \theta_0 \right) \right\}$$

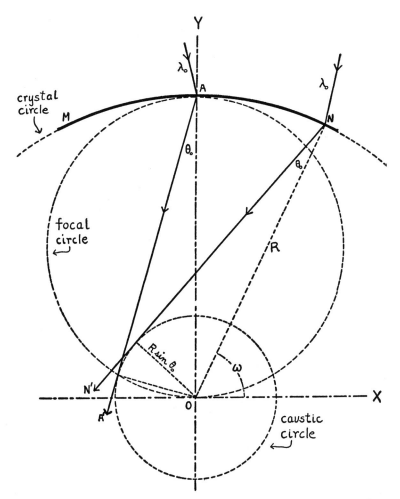

FIG. IX–18. Principle of a bent crystal focussing spectrograph according to Mlle. Cauchois.

which may be written

$$x = - R \sin \theta_0 \sin (\omega - \theta_0)$$
$$y = R \sin \theta_0 \cos (\omega - \theta_0). \tag{9.87}$$

In any actual experiment with the instrument, the segment of the bent crystal actually used, although very large compared to the slit widths used in an ordinary spectrograph, nevertheless is restricted to a small angular range near $\omega = 90°$. Inserting this value in eqs. (9.87), we find that the points of tangency of the diffracted rays on the caustic circle lie near the points

$$x = - R \sin \theta_0 \cos \theta_0$$
$$y = R \sin^2 \theta_0. \tag{9.88}$$

There is, of course, no sharp focus near these points, but the finite angular width of the diffracted rays overlapping here will cause a considerable concentration of power. We are interested in the locus of the points defined by eq. (9.88) as the wave-length varies, which means as θ_0 varies. Equation (9.88) gives

$$x^2 + (y - \tfrac{1}{2}R)^2 = \tfrac{1}{4}R^2, \tag{9.89}$$

which is the equation of the focal circle APO. If a photographic film is placed along this circle, the various wave-lengths will be in this inexact sense, focussed upon it. It is seen that the lines should be sharp on the edge near the point O and somewhat diffuse on the far edge.

If the spectra are not located too far from the point O, and s represents the distance along the photographic film, the dispersion

$$\frac{ds}{d\lambda} = \frac{d}{d\lambda} R \sin \theta_0 = \frac{nR}{2d}. \tag{9.90}$$

In some crystals, mica, for instance, the transverse planes do not lie normal to the surface, but may make an angle α with this normal. The previous development holds in this case, except that θ_0 must be replaced by $\theta_0 \pm \alpha$.

Mlle. Cauchois used a spectrograph constructed on this principle, with a diameter of the focal circle of 20 cm. Mica and gypsum crystals were used. In the case of mica, $\alpha = 10° \, 19' \pm 1'$ and $d = 2.554 \pm 0.005$ A. With this instrument the K spectra of the rare gases excited by electron bombardment were readily photographed. The focussing, although theoretically not perfect, is actually sufficient to give good resolving power; the $K\beta_1\beta_3$ doublet being resolved in the first order.

Independently of this development, Johann[83] designed a spectrograph using the reflection from the surface planes of a bent mica crystal. By this method wave-lengths can be studied which would be absorbed in passing through a crystal sheet. The method is illustrated by Fig. IX–19. The error in focussing becomes more

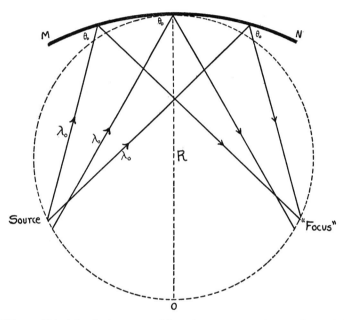

Fɪɢ. IX–19.   Principle of a bent crystal focussing spectrograph according to Johann.

serious at shorter wave-lengths, so that the arrangement is best used for the longer wave-length region, or for higher orders of the shorter wave-lengths. Using mica crystals, Johann obtained a photograph of the Cu $K\alpha$ doublet in the fifth order in one milliampere second.

Du Mond and Kirkpatrick[81] have shown that if a crystal is both cut and bent, perfect focussing may be obtained. Let the crystal be bent until the atomic planes coincide with concentric circles of radius R, and then grind a surface of radius $\frac{1}{2}R$ into the bent crystal.

[83] H. H. Johann, Zeitschr. f. Physik **69**, 185 (1931).

This same suggestion has recently been made by Johansson,[84] and a spectrograph on this principle constructed. The scheme is shown in Fig. IX–20.

Because of the difficulty of cutting and bending a crystal in this manner, Du Mond and Kirkpatrick constructed a multicrystal spectrograph, in which 50 small crystals were arranged as shown in Fig. IX–21. Each crystal was a small piece of calcite, with a Seeman wedge near the center of its reflecting surface to limit the aper-

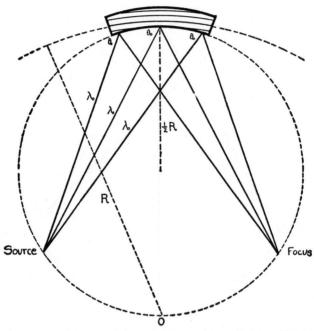

Fig. IX–20. A type of spectrograph suggested by Du Mond and Kirkpatrick in which accurate focussing may be obtained.

ture. When in adjustment, the reflecting surfaces of the crystals would, if prolonged, intersect in a line which cuts the figure at O, a distance R from the crystals. The circle of radius $\frac{1}{2}R$ is then the focal circle, and if divergent radiation is incident on the crystals from above, the wave-lengths are focussed at points on this circle. The instrument has been used with considerable success in the study of the spectrum of radiation scattered with change in wave-length.

[84] Johansson, Naturwiss. **20**, 758 (1932); Zeitschr. f. Physik **82**, 507 (1933).

Carlsson, and Sandström and Carlsson[85] have studied the weak lines in the K series by means of a spectrograph constructed according to the design of Mlle. Cauchois. The crystal was a gypsum sheet 0.02 cm. thick, bent to a radius of 50 cm. The area on the crystal through which radiation was transmitted varied from 0.060 to 0.120 cm.², and was 0.15 cm. high. Later, a second instrument was con-

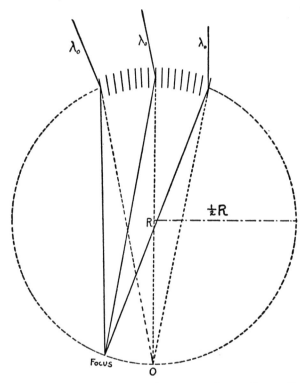

Fig. IX–21. Principle of the multicrystal spectrograph according to Du Mond and Kirkpatrick.

structed in which the radius of the bent crystal could be varied from 70 to 103 cm. The used portion of the crystal was 0.65 to 0.8 cm. wide and 0.1 cm. high. Carlsson obtained with this instrument in 10 minutes' exposure a photograph of the $K\beta_1 K\beta_3$ doublet of 38 Sr, showing good separation. A comparable photograph, obtained by

[85] Sandström and Carlsson, Zeitschr. f. Physik 80, 597 (1933).
Carlsson, Zeitschr. f. Physik 80, 604; 84, 119 (1933).

Edlén[86] with the tube spectrograph, necessitated an exposure of 6 hours.

Some of the new K series lines which have been discovered by this method and by the double spectrometer method are discussed under the topic " violations of the selection rules " in the chapter on the interpretation of x-ray spectra.   In addition, Carlsson has given the wave-lengths of two new lines, which cannot be correlated with terms in the ordinary x-ray diagram.   These lines are called $K\beta_6$ and $K\beta_7$, and the wave-lengths given by Carlsson for them are listed in Table IX–24.

TABLE IX–24

WAVE-LENGTHS OF THE LINES $K\beta_6$ AND $K\beta_7$

Element	$K\beta_6$	$K\beta_7$	Element	$K\beta_6$	$K\beta_7$
	X.U.	X.U.		X.U.	X.U.
37 Rb	821.64		40 Zr	695.85	697.8
38 Sr	776.23	778.8	42 Mo	627.21	629.15
39 Y	734.58	737.1			

Hulubei and Cauchois[87] have also reported new lines in the K series found by the method of the bent crystal spectograph, some of which are included in the above table.

[86] B. Edlén, Zeitschr. f. Physik **52**, 364 (1928).
[87] Hulubei and Cauchois, Compt. rend. **196**, 1294 (1933).

APPENDICES

APPENDIX I

Radiation from an Electron Moving with a Velocity Approaching that of Light

(References: E. Cunningham, "The Principle of Relativity," Chaps. IV, V and VI; A. Sommerfeld, "Atomic Structure and Spectral Lines," English translation, pp. 452–466.)

In view of the fact that we shall have frequent use throughout this work for the results of the special theory of relativity, it will be valuable to outline briefly the derivation of these results.

A. THE LORENTZ TRANSFORMATION EQUATIONS

1. *Einstein's Derivation of the Fundamental Transformations*

The relativity method of solving a problem relating to a body in motion is to solve first the problem for such a body when at rest, and then by the application of certain "transformation equations" find the corresponding solution for a body in motion. In deriving these transformation equations, Einstein imagines two similar systems, S and S', the system S remaining at rest while the system S', which was coincident with the system S at the instant $t = 0$, moves along the X axis with a velocity v. The equations are then derived by the use of two assumptions: (1) that the velocity of light has the same value c in both systems, and (2) that the changes between the variables x, y, z and t are linear, i.e., that the space is homogeneous and that the motion is unaccelerated.

The mathematical formulation of the second assumption is that

$$x' = k(x - vt), \qquad y' = ly,$$
$$z' = lz, \qquad t' = \alpha x + \beta y + \gamma z + \delta t, \qquad (2)$$

where the primed coordinates refer to the moving system S', the unprimed ones to the stationary system, and the coefficients k, l, α, β, γ, δ are functions only of the velocity. The coefficients of y and z

759

are taken to be the same by symmetry, since the motion is perpendicular to both the Y and Z axes. An expression of the first assumption is that for a particle moving from the origin with the velocity of light,

$$x^2 + y^2 + z^2 = c^2 t^2 \tag{1}$$

is equivalent to

$$x'^2 + y'^2 + z'^2 = c^2 t'^2.$$

It is from these assumptions, equations (1) and (2), that all the transformation equations are derived.

If in the second of eqs. (1) we introduce the values of the primed coordinates given in eqs. (2), we obtain

$$k^2(x - vt)^2 + l^2 y^2 + l^2 z^2 = c^2(\alpha x + \beta y + \gamma z + \delta t)^2,$$

or on expanding and collecting coefficients,

$$(k^2 - c^2\alpha^2)x^2 + (l^2 - c^2\beta^2)y^2 + (l^2 - c^2\gamma^2)z^2$$

$$- 2c^2\alpha\beta \cdot xy - 2c^2\alpha\gamma \cdot xz - 2c^2\beta\gamma \cdot yz$$

$$= (c^2\delta^2 - k^2 v^2)t^2 + 2(k^2 v + c^2\alpha\delta)xt + 2c^2\beta\delta \cdot yt + 2c^2\gamma\delta \cdot zt.$$

But by our first assumption this is equivalent to

$$x^2 + y^2 + z^2 = c^2 t^2.$$

Since the particle may be assumed to move in any direction, the coordinates may be varied independently of each other, so that the coefficients of x, x^2, y, y^2, etc., in the two expressions must be equivalent to each other except for an arbitrary factor m^2 by which both sides of the latter expression may be multiplied without changing its significance. Thus we have,

$$\alpha\beta = \alpha\gamma = \beta\gamma = \beta\delta = \gamma\delta = 0, \qquad k^2 v + c^2\alpha\delta = 0,$$

$$k^2 - c^2\alpha^2 = m^2, \qquad\qquad l^2 - c^2\beta^2 = m^2,$$

$$l^2 - c^2\gamma^2 = m^2, \qquad\qquad c^2\delta^2 - k^2 v^2 = m^2 c^2.$$

It follows that

$$\beta = \gamma = 0, \qquad \alpha = -\, kv/c^2, \qquad \delta = k,$$

$$k = \left(1 - \frac{v^2}{c^2}\right)^{-\frac{1}{2}} m, \qquad\qquad l = m.$$

Our simplest assumption is that $m = 1$, which merely means that we are measuring distances on the same scale in the two systems. For at the instant at which the $Y'Z'$ plane of the system S' is coincident with the YZ plane of the system S, the corresponding points in the two planes coincide, that is,

$$y' = y \quad \text{and} \quad z' = z.$$

Introducing this value of m, therefore,

$$k = \left(1 - \frac{v^2}{c^2}\right)^{-\frac{1}{2}}, \quad l = 1, \quad \alpha = -\frac{v}{c^2}k, \qquad (3)$$

$$\beta = \gamma = 0, \qquad\qquad\qquad \delta = k.$$

Consequently by equations (2),

$$x' = (x - vt)k, \quad y' = y, \quad z' = z, \quad t' = k(t - vx/c^2). \qquad (4)$$

On solving for x, y, z and t, we find conversely,

$$x = (x' + vt')k, \quad y = y', \quad z = z', \quad t = k(t' + vx'/c^2). \qquad (4')$$

2. *Displacement, Velocity and Acceleration*

Consider two points whose coordinates at the instant t in the stationary system are x_1, y_1, z_1, and x_2, y_2, z_2. In the moving system the distance between the two points, as measured along the three axes, is by eq. (4),

$$\left.\begin{aligned}
x_2' - x_1' &= k(x_2 - vt) - k(x_1 - vt) = k(x_2 - x_1) \\
y_2' - y_1' &= y_2 - y_1 \\
z_2' - z_1 &= z_2 - z_1
\end{aligned}\right\} \qquad (5)$$

To an observer moving with the system S', though the distances along the Y and Z axes remain unchanged, the distance along the direction of motion thus appears to be shortened by the factor k. Conversely, if two points in the moving system are a distance $x_2' - x_1'$ apart, application of eq. (4') shows that in the system at rest their separation is $x_2 - x_1 = k(x_2' - x_1')$. This apparent contraction in the direction of motion is that postulated originally by Fitzgerald to account for the results of the Michelson-Morley experiment.

Addition of Velocities.—Imagine a particle which is moving with a velocity whose components, as measured in the stationary system, are u_x, u_y and u_z. The X component of the velocity in the system S' is then dx'/dt', where

$$dx' = d\{k(x - vt)\} = k(dx - vdt),$$

and

$$dt' = d\left\{k\left(t - \frac{vx}{c^2}\right)\right\} = k\left(dt - \frac{vdx}{c^2}\right).$$

Thus

$$u_x' = \frac{dx'}{dt'} = \frac{dx - vdt}{dt - \dfrac{v}{c^2}dx} = \frac{\dfrac{dx}{dt} - v}{1 - \dfrac{v}{c^2}\dfrac{dx}{dt}}$$

$$= \frac{u_x - v}{1 - \dfrac{v}{c^2}u_x}. \tag{6}$$

Similarly we find,

$$u_y' = \frac{u_y}{k\left(1 - \dfrac{v}{c^2}u_x\right)} \quad \text{and} \quad u_z' = \frac{u_z}{k\left(1 - \dfrac{v}{c^2}u_x\right)}. \tag{7}$$

Conversely we can show that if as measured in system S' the particle's velocity components are u_x', u_y' and u_z', in system S its velocity is given by

$$u_x = \frac{u_x' + v}{1 + \dfrac{v}{c^2}u_x'} \tag{6'}$$

$$u_y = \frac{u_y'}{k\left(1 + \dfrac{v}{c^2}u_x'\right)} \quad \text{and} \quad u_z = \frac{u_z'}{k\left(1 + \dfrac{v}{c^2}u_x'\right)}. \tag{7'}$$

From eq. (6') we see that the velocity u_x of a particle moving with a velocity u_x' relative to the system S', which itself is moving with a velocity v, is less than $u_x' + v$, and is always less than c if both u_x' and v are less than c. For velocities comparable with that of light, therefore, the simple rules of vector addition cannot be applied. We also see that c represents a limiting velocity which cannot be exceeded by a particle which gains velocity in increments less than c. An interesting and important confirmation of this result is that whereas β-particles ejected by radioactive materials have been found to have velocities up to $0.998c$, none have ever been observed with velocities greater than c.

Accelerations.—We define the acceleration of the particle as measured in the stationary system as the vector having the components $a_x = du_x/dt$, $a_y = du_y/dt$ and $a_z = du_z/dt$. As measured from the moving axes,

$$du_x' = d\left[\frac{u_x - v}{1 - \dfrac{vu_x}{c^2}} \right]$$

$$= \frac{du_x}{k^2\left(1 - \dfrac{vu_x}{c^2}\right)^2}.$$

But we have seen that

$$dt' = k\left(dt - \frac{v}{c^2}dx\right) = k\left(dt - \frac{v}{c^2}u_x dt\right)$$

$$= dt \cdot k\left(1 - \frac{vu_x}{c^2}\right).$$

Thus

$$a_x' = \frac{du_x'}{dt'} = \frac{du_x}{dt} \cdot \frac{1}{k^3\left(1 - \dfrac{vu_x}{c^2}\right)^3}.$$

If we write

$$\phi = k\left(1 - \frac{vu_x}{c^2}\right),$$

then

$$a_x' = \frac{1}{\phi^3}a_x. \tag{8}$$

In a similar manner we can show that

$$a_y' = \frac{1}{\phi^2}a_y + \frac{kvu_y}{\phi^3 c^2}a_x,$$

$$a_z' = \frac{1}{\phi^2}a_z + \frac{kvu_z}{\phi^3 c^2}a_x. \tag{9}$$

3. *The Electromagnetic Field*

In the stationary system the equations of the electromagnetic field are:

$$\frac{1}{c}\frac{\partial E_x}{\partial t} + 4\pi\rho\,\frac{u_x}{c} = \frac{\partial H_z}{\partial y} - \frac{\partial H_y}{\partial z}, \tag{A}$$

$$\frac{1}{c}\frac{\partial E_y}{\partial t} + 4\pi\rho\,\frac{u_y}{c} = \frac{\partial H_x}{\partial z} - \frac{\partial H_z}{\partial x}, \tag{B}$$

$$\frac{1}{c}\frac{\partial E_z}{\partial t} + 4\pi\rho\,\frac{u_z}{c} = \frac{\partial H_y}{\partial x} - \frac{\partial H_x}{\partial y}, \tag{C}$$

$$-\frac{1}{c}\frac{\partial H_x}{\partial t} = \frac{\partial E_z}{\partial y} - \frac{\partial E_y}{\partial z}, \tag{D}$$

$$-\frac{1}{c}\frac{\partial H_y}{\partial t} = \frac{\partial E_x}{\partial z} - \frac{\partial E_z}{\partial x}, \tag{E}$$

$$-\frac{1}{c}\frac{\partial H_z}{\partial t} = \frac{\partial E_y}{\partial x} - \frac{\partial E_x}{\partial y}, \tag{F}$$

$$\frac{\partial E_x}{\partial x} + \frac{\partial E_y}{\partial y} + \frac{\partial E_z}{\partial z} = 4\pi\rho, \tag{G}$$

$$\frac{\partial H_x}{\partial x} + \frac{\partial H_y}{\partial y} + \frac{\partial H_z}{\partial z} = 0. \tag{H}$$

In these equations E is the electric intensity expressed in e.s.u., H is the magnetic intensity in e.m.u., and ρ is the volume density of electrification. In order to express the corresponding relations as referred to the moving system S', let us consider the partial derivatives of any function Ψ of the coordinates x, y, z and t. By virtue of eqs. (4) and (4') we have:

$$\frac{\partial \Psi}{\partial x} = \frac{\partial \Psi}{\partial x'}\frac{dx'}{dx} + \frac{\partial \Psi}{\partial t'}\frac{dt'}{dx} = \frac{\partial \Psi}{\partial x'}k - \frac{\partial \Psi}{\partial t'}k\,\frac{v}{c^2}$$

$$= k\left(\frac{\partial \Psi}{\partial x'} - \frac{v}{c^2}\frac{\partial \Psi}{\partial t'}\right);$$

$$\frac{\partial \Psi}{\partial y} = \frac{\partial \Psi}{\partial y'}; \qquad \frac{\partial \Psi}{\partial z} = \frac{\partial \Psi}{\partial z'};$$

$$\frac{\partial \Psi}{\partial t} = \frac{\partial \Psi}{\partial t'}\frac{dt'}{dt} + \frac{\partial \Psi}{\partial x'}\frac{dx'}{dt} = k\left(\frac{\partial \Psi}{\partial t'} - v\frac{\partial \Psi}{\partial x'}\right).$$

Expressing eqs. (A), (B), and (C) in terms of x', y', z' and t' by the use of these relations we obtain,

$$\frac{k}{c}\frac{\partial E_x}{\partial t'} - \frac{kv}{c}\frac{\partial E_x}{\partial x'} + 4\pi\rho\frac{u_x}{c} = \frac{\partial H_z}{\partial y'} - \frac{\partial H_y}{\partial z'}, \tag{a}$$

$$\frac{k}{c}\frac{\partial E_y}{\partial t'} - \frac{kv}{c}\frac{\partial E_y}{\partial x'} + 4\pi\rho\frac{u_y}{c} = \frac{\partial H_x}{\partial z'} - k\frac{\partial H_z}{\partial x'} + \frac{kv}{c^2}\frac{\partial H_z}{\partial t'}, \tag{b}$$

$$\frac{k}{c}\frac{\partial E_z}{\partial t'} - \frac{kv}{c}\frac{\partial E_z}{\partial x'} + 4\pi\rho\frac{u_z}{c} = k\frac{\partial H_y}{\partial x'} - \frac{kv}{c^2}\frac{\partial H_y}{\partial t'} - \frac{\partial H_x}{\partial y'}. \tag{c}$$

It is an essential assumption of the theory of relativity that physical laws have the same form whether expressed in the coordinates of system S' or in those of system S. For if this were not true, by the form of the physical law it should be possible to determine the state of motion of the system. It will be seen that our assumption (1) is a special case of this more general principle. We accordingly seek for quantities E', H' and ρ' which will be related to E, H and ρ in such a way that when substituted in eqs. (a), (b), (c), etc., these will be of the same form as eqs. (A), (B), (C), etc. The desired values are:

$$\left.\begin{array}{l} E_x' = E_x; \quad E_y' = k\left(E_y - \frac{v}{c}H_z\right); \quad E_z' = k\left(E_z + \frac{v}{c}H_y\right); \\[2mm] H_x' = H_x; \quad H_y' = k\left(H_y + \frac{v}{c}E_z\right); \quad H_z' = k\left(H_z - \frac{v}{c}E_y\right); \end{array}\right\} \tag{10}$$

and the equivalent reciprocal expressions are,

$$\left.\begin{array}{ll} E_y = k\left(E_y' + \frac{v}{c}H_z'\right); & E_z = k\left(E_z' - \frac{v}{c}H_y'\right); \\[2mm] H_y = k\left(H_y' - \frac{v}{c}E_z'\right); & H_z = k\left(H_z' + \frac{v}{c}E_y'\right); \end{array}\right\} \tag{10'}$$

also

$$\rho' = k\rho\left(1 - \frac{vu_x}{c^2}\right); \qquad \rho = k\rho'\left(1 + \frac{vu_x'}{c^2}\right). \tag{11}$$

When these values for E, H and ρ are inserted in eqs. (b) and (c), using the values of u_y and u_z given by eqs. (7'), we obtain, after some reduction,

$$\frac{1}{c}\frac{\partial E_y'}{\partial t'} + 4\pi\rho'\frac{u_y'}{c} = \frac{\partial H_x'}{\partial z'} - \frac{\partial H_z'}{\partial x'}, \qquad (B')$$

$$\frac{1}{c}\frac{\partial E_z'}{\partial t'} + 4\pi\rho'\frac{u_z'}{c} = \frac{\partial H_y'}{\partial x'} - \frac{\partial H_x'}{\partial y'}. \qquad (C')$$

These are of precisely the same form as equations (B) and (C).

The substitution in eq. (a) is somewhat complex. Introducing the new values for E and H we obtain directly

$$\frac{k}{c}\left\{\frac{\partial E_x'}{\partial t'} - v\left(\frac{\partial E_x'}{\partial x'} + \frac{\partial E_y'}{\partial y'} + \frac{\partial E_z'}{\partial z'}\right)\right\} + 4\pi\rho\frac{u_x}{c} = k\left(\frac{\partial H_z'}{\partial y'} - \frac{\partial H_y'}{\partial z'}\right).$$

But from eq. (G) we get,

$$\frac{kv}{c}\left(\frac{\partial E_x'}{\partial x'} + \frac{\partial E_y'}{\partial y'} + \frac{\partial E_z'}{\partial z'}\right) - \frac{kv^2}{c^3}\frac{\partial E_x'}{\partial t'} - \frac{kv^2}{c^2}\left(\frac{\partial H_y'}{\partial z'} - \frac{\partial H_z'}{\partial y'}\right) = 4\pi\rho\frac{v}{c}.$$

Thus

$$\frac{\partial E_x'}{\partial t'}\frac{k}{c}\left(1 - \frac{v^2}{c^2}\right) - 4\pi\rho\frac{v}{c} + 4\pi\rho\frac{u_x}{c} = k\left(1 - \frac{v^2}{c^2}\right)\left(\frac{\partial H_z'}{\partial y'} - \frac{\partial H_y'}{\partial z'}\right),$$

or

$$\frac{1}{c}\frac{\partial E_x'}{\partial t'} - k\frac{4\pi\rho}{c}(v - u_x) = \frac{\partial H_z'}{\partial y'} - \frac{\partial H_y'}{\partial z'},$$

since $(1 - v^2/c^2) = 1/k^2$. Introducing the values of ρ and u_x given by equations (11) and (6') we then have at once,

$$\frac{1}{c}\frac{\partial E_x'}{\partial t'} + 4\pi\rho'\frac{u_x'}{c} = \frac{\partial H_z'}{\partial y'} - \frac{\partial H_y'}{\partial z'}, \qquad (A')$$

which is identical in form with eq. (A).

In a similar manner it can be shown that, using the values of E, H and ρ given by eqs. (10) and (11), eqs. (D), (E), (F), (G) and (H) transform into precisely similar equations in the system S'. Thus expressions (10) and (11) are the desired transformation equations for the electromagnetic field.

Constancy of Electric Charge.—If we consider a volume element moving with system S' with a velocity $u_x = v$, whose edges are $\delta x'$, $\delta y'$, $\delta z'$, and which contains an electric charge of volume density ρ', the total charge within the element as measured in system S' is $\rho' \delta x' \delta y' \delta z'$. From eqs. (4) and (11), however,

$$\rho' \delta x' \delta y' \delta z' = k\rho \left(1 - \frac{v^2}{c^2}\right) \cdot k \delta x \delta y \delta z$$

$$= \rho \delta x \delta y \delta z \qquad (12)$$

$$= \text{charge measured in system } S,$$

since

$$(1 - v^2/c^2) = 1/k^2.$$

Thus an electric charge has the same value whether referred to axes at rest or to axes moving with the charge.

4. *Variation of Mass with Velocity*

Let us consider a particle, whose mass when at rest is m_0, moving in the XY plane, with a velocity which at the instant $t = 0$ is the same as that of the moving system S'. In this system the compo nents of the force acting on the particle are let us say X', Y', whence by Newton's second law of motion,

$$\frac{d}{dt'}\left(m'\frac{dx'}{dt'}\right) = X', \quad \text{and} \quad \frac{d}{dt'}\left(m'\frac{dy'}{dt'}\right) = Y'. \qquad (13)$$

At the initial instant $m' = m_0$, and $dx'/dt' = dy'/dt' = 0$, so that

$$m_0\frac{d^2x'}{dt'^2} = X' \quad \text{and} \quad m_0\frac{d^2y'}{dt'^2} = Y'. \qquad (14)$$

But from equations (8) and (9), noting that $u_x = v$, $u_y = 0$, and $\phi = 1/k$ where $k = 1/\sqrt{1 - v^2/c^2}$, we find

$$\frac{d^2x'}{dt'^2} = k^3\frac{d^2x}{dt^2}, \quad \text{and} \quad \frac{d^2y'}{dt'^2} = k^2\frac{d^2y}{dt^2}. \qquad (15)$$

Let us suppose that the force X', Y' is that due to an electric field of components E_x' and E_y' acting on a charge e on the particle. Then noting that the charge e has the same value in both systems, whereas by eqs. (10) $E_x' = E_x$ and $E_y' = kE_y$, since $H_z = 0$, the com ponents of the force are

$$X' = E_x'e = E_xe = X,$$

and

$$Y' = E_y'e = kE_ye = kY. \qquad (16)$$

Substituting from eqs. (15) and (16) in eq. (14) we get

$$k^3 m_0 \frac{d^2x}{dt^2} = X \quad \text{and} \quad km_0 \frac{d^2y}{dt^2} = Y. \tag{17}$$

The quantities $k^3 m_0$ and km_0 are (or have been) frequently though disadvantageously referred to respectively as the longitudinal and the transverse mass. The fundamental definition of mass is however not the coefficient of the acceleration in the expression for the force, as this would imply, but rather the coefficient of the velocity in the expression for the momentum, or what Newton calls the " quantity of motion." That is, the mass is correctly defined by relations similar to eq. (13), namely.

$$\frac{d}{dt}\left(m \frac{dx}{dt} \right) \equiv X, \quad \text{and} \quad \frac{d}{dt}\left(m \frac{dy}{dt} \right) \equiv Y. \tag{18}$$

If in eqs. (18) we use $m = km_0$, we get

$$X = \frac{d}{dt}\left(km_0 \frac{dx}{dt} \right) = km_0 \frac{d^2x}{dt^2} + m_0 \frac{dx}{dt} \frac{dk}{dt},$$

$$Y = \frac{d}{dt}\left(km_0 \frac{dy}{dt} \right) = km_0 \frac{d^2y}{dt^2} + m_0 \frac{dy}{dt} \frac{dk}{dt}.$$

But

$$\frac{dk}{dt} = \frac{d}{dt}\left(1 - \frac{v^2}{c^2} \right)^{-\frac{1}{2}} = \frac{v}{c^2}\left(1 - \frac{v^2}{c^2} \right)^{-\frac{3}{2}} \frac{dv}{dt} = k^3 \frac{v}{c^2} \frac{d^2x}{dt^2}, \tag{19}$$

also $dx/dt = v$, and $dy/dt = 0$. Thus,

$$X = km_0 \frac{d^2x}{dt^2} + k^3 m_0 \frac{v^2}{c^2} \frac{d^2x}{dt^2} = k^3 m_0 \frac{d^2x}{dt^2}\left[\left(1 - \frac{v^2}{c^2} \right) + \frac{v^2}{c^2} \right]$$

$$= k^3 m_0 \frac{d^2x}{dt^2},$$

$$Y = km_0 \frac{d^2y}{dt^2}.$$

These expressions are identical with eqs. (17), showing that the mass, as defined by eq. (18), is given by

$$m = km_0 = m_0/\sqrt{1 - \beta^2}, \tag{20}$$

where $\beta = v/c$.

Kinetic Energy.—Imagine a particle of rest mass m_0 moving along the X axis with a velocity $v = \beta c$, and acted on by a force of magnitude X. The rate at which this force does work, increasing the kinetic energy T of the particle, is

$$X \frac{dx}{dt} = \frac{dT}{dt}.$$

Using the value of X given by eq. (17), this expression becomes,

$$\frac{dT}{dt} = \frac{dx}{dt} \cdot k^3 m_0 \frac{d^2x}{dt^2}$$

$$= m_0 c^2 k^3 \beta \frac{d\beta}{dt}.$$

But by (19)

$$\frac{dk}{dt} = k^3 \frac{v}{c^2} \frac{d^2x}{dt^2} = k^3 \beta \frac{d\beta}{dt}.$$

Thus

$$\frac{dT}{dt} = m_0 c^2 \frac{dk}{dt},$$

whence

$$T = k m_0 c^2 + \text{const.}$$

Since $T = 0$ when $v = 0$ or when $k = 1$, const $= -m_0 c^2$. Therefore

$$T = m_0 c^2 (k - 1)$$

$$= m_0 c^2 \left(\frac{1}{\sqrt{1 - \beta^2}} - 1 \right). \tag{21}$$

If this is expanded into a series, recalling that $\beta = v/c$, we obtain

$$T = \tfrac{1}{2} m_0 v^2 (1 + \tfrac{3}{4}\beta^2 + \tfrac{5}{8}\beta^4 + \ldots). \tag{22}$$

For small velocities, this calculation therefore gives the same value $\tfrac{1}{2}mv^2$ as is employed in the usual mechanics.

The Inertia of Energy.—Equation (21) may be written, since $km_0 = m$, as

$$T = c^2(m - m_0), \quad \text{or} \quad m - m_0 = T/c^2.$$

That is, the increase in the mass of the body due to its motion is equal to the energy due to its motion divided by c^2.

This is one example of a general principle propounded by Einstein as the result of an extensive application of the principles of special relativity to a large variety of problems. His conclusion is: every quantity of energy, of any kind whatever, has associated with it an amount of mass

$$M = W/c^2, \tag{23}$$

where W is the amount of energy.

A corollary to this proposition is that, since momentum is defined as mass × velocity, if a quantity of energy is moving with a velocity v, it carries with it an amount of momentum

$$p = Wv/c^2. \tag{24}$$

An important application of this corollary is to the case of radiant energy, propagated in a definite direction with a velocity c. In this case the momentum p carried by the radiant energy W is

$$p = W/c, \tag{25}$$

a result identical with that required according to electromagnetic theory to account for radiation pressure.

In the following table are collected the more important transformation equations.

TABLE I

Transformation equations from system S at rest to system S' moving along X axis with velocity $v = \beta c$, and vice versa:

$$\beta \equiv \frac{v}{c}; \quad k \equiv (1 - \beta^2)^{-\frac{1}{2}}; \quad \phi \equiv k\left(1 - \frac{vu_x}{c^2}\right); \quad \phi' \equiv k\left(1 + \frac{vu_x'}{c^2}\right).$$

Displacement:

$$x' = k(x - vt), \qquad\qquad x = k(x' + vt'),$$
$$y' = y, \qquad z' = z, \qquad\qquad y = y', \qquad z = z', \tag{4}$$
$$t' = k\left(t - \frac{vx}{c^2}\right), \qquad\qquad t = k\left(t' + \frac{vx'}{c^2}\right).$$

Velocity:

$$u_x' = \frac{k}{\phi}(u_x - v), \qquad\qquad u_x = \frac{k}{\phi'}(u_x' + v), \tag{6}$$

$$u_y' = u_y/\phi, \qquad\qquad u_y = u_y'/\phi',$$
$$u_z' = u_z/\phi, \qquad\qquad u_z = u_z'/\phi'. \tag{7}$$

Acceleration:

$$a_x' = a_x/\phi^3, \qquad\qquad a_x = a_x'/\phi'^3,$$

$$a_y' = \frac{a_y}{\phi^2} + \frac{kvu_y}{\phi^3 c^2} a_x, \qquad\qquad a_y = \frac{a_y'}{\phi'^2} - \frac{kvu_y'}{\phi'^3 c^2} a_x',$$

$$a_z' = \frac{a_z}{\phi^2} + \frac{kvu_z}{\phi^3 c^2} a_x, \qquad\qquad a_z = \frac{a_z'}{\phi'^2} - \frac{kvu_z'}{\phi'^3 c^2} a_x'. \qquad (9)$$

Electromagnetic Field:

$$E_x' = E_x, \qquad\qquad E_x = E_x',$$
$$E_y' = k(E_y - \beta H_z), \qquad\qquad E_y = k(E_y' + \beta H_z'),$$
$$E_z' = k(E_z + \beta H_y), \qquad\qquad E_z = k(E_z' - \beta H_y'), \qquad (10)$$

$$H_x' = H_x, \qquad\qquad H_x = H_x',$$
$$H_y' = k(Hy + \beta E_z), \qquad\qquad H_y = k(H_y' - \beta E_z'),$$
$$H_z' = k(H_z - \beta E_y), \qquad\qquad H_z = k(H_z' + \beta E_y').$$
$$\rho' = \phi\rho, \qquad\qquad \rho = \phi'\rho', \qquad (11)$$

$$e = e' \qquad (12)$$

Dynamics:

$$m = km_0 \quad (20); \qquad T = m_0 c^2(k - 1) \quad (21); \qquad M = W/c^2 (23);$$

$$p = Wv/c^2 \quad (24); \qquad p_{\text{radiation}} = W/c \quad (25).$$

B. FIELD DUE TO ELECTRON ACCELERATED IN DIRECTION OF MOTION

In Appendix II we show that if an electron moving with negligible velocity is accelerated along the X axis, an electric field results whose intensity is

$$E = H = \frac{ae}{rc^2} \sin \theta. \qquad (2.01)$$

In order to calculate the radiation from this electron when moving with a velocity v, we imagine the system S' moving with the electron at the moment $t = 0$ with the uniform velocity v. Referred to this system the electron is at this instant at rest, so that the field due to the radiation is,

$$E' = H' = \frac{a'e \sin \theta'}{r'c^2}. \qquad (26)$$

Referring to Fig. I, it will be seen that

$$E_x' = - E' \sin \theta'; \qquad E_y' = E' \cos \theta'; \qquad E_z' = 0;$$

$$H_x' = 0; \qquad H_y' = 0; \qquad H_z' = H'. \qquad (27)$$

By eqs. (10), therefore,

$$E_z = E_z' = -\frac{e}{c^2}\frac{a'}{r'}\sin^2\theta',$$

$$E_y = k\left(\frac{e}{c^2}\frac{a'}{r'}\sin\theta'\cos\theta' + \beta\frac{e}{c^2}\frac{a'}{r'}\sin\theta'\right),$$

$$E_z = 0, \qquad H_z = 0, \qquad H_y = 0, \tag{28}$$

$$H_z = k\left(\frac{e}{c^2}\frac{a'}{r'}\sin\theta' + \beta\frac{e}{c^2}\frac{a'}{r'}\sin\theta'\cos\theta'\right).$$

To complete the transformation, we note from eq. (8), since $u_x = v$ and thus $\phi = 1/k$, that

$$a' = a_x' = k^3 a_x = k^3 a. \tag{29}$$

Also, from eq. (4),

$$r' = \sqrt{x'^2 + y'^2} = \sqrt{k^2(x^2 - 2vxt + v^2t^2) + y^2},$$

where t, the time at which the field is evaluated at P (Fig. I) is r/c. Thus

$$r' = \sqrt{k^2(x^2 - 2xv\,r/c + v^2r^2/c^2) + y^2},$$

$$= k\sqrt{x^2 - 2\beta xr + \beta^2 r^2 + y^2 - \beta^2 y^2},$$

$$= k(r - \beta x). \tag{30}$$

$$\sin\theta' = \frac{y'}{r'} = \frac{y}{k(r - \beta x)} = \frac{\sin\theta}{k(1 - \beta\cos\theta)}, \tag{31}$$

$$\cos\theta' = \sqrt{1 - \sin^2\theta'} = \frac{\cos\theta - \beta}{1 - \beta\cos\theta}. \tag{32}$$

Substituting these values in eqs. (28) we get

$$E_z = -\frac{e}{c^2}\frac{a}{r}\frac{\sin^2\theta}{(1 - \beta\cos\theta)^3},$$

$$E_y = \frac{e}{c^2}\frac{a}{r}\frac{\sin\theta\cos\theta}{(1 - \beta\cos\theta)^3},$$

or

$$E = \sqrt{E_x{}^2 + E_y{}^2} = \frac{ea}{rc^2} \frac{\sin\theta}{(1 - \beta\cos\theta)^3};$$

and

$$H = H_z = \frac{ea}{rc^2} \frac{\sin\theta}{(1 - \beta\cos\theta)^3}.$$

(33)

The equations (33), representing the field due to a charge in accelerated motion along the axis, are those employed in Chapter II as eqs. (2.02). They were used by Sommerfeld (" Atomic Structure and Spectral Lines," pp. 33 and 532) in discussing the pulse theory of x-rays.

APPENDIX II

ELECTROMAGNETIC FIELD OF A MOVING ELECTRON

The intensity of the radiation emitted by an accelerated electron may be calculated by an application of Maxwell's conception of displacement currents. Just as an electromotive force is induced in a circuit toward which a magnetic pole is moving, so a magnetomotive force is induced by the motion of an electric charge. The use of the idea of displacement currents may be illustrated by calculating on this basis the magnetic field due to a moving electron.

Field Due to an Electron in Slow, Uniform Motion

Imagine, as in Fig. II–A, an electron moving along the X-axis with a velocity v small compared with the velocity of light c. We wish to determine the magnetic field at a point $P(r, \theta)$. If we draw through P a sphere about the electron at O as a center, the number of unit lines of electric force, or the electric "displacement" across the sphere is equal to the charge e. If, however, we consider the circle PSQ, perpendicular to OX, the displacement through this circle is

$$D = e. \ \frac{\text{Area of Zone } PRQ}{\text{Area of whole sphere}}$$

$$= e. \ \frac{MR}{2OR}$$

$$= \tfrac{1}{2}e(1 - \cos \theta). \tag{1}$$

The *displacement current* passing through the circle PSQ is $i_D = dD/dt$, and this is supposed to produce precisely the same magnetic effect as if dD/dt were the rate at which electric charge traversed the circle. The work done in carrying unit magnetic pole about this circuit is thus

$$\int H ds = \frac{4\pi}{c} i_D, \tag{2}$$

774

where the magnetic field H is in e.m.u., and the displacement current i_D is in e.s.u., or,

$$H \cdot 2\pi r \sin \theta = \frac{4\pi}{c} \frac{d}{dt} \left[\tfrac{1}{2} e (1 - \cos \theta) \right]$$

$$= \frac{2\pi e}{c} \sin \theta \frac{d\theta}{dt}.$$

That is,

$$H = \frac{e}{rc} \frac{d\theta}{dt}.$$

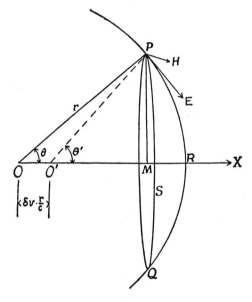

Fɪɢ. II–A.

Since

$$d\theta = (dx \sin \theta)/r, \, d\theta/dt = \frac{1}{r} \sin \theta \frac{dx}{dt} = \frac{v}{r} \sin \theta.$$

Thus

$$H = \frac{ev}{r^2c} \sin \theta. \tag{3}$$

It will be seen that this is the same magnetic field at P as one calculates from Ampere's rule,

$$dH = \frac{ids}{r^2c} \sin \theta,$$

if ev is taken as equivalent to the element of current ids.

Field Due to Accelerated, Slowly Moving, Electron

Referring again to Fig. II–A, let us now imagine an electron moving with a small uniform velocity δv along the X axis, which is stopped at the point O in a short interval of time δt. We wish to calculate the intensity of the electromagnetic pulse at P resulting from this change in the electron's motion.

At the instant $t = o$, the electron is at the point O, and since it has been in slow uniform motion, its field is the same in all directions.[1] The displacement through the circle PSQ is now, as in equation (1),

$$\tfrac{1}{2}e(1 - \cos\theta).$$

After the additional short time interval δt the electron has stopped close to O. But an observer at P is unaware of this change in the electron's motion until after the time r/c, required for an electromagnetic pulse to move from O to P. At the instant $t = r/c$, therefore, the field at P is just as it would be if the electron had continued to move with uniform velocity δv during this interval, reaching a point O' at a distance $\delta x = \delta v \cdot r/c$ from O. The displacement through PSQ is now therefore $\tfrac{1}{2}e(1 - \cos\theta')$. But at the moment $t = r/c + \delta t$, and forever after, the field at P is that due to an electron at rest at O, so the displacement is again $\tfrac{1}{2}e(1 - \cos\theta)$.

During the short interval from $t = r/c$ to $t = r/c + \delta t$ the displacement has accordingly changed at the average rate,

$$\frac{\delta D}{\delta t} = \tfrac{1}{2}e(\cos\theta' - \cos\theta)/\delta t,$$

or

$$i_D = \tfrac{1}{2}e\,\frac{\delta\cos\theta}{\delta t}$$

$$= -\tfrac{1}{2}e\sin\theta\,\frac{\delta\theta}{\delta t}.$$

But

$$\delta\theta = \frac{\delta x}{r}\sin\theta = \frac{\delta v}{c}\sin\theta,$$

whence

$$\frac{\delta\theta}{\delta t} = \frac{1}{c}\sin\theta\,\frac{\delta v}{\delta t} = -\frac{a}{c}\sin\theta,$$

---

[1] Equations (10) of Appendix I state that to the first power of v/c the electric field of a charge in uniform motion is the same as for the charge at rest.

where $a = -\dfrac{\delta v}{\delta t}$ is the acceleration to which the electron is subject.

It follows that

$$i_D = \frac{1}{2} \frac{ae}{c} \sin^2 \theta.$$

As in eq. (2) we have therefore

$$H \cdot 2\pi r \sin \theta = \frac{4\pi}{c} \frac{1}{2} \frac{ae}{c} \sin^2 \theta,$$

whence

$$H = \frac{ae \sin \theta}{rc^2}. \tag{4}$$

When a magnetic field moves perpendicular to itself with a velocity v, it gives rise to an electric field of strength $E = H \cdot \dfrac{v}{c}$ if E is expressed in electrostatic and H in electromagnetic units. In the present case, since the velocity of propagation of the pulse is $v = c$, the intensity of the electric field of the pulse in these units is identical with that of the magnetic field, i.e.,

$$E = H = \frac{ae}{rc^2} \sin \theta. \tag{5}$$

This equation is used in the text as eq. (2.01).

It will be noticed that these electric and magnetic intensities due to the electron's acceleration vary inversely as the distance r at which they are observed. But the electric intensity due to a stationary charge, and the magnetic intensity (eq. (3)), due to a charge in uniform motion, vary inversely as the square of the distance. Thus the radiation from the electron may be perceptible at distances so great that its electrostatic field is negligible.

APPENDIX III

VELOCITY OF A WAVE GROUP

Consider two infinite trains of waves of wave-length λ and $\lambda + \delta\lambda$, superposed, as represented by Fig. III–A, and let u and $u + \delta u$ be their velocities of propagation. If at time $t = 0$ the wave trains are in the same phase at A, the adjacent crests, B and C will be

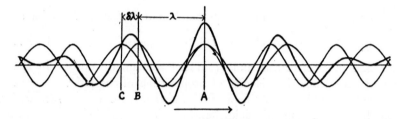

FIG. III–A. If the longer of the two wave trains moves the faster, the wave group will travel more slowly than the waves themselves.

superposed after an interval $\delta t = \delta\lambda/\delta u$. Thus the group velocity is less than the wave or phase velocity by $\lambda/\delta t$, i.e.,

$$w = u - \lambda \frac{\delta u}{\delta\lambda}.$$

Writing the increments as differentials, this becomes

$$w = u\left(1 - \frac{\lambda}{u}\frac{du}{d\lambda}\right). \tag{1}$$

In order to express w in terms of the frequency instead of the wave-length, we note that

$$\frac{\lambda}{u} = \frac{1}{\nu}$$

and

$$\frac{du}{d\lambda} = \frac{du}{d\nu}\frac{d\nu}{d\lambda}.$$

778

But since $\qquad\qquad \lambda = u/v,$

$$\frac{d\lambda}{dv} = \frac{1}{v}\frac{du}{dv} - \frac{u}{v^2},$$

whence

$$\frac{du}{d\lambda} = \frac{du}{dv}\bigg/\left(\frac{1}{v}\frac{du}{dv} - \frac{u}{v^2}\right)$$

$$= 1\bigg/\left(\frac{1}{v} - \frac{u}{v^2}\frac{dv}{du}\right).$$

Thus by eq. (1),

$$w = u\left[1 - \frac{1}{v}\bigg/\left(\frac{1}{v} - \frac{u}{v^2}\frac{dv}{du}\right)\right],$$

or after some reduction,

$$\frac{1}{w} = \frac{1}{u}\left(1 - \frac{v}{u}\frac{du}{dv}\right)$$

$$= \frac{d}{dv}\left(\frac{v}{u}\right). \qquad\qquad (2)$$

This is eq. (2.11) as used in the text.

APPENDIX IV

Atomic Structure or Form Factors

In order to calculate the intensity of scattered and reflected x-rays, both from gases and crystals, two types of structure factor are useful. The first,

$$F_a = \sum_1^Z f_n = \sum_1^Z \int_0^\infty u_n(a) \frac{\sin ka}{ka} \, da, \qquad (1)$$

is called the *atomic structure factor*, and is the ratio of the amplitude of the *coherent* ray scattered by the atom to the amplitude due to a single electron. Here f_n is the structure factor for the nth electron; Z is the number of the electrons in the atom; $u_n(a)da$ is the probability that the nth electron will lie between the radii a and $a + da$ from the center of the atom, and according to quantum mechanics is given by

$$u_n(a) = 4\pi a^2 |\psi_n|^2, \qquad (2)$$

where ψ_n is Schrödinger's function for the nth quantum state. Also,

$$k = \frac{4\pi}{\lambda} \sin \tfrac{1}{2}\phi. \qquad (3)$$

The quantity F_a as evaluated from eq. (1) for any particular atom is thus a function of k, i.e., of $\sin(\phi/2)/\lambda$. The values of F_a for a large number of different atoms have been calculated and tabulated by James and Brindley,[1] based on values of ψ_n calculated by Hartree and by Thomas and Fermi. The values of F given in Table I are selected from their more extensive list, with the exception of that for krypton, which has been got by interpolation between their values, and those for xenon and mercury, which have been calculated from the formula of Thomas and Fermi (cf. text, p. 145).

The part of the incoherent scattering which is represented by the modified line in the spectrum of scattered x-rays is proportional to

$$Z - \sum_1^Z f_n^2 \qquad (4)$$

(cf. eq. (3.57)), where Z and f have the meanings assigned above.

[1] R. W. James and G. W. Brindley, Phil. Mag. **12**, 104 (1931).

Values of Σf^2 are accordingly given in Table II. These have been calculated using the f_n values listed by James and Brindley as based on Hartree's theory. It may be noted that the Thomas-Fermi atom, though giving a good approximation for the calculation of $F = \Sigma f$, does not give a good approximation for Σf^2. A method of calculat-

TABLE I

ATOMIC SCATTERING FACTORS, F *

(Based on R. W. James and G. W. Brindley, Phil. Mag. **12**, 104 (1931))

$$\frac{1}{\lambda}\sin\tfrac{1}{2}\phi$$

Element	0	0.1	0.2	0.3	0.4	0.5	0.6	0.7	0.8	0.9	1.0	1.1	Remarks
1 H	1.0	0.81	0.48	0.25	0.13	0.07	0.04	0.03	0.02	0.01	0.00	0.00	W
2 He	2.0	1.88	1.46	1.05	0.75	0.52	0.35	0.24	0.18	0.14	0.11	0.09	H
3 Li$^+$	2.0	1.96	1.8	1.5	1.3	1.0	0.8	0.6	0.5	0.4	0.3	0.3	H
3 Li	3.0	2.2	1.8	1.5	1.3	1.0	0.8	0.6	0.5	0.4	0.3	0.3	H
4 Be^{+2}	2.0	2.0	1.9	1.7	1.6	1.4	1.2	1.0	0.9	0.7	0.6	0.5	I
4 Be	4.0	2.9	1.9	1.7	1.6	1.4	1.2	1.0	0.9	0.7	0.6	0.5	I
5 B	5.0	3.5	2.4	1.9	1.7	1.5	1.4	1.2	1.2	1.0	0.9	0.7	I
6 C	6.0	4.6	3.0	2.2	1.9	1.7	1.6	1.4	1.3	1.2	1.0	0.9	I
7 N	7.0	5.8	4.2	3.0	2.3	1.9	1.65	1.55	1.5	1.4	1.3	1.15	I
8 O	8.0	7.1	5.3	3.9	2.9	2.2	1.8	1.6	1.5	1.4	1.35	1.25	H
8 O^{-2}	10.0	8.0	5.5	3.8	2.7	2.1	1.8	1.5	1.5	1.4	1.35	1.25	I + H
9 F$^-$	10.0	8.7	6.7	4.8	3.5	2.8	2.2	1.9	1.7	1.55	1.5	1.35	H
9 F	9.0	7.8	6.2	4.45	3.35	2.65	2.15	1.9	1.7	1.6	1.5	1.35	H
10 Ne	10.0	9.3	7.5	5.8	4.4	3.4	2.65	2.2	1.9	1.65	1.55	1.5	I
11 Na$^+$	10.0	9.5	8.2	6.7	5.25	4.05	3.2	2.65	2.25	1.95	1.75	1.6	H
11 Na	11.0	9.65	8.2	6.7	5.25	4.05	3.2	2.65	2.25	1.95	1.75	1.6	H
12 Mg^{+2}	10.0	9.75	8.6	7.25	6.05	4.8	3.85	3.15	2.55	2.2	2.0	1.8	I
12 Mg	12.0	10.5	8.6	7.22	6.05	4.8	3.85	3.15	2.55	2.2	2.0	1.8	I
13 Al	13.0	11.0	8.95	7.75	6.6	5.5	4.5	3.7	3.1	2.65	2.3	2.0	H + I
14 Si	14.0	11.4	9.4	8.2	7.15	6.1	5.1	4.2	3.4	2.95	2.6	2.3	H + I
15 P	15.0	12.4	10.0	8.45	7.45	6.5	5.65	4.8	4.05	3.4	3.0	2.6	I
16 S	16.0	13.6	10.7	8.95	7.85	6.85	6.0	5.25	4.5	3.9	3.35	2.9	I
17 Cl	17.0	14.6	11.3	9.25	8.05	7.25	6.5	5.75	5.05	4.4	3.85	3.35	H + I
17 Cl$^-$	18.0	15.2	11.5	9.3	8.05	7.25	6.5	5.75	5.05	4.4	3.85	3.35	H
18 A	18.0	15.9	12.6	10.4	8.7	7.8	7.0	6.2	5.4	4.7	4.1	3.6	I
19 K$^+$	18.0	16.5	13.3	10.8	8.85	7.75	7.05	6.44	5.9	5.3	4.8	4.2	H
20 Ca^{+2}	18.0	16.8	14.0	11.5	9.3	8.1	7.35	6.7	6.2	5.7	5.1	4.6	H
29 Cu	29.0	25.8	21.4	17.8	15.2	13.3	11.7	10.2	9.1	8.1	7.3	6.7	I
36 Kr	36.0	33.0	28.0	24.2	21.2	18.9	16.7	14.4	12.3	10.6	9.2	8.3	I
37 Rb$^+$	36.0	33.6	28.7	24.6	21.4	18.9	16.7	14.6	12.8	11.2	9.9	8.9	H
54 Xe	54	50	43	37	32	28	25	23	20	18	17	15	F
80 Hg	80	75	66	58	50	45	41	36	33	30	28	26	F

W = from hydrogen wave-function   I = interpolated values
H = from Hartree distribution   F = Thomas-Fermi distribution

* The symbol F is used in Chap. III of this book to represent the atomic structure factor; in the remainder of the book it is represented by f.

ing the incoherent scattering, based on this type of atom, has, however, been given by W. Heisenberg.[1]

TABLE II

INCOHERENT SCATTERING FUNCTION, Σf^2

$$\frac{1}{\lambda} \sin \tfrac{1}{2}\phi$$

Element	0	0.1	0.2	0.3	0.4	0.5	0.6	0.7	0.8	0.9	1.0	1.1
1 H	1.0	0.66	0.23	0.06	0.02	0.00	0.00	0.00	0.00	0.00	0.00	0.00
2 He	2.0	1.76	1.06	0.55	0.28	0.14	0.06	0.03	0.02	0.01	0.01	0.00
3 Li$^+$	2.0	1.9	1.6	1.1	0.8	0.5	0.2	0.1	0.1	0.05	0.0	0.00
3 Li	3.0	1.9	1.6	1.1	0.8	0.5	0.2	0.1	0.1	0.05	0.0	0.0
4 Be	4.0	2.2	1.9	1.6	1.2	0.9	0.6	0.3	0.2	0.2	0.1	0.0
5 B	5.0	3.0	2.3	1.8	1.5	1.2	0.8	0.5	0.5	0.4	0.3	0.2
6 C	6.0	4.0	2.7	1.8	1.5	1.3	1.0	0.8	0.7	0.6	0.5	0.4
7 N	7.0	5.2	3.3	1.9	1.7	1.4	1.2	1.0	0.9	0.9	0.8	0.6
8 O	8.0	6.4	3.9	2.4	2.0	1.6	1.5	1.3	1.2	1.1	0.9	0.8
8 O^{-2}	10.0	6.9	4.0	2.3	1.8	1.6	1.5	1.3	1.2	1.1	0.9	0.8
9 F	9.0	7.3	4.7	3.0	2.3	1.8	1.6	1.5	1.4	1.2	1.1	1.0
9 F$^-$	10.0	7.6	4.8	2.9	2.2	1.8	1.6	1.5	1.4	1.2	1.1	1.0
10 Ne	10.0	8.3	5.6	3.8	2.7	2.1	1.8	1.6	1.5	1.3	1.2	1.1
11 Na$^+$	10.0	9.0	6.3	4.6	3.2	2.4	2.0	1.7	1.6	1.4	1.3	1.2
11 Na	11.0	9.0	6.3	4.6	3.2	2.4	2.0	1.7	1.6	1.4	1.3	1.2
12 Mg^{+2}	10.0	9.2	7.1	5.3	3.8	2.9	2.3	1.9	1.7	1.5	1.4	1.3
12 Mg	12.0	9.6	7.1	5.3	3.8	2.9	2.3	1.9	1.7	1.5	1.4	1.3
13 Al	13.0	10.2	7.8	6.0	4.5	3.4	2.6	2.2	1.9	1.7	1.5	1.4
14 Si	14.0	10.4	8.3	6.5	5.0	3.9	3.0	2.4	2.0	1.8	1.6	1.4
17 Cl	17.0	13.1	9.7	7.8	6.5	5.4	4.4	3.6	3.0	2.5	2.2	2.0
17 Cl$^-$	18.0	13.4	9.8	7.8	6.5	5.4	4.4	3.6	3.0	2.5	2.2	2.0
18 A	18.0	14.2	10.3	8.2	6.9	5.8	4.8	4.0	3.4	2.8	2.4	2.2
19 K$^+$	18.0	15.1	10.8	8.7	7.3	6.2	5.2	4.4	3.7	3.1	2.7	2.3
20 Ca^{+2}	18.0	16.0	11.3	9.2	7.7	6.6	5.6	4.8	4.0	3.4	3.0	2.4
29 Cu	29	24	18	14	12	10	9	7	6	6	5	4
36 Kr	36	30	25	20	16	14	12	10	8	7	6	6
37 Rb$^+$	36	32	25	21	17	14	12	10	8	8	7	6
54 Xe	54	48	40	33	27	23	20	17	15	13	12	10
80 Hg	80	72	60	50	42	35	30	27	24	22	20	18

[1] W. Heisenberg, Phys. Zeits. **32**, 737 (1931). See also L. Bewilogua, Phys. Zeits. **32**, 740 (1931), for numerical calculations.

APPENDIX V

Wave-lengths of X-ray Spectrum Lines

TABLE I

Complete K Series of 13 Al, 29 Cu, and 42 Mo. Wave-lengths in Angstroms Calculated from the Uncorrected Bragg Equation Using for the Grating Space of Calcite in the First Order $d_1 = 3.02904 \times 10^{-8}$ cm.

	α_2	α_1	α'	α_3	α_4	α_5
	W		W	W	W	W
13 Al	8.3205		8.2863	8.2669	8.2512	8.2099
		B				
	$\Delta\lambda = 0.00244$					
	Wf	Wf			Wf	
29 Cu	1.541232	1.537395	....	1.53091		....
	L	L				
42 Mo	0.712105	0.707831	....	....	....	....

	α_6	β'	β_3	β_1	β''	β_x
	W	W		W		W
13 Al	8.1897	8.043	....	7.965	....	7.944
				Wf	K	
29 Cu	....	....	....	1.38935	1.38219	
			L	L		
42 Mo	....	....	0.631543	0.630978	....	....

	β_7	β_6	β_5	β_2	β_4	β'''
						D
13 Al	....	....	....	....	....	7.819; 7.789
			Wf			
29 Cu	....	....	1.37824			
	C2	C2	C1	L	C1	
42 Mo	0.62915	0.62721	0.62575	0.619698	0.61873	

References for Table I

B = Bäcklin, Zeitschr. f. Physik **33**, 547 (1925). The separation varies in different chemical compounds.

C1 = Carlsson, Zeitschr. f. Physik **80**, 604 (1933).

C2 = Carlsson, Zeitschr. f. Physik **84**, 119 (1933).

D = Druyvesteyn, Diss. Groningen (1928). The line is apparently double.

K = Kawata, Mem. Coll. Sci. Kyoto Imp. Univ. (A), **13**, 383 (1930).

L = Larsson, Phil. Mag. (7), **3**, 1136 (1927).

W = Wetterblad, Zeitschr. f. Physik **42**, 603; 611 (1927) β_x is obtained from metallic Al, β_1 from Al$_2$O$_3$.

Wf = Wennerlöf, Ark. Mat. Astr. o. Fys. Stockholm (A), **22**, No. 8 (1930). Reported in Siegbahn, Spektroskopie der Röntgenstrahlen (1931).

APPENDICES

TABLE II

WAVE-LENGTHS IN ANGSTROMS OF K SERIES LINES REPRESENTING TRANSITIONS IN THE
ORDINARY X-RAY ENERGY LEVEL DIAGRAM * ALLOWED BY THE SELECTION PRINCIPLES

Siegbahn Sommerfeld Transition	$K\alpha_2$ $K\alpha'$ $K-L_{II}$	$K\alpha_1$ $K\alpha$ $K-L_{III}$	$K\beta_3$ $K\beta'$ $K-M_{II}$	$K\beta_1$ $K\beta$ $K-M_{III}$	$K\beta_2$ $K\gamma$ $K-N_{II}N_{III}$	Reference
4 Be	115.7					Sö
5 B	67.71					Sö
6 C	44.54					Sö
7 N	31.557					Sö
8 O	23.567					Sö
9 F	18.275					Sö
11 Na	11.885		11.594			W
12 Mg	9.869		9.539			W
13 Al	8.3205		7.965			W
14 Si	7.11106		6.7545			L1; B
15 P	6.1425		5.7921			H1; L, L
16 S	5.3637	5.3613	5.0211			H2; S, D; L, L
17 Cl	4.7212	4.7182	4.3942			S, D; D; L, L
19 K	3.73707	3.73368	3.4468			S, D
20 Ca	3.35495	3.35169	3.0834			S, D
21 Sc	3.02840	3.02503	2.7739			S, D
22 Ti	2.74681	2.74317	2.5090			S, D
23 Va	2.50213	2.49835	2.2797			S, D
24 Cr	2.28891	2.28503	2.0806			E
25 Mn	2.10149	2.09751	1.90620			E
26 Fe	1.936012	1.932076	1.753013			E
27 Co	1.78919	1.78529	1.61744			E
28 Ni	1.65835	1.65450	1.47905	1.48561		E
29 Cu	1.541232	1.537395	1.38935	1.37824		Wf
30 Zn	1.43603	1.43217	1.29255	1.28107		Ed
31 Ga	1.34087	1.33715	1.20520	1.1938		U, C
32 Ge	1.25521	1.25130	1.12671	1.11459		Ld
33 As	1.17743	1.17344	1.05510	1.04281		Ed
34 Se	1.10652	1.10248	0.99013	0.97791		Ed
35 Br	1.04166	1.03759	0.93087	0.91853		Ed
36 Kr	0.9821	0.9781	0.8767		0.8643	C, H
37 Rb	0.92776	0.92364	0.82749	0.82696	0.81476	Ed
38 Sr	0.87761	0.87345	0.78183	0.78130	0.76921	Ed
39 Y	0.83132	0.82712	0.73972	0.73919	0.72713	Ed
40 Zr	0.78851	0.78430	0.70083	0.70028	0.68850	Ed
41 Cb	0.74889	0.74465	0.66496	0.66438	0.65280	Ed
42 Mo	0.712105	0.707831	0.631543	0.630978	0.619698	L2
43 Ma	0.675	0.672	0.601			B, T
44 Ru	0.64606	0.64174	0.57193	0.57131	0.56051	Ed
45 Rh	0.61637	0.61202	0.54509	0.54449	0.53396	En
46 Pd	0.58863	0.58427	0.52009	0.51947	0.50918	K
47 Ag	0.56267	0.55828	0.49665	0.49601	0.48603	K
48 Cd	0.53832	0.53390	0.47471	0.47408	0.46420	V
49 In	0.51548	0.51106	0.45423	0.45358	0.44408	V
50 Sn	0.49402	0.48957	0.43495	0.43430	0.42499	St
51 Sb	0.47387	0.46931	0.41623		0.40710	Ld
52 Te	0.45491	0.45037	0.39926		0.39037	Ld
53 I	0.43703	0.43249	0.38392	0.38315	0.37471	Ld
54 Xe	0.417		0.360			Dv
55 Cs	0.40411	0.39959	0.35436	0.35360	0.34516	Ld; C, S
56 Ba	0.38899	0.38443	0.34089	0.34022	0.33222	Ld; C, S
57 La	0.37466	0.37004	0.32809	0.32726	0.31966	Ld; C, S

TABLE II—*Continued*

Siegbahn Sommerfeld Transition	$K\alpha_2$ $K\alpha'$ $K\text{-}L_{II}$	$K\alpha_1$ $K\alpha$ $K\text{-}L_{III}$	$K\beta_3$ $K\beta'$ $K\text{-}M_{II}$	$K\beta_1$ $K\beta$ $K\text{-}M_{III}$	$K\beta_2$ $K\gamma$ $K\text{-}N_{II}N_{III}$	Reference
58 Ce	0.36110	0.35647	0.31572	0.31501	0.30770	Ld; C, S
59 Pr	0.34805	0.34340	0.30439	0.30360	0.29625	C, S
60 Nd	0.33595	0.33125	0.29351	0.29275	0.28573	Ld; C, S
62 Sa	0.31302	0.30833	0.27325	0.27250	0.26575	Ld; C, S
63 Eu	0.30265	0.29790	0.26386	0.26307	0.25645	Ld; C, S
64 Gd	0.29261	0.28782	0.25471	0.25394	0.24762	Ld; C, S
65 Tb	0.28286	0.27820	0.24629	0.24551	0.23912	Ld; C, S
66 Dy	0.27375	0.26903	0.23787	0.23710	0.23128	Ld; C, S
67 Ho	0.26499	0.26030	......	......	......	Ld
68 Er	0.25664	0.25197	0.22300	0.22215	0.21671	Ld; C, S
69 Tu	0.24861	0.24387	0.21558	0.21487	......	C, S
70 Yb	0.24098	0.23628	0.20916	0.20834	0.20322	Ld; C, S
71 Lu	0.23358	0.22882	0.20252	0.20171	0.19649	C, S
72 Hf	0.22653	0.22173	0.19583	0.19515	0.19042	C, S
73 Ta	0.21973	0.21488	0.18991		0.18452	C, S
74 W	0.21337	0.20856	0.18475	0.18397	0.17906	Wm
76 Os	0.20131	0.19645	0.17361		0.16875	C, S
77 Ir	0.19550	0.19065	0.16850		0.16376	C, S
78 Pt	0.19004	0.18223	0.16370		0.15887	C, S
79 Au	0.18483	0.17996	0.15902		0.15426	C, S
81 Tl	0.17466	0.16980	0.15011		0.14539	C, S
82 Pb	0.17004	0.16516	0.14606		0.14125	C, S
83 Bi	0.16525	0.16041	0.14205		0.13621	C, S; R
92 U	0.13095	0.12640	0.11187		0.10842	R

* This criterion cannot be strictly applied to the $K\alpha$ line from 4 Be to 9 F, nor to the $K\beta_1$ line from 11 Na to 29 Cu as reported in this table.

References:

B = Bäcklin, Zeitschr. f. Physik **33**, 547 (1925).

B, T = Berg and Tacke, Naturwiss. **13**, 571 (1925).

C, H = Cauchois and Hulubei, Compt. rend. **196**, 1590 (1933).

C, S = Cork and Stephenson, Phys. Rev. (2), **27**, 103; 530 (1926).

Dv = Dauvillier, Compt. rend. **191**, 937 (1930).

D = Dolejsek, Compt. rend. **174**, 441 (1922).

Ed = Edlén, Zeitschr. f. Physik **52**, 364 (1928).

En = Enger, Zeitschr. f. Physik **46**, 826 (1928).

E = Eriksson, Zeitschr. f. Phys. **48**, 360 (1928).

H1 = Hjalmar, Zeitschr. f. Physik **1**, 489 (1920).

H2 = Hjalmar, Zeitschr. f. Physik **7**, 341 (1921).

K = Kellström, Zeitschr. f. Physik **41**, 516 (1927).

L1 = Larsson, Uppsala Univ. Arsk. (1929).

L2 = Larsson, Phil. Mag. (7), **3**, 1136 (1927).

Ld = Leide, Compt. rend. **180**, 1203 (1925) and Diss. Lund. 1925.

L, L = Lindh and Lundquist, Ark. Mat. Astr. o. Fys **18**, 14, 3 (1924); Zeitschr. f. Phys. **33**, 901 (1925).

R = Réchou, Compt. rend. **180**, 1107 (1925).

S, D = Siegbahn and Dolejsek, Zeitschr. f. Phys. **10**, 159 (1922).

Sö = Södermann, Zeitschr. f. Phys. **52**, 795 (1929), Phil. Mag. **1**, 600 (1930).

St = Stenström, Zeitschr. f. Phys. **48**, 349 (1928).

U, C = Uhler and Cooksey, Phys. Rev. **10**, 645 (1917).

V = Valasek, Phys. Rev, **34**, 1231 (1929).

Wf = Wennerlöf, Ark. Mat. Astr. o. Fys (A), **22**, No. 8 (1930).

W = Wetterblad, Zeitschr. f. Phys. **42**, 603; 611 (1927).

Wm = Williams, Phys. Rev. **40**, 791 (1932); Hudson and Vogt, Proc. Nat. Acad. Sci. U. S. A, **19**, 444 (1933), resolve $K\beta_2$, $\Delta\lambda = 0.00018$ A.

TABLE III

THE COMPLETE L SPECTRUM OF 29 Cu, 47 Ag, AND 74 W WITH THE EXCEPTION OF SPARK LINES

Line	Transition	29 Cu	47 Ag	74 W
l	$L_{III}-M_I$	15.26^K	4.6976^C	1.6750^F
t	$L_{III}-M_{II}$	....	....	1.6216^D
s	$L_{III}-M_{III}$	....	....	1.5610^D
α_2	$L_{III}-M_{IV}$	$\}\ 13.306^K\ \{$	4.15430^H	1.48438^F
α_1	$L_{III}-M_V$		4.14575^H	1.47336^F
η	$L_{II}-M_I$	14.87^K	4.4101^C	1.4181^F
β_4	L_I-M_{II}	12.07^K	3.8611^{HJ}	1.29879^F
β_6	$L_{III}-N_I$	....	3.7986^C	1.2870^F
β_1	$L_{II}-M_V$	13.027^K	3.92650^H	1.27917^F
β_3	L_I-M_{III}	12.07^K	3.8245^{HJ}	1.25992^F
β_{15}	$L_{III}-N_{IV}$	....	....	1.2439^I
β_2	$L_{III}-N_V$	....	3.69560^H	1.24203^F
β_7	$L_{III}-O_I$	....	....	1.2217^I
u	$L_{III}-N_{VI}N_{VII}$	....	.. ..	1.2161^I
β_5	$L_{III}-O_{IV}O_V$	....	....	1.2129^l
β_{10}	L_I-M_{IV}	....	3.630^C	1.2096^I
β_9	L_I-M_V	....	3.620^C	1.2023^I
γ_5	$L_{II}-N_I$	....	3.6073^C	1.1298^I
γ_1	$L_{II}-N_{IV}$	....	3.51545^H	1.09630^F
γ_8	$L_{II}-O_I$	....	....	1.0791^I
v	$L_{II}-N_{VI}N_{VII}$	....	....	1.0752^I
γ_6	$L_{II}-O_{IV}$	....	....	1.0721^I
γ_2	L_I-N_{II}	....	$\}\ 3.2998^C$	1.06588^F
γ_3	L_I-N_{III}	....		1.05987^F
γ_{11}	L_I-N_V	....	....	1.0437^I
γ_4	$L_I-O_{II}O_{III}$	....	....	1.0258^F

References:

C = Coster, Phil. Mag. **44**, 545 (1922), and Coster and Mulder, Zeitschr. f. Phys. **38**, 264 (1926); also Coster, Phil. Mag. **43**, 1070 (1922).

D = Dauvillier, Compt. rend. **174**, 1347 (1922).

F = Friman, Zeitschr. f. Phys. **39**, 813 (1926).

H = Haglund, Zeitschr. f. Phys. **84**, 248 (1933).

Hj = Hjalmar, Zeitschr. f. Phys. **7**, 341 (1921)

I = Idei, Sci. Rep. Tohoku Imp. Univ. **19**, 559 (1930).

K = Karlsson, Ark. Mat. Astr. o. Fys, Stockholm (A) **22**, No. 9 (1930).

TABLE IV

Wave-lengths of the More Prominent L Group Lines in Angstroms

Siegbahn Sommerfeld Transition	α_2 α' $L_{III}-M_{IV}$	α_1 α $L_{III}-M_V$	β_1 β $L_{II}-M_V$	l ϵ $L_{III}-M_I$	η η $L_{II}-M_I$	Authority
16 S	......	......		83.75		P, T
20 Ca	36.27			40.90	......	K
21 Sc	31.37			35.71	......	K
22 Ti	27.37			31.33	......	K
23 Va	24.31			27.70	......	H
24 Cr	21.53	21.19		23.84	23.28	Kn
25 Mn	19.40	19.04		22.34	......	K; Kn
26 Fe	17.57	17.23		20.09	19.76	Kn
27 Co	15.93	15.63		18.25	17.86	Kn
28 Ni	14.53	14.25		16.66	16.28	Kn
29 Cu	13.306	13.027		15.26	14.87	Kn
30 Zn	12.229	11.960		13.97	13.61	Kn
31 Ga	11.27	11.01		12.89	12.56	T
32 Ge	10.415	10.153		11.922	11.587	Hj; S, Th
33 As	9.652	9.395		11.048	10.711	Hj; S, Th
34 Se	8.972	8.718		10.272	9.939	Th
35 Br	8.358	8.109		9.564	9.235	Hj; T
37 Rb	7.3027	......		......	......	R, R; Hj
38 Sr	6.8486	6.610		7.822	7.506	Hj
39 Y	6.4357	6.2039		......	7.0310	C

Siegbahn Sommerfeld Transition	α_2 α' $L_{III}-M_{IV}$	α_1 α $L_{III}-M_V$	β_1 β $L_{II}-M_V$	β_2 γ $L_{III}-N_V$	γ_1 δ $L_{II}-N_{IV}$	Authority
40 Zr	6.057		5.8236	5.5742	5.3738	Hj; C
41 Cb	5.718	5.7120	5.4803	5.2260	5.0248	Hj; C
42 Mo	5.401	5.3950	5.1665	4.9100	......	Hj; C
44 Ru	4.8437	4.8357	4.6110	4.3619	4.1728	Hj; C
45 Rh	4.5956	4.5878	4.3640	4.1221	3.9357	Hj; C
46 Pd	4.3666	4.3585	4.1373	3.9007	3.7164	Hj; C
47 Ag	4.1538	4.1456	3.9266	3.6938	3.5149	Hj
48 Cd	3.9564	3.9478	3.7301	3.5064	3.3280	Hj; C
49 In	3.7724	3.7637	3.5478	3.3312	3.1553	Hj; C
50 Sn	3.60151	3.59257	3.3779	3.16861	2.99494	Wf
51 Sb	3.4408	3.4318	3.2184	3.0166	2.8451	Hj; C
52 Te	3.2910	3.2820	3.0700	2.8761	2.7065	Hj; C
53 I	3.1509	3.1417	2.9309	2.7461	2.5775	Hj
55 Cs	2.8956	2.8861	2.6778	2.5064	2.3425	Hj; C
56 Ba	2.7790	2.7696	2.5622	2.3993	2.2366	Hj
57 La	2.6689	2.6597	2.4533	2.2980	2.1372	Hj; C
58 Ce	2.5651	2.5560	2.3510	2.2041	2.0443	Hj; C
59 Pr	2.4676	2.4577	2.2539	2.1148	1.9568	Hj; C

TABLE IV—(*Continued*)

Siegbahn Sommerfeld Transition	α_2 α' $L_{III}-M_{IV}$	α_1 α $L_{III}-M_V$	β_1 β $L_{II}-M_V$	β_2 γ $L_{III}-N_V$	γ_1 δ $L_{II}-N_V$	Authority
60 Nd	2.3756	2.3653	2.1622	2.0314	1.8738	Hj; C
62 Sa	2.2057	2.1950	1.9936	1.8781	1.7231	Hj; C
63 Eu	2.1273	2.1163	1.9163	1.8082	1.6543	Hj; C
64 Gd	2.0526	2.0419	1.8425	1.7419	1.5886	Hj; C
65 Tb	1.9823	1.9715	1.7727	1.6790	1.5266	Hj; C
66 Dy	1.9156	1.9046	1.7066	1.6198	1.4697	Hj; C
67 Ho	1.8521	1.8410	1.6435	1.5637	1.4142	Hj; C
68 Er	1.79202	1.78068	1.58409	1.51094	1.3611	Wf
69 Tu	1.7339	1.7228	1.5268	1.4602	1.3127	C
70 Yb	1.67942	1.66844	1.4725	1.41261	1.26512	C; Wf
71 Lu	1.6270	1.61617	1.42067	1.36731	1.21974	Wf
72 Hf	1.57704	1.56607	1.3711	1.3235	1.1765	C'
73 Ta	1.52978	1.51885	1.32423	1.28190	1.13558	Wf
74 W	1.48438	1.47336	1.27917	1.24203	1.09630	F
75 Re	1.4410	1.42997	1.23603	1.2041	1.0587	B; Wf
76 Os	1.39866	1.38859	1.19490	1.16884	1.02296	L
77 Ir	1.3598	1.34847	1.15540	1.13297	0.98876	F
78 Pt	1.32155	1.31033	1.11758	1.09974	0.95599	F
79 Au	1.28502	1.27377	1.08128	1.06801	0.92461	F
80 Hg	1.24951	1.23863	1.04652	1.03770	0.8946	F; E, T
81 Tl	1.21626	1.20493	1.01299	1.00822	0.86571	F; I
82 Pb	1.18408	1.17258	0.98083	0.98083	0.83801	F; I
83 Bi	1.15301	1.14150	0.95002	0.95324	0.81143	F; I
90 Th	0.96585	0.95405	0.76356	0.79192	0.65176	F; I
91 Pa	0.9427	0.9309	0.7407	0.7721	0.6325	B; v. G
92 U	0.92062	0.90874	0.71851	0.75307	0.61359	F; I

References:

B = Beuthe, Zeitschr. f. Phys. **46**, 873 (1928).
B, v. G = Beuthe and von Grosse, Zeitschr. f. Phys. **60**, 603 (1930).
C = Coster, Phil. Mag. **44**, 545; **43**, 1070 (1922); Coster and Mulder, Zeitschr. f. Phys. **38**, 264 (1926).
C' = Coster, Phil. Mag. **46**, 956 (1923).
E, T = Eddy and Turner, Proc. Roy. Soc. Lond. A **111**, 117 (1926).
F = Friman, Zeitschr. f. Physik **39**, 813 (1926).
Hj = Hjalmar, Zeitschr. f. Phys. **7**, 341 (1921).
H = Howe, Phys. Rev. **37**, 717 (1930).
I = Idei, Sci. Rep. Tohoku Imp. Univ. **19**, 559 (1930).
Kn = Karlsson, Ark. Mat. Astr. o. Fys, Stockholm A **22**, No. 9 (1930).
K = Kellström, Zeitschr. f. Physik, **58**, 511 (1929). Grating measurement.
L = Lang, Annalen der Physik (4), **75**, 489 (1924).
P, T = Prins and Takens, Zeitschr. f. Physik, **77**, 795 (1932).
R, R = F. K. and R. D. Richtmyer, Phys. Rev. **34**, 574 (1929).
S, Th = Siegbahn and Thoraeus, Ark. Mat. Astr. o. Fys, Stockholm **18**, 19 (1924).
Th = Thoraeus, Phil. Mag. (7), **2**, 1007 (1926).
T = van der Tuuk, Zeitschr. f. Physik **41**, 326 (1927).
Wf = Wennerlöf, Zeitschr. f. Physik, **41**, 524 (1927); Ark. Mat. Astr. o. Fys. Stockholm, A **22**, No. 8 (1930).

TABLE V

Wave-lengths of M Series Lines in Angstroms from 73 Ta to 92 U *

Transition	73 Ta	74 W	75 Re	76 Os	77 Ir	78 Pt	79 Au	81 Tl	82 Pb	83 Bi	90 Th	92 U
$M_{II}O_{IV}$	....	....	....	....	....	....	....	....	....	....	2.613	2.440
$M_{I}N_{III}$	....	5.163	....	....	....	4.451	4.291	4.005	3.864	3.732	2.938	2.745
$M_{II}N_{IV}$	5.558	5.342	....	4.944	4.770	4.590	4.424	4.110	3.964	3.829	3.006	2.813
$M_{III}O_{V}$	....	....	....	....	4.859	4.682	4.514	4.207	4.063	3.926	3.124	2.941
$M_{III}O_{I}$	....	5.620	....	....	....	....	....	....	4.235	4.096	....	3.114
$M_{II}N_{I}$	....	....	....	....	....	....	....	....	....	....	....	3.322
γ'	....	....	....	....	....	....	....	4.800	4.650	4.506	3.661	3.463
$M_{III}N_{V}$	6.299	6.076	5.875	5.670	5.490	5.309	5.135	4.815	4.665	4.522	3.672	3.473
$M_{III}N_{IV}$	6.340	6.121	5.919	5.712	5.529	5.346	5.175	4.855	4.705	4.560	3.710	3.514
$M_{IV}O_{II}$	7.083	6.794	....	....	....	....	....	....	....	4.813	3.804	3.570
β'	6.984	6.718	....	6.233	6.009	5.796	5.595	5.220	5.045	4.881	3.924	3.698
$M_{IV}N_{VI}$	7.008	6.743	6.491	6.254	6.025	5.816	5.612	5.239	5.065	4.899	3.934	3.708
$M_{V}O_{III}$	....	....	....	....	....	5.975	5.755	....	....	....	....	....
α''	7.201	6.932	....	6.440	6.215	5.997	5.794	5.416	5.239	....	....	....
α'	7.219	6.948	....	6.459	6.231	6.011	5.811	5.433	5.256	5.087	4.112	3.886
$M_{V}N_{VII}$	7.237	6.969	6.715	6.477	6.249	6.034	5.828	5.450	5.274	5.108	4.130	3.902
$M_{V}N_{VI}$	....	....	....	....	6.262	6.045	5.842	5.461	5.288	5.119	4.143	3.916
$M_{III}N_{I}$	7.596	7.346	....	....	6.653	6.442	6.241	5.870	5.694	5.526	4.554	4.322
$M_{IV}N_{III}$	....	8.559	8.222	....	7.629	7.356	7.086	....	6.371	6.149	4.901	4.615
$M_{V}N_{III}$	9.297	8.943	8.612	8.293	8.002	7.722	7.451	6.960	6.726	6.508	5.229	4.937
$M_{IV}N_{II}$	9.311	8.977	8.646	8.344	8.048	7.774	7.507	7.017	6.788	6.571	5.329	5.040

* E. Lindberg, Dissertation, Uppsala (1931). In addition to the values listed here, measurements have been made in the range from Ce 58 to 72 Hf. These wave-lengths may be found in the dissertation, or in Siegbahn, Spektroskopie der Röntgenstrahlen, (1931).

It has been found that transitions between the various N levels occur with sufficient frequency to be detected. This is in contradiction to the empirical rule, observed in x-ray spectra, that the total quantum number must change in an observable transition. The existence of lines in which the total quantum number does not change is discussed in the treatment of selection principles in Chap. VIII.

TABLE VI

WAVE-LENGTHS OF N SERIES LINES IN ANGSTROMS

Thibaud and Soltan	Journal de Physique **8**, 484 (1927)
C. del Rosario	Physical Review **41**, 136 (1932)
T. Magnusson	Zeitschrift für Physik **79**, 161 (1932)
Prins and Takens	Zeitschrift für Physik **77**, 795 (1932)

Element	Transition	Thibaud and Soltan	del Rosario	Prins and Takens	Magnusson
73 Ta	$N_{IV}-N_{VI}$	58.3	58.3	....	58.1
73 Ta	$N_V-N_{VI, VII}$	61.4	61.3	....	61.0
74 W	$N_{IV}-N_{VI}$	56.0	56.0	....	55.8
74 W	$N_V-N_{VI, VII}$	59.1	59.0	....	58.5
76 Os	$N_{IV}-N_{VI}$	....	....	....	51.8
76 Os	$N_V-N_{VI, VII}$	....	....	....	54.6
77 Ir	$N_{IV}-N_{VI}$	....	....	50.00	50.1
77 Ir	$N_V-N_{VI, VII}$	....	53.0	52.54	52.8
78 Pt	$N_{IV}-N_{VI}$	48.0	....	....	48.0
78 Pt	$N_V-N_{VI, VII}$	51.0	....	....	50.9
79 Au	$N_{IV}-N_{VI}$	46.8	46.2	....	46.8
79 Au	$N_V-N_{VI, VII}$	49.4	48.9	....	49.4
80 Hg	$N_{IV}-N_{VI}$	....	43.6		
80 Hg	$N_V-N_{VI, VII}$	....	46.4		
81 Tl	$N_V-N_{VI, VII}$	....	....	....	46.6

APPENDIX VI

The Critical Absorption Wave-lengths of the Elements

The critical absorption wave-lengths shown in this table are, with certain exceptions, those which have been directly obtained from absorption measurements by standard x-ray methods. The exceptions are cases in which the values are known as series limits of optical spectra, which for the present classification we may consider to include the ultra-violet. Thus it is known that the terms in the spectrum of Ne I converge to two limits, which are the terms arising from the configuration $1s^2\,2s^2 2p^5$ of Ne II. These are the L_{II} and L_{III} terms of neon. Similarly the term arising from $1s^2\,2s$ of Be II is known and correctly interpreted as L_I of 4 Be.

Cases such as $1s^2\,2s^2 2p^5\,3s$, of Na II, in which the terms arising from the configuration are known, were excluded from the table, although in a certain sense it might be said that $L_{II}L_{III}$ of sodium arise from this configuration. Actually, the coupling between the $3s$ and the $2p$ electrons is sufficient to split the doublet which would arise in the absence of this $3s$ electron into four terms, of J values 2, 1, 1, 0. These are not given in the table on the ground that they are too far removed from the doublet types to which bona fide x-ray terms closely approximate.

TABLE I

CRITICAL ABSORPTION WAVE-LENGTHS IN ANGSTROMS

	K	L_I	L_{II}	L_{III}	M_I	M_{II}	M_{III}	M_{IV}	M_V	Longer Wave-lengths
1 H										
2 He	504.29 [10]									
3 Li		1329.89 [10]								
4 Be	64.37 [7]									
5 B	43.5 [8]									
6 C	31.1 [8]									
7 N	23.5 [8]									
8 O	18.0 [7]									
9 F										
10 Ne		255.77 [10]	572.4 [10]	574.9 [10]						
11 Na										
12 Mg	9.4962 [1]				1621.48 [10]					
13 Al	7.9356 [1]			181 [7]						
14 Si	6.7310 [2]			126 [7]						
15 P	5.7749 [2]			96.4 [7]						
16 S	5.0088 [2]			75.7 [7]						
17 Cl	4.3838 [2]			60.9 [7]						
18 A	3.8657 [3]			50.1 [7]	424.03 [10]	778.0 [10]	786.8 [10]			
19 K	3.4310 [2]									
20 Ca	3.0643 [2]			35.63 [9]						N_I 2028.20 [10]
21 Sc	2.7517 [3]									
22 Ti	2.4912 [3]			27.29 [9]						
23 Va	2.2630 [2]									
24 Cr	2.0659 [1]									
25 Mn	1.8916 [1]									
26 Fe	1.7394 [1]									
27 Co	1.6040 [1]									
28 Ni	1.4839 [1]									
29 Cu	1.3774 [1]		12.9 [9]	13.15 [9]				708.18 [10]	722.08 [10]	N_I 1319.84 [10]
30 Zn	1.2805 [1]									
31 Ga	1.1902 [4]									
32 Ge	1.1164 [4]									
33 As	1.04263 [5]									
34 Se	0.97773 [5]									
35 Br	0.91809 [5]									
36 Kr	0.86372 [12]									N_{II} 845.42 [10] N_{III} 855.63 [10]

37 Rb	0.81410 [5]	5.9854 [6]	....	6.8413 [6]						*O*I		
38 Sr	0.76837 [5]	5.5713 [6]	6.1621 [6]	6.3620 [6]	....	....	....	....	....	2177.46 [10]		
39 Y	0.7255 [4]	5.2216 [6]	5.7373 [6]	5.9444 [6]								
40 Zr	0.68738 [5]	4.8574 [6]	5.3659 [6]	5.5610 [6]								
41 Cb	0.65158 [5]	4.5717 [6]	....	5.2121 [6]								
42 Mo	0.61848 [5]	4.2897 [6]	4.7120 [6]	4.9042 [6]								
43 Ma												
44 Ru	0.5584 [4]	....	4.1648 [18]	4.3577 [18]								
45 Rh	0.53303 [5]	3.61860 [18]	3.9340 [18]	4.1212 [18]						*N*IV	*N*V	
46 Pd	0.50795 [5]	3.4206 [18]	3.7512 [18]	3.9005 [18]	....	....	....	....	....	1412.93 [32]	1487.30 [32]	
47 Ag	0.48448 [14]	3.2474 [18]	3.5067 [18]	3.6908 [18]	....	....	....	30.82 [9]	31.14 [9]	*N*V	*N*VI	*O*I
48 Cd	0.46313 [5]	3.0773 [18]	3.3192 [18]	3.4963 [18]	....	....	....	28.13 [9]		678.28 [10]	705.23 [10]	1378.57 [10]
49 In	0.44298 [5]	2.9194 [18]	3.1395 [18]	3.3155 [18]								
50 Sn	0.42394 [5]	2.7696 [18]	2.9723 [18]	3.1493 [18]	....	....	....	24.28 [9]				
51 Sb	0.40609 [5]	2.6317 [19]	2.8219 [19]	2.9907 [19]								
52 Te	0.38926 [5]	2.5039 [19]	2.6793 [19]	2.8457 [19]								
53 I	0.37344 [5]	2.3839 [19]	2.5475 [19]	2.7139 [19]	....	....	....	19.66 [9]		*O*II, III		
54 Xe	0.35777 [13]	2.2691 [12]	2.4241 [12]	2.5872 [12]	....	....	....	....	....	1022.13 [10]		
55 Cs	0.34404 [5]	2.1605 [20]	2.3073 [20]	2.4678 [20]						*P*I		
56 Ba	0.33070 [5]	2.0620 [21]	2.1993 [21]	2.3568 [21]	....	....	....	15.56 [9]	15.89 [9]	2379.29 [10]		
57 La	0.31814 [5]	1.9689 [22]	2.0989 [22]	2.2537 [22]								
58 Ce	0.30626 [5]	1.8856 [22]	2.0067 [22]	2.1579 [22]								
59 Pr	0.2951 [15]	1.808 [21]	1.9197 [21]	2.0727 [21]								
60 Nd	0.28458 [5]	1.7317 [21]	1.8391 [21]	1.9907 [21]								
61 Il												
62 Sm	0.2644 [15]	1.5954 [21]	1.6991 [21]	1.8408 [21]								
63 Eu	0.2548 [15]	1.5333 [21]	1.6228 [21]	1.7717 [21]								
64 Gd	0.2462 [15]	1.4740 [21]	1.5587 [22]	1.7062 [22]								
65 Tb	0.2376 [15]	1.4181 [21]	1.4981 [21]	1.6453 [21]								
66 Dy	0.2301 [15]	1.3648 [22]	1.4414 [22]	1.5870 [22]								
67 Ho	0.22264 [5]	1.3146 [21]	1.3869 [21]	1.5322 [21]								
68 Er	....	1.2660 [22]	1.3349 [22]	1.4796 [22]								
69 Tu	0.2085 [15]	1.2196 [22]	1.2849 [22]	1.4299 [22]								
70 Yb	0.2016 [15]	1.1764 [25]	1.2381 [25]	1.38264 [25]								
71 Lu	0.1951 [15]	1.1362 [22]	1.1945 [22]	1.3377 [22]								
72 Hf	0.1901 [15]	1.097 [24]	1.1515 [24]	1.2930 [24]								
73 Ta	0.1836 [15]	1.057 [21]	1.1102 [21]	1.2517 [21]								
74 W	0.17822 [16]	1.0205 [21]	1.0713 [21]	1.2116 [21]	4.365 [28]	4.800 [28]	5.427 [29]	6.487 [29]	6.702 [29]			
75 Re	0.1735 [17]	0.9873 [26]	1.0354 [26]	1.1755 [26]								
76 Os	0.16755 [16]	0.9558 [26]	0.9998 [26]	1.1390 [26]	4.037 [30]	4.412 [30]	5.027 [30]	5.975 [30]	6.194 [30]			

TABLE I—*Continued*

	K	L_I	L_{II}	L_{III}	M_I	M_{II}	M_{III}	M_{IV}	M_V	Longer Wave-lengths
77 Ir	0.16209 [16]	0.9223 [26]	0.9654 [26]	1.1038 [26]		4.270 [30]	4.851 [30]	5.754 [30]	5.961 [30]	
78 Pt	0.15770 [16]	0.8914 [26]	0.9321 [26]	1.0710 [26]		3.738 [30]	4.676 [29]	5.544 [29]	5.746 [29]	
79 Au	0.15320 [16]	0.8622 [26]	0.9009 [26]	1.0382 [26]	3.603 [31]	4.085 [31]	4.508 [29]	5.330 [29]	5.529 [29]	
80 Hg	0.14893 [16]	0.8342 [26]	0.8768 [26]	1.0075 [26]	3.742 [31]		4.340 [29]	5.139 [29]	5.331 [29]	O_{IV} 742.22 [10]
81 Tl	0.14441 [16]	0.8072 [26]	0.8419 [26]	0.9778 [26]			4.184 [29]	4.936 [29]	5.136 [29]	O_V 835.47 [10] P_I 1187.95 [10]
82 Pb	0.14049 [16]	0.7812 [26]	0.8143 [26]	0.9492 [26]			4.034 [29]	4.747 [29]	4.945 [29]	
83 Bi	0.13678 [16]	0.7559 [26]	0.7878 [26]	0.9221 [26]			3.893 [29]	4.568 [29]	4.762 [29]	
84 Po	....									
85	....									$P_{II\ III}$ 1153.52 [10]
86 Rn	....									
87	....									
88 Ra	....	....	0.670 [27]	0.802 [27]						
89 Ac										
90 Th	0.11270 [16]	0.6039 [26]	0.6293 [26]	0.7600 [26]	2.388 [24]	2.571 [24]	3.062 [29]	3.550 [29]	3.722 [29]	
91 Pa										
92 U	0.10658 [16]	0.5680 [26]	0.5913 [26]	0.7208 [26]	2.228 [24]	2.385 [24]	2.877 [29]	2.327 [29]	3.491 [29]	

REFERENCES

1 Åse, reported in Siegbahn, Spektroskopie der Röntgenstrahlen (1931).
2 Lindh, Ark. Mat. Astr. o. Fys., Stockholm, 18, 14 (1924).
3 Fricke, Phys. Rev. 15, 202 (1920).
4 Duane, Blake, and Hu, from W. Duane, Bull. Nat. Res. Counc. U.S.A. 1, 6 (1920).
5 Leide, Dissertation, Lund (1925).
6 Coster and Mulder, Zeitschr. f. Physik 38, 264 (1926).
7 Holweck, De la Lumière aux Rayons-X, Paris (1927).
8 Thibaud, Journ. de Physique et le Rad. 8, 13; 447 (1927).
9 J. A. Prins and A. J. Takens, Zeitschr. f. Physik 84, 65 (1933).
10 Bacher and Goudsmit, Atomic Energy States, McGraw-Hill (1932).
12 J. D. Hanawalt, Phys. Rev. 37, 715 (1931).
13 Cauchois and Hulubei, Compt. rend. 197, 644 (1933).
14 F. Enger, Zeitschr. f. Physik 46, 826 (1928).
15 Cabrera, Compt. rend. 176, 740 (1923).

16 Mack and Cork, Phys. Rev. 30, 741 (1927).
17 Polland, Compt. rend. 183, 737 (1926).
18 van Dyke and Lindsay, Phys. Rev. 29, 205; 30, 562 (1927).
19 Chamberlain and Lindsay, Phys. Rev. 30, 369 (1927).
20 Lindsay, Compt. rend. 175, 150 (1922).
21 Nishina, Phil. Mag. 49, 521 (1925).
22 Coster, Nishina, and Werner, Zeitschr. f. Physik 18, 207 (1923).
23 Hertz, Zeitschr. f. Physik 3, 19 (1920).
24 Coster, Phil. Mag. 44, 545; 1070 (1922).
25 Eddy, Proc. Roy. Soc. Melbourne, July, 1925.
26 Sandström, Zeitschr. f. Physik 65, 632 (1930).
27 de Broglie, Compt. rend. 168, 854 (1919).
28 Zumstein, Phys. Rev. 25, 106 (1925).
29 Lindberg, Zeitschr. f. Physik 54, 632 (1929).
30 Rogers, Phys. Rev. 29, 205; 30, 747 (1927).
31 Johnson, Phys. Rev. 34, 1106 (1929).

APPENDIX VII

Terms in the X-ray Spectra of 13 Al, 20 Ca, 29 Cu, 42 Mo, 47 Ag, 74 W and 92 U

In constructing a term table, it is best to use the combination principle in such a way as to depend upon the smallest possible number of absorption measurements, since these are less accurate than wave-length measurements of lines.[1] In the term table for uranium, given below, the L_{III} term is located from the measurements of the L_{III} absorption limit reported in the table of critical absorption wave-lengths. The other terms are located by means of the combination principle, using wave-lengths of uranium lines. A similar procedure is followed in tungsten. In silver, the measured K absorption wave-length is used to locate the K term. The terms L_{II} and L_{III} are then found by means of the measured wave-lengths of the Ag $K\alpha$ lines. Since screening doublets do not appear in the x-ray emission spectrum, the term L_I is located by applying the observed ν/R difference between L_I and L_{III} found in absorption experiments to the L_{III} term located as above. The other terms may then be found from emission wave-lengths. A similar procedure has been followed in molybdenum and the lighter elements. The L_I levels of 92 U and 74 W can be located with respect to L_{III} by combining lines in the L and M group.

As explained in the chapter on x-ray spectra, the term values are negative if the configuration resulting from the removal of the most loosely bound electron (the limit of the arc spectrum), is assigned the wave-number zero. If such a configuration has the energy zero, the energies of the x-ray levels are positive.

[1] A. E. Ruark, Phys. Rev. **45**, 827 (1934), has proposed constructing x-ray term tables without the use of x-ray absorption limit wave-lengths, substituting for these terms determined optically. For instance the term table of 36 Kr might be built up from the optically measured N_{II} and N_{III} levels listed in Table I, Appendix VI. If the energy of a photo-electron ejected from an atom is computed from this term table and compared with that measured (i.e. Kretschmar, Chap. VII, Sec. 5), independent evidence as to the true value of e may be obtained. Ruark's calculations are not decisive, but favor the oil-drop value.

A complete table of x-ray terms is given in Siegbahn, Spektro-skopie der Röntgenstrahlen (1931). Some of the terms for 47 Ag given here differ from those in Siegbahn's book because of the recent measurements of Haglund, listed in the table showing the L series of silver. The K term of 74 W is located from the double spectrometer measurements of Williams on the K series lines.

TABLE I

X-RAY TERMS FOR VARIOUS ELEMENTS

ν/R Values; ν in Cm.$^{-1}$, $R = 109{,}737$ Cm.$^{-1}$

Term	13 Al	20 Ca	29 Cu	42 Mo	47 Ag	74 W	92 U
K	10.71	297.4	661.6	1473.4	1880.9	5120.7	8474
L_I	....	....	81.0	211.3	282.7	890.8	1602.6
L_{II}	2.30	25.8	70.3	193.7	260.9	849.9	1542.7
L_{III}	2.30	25.5	68.9	186.0	248.6	751.3	1264.2
M_I	....	....	8.9	37.5	54.4	207.3	408.5
M_{II}	0.63	1.9	5.7	30.5	46.7	189.3	381.5
M_{III}	0.63	1.9	5.7	29.2	44.4	167.5	316.8
M_{IV}	....	0.4	0.4	17.3	29.2	137.5	274.2
M_V	....	0.4	0.4	17.1	28.8	132.9	261.2
N_I	....	....	....	5.1	8.7	43.3	106.0
N_{II}	....	....	....	2.9	6.5	36.0	93.5
N_{III}	....	....	....	2.9	6.5	31.0	76.6
N_{IV}	....	....	....	....	1.1	18.7	57.5
N_V	....	....	....	0.4	2.0	17.6	54.3
N_{VI}	....	....	....	....	....	2.3	28.5
N_{VII}	....	....	....	....	....	2.0	27.6
O_I	....	....	....	....	....	5.4	23.7
O_{II}	....	....	....	....	....	2.9	18.3
O_{III}	....	....	....	....	....	2.9	13.9
$O_{IV}O_V$	....	....	....	....	....	....	7.0
$P_{II}P_{III}$	....	....	....	....	....	....	0.8

APPENDIX VIII

THE ELECTRONIC STRUCTURES OF THE ELEMENTS

References:

Pauling and Goudsmit, The Structure of Line Spectra, McGraw-Hill, New York (1930).

Bacher and Goudsmit, Atomic Energy States, McGraw-Hill, New York (1932).

The locations given for the outermost electrons are those obtained from optical spectroscopic data on isolated atoms in a gas, except in cases where the symbol of the element is enclosed in parentheses. In such cases no optical data appear in the tabulation of Bacher and Goudsmit. It should be emphasized that the outer electron locations do not necessarily apply to molecular compounds, or to the atoms in a liquid or solid state, i.e., on the target of an x-ray tube.

TABLE I

ELECTRONIC STRUCTURES FROM HYDROGEN TO KRYPTON

n	1	2	2	3	3	3	4	4	n	1	2	2	3	3	3	4	4
l	0	0	1	0	1	2	0	1	l	0	0	1	0	1	2	0	1
Symbol	$1s$	$2s$	$2p$	$3s$	$3p$	$3d$	$4s$	$4p$	Symbol	$1s$	$2s$	$2p$	$3s$	$3p$	$3d$	$4s$	$4p$
1 H	1								19 K	2	2	6	2	6	...	1	
2 He	2								20 Ca	2	2	6	2	6	...	2	
3 Li	2	1							21 Sc	2	2	6	2	6	1	2	
4 Be	2	2							22 Ti	2	2	6	2	6	2	2	
5 B	2	2	1						23 Va	2	2	6	2	6	3	2	
6 C	2	2	2						24 Cr	2	2	6	2	6	5	1	
7 N	2	2	3						25 Mn	2	2	6	2	6	5	2	
8 O	2	2	4						26 Fe	2	2	6	2	6	6	2	
9 F	2	2	5						27 Co	2	2	6	2	6	7	2	
10 Ne	2	2	6						28 Ni	2	2	6	2	6	8	2	
11 Na	2	2	6	1					29 Cu	2	2	6	2	6	10	1	
12 Mg	2	2	6	2					30 Zn	2	2	6	2	6	10	2	
13 Al	2	2	6	2	1				31 Ga	2	2	6	2	6	10	2	1
14 Si	2	2	6	2	2				32 Ge	2	2	6	2	6	10	2	2
15 P	2	2	6	2	3				33 As	2	2	6	2	6	10	2	3
16 S	2	2	6	2	4				34 Se	2	2	6	2	6	10	2	4
17 Cl	2	2	6	2	5				35 Br	2	2	6	2	6	10	2	5
18 A	2	2	6	2	6				36 Kr	2	2	6	2	6	10	2	6

TABLE I—*Continued*

ELECTRONIC STRUCTURES FROM RUBIDIUM TO URANIUM, THE LEVELS FROM 1s TO 4p BEING POPULATED AS IN KRYPTON

n	4	4	5	5	5	6	6	6	7
l	2	3	0	1	2	0	1	2	0
Symbol	4d	4f	5s	5p	5d	6s	6p	6d	7s
37 Rb	...	...	1						
38 Sr	...	...	2						
39 Y	1	...	2						
40 Zr	2	...	2						
41 Cb	4	...	1						
42 Mo	5	...	1						
(43 Ma)	6	...	1						
44 Ru	7	...	1						
45 Rh	8	...	1						
46 Pd	10								
47 Ag	10	...	1						
48 Cd	10	...	2						
49 In	10	...	2	1					
50 Sn	10	...	2	2					
51 Sb	10	...	2	3					
52 Te	10	...	2	4					
(53 I)	10	...	2	5					
54 Xe	10	...	2	6					
55 Cs	10	...	2	6	...	1			
56 Ba	10	...	2	6	...	2			
57 La	10	...	2	6	1	2			
(58 Ce)	10	1	2	6	1	2			
(59 Pr)	10	2	2	6	1	2			
(60 Nd)	10	3	2	6	1	2			
(61 Il)	10	4	2	6	1	2			
(62 Sa)	10	5	2	6	1	2			
(63 Eu)	10	6	2	6	1	2			
(64 Gd)	10	7	2	6	1	2			

n	4	4	5	5	5	6	6	6	7
l	2	3	0	1	2	0	1	2	0
Symbol	4d	4f	5s	5p	5d	6s	6p	6d	7s
(65 Tb)	10	8	2	6	1	2			
(66 Ds)	10	9	2	6	1	2			
(67 Ho)	10	10	2	6	1	2			
(68 Er)	10	11	2	6	1	2			
(69 Tu)	10	12	2	6	1	2			
(70 Yb)	10	13	2	6	1	2			
(71 Lu)	10	14	2	6	1	2			
72 Hf	10	14	2	6	2	2			
(73 Ta)	10	14	2	6	3	2			
74 W	10	14	2	6	4	2			
75 Re	10	14	2	6	5	2			
(76 Os)	10	14	2	6	6	2			
77 Ir	10	14	2	6	9				
78 Pt	10	14	2	6	9	1			
79 Au	10	14	2	6	10	1			
80 Hg	10	14	2	6	10	2			
81 Tl	10	14	2	6	10	2	1		
82 Pb	10	14	2	6	10	2	2		
83 Bi	10	14	2	6	10	2	3		
(84 Po)	10	14	2	6	10	2	4		
(85)	10	14	2	6	10	2	5		
86 Rn	10	14	2	6	10	2	6		
(87)	10	14	2	6	10	2	6	...	1
(88 Ra)	10	14	2	6	10	2	6	...	2
(89 Ac)	10	14	2	6	10	2	6	1	2
(90 Th)	10	14	2	6	10	2	6	2	2
(91 Pa)	10	14	2	6	10	2	6	3	2
(92 U)	10	14	2	6	10	2	6	4	2

APPENDIX IX

MEAN VALUES OF THE MASS ABSORPTION COEFFICIENTS OF THE
ELEMENTS

The values of the mass absorption coefficient given in Tables I, II, and III were compiled by S. J. M. Allen, and very kindly sent to the authors with permission to publish them in this book. The tabulated values are weighted and averaged observations from various sources, including previously unpublished values obtained by Allen. Values inclosed in parentheses have been interpolated with an accuracy of approximately 1 per cent. Values enclosed in square brackets have been extrapolated with an accuracy of probably better than 10 per cent.

In Table II, which includes the values for wave-lengths between the K and L_{III} critical absorption wave-lengths, the maximum and minimum values of the mass absorption coefficient at the K limit of various elements is given, and the corresponding ratio at the L_{II} limit of 90 Th is included. Values of the absorption jump for the three L limits of various elements are tabulated elsewhere in this book. Attention is also called to the fact that the book includes a separate table of the values of the mass absorption coefficients of gases (pp. 521–525).

A compilation of the data on mass absorption coefficients available in 1928 has been published by E. Jönsson.[1]

[1] E. Jönsson, Thesis, Uppsala (1928).

TABLE I

THE MASS ABSORPTION COEFFICIENTS FOR THE ELEMENTS FOR WAVE-LENGTHS SHORTER THAN THE *K* CRITICAL ABSORPTION WAVE-LENGTH, ACCORDING TO S. J. M. ALLEN

Part A. Wave-lengths between 0.05 and 0.710 Angstrom

Element	λ												Element
	0.05	0.064	0.072	0.098	0.130	0.175	0.200	0.260	0.417	0.497	0.631	0.710	
1 H	...	0.245	0.250	0.280	0.320	0.360	0.375	0.375	0.390	0.435	0.435	0.435	1 H
3 Li	...	0.110	0.118	0.125	0.132	0.144	0.151	0.156	0.180	0.198	0.225	0.260	3 Li
4 Be	...	...	....	....	....	0.150	0.160	0.166	0.185	0.210	0.255	0.315	4 Be
5 B	...	0.126	0.132	0.138	0.149	0.155	0.165	0.175	0.198	0.220	0.303	0.365	5 B
6 C	0.120	0.130	0.136	0.142	0.152	0.163	0.175	0.188	0.256	0.315	0.474	0.605	6 C
7 N	...	...	....	0.143	.....	....	....	....	....	....	....	0.870	7 N
8 O	...	0.130	0.137	0.144	0.157	0.169	0.183	0.210	0.372	0.520	0.900	1.22	8 O
9 F	...	...	....	(0.146)	.....	....	....	....	....	....	....	1.85	9 F
10 Ne	...	...	....	0.148	0.159	0.185	0.210	0.270	0.580	0.930	1.80	2.50	10 Ne
11 Na	...	0.130	0.139	0.150	.....	0.195	0.225	0.305	0.750	1.18	2.30	3.30	11 Na
12 Mg	...	0.130	0.140	0.152	0.168	0.205	0.250	0.343	0.945	1.52	3.00	4.30	12 Mg
13 Al	0.115	0.130	0.143	0.156	0.186	0.228	0.270	0.402	1.18	1.90	3.73	5.22	13 Al
14 Si	...	...	....	(0.159)	.....	....	....	....	....	....	....	6.35	14 Si
15 P	...	...	....	(0.162)	.....	....	....	....	....	....	....	8.00	15 P
16 S	...	0.139	0.150	0.166	0.220	0.335	0.400	0.650	2.10	3.50	6.90	9.90	16 S
17 Cl	...	0.142	0.15	0.176	.....	....	....	....	2.47	4.20	8.40	11.6	17 Cl
18 A	...	...	....	0.184	0.245	0.400	0.445	0.850	2.95	5.00	9.80	13.0	18 A
19 K	...	...	....	0.191	.....	....	....	....	....	....	....	15.4	19 K
20 Ca	...	0.155	0.180	0.200	0.290	0.460	0.52	1.10	3.95	6.60	13.3	18.6	20 Ca
21 Sc	...	...	....	(0.208)	.....	....	....	....	....	....	....	....	21 Sc
22 Ti	...	...	....	(0.217)	(0.330)	(0.55)	(0.78)	(1.42)	(5.17)	(8.9)	(17.0)	(24.2)	22 Ti
23 Va	...	...	....	(0.227)	.....	....	....	....	....	....	....	....	23 Va
24 Cr	...	...	....	(0.238)	(0.375)	(0.69)	(0.92)	(1.85)	(6.75)	(11.3)	(22.0)	(32.0)	24 Cr
25 Mn	...	...	....	(0.250)	.....	....	....	....	....	....	....	....	25 Mn
26 Fe	0.140	0.178	0.202	0.265	0.424	0.85	1.10	2.30	8.45	14.0	27.5	38.5	26 Fe
27 Co	...	...	.....	0.287	0.46	0.92	1.26	2.60	9.45	15.9	30.7	43.0	27 Co
28 Ni	...	...	....	0.310	0.50	1.01	1.42	2.90	10.45	17.9	34.2	48.1	28 Ni
29 Cu	...	0.198	0.232	0.325	0.57	1.12	1.59	3.25	11.4	18.9	37.2	51.0	29 Cu
30 Zn	0.155	...	....	0.350	0.62	1.23	1.76	3.55	12.4	21.0	41.6	58.0	30 Zn
31 Ga	...	...	....	(0.380)	.....	....	....	....	....	....	....	....	31 Ga
32 Ge	...	...	....	(0.41)	(0.75)	(1.48)	(2.10)	(4.15)	(14.9)	(25.2)	(48.0)	(67.0)	32 Ge
33 As	...	...	....	(0.44)	.....	....	....	....	....	....	....	....	33 As
34 Se	...	...	....	(0.48)	.....	(1.73)	....	....	....	....	....	....	34 Se
35 Br	...	...	....	0.52	0.87	1.89	2.67	5.26	19.1	32.0	59.0	84.0	35 Br
36 Kr	...	...	....	(0.56)	.....	....	(2.90)	(5.65)	(20.7)	(34.7)	(64.0)	(91.0)	36 Kr
37 Rb	...	...	....	(0.59)	.....	....	....	....	....	....	....	....	37 Rb
38 Sr	...	...	....	0.61	(1.07)	(2.30)	3.30	6.50	24.0	40.2	72.5	106	38 Sr
39 Y	...	...	....	(0.66)	.....	....	....	....	....	....	....	(114)	39 Y
40 Zr	...	...	....	(0.71)	.....	(2.62)	(3.74)	(7.35)	(27.1)	(45.1)	(82.0)	....	40 Zr
41 Cb	...	...	....	(0.75)	.....	....	....	....	....	....	(87.0)	....	41 Cb
42 Mo	...	0.413	....	0.79	1.39	2.98	4.20	8.30	30.3	50.2	....	....	42 Mo
43 Ma	...	...	....	(0.85)	.....	....	....	....	....	....	....	....	43 Ma
44 Ru	...	...	....	(0.90)	(1.60)	(3.32)	(4.66)	(9.30)	(34.3)	(56.0)	....	....	44 Ru
45 Rh	...	...	....	(0.95)	.....	....	....	....	....	....	....	....	45 Rh
46 Pd	...	...	....	0.99	1.81	3.70	5.15	10.5	38.2	62.0	....	....	46 Pd
47 Ag	...	0.465	0.584	1.05	1.94	3.92	5.40	11.4	40.5	....	....	....	47 Ag

TABLE I—*Continued*

Element	λ												Element
	0.05	0.064	0.072	0.098	0.130	0.175	0.200	0.260	0.417	0.497	0.631	0.710	
48 Cd	...	...	....	(1.09)	.....	....	....	....	....	....	....	....	48 Cd
49 In	...	...	....	(1.13)	.....	....	....	....	....	....	....	....	49 In
50 Sn	0.32	0.490	0.614	1.17	2.15	4.50	6.10	12.8	45.5	....	....	....	50 Sn
51 Sb	...	...	....	(1.21)	.....	....	....	....	....	....	....	....	51 Sb
52 Te	...	...	....	(1.25)	.....	....	(6.60)	(14.4)	....	....	....	....	52 Te
53 I	...	...	....	1.33	2.52	5.10	6.94	14.8	....	....	....	....	53 I
54 Xe	...	...	....	(1.4c)	.....	(5.35)	....	....	....	....	....	....	54 Xe
55 Cs	...	...	....	(1.46)	.....	....	....	....	....	....	....	....	55 Cs
56 Ba	...	...	....	1.52	2.88	5.80	8.0	16.2	....	....	....	....	56 Ba
57 La	...	...	....	(1.60)	.....	....	....	....	....	....	....	....	57 La
58 Ce	...	...	....	(1.68)	.....	....	(8.6)	(17.2)	....	....	....	....	58 Ce
59 Pr	...	...	....	(1.75)	.....	....	....	....	....	....	....	....	59 Pr
60 Nd	...	...	....	(1.81)	(3.40)	(6.70)	(9.2)	(18.4)	....	....	....	....	60 Nd
65 Tb	...	...	....	(2.13)	(4.00)	(7.90)	(11.4)	....	....	....	....	....	65 Tb
73 Ta	...	1.35	1.75	2.80	5.10	10.0	....	....	....	....	....	....	73 Ta
74 W	...	...	....	2.88	5.35	....	....	....	....	....	....	....	74 W
75 Re	...	...	....	(2.95)	.....	....	....	....	....	....	....	....	75 Re
76 Os	...	...	....	(3.02)	.....	....	....	....	....	....	....	....	76 Os
77 Ir	...	...	....	(3.09)	.....	....	....	....	....	....	....	....	77 Ir
78 Pt	0.86	1.52	2.00	3.15	6.30	....	....	....	....	....	....	....	78 Pt
79 Au	0.88	1.55	2.05	3.21	6.40	....	....	....	....	....	....	....	79 Au
80 Hg	...	...	....	3.31	.....	....	....	....	....	....	....	....	80 Hg
81 Tl	...	...	....	(3.41)	.....	....	....	....	....	....	....	....	81 Tl
82 Pb	1.00	1.64	2.10	3.50	6.55	....	....	....	....	....	....	....	82 Pb
83 Bi	...	...	....	3.57	6.70	....	....	....	....	....	....	....	83 Bi
88 Ra	...	...	....	(3.75)	.....	....	....	....	....	....	....	....	88 Ra
90 Th	...	...	2.22	3.80	.....	....	....	....	....	....	....	....	90 Th
92 U	...	1.80	2.25	3.90	.....	....	....	....	....	....	....	....	92 U

TABLE I

THE MASS ABSORPTION COEFFICIENTS OF THE ELEMENTS FOR WAVE-LENGTHS SHORTER THAN THE K CRITICAL ABSORPTION WAVE-LENGTH, ACCORDING TO S. J. M. ALLEN

Part B.　Wave-lengths between 0.880 and 8.32 Angstroms

Ele-ment	λ												Ele-ment
	0.880	1.00	1.235	1.389	1.54	1.934	2.50	3.57	4.36	5.17	6.97	8.32	
1 H	0.440	0.44	0.45	0.47	0.48	0.50	0.55	[1.0]	[1.50]	[2.2]	[4.8]	[7.9]	1 H
2 He	....	0.253	....	....	....	....	....	[2.6]	[4.6]	[7.5]	[18]	[33]	2 He
3 Li	0.350	0.43	0.67	0.86	1.10	2.10	4.0	[10.7]	[19.2]	[32]	[78]	[130]	3 Li
4 Be	0.425	0.55	0.95	1.25	1.60	3.05	6.1	[16.2]	[29.2]	[49]	[119]	[200]	4 Be
5 B	0.580	0.76	1.35	1.87	2.45	4.70	9.1	[25.2]	[46.0]	[75]	[185]	[320]	5 B
6 C	0.990	1.365	2.42	3.35	4.52	8.77	18.0	55.2	97.8	160	390	656	6 C
7 N	1.50	2.11	3.95	5.50	7.40	14.0	29.0	96	166	273	645	1109	7 N
8 O	2.20	3.15	5.70	8.10	11.16	22.0	45.5	150	258	413	976	1589	8 O
9 F	3.30	4.80	9.5	12.5	17.0	35.0	71.0	(210)	(370)	(570)	(1330)	(2100)	9 F
10 Ne	4.55	6.50	12.4	17.0	24.0	49.0	100	275	478	763	1727	(2750)	10 Ne
11 Na	6.10	8.80	17.1	23.4	32.1	61.3	128	(345)	(600)	(930)	(2070)	(3300)	11 Na
12 Mg	8.34	11.5	21.4	30.0	40.8	77.2	161	(420)	(750)	(1130)	(2440)	(3900)	12 Mg
13 Al	9.75	14.12	26.3	36.8	49.0	93.5	193	500	880	1370	2800	....	13 Al
14 Si	11.8	17.0	33.0	44	60.0	111	(225)	(610)	(1100)	(1650)	....	....	14 Si
15 P	14.8	21.2	40.0	54	73.0	134	(275)	(740)	(1330)	(2010)	....	....	15 P
16 S	18.2	26.5	49.5	65.5	90	173	355	900	1550	....	....	....	16 S
17 Cl	20.7	30.5	55.5	76.7	103	198	400	1020	1800	....	....	....	17 Cl
18 A	24.0	35.0	62.5	85.7	116	235	475	1210	....	....	....	....	18 A
19 K	29.0	41.5	78.0	106	137	272	540	....	....	....	....	....	19 K
20 Ca	34.8	49.0	90	120	163	310	600	....	....	....	....	....	20 Ca
21 Sc	....	....	....	....	....	(350)	(685)	....	....	....	....	....	21 Sc
22 Ti	(46.0)	(64.5)	(118)	(163)	(213)	(395)	(780)	....	....	....	....	....	22 Ti
23 Va	....	....	....	....	....	(445)	....	....	....	....	....	....	23 Va
24 Cr	(57.5)	(81.5)	(147)	(203)	(240)	(500)	....	....	....	....	....	....	24 Cr
25 Mn	....	....	....	....	(295)	....	....	....	....	....	....	....	25 Mn
26 Fe	69.5	101	181	250	328	....	....	....	....	....	....	....	26 Fe
27 Co	75.0	110	195	267	358	....	....	....	....	....	....	....	27 Co
28 Ni	81.3	118.5	208	286	....	....	....	....	....	....	....	....	28 Ni
29 Cu	92.0	130	238	....	....	....	....	....	....	....	....	....	29 Cu
30 Zn	105	147	262	....	....	....	....	....	....	....	....	....	30 Zn
31 Ga	....	(155)	....	....	....	....	....	....	....	....	....	....	31 Ga
32 Ge	(123)	(166)	....	....	....	....	....	....	....	....	....	....	32 Ge
33 As	....	(178)	....	....	....	....	....	....	....	....	....	....	33 As
34 Se	(141)	....	....	....	....	....	....	....	....	....	....	....	34 Se
35 Br	151	....	....	....	....	....	....	....	....	....	....	....	35 Br

TABLE I

THE MASS ABSORPTION COEFFICIENTS OF THE ELEMENTS FOR WAVE-LENGTHS SHORTER
THAN THE K CRITICAL ABSORPTION WAVE-LENGTH, ACCORDING TO S. J. M. ALLEN

Part C.   Wave-lengths from 9.87 to 68.0 Angstroms

Element	λ					Element
	9.87	13.37	17.67	44.5	68.0	
1 H	[13]	[31]	[71]	1,000	3000	1 H
2 He	[56]	[126]	[286]	3,600	....	2 He
3 Li	[220]	[530]	[1,250]	(12,000)	....	3 Li
4 Be	[340]	[800]	[1,870]	[20,000]	....	4 Be
5 B	[520]	[1150]	[2,400]	[27,000]	....	5 B
6 C	1063	2170	[4,300]	....	....	6 C
7 N	1796	3836	6,980	....	....	7 N
8 O	2540	5456	10,000	....	....	8 O
9 F	(3000)	(6950)	[12,000]	....	....	9 F
10 Ne	4310	8500	....	....	....	10 Ne
11 Na	(5000)	....	....	....	....	11 Na

TABLE II

THE MASS ABSORPTION COEFFICIENTS OF THE ELEMENTS FOR WAVE-LENGTHS IN THE
REGION BETWEEN THE K AND THE L_{III} CRITICAL ABSORPTION WAVE-LENGTHS,
ACCORDING TO S. J. M. ALLEN

Part A.   Wave-lengths from 0.1075 to 0.260 Angstrom

(When two values are given for the same wave-length, they represent the maximum and minimum values at a critical absorption limit).

Element	λ										Element
	0.1075	0.130	0.142	0.155	0.158	0.175	0.178	0.184	0.200	0.260	
73 Ta	......	......	......	......	......	......	......	11.8			73 Ta
								2.8	3.40	6.70	
74 W	......	......	......	......	......	......	11.3				74 W
							2.7	....	3.50	6.85	
78 Pt	......	......	......	......	9.40						78 Pt
					2.45	2.97	....	....	4.25	8.0	
79 Au	......	......	......	8.80							79 Au
				2.30	2.43	3.13	....	....	4.40	8.3	
82 Pb	......	......	7.75								82 Pb
			2.10	......	2.60	3.48	....	....	4.90	10.0	
83 Bi	......	......	2.18	......	2.70	3.60	....	....	5.10	11.0	83 Bi
90 Th	......	2.05	......	......		3.82	....	....	5.30	12.0	90 Th
92 U	4.65	2.05									92 U
	1.62	2.10	......	......	......	3.95	....	....	5.40	....	

TABLE II

The Mass Absorption Coefficients of the Elements for Wave-lengths in the Region between the K and the L_{III} Critical Absorption Wave-lengths, According to S. J. M. Allen

Part B. Wave-lengths from 0.331 to 1.00 Angstrom

The wave-length values (λ) head the columns below. Cells for an element at its own K-critical wave-length give the two (high/low) values of the absorption jump.

Element	0.331	0.374	0.417	0.424	0.485	0.497	0.618	0.631	0.710	0.769	0.880	0.918	1.00	Element
35 Br												170 / 22	28.0	35 Br
38 Sr										125.0 / 17.0	22.0			38 Sr
42 Mo							88.0 / 12.5				36.0		52.0	42 Mo
47 Ag					62.5 / 9.8	10.5		15.0	19.9		50.0		73.0	47 Ag
50 Sn				46.6 / 8.0		11.8		19.6	27.5		60.0		86.0	50 Sn
53 I		35.7 / 6.5	9.2			15.6		23.0	34.0				98.0	53 I
56 Ba	28.0 / 5.4					17.8		26.4	38.5					56 Ba
73 Ta			10.5					31.1	42.0					73 Ta
74 W			21.5			36.0		72.0	100				260	74 W
78 Pt			22.5			38.0		75.0	104		19.5		165	78 Pt
79 Au			27.4			47.0		84.5	115		170		178	79 Au
80 Hg			28.4			48.5		87	120				180	80 Hg
82 Pb			32			52.8		98	136		135			82 Pb
90 Th						59		71	91					90 Th

TABLE II

The Mass Absorption Coefficients of the Elements for Wave-lengths in the Region between the K and the L_{III} Critical Absorption Wave-lengths, According to S. J. M. Allen

Part C. Wave-lengths from 1.235 to 4.36 Angstroms

(When two values are given for the same wave-length, they represent maximum and minimum values at the critical absorption limit.)

Element	λ											Element
	1.235	1.28	1.377	1.484	1.54	1.739	1.934	2.5	3.57	3.87	4.36	
18 A	.....	.....	.....	.....	.....	.....	.....	.....	....	1460		18 A
										148	202	
26 Fe	.....	.....	.....	.....	.....	460						26 Fe
						54	71.2	147	375	....	610	
28 Ni	.....	.....	.....	340								28 Ni
				40.5	48	.....	89.5	180	450	....	715	
29 Cu	.....	.....	307									29 Cu
			37	.....	50.9	.....	96.3	197	495	....	760	
30 Zn	.....	287										30 Zn
		36	.....	.....	58.6	.....	110	228	575	....	910	
35 Br	.....	.....	.....	.....	89	.....	.....	.....	....	....	....	35 Br
47 Ag	126	.....	.....	.....	217	.....	405	710	1360	....	....	47 Ag
50 Sn	150	.....	.....	.....	247	.....	470	850	....	....	....	50 Sn
53 I	.....	.....	.....	.....	290	.....	.....	.....	....	....	....	53 I

TABLE II

The Mass Absorption Coefficients of the Elements for Wave-lengths in the Region between the K and the L_{III} Critical Absorption Wave-lengths, According to S. J. M. Allen

Part D. Wave-lengths from 4.38 to 68.0 Angstroms

Element	λ										Element
	4.38	5.01	5.17	6.97	7.95	8.32	9.87	11.9	44.5	68.0	
7 N	.....	.....	.....	.....	.....	.....	.....	.....	3820	10,900	7 N
8 O	.....	.....	.....	.....	.....	.....	.....	.....	5800	16,250	8 O
10 Ne	.....	.....	.....	.....	.....	.....	.....	.....	13,100	....	10 Ne
13 Al	.....	.....	.....	.....	3600						13 Al
					280	330	500	850	.....	....	
16 S	.....	2100									16 S
		210	221	500	.....	794	1320	2100	.....	....	
17 Cl	1830										17 Cl
	178	.....	277	610	.....	962	1570	2500	.....	....	
18 A	.....	.....	324	748	.....	1160	1860	3000	.....	....	18 A
28 Ni	.....	.....	1150	2000	.....	3140	4540	6900	.....	....	28 Ni
29 Cu	.....	.....	1190	2130	.....	3450	5036	7550	.....	....	29 Cu

TABLE III

THE MASS ABSORPTION COEFFICIENTS OF THE ELEMENTS FOR WAVE-LENGTHS LONGER THAN THE L_{III} CRITICAL ABSORPTION WAVE-LENGTH; ACCORDING TO S. J. M. ALLEN

Element	λ															Element
	1.0	1.104	1.235	1.389	1.54	1.934	2.50	3.35	4.15	5.37	6.97	9.8	6.97	8.32	11.9	
47 Ag	...	...	...	...	...	...	...	...	461	845	1300	2700	...	...	...	47 Ag
50 Sn	...	...	...	...	...	...	...	...	550	...	...	...	...	...	...	50 Sn
74 W	...	...	95	...	176	300	...	...	...	...	...	...	...	...	...	74 W
78 Pt	...	86	115	155	202	358	596	1120	1290	1640	...	...	1190	1560	2440	78 Pt
79 Au	...	93	122	166	213	385	...	...	...	...	...	...	...	...	...	79 Au
80 Hg	...	94	125	172	...	...	...	...	...	...	...	...	...	...	...	80 Hg
82 Pb	75	103	137	185	230	428	...	...	...	...	...	...	...	...	...	82 Pb
90 Th	95	...	...	...	...	...	...	...	...	...	...	...	...	...	...	90 Th

APPENDIX X

TABLE I

ABSORPTION OF W $K\alpha_1$, $\lambda = 0.2086$ A, BY VARIOUS SUBSTANCES

Substance	Mass Absorption Coefficient	Probable Error
1 H	0.40	
Paraffin	0.209	0.002
6 C	0.176	0.002
13 Al	0.278	0.002
29 Cu	1.617	0.012
47 Ag	5.99	0.09
73 Ta	3.62	0.02
74 W	3.81	0.03
82 Pb	5.07	0.04

Reference, T. M. Hahn, Phys. Rev. **46**, 149 (1934).

APPENDIX XI

SOME APPLICATIONS OF RECIPROCAL VECTORS TO CRYSTAL STRUCTURE PROBLEMS

Ewald[1] has called attention to the fact that the introduction of reciprocal vectors into calculations concerning crystal lattices often greatly simplifies the problem, especially when a non-orthogonal lattice of low symmetry is being treated. We may imagine a given set of vectors $\tau_1 \tau_2 \tau_3$ which may have any inclination to each other, but are not coplanar in any case applicable to crystal structure considerations. These may represent the primitive translations of the lattice. A set of vectors reciprocal to these, denoted by $t_1 t_2 t_3$ is defined as follows:

$$t_1 \cdot \tau_1 = t_2 \cdot \tau_2 = t_3 \cdot \tau_3 = 1. \tag{1}$$

$$t_1 \cdot \tau_2 = t_1 \cdot \tau_3 = t_2 \cdot \tau_1 = t_2 \cdot \tau_3 = t_3 \cdot \tau_1 = t_3 \cdot \tau_1 = 0. \tag{2}$$

The second of these relations shows that t_1 is perpendicular to τ_2 and τ_3; it must then be capable of representation as

$$t_1 = \pi_1 \tau_2 \times \tau_3, \tag{3}$$

where π_1 is an appropriate numerical coefficient. To determine π_1 we set up the scalar product $\tau_1 \cdot t_1$, which must be unity from eq. (1). This gives

$$\tau_1 \cdot t_1 = \pi_1 \tau_1 \cdot \tau_2 \times \tau_3 = 1 \tag{4}$$

which means that

$$\pi_1 = \frac{1}{\tau_1 \cdot \tau_2 \times \tau_3},$$

so that

$$t_1 = \frac{\tau_2 \times \tau_3}{\tau_1 \cdot \tau_2 \times \tau_3} \tag{5}$$

[1] P. P. Ewald, Kristalle und Röntgenstrahlen, Julius Springer, Berlin (1923), p. 246.

and similarly

$$t_2 = \frac{\tau_3 \times \tau_1}{\tau_1 \cdot \tau_2 \times \tau_3} \tag{6}$$

$$t_3 = \frac{\tau_1 \times \tau_2}{\tau_1 \cdot \tau_2 \times \tau_3}. \tag{7}$$

If, on the other hand, we start from the definitions of eqs. (1) and (2), considering $t_1 t_2 t_3$ as the given vectors, we can deduce expressions for the τ's in terms of the t's. Thus eqs. (2) require that τ_1 be perpendicular to t_2 and t_3, and proceeding exactly as before, we find

$$\tau_1 = \frac{t_2 \times t_3}{t_1 \cdot t_2 \times t_3} \tag{8}$$

and similar expressions for τ_2 and τ_3 obtained by interchanging the symbols τ and t in eqs. (6) and (7).

The volume of the unit cell for which $\tau_1 \tau_2 \tau_3$ are the primitive translations is given by the triple product

$$v_r = \tau_1 \cdot \tau_2 \times \tau_3. \tag{9}$$

If we consider that the vectors $t_1 t_2 t_3$ are the primitive translations of a lattice reciprocal to that characterized by the τ's, then v_t, the volume of the reciprocal unit cell, is

$$v_t = t_1 \cdot t_2 \times t_3. \tag{10}$$

It may be shown as follows that v_t is the numerical reciprocal of v_r. Considering the scalar product $\tau_1 \cdot t_1$ we obtain

$$\tau_1 \cdot t_1 = 1 = \frac{t_2 \times t_3}{t_1 \cdot t_2 \times t_3} \cdot \frac{\tau_2 \times \tau_3}{\tau_1 \cdot \tau_2 \times \tau_3} = \frac{1}{v_t v_r} \{t_2 \times t_3 \cdot \tau_2 \times \tau_3\}. \tag{11}$$

The multiple vector product occurring in eq. (11) can be expanded into scalar products by considering for the moment that $\tau_3 \times \tau_2$ may be represented by some vector R, so that we have[2]

$$t_2 \times t_3 \cdot R = t_2 \cdot t_3 \times R.$$

We then expand the triple vector product involved:

$$t_3 \times R = t_3 \times (\tau_2 \times \tau_3) = t_3 \cdot \tau_3 \tau_2 - t_3 \cdot \tau_2 \tau_3 = \tau_2,$$

[2] The interchange of dot and cross in this operation is discussed in any treatise on vector analysis, e.g., Page, Introduction to Theoretical Physics, D. Van Nostrand, New York (1928), p. 9.

so that finally

$$t_2 \times t_3 \cdot \mathbf{\tau}_2 \times \mathbf{\tau}_3 = t_2 \cdot \mathbf{\tau}_2 = 1,$$

which means that with eqs. (10) and (11) that

$$t_1 \cdot t_2 \times t_3 = 1/v_r, \tag{12}$$

which is the relation used as eq. (6.73), Chap. VI.   Many further applications of reciprocal vectors to crystal structure problems are given by Ewald, loc. cit.

AUTHOR INDEX

SUBJECT INDEX